Research in Geophysics

VOLUME 1

Sun, Upper Atmosphere, and Space

Research in Geophysics

Edited by
Hugh Odishaw
National Academy of Sciences
Washington, D.C.

Volume 1
Sun, Upper Atmosphere, and Space

The M.I.T. Press
Massachusetts Institute of Technology
Cambridge, Massachusetts

Library of Congress Catalog Card Number 64-23354

Manufactured in the United States of America

PREFACE

From time to time a critical survey of a large field of research serves the interests of science well. We believe that this survey does so for the geophysical sciences. Growing out of an international symposium in the summer of 1963 on research in geophysics, the critical reviews in these two volumes, together called *Research in Geophysics*, bring together results in the major areas of geophysics, ranging from the disciplines concerned with the solid earth to those dealing with the interplanetary medium. Experiments and theories are assessed; hopefully, a direct and effective entrance to the now vast literature is provided.

For many reasons the National Academy of Sciences welcomed the opportunity to sponsor this symposium. Apart from the scientific needs and interests, there was our desire, shared by many throughout the world, to mark in a significant way a kind of culmination of the International Geophysical Year, which had technically come to an end but had given birth to lusty successors such as the Years of the Quiet Sun, begun this year and to continue until the end of 1965. Also, the Academy marked its 100th anniversary in 1963, and the nature of the symposium was clearly in keeping with the broad reviewing and summarizing character of the distinguished scientific sessions that were to mark our Centennial Celebration last October.

At every hand we had the generous help and ready participation of our colleagues at home and abroad in the planning and conduct of the symposium. It is a particular pleasure to record the appreciation of the Academy for the assistance of the several committees and constituent unions of the International Council of Scientific Unions that cooperated with us. Special mention should be made in this connection of the Bureau of the Special Committee for the International Geophysical Year, and the International Geophysical Committee. Above all, our gratitude goes to those eminent scientists who contributed the several chapters incorporated herein.

FREDERICK SEITZ
President
National Academy of Sciences

Washington, D.C.
August, 1964

FOREWORD

This volume is devoted to the nature of magnetic fields, charged particles, and radiations in the upper atmosphere and space (particularly between sun and earth) and to the many, often intricate, relationships among these phenomena. In more conventional terms, the disciplines here dealt with are solar physics, cosmic rays, magnetic fields, ionospheric physics, and auroral and airglow physics and chemistry. The contributors are concerned with the upper atmosphere, with the interplanetary medium beyond and especially that portion lying between earth and sun, and with solar-terrestrial relationships. A companion volume takes up topics on the solid earth (seismology, geodesy, gravity, etc.) and on interface phenomena (glaciology, oceanography, and meteorology). The two together, generically entitled *Research in Geophysics,* provide a survey of our present knowledge and current research efforts throughout the world in these major geophysical areas.

These two volumes are, in fact, a reflection of geophysics today: the last decade has seen a remarkable expansion—in fact, a revolution—in the scope and intensity of geophysical research. Many factors account for this, including the development in modern times of sensitive electronic instrumentation, powerful tools such as sounding rockets and spacecraft, and the availability of high-speed computing machinery, but it is not our purpose here to look into causes. The consequences of this unparalleled acceleration in geophysical research are directly linked to these two volumes, for so much has happened in observation, experimentation, analysis, and theory during the last decade, that an assessment of the status of our knowledge in major areas appeared both necessary and useful.

Where did we stand, in a given area, about ten years ago? What were the results of investigations during the International Geophysical Year, which was perhaps the most powerful force in the research explosion of geophysics? What have we learned in the half-decade or so following the IGY? Hence, where do we stand today? And finally, what problems confront us now? These were the questions which we felt to be of compelling interest to all, and these were the questions which we put to the authors of the various chapters, authors chosen by virtue of their internationally acknowledged competence in their specialty. In short, the authors were asked to prepare critical review papers which would serve as syntheses of our knowledge, as assessments of important research (particularly in recent years), and as guides to directions and trends.

These volumes are also a reflection of the International Geophysical Year and the succeeding programs which it inspired. The IGY, at the heart of the revolution in geophysics, was responsible for so rich a harvest of results that a fresh assessment became mandatory. It served as the point of departure in planning these volumes. Plans for this world review began to crystallize in 1961, following much earlier preliminary discussions within the international community. Our concept then was to hold a symposium in 1963 when the Academy was due to celebrate its one hundredth anniversary in Washington and when the International Union of Geodesy and Geophysics was to hold its XIIIth General Assembly on the campus of the University of California at Berkeley. The latter event was significant in part because the International Scientific Radio Union, the International Union of Pure and Applied Physics, and the International Astronomical Union, had played important roles in IGY planning, in part because many geophysicists from distant parts of the world would be in the United States for the assembly and therefore easily able to participate in the symposium. A symposium also seemed a suitable, festive but scientifically substantive, way to mark the Academy's centennial, although the formal celebration had been planned for a later period in Washington.

We were fortunate in having support both at home and abroad for the proposed review symposium. Thus endorsement, counsel, and suggestions came to us from the International Council of Scientific Unions, International Scientific Radio Union, the International Union of Geodesy and Geophysics, the International Union of Pure and Applied Physics, International Geophysics Committee, Committee on Space Research, and Scientific Committee on Antarctic Research. In fact, the International Geophysics Committee, which succeeded the Special Committee for the International Geophysical Year and took on completion tasks for the IGY endeavor, cosponsored the symposium. In the United States, too, interest and assistance were forthcoming at every hand. The Geophysics Research Board of the Academy and the U.S. National Committee for the International Geophysical Year, which had been incorporated into the Board, took on the task of planning and coordinating the sessions. The General Arrangements Committee for the General Assembly of the International Union of Geodesy and Geophysics—a domestic group established by the American Geophysical Union—provided much of the financial support, to which public and private institutions and foundations contributed generously. Especial mention needs to be made of the National Science Foundation, which had worked so closely with the Academy in support of the IGY, the International Geophysical Cooperation of 1959, and various major post-IGY research endeavors such as the continuing work in Antarctica, the Indian Ocean Expedition, The World Magnetic Survey, the Upper Mantle Project, the International Years of the Quiet Sun, and so on.

Although the concept thus received gratifying response from international scientific bodies and from domestic institutions, and while support was generously forthcoming, the task of formulating the details of the symposium was before us. We turned, both in 1961 and 1962, to some three hundred active scientists in various fields of geophysics and in various countries, soliciting their views as to the most important, major subjects. With these in hand, we then established the Symposium Program Committee, which consisted of the members of the Bureau of the Special Committee for the International Geophysical Year (Sydney Chapman, Lloyd V. Berkner, V. V. Beloussov, J. Coulomb, and M. Nicolet) and the members of the Executive Committee of the U.S. National Committee (W. W. Atwood, L. M. Gould, J. W. Joyce, Joseph Kaplan, Hugh Odishaw, F. W. Reichelderfer, A. H. Shapley, A. F. Spilhaus, and M. A. Tuve). The Symposium Program Committee reviewed the recommendations noted above, selected the topics of greatest interest, and nominated leading experts as prospective authors. Invitations to the latter were issued in early 1963, and the dates and site for the symposium were set: 12–16 August 1963 at the University of California, Los Angeles. To cope with the many local problems that an international symposium entails, an Arrangements Committee at the University of California was created, whose members consisted of the following scientists: G. J. Fergusson, Chairman; L. H. Adams, J. A. Bjerknes, D. T. Griggs, Joseph Kaplan, Leon Knopoff, W. F. Libby, G. J. F. MacDonald, Walter Munk, W. W. Rubey, and L. B. Slichter. We take special pleasure in noting our deep obligation to Professor Fergusson, whose efforts made the week in Los Angeles pleasant and fruitful for every participant.

The symposium began with a plenary session on the afternoon of 12 August 1963. W. F. Libby welcomed the participants on behalf of the University of California and Chancellor Franklin D. Murphy. L. V. Berkner represented the Academy's President Frederick Seitz, and conveyed the Academy's greetings. Professor Sydney Chapman concluded the session with a discussion of the scientific meaning of the IGY and of its successor programs. Four special lectures on broad topics were presented: Thomas F. Malone on international cooperation in meteorology and the atmospheric sciences, Roger Revelle on international cooperation in oceanography, V. V. Beloussov on the Upper Mantle Project, and W. J. G. Beynon on the International Years of the Quiet Sun.

Presentation of the review papers began on Tuesday morning, 13 August, and concluded at noon of Friday, 16 August. Some forty papers were delivered by as many leading authorities. The symposium was divided into two parallel sets of sessions: one devoted to topics on the solid earth and interface phenomena, the other to the sun, upper atmosphere, and space. This permitted limiting each three-hour morning and afternoon session to three papers, providing time for discussion: discussion was deemed important. To this end a large attendance was not sought, and invitations were sent to active workers. Each of the two parallel sessions thus saw some one hundred research scientists participating, together with an almost equal number of auditors—largely faculty and students from California universities. The discussions were lively and useful: useful both in the analysis of recent research results and in the final preparation of the papers for publication.

In the winter and spring of 1963–1964 gathering and editing of the written papers got under way. Our gratitude goes to all the authors—first for their oral presentations, then for their manuscripts, and finally for patiently but promptly reviewing edited copy and checking proof. Our thanks, too, go to many members of the Academy's staff for their continuous and effective help through all phases of this effort. We wish also to acknowledge appreciation to the staff of the MIT Press, which worked most expeditiously in the publication of these volumes.

JOSEPH KAPLAN
HUGH ODISHAW
MERLE A. TUVE

National Academy of Sciences
Washington, D.C.
August, 1964

CONTENTS

CHAPTER 8

CHAPTER 9

CHAPTER 10

CHAPTER 11

CHAPTER 15

THE AURORA 367

SYDNEY CHAPMAN AND SYUN-ICHI AKASOFU

CHAPTER 16

AIRGLOW 401

D. BARBIER

CHAPTER 17

MAGNETIC FIELD AT THE POLES 423

TAKESI NAGATA

CONTRIBUTORS AND CHAPTERS

List of Contributors

Syun-Ichi Akasofu, Geophysical Institute, University of Alaska, College, Alaska.

Daniel Barbier, Paris Observatory and the Astrophysical Institute of Paris, Paris, France.

V. V. Beloussov, President, Soviet Geophysical Committee, Academy of Sciences of the USSR, Moscow, USSR (Member of Bureau, Special Committee for the International Geophysical Year [CSAGI]; President, Upper Mantle Committee).

Charles R. Bentley, Geophysical and Polar Research Center, University of Wisconsin, Madison, Wisconsin.

W. J. G. Beynon, Professor of Physics, University College of Wales, Aberystwyth, Wales (President, Special Committee for the International Years of the Quiet Sun [SC-IQSY]; President, International Geophysical Committee [CIG]).

Bert Bolin, Professor of Meteorology, University of Stockholm, Stockholm, Sweden.

M. I. Budyko, Main Geophysical Observatory, Hydrometeorological Service of the USSR, Leningrad, USSR.

Joseph W. Chamberlain, Associate Director, Kitt Peak National Observatory, Tucson, Arizona.

Sydney Chapman, Geophysical Institute, University of Alaska, College, Alaska; High Altitude Observatory, Boulder, Colorado (President of the Special Committee for the International Geophysical Year [CSAGI]).

Günter Dietrich, Professor of Oceanography and Director of the Institute of Marine Research, University of Kiel, Kiel, Germany.

William L. Donn, Senior Research Scientist, Lamont Geological Observatory; Professor of Geology, the City College of New York, New York.

Mervyn A. Ellison, Senior Professor, School of Cosmic Physics, Dublin Institute for Advanced Studies; Director of Dunsink Observatory, Dublin, Ireland.

E. P. Fedorov, Main Astronomical Observatory, Academy of Sciences of the Ukrainian SSR, Kiev, USSR.

Louis A. Frank, Department of Physics, State University of Iowa, Iowa City, Iowa.

Herbert Friedman, E. O. Hulburt Center for Space Research, U. S. Naval Research Laboratory, Washington, D.C.

Robert A. Helliwell, Professor of Electrical Engineering, Stanford University, Stanford, California.

Colin O. Hines, Professor of Aeronomy, University of Chicago, Chicago, Illinois.

John H. Hodgson, Chief, Division of Seismology, Dominion Observatory, Ottawa, Canada.

Herfried C. Hoinkes, Professor of Meteorology and Director of the Institute of Meteorology and Geophysics, University of Innsbruck, Innsbruck, Austria.

C. de Jager, Professor of Astrophysics and Director of Sonnenborgh Observatory, University of Utrecht, Utrecht, The Netherlands.

Joseph Kaplan, Professor, Department of Physics, University of California, Los Angeles, California (Chairman, U.S. National Committee for the International Geophysical Year; President, International Union of Geodesy and Geophysics).

V. I. Keilis-Borok, Institute of Physics of the Earth, Academy of Sciences of the USSR, Moscow, USSR.

John A. Knauss, Professor of Oceanography and Dean of the Graduate School of Oceanography, University of Rhode Island, Kingston, Rhode Island.

K. I. Kondratiev, Professor, University of Leningrad, Leningrad, USSR.

V. G. Kort, Director, Institute of Oceanology, Academy of Sciences of the USSR, Moscow, USSR.

I. P. Kosminskaya, Institute of Physics of the Earth, Academy of Sciences of the USSR, Moscow, USSR.

A. N. Krenke, Institute of Geography, Academy of Sciences of the USSR, Moscow, USSR.

Thomas F. Malone, Chairman, Committee on Atmospheric Sciences, National Academy of Sciences, Washington, D.C. (Director and Vice-President for Research, Travelers Insurance Company, Hartford, Connecticut).

William Markowitz, Director, Time Service Division, U.S. Naval Observatory, Washington, D. C.

Sadami Matsushita, Senior Research Staff, High Altitude Observatory-National Center for Atmospheric Research; Professor Adjoint of Astrogeophysics, University of Colorado, Boulder, Colorado.

Paul J. Melchior, Astronomer at the Royal Observatory of Belgium; Director of the International Center for Earth Tides, Brussels, Belgium.

Peter Meyer, Enrico Fermi Institute for Nuclear Studies and Department of Physics, University of Chicago, Chicago, Illinois.

Takesi Nagata, Geophysical Institute, University of Tokyo, Tokyo, Japan; Department of Earth and Planetary Sciences, University of Pittsburgh, Pittsburgh, Pennsylvania.

M. Nicolet, Director, National Center for Space Research, Brussels, Belgium (Secretary-General of the Special Committee for the International Geophysical Year [CSAGI]).

Tatsuzo Obayashi, Professor, Ionosphere Research Laboratory, Kyoto University, Kyoto, Japan.

Hugh Odishaw, National Academy of Sciences, Washington, D.C. (Executive Director, U.S. National Committee for the International Geophysical Year; Executive Secretary, Geophysics Research Board, National Academy of Sciences).

L. C. Pakiser, Geophysicist and Chief, Branch of Crustal Studies, U.S. Geological Survey, Denver, Colorado.

E. N. Parker, Enrico Fermi Institute for Nuclear Studies and Department of Physics, University of Chicago, Chicago, Illinois.

June G. Pattullo, Professor, Department of Oceanography, Oregon State University, Corvallis, Oregon.

W. R. Piggott, D.S.I.R. Radio Research Station, Slough, Bucks., England.

Frank Press, Director, Seismological Laboratory, California Institute of Technology, Pasadena, California.

Russell W. Raitt, Department of Earth Sciences and Marine Physical Laboratory of the Scripps Institution of Oceanography, University of California, San Diego, California.

John H. Reid, Assistant Professor, School of Cosmic Physics, Dublin Institute for Advanced Studies; Chief Assistant, Dunsink Observatory, Dublin, Ireland.

Roger Revelle, Director, Scripps Institution of Oceanography, La Jolla, California; University Dean of Research, University of California, Berkeley, California.

Y. V. Riznichenko, Institute of Physics of the Earth, Academy of Sciences, Moscow, USSR.

Juan G. Roederer, Faculty of the Natural Sciences, University of Buenos Aires, Buenos Aires, Argentina.

Morton J. Rubin, Chief, Office of Special Programs, U.S. Weather Bureau, Washington, D.C.

Frederick Seitz, President, National Academy of Sciences, Washington, D.C.

David M. Shaw, Research Assistant, Lamont Geological Observatory, Palisades, New York.

P. A. Shumskiy, Soviet Committee on Antarctic Research, Academy of Sciences of the USSR, Moscow, USSR.

S. F. Smerd, Division of Radiophysics, C.S.I.R.O., Sydney, Australia.

John Steinhart, Department of Terrestrial Magnetism, Carnegie Institution of Washington, Washington, D.C.

Anne E. Stevens, Seismologist, Dominion Observatory, Ottawa, Canada.
N. Stoyko, International Time Bureau, Paris Observatory, Paris, France.
Sidney Teweles, Stratospheric Meteorology Research Project, U.S. Weather Bureau, Washington, D.C.
V. A. Troitskaya, Institute of Physics of the Earth, Academy of Sciences of the USSR, Moscow, USSR.
Merle A. Tuve, Chairman, Geophysics Research Board, National Academy of Sciences, Washington, D.C. (Director, Department of Terrestrial Magnetism, Carnegie Institution of Washington, Washington, D.C.).
James A. Van Allen, Professor of Physics, State University of Iowa, Iowa City, Iowa.
George P. Woollard, Director, Hawaii Institute of Geophysics, Honolulu, Hawaii.
I. A. Zotikov, Institute of Geography, Academy of Sciences of the USSR, Moscow, USSR.

List of Chapters and Authors

Volume 1: Sun, Upper Atmosphere, and Space

Volume 2: Solid Earth and Interface Phenomena

Research in Geophysics

CHAPTER 1

SOLAR ULTRAVIOLET AND X-RAY RADIATION

C. de Jager

1. Introduction

Since the International Geophysical Year, available information on solar ultraviolet and X-ray radiation has grown appreciably: recent review papers are those by Tousey [84] on the extreme ultraviolet spectrum of the sun and by Friedman [36] on ultraviolet and X-rays from the sun and on rocket spectroscopy. The latter deals not only with solar ultraviolet radiation but also with X-rays and also has an interesting historical review of the subject.

More specifically dealing with solar X-rays are a review paper by Kundu [55] on centimeter wave radio emissions and X-rays from the sun, and one by Elwert [31] on solar X-rays. The latter also discusses extensively the theoretical aspects of the problem. Finally there is Pecker's somewhat older but still very interesting review "La prédiction du spectre ultraviolet des étoiles et du soleil" [74].

With so many excellent review papers available, we prefer to follow another line of thought. We shall treat the different parts of the solar atmosphere that contribute to the observed ultraviolet and X-ray radiation, summarize our knowledge about these solar regions, review the observations of uv and X-radiation from these sources, compare them with existing theories, and enumerate for the various spectral ranges possible future observations, which may be helpful for a better understanding of some topical problems on the relevant parts of the sun.

The following wavelength regions are very approximate, and serve only to give a rough indication.

Section	Source of radiation	Very approximative wavelength region
2	The photosphere	>1800 Å
	Transition photosphere-chromosphere	1200–2000 Å
3	The chromosphere	900–1800 Å
	Transition to the corona	100–1000 Å, Ly α
4	The quiet corona	10–200 Å
5	The coronal activity regions	5–100 Å
6	Solar flares: "Thermal" radiation	1–50 Å
	Solar flares: Nonthermal bursts	0.01–10 Å

2. The Photosphere and the Transition Photosphere-Chromosphere

2.1. Structure

The essential features (Fig. 1) of the deep photospheric structure are represented in a model given in 1959 [45] and worked out later [47]. The model, as suggested initially, is a so-called three-column model with hot rising columns, cool descending masses of gas, and a stationary average kind of column. For optical depths $\tau_{5000\,\text{Å}} (\equiv \tau_0 < 0.08)$ there is only one kind of element; in deeper regions there are three, with increasingly greater temperature differences. At an optical depth $\tau_0 = 1$, the temperature differences between the two extreme columns is about 1000°. This model predicts maximum brightness differences between the granules of 21 per cent, or a root-mean-square value of 7.4 per cent (assuming a sinusoidal brightness

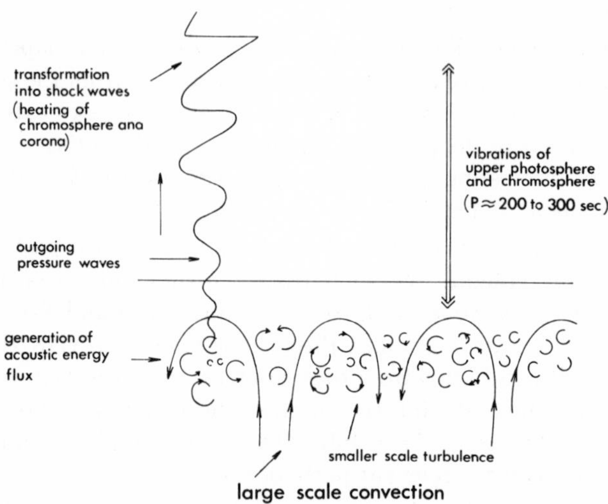

FIG. 1. Schematic drawing of the photosphere.

distribution). This is in reasonable agreement with observations of Rösch [80], who found an average intensity ratio of 1.23 between maxima and minima in the photosphere, and with the observations of Bahng and Schwarzschild [6] who gave an rms value of 7.2 per cent. Hence our temperature differences are fairly well correct (further on photospheric intensity of fluctuations, see [47]).

Recent investigation [50] has shown that the greater part of photospheric matter is contained in the two extreme kinds of columns and that the central elements, having the average temperature and no upward motion component, contain presumably very little matter. So the actual photospheric model is essentially a two-column model; the third, average element has only significance for problems dealing with the average properties of the photosphere.

As to the dynamic properties of the photosphere, we assume that the systematic large-scale convective up-and-downward motions decrease from 2 km/sec at $\tau_0 = 1.0$ to zero at $\tau_0 = 0.08$. Above that level no convective motions are assumed. However, there are two other kinds of motions occurring in these upper levels:

1. A field of pressure waves, originating from the solar convection zone, manifests itself in the higher layers as a "microturbulent" vertical velocity component. It increases from small values in the deep photospheric regions to 1.5 km/sec at $\tau_0 = 0.12$ and to 2.5 km/sec at $\tau_0 = 0.012$.
2. Apart from this system of motions, a field with an oscillatory character has been discovered by Leighton [58], and rediscussed by Leighton [59, 69] and by Evans, Michard, and others [33, 64]. The period of this oscillation is nearly 300 sec in the photospheric regions and decreases to about 200 sec in the high chromosphere ($\sim$4000 km).

If the photosphere were in strict radiative equilibrium, its temperature would monotonically decrease outward down to values of the order of 3400° for very small optical depths [10, 11]. However, there are many indications that the temperature decreases to 4500° only, and increases outward into the chromosphere. This is due to the dissipation of pressure-wave energy in high photospheric layers. In higher and higher layers this dissipation becomes increasingly effective and leads to the formation of the chromosphere and corona.

2.2. Ultraviolet Spectra

A great number of excellent spectra has been secured, mainly by the Naval Research Laboratory (N.R.L.) by Behring, McAllister, and Rense [8], see also McAllister [60], and by Kačalov and Yakovleva [51]; see Tousey's review [84]. The dispersion, initially small, has been increased in the course of the years till ultimately a resolving power could be reached, comparable to that of ground observations. On 29 August 1961, solar spectra were obtained from 3500–2200 Å by Purcell, Garrett, and Tousey [79], using an echelle spectrograph (Fig. 2). The resolving power at 2700 Å is 0.03 Å, whereas good ground observations (see, e.g., a description of the Liège spectrograph at the Jungfraujoch; L. Delbouille, L. Neven, and G. Roland [19]) have in the near uv an apparatus profile with a half-width of 0.01 Å. Interesting features in this spectral region are:

(*a*) The Mg II absorption lines, with their strong central emission peaks, at 2802.70 Å and 2795.52 Å (Fig. 3*a*).

(*b*) The abrupt and as yet unexplained change in the aspect of the spectrum between 2085 Å and 2100 Å (Fig. 3*b*). For longer wavelengths the continuum between the lines can be represented by a radiation temperature of 5500°K and the spectrum shows a wealth of many absorption lines, but for wavelengths <2085 Å the radiation temperature of the continuum is

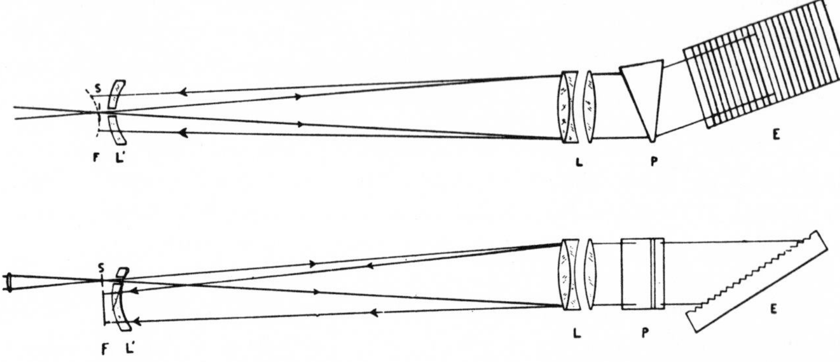

FIG. 2. NRL echelle spectrograph 4000–2000 Å range (Purcell *et al.*, [79]).

depressed down to T_R = 5000°K. Furthermore the spectral lines are greatly reduced in equivalent width: the intensities in the line cores are represented by T_R = 4900°K below as well as above the wavelength of the jump.

The available data are interesting and challenging to the theorist; however, no theoretical investigations were made to explain the observed line profiles in this spectral range; this may mainly be due to the fact that no thorough photometric intensity recordings have as yet been published. A first Photometric Atlas of the Solar Spectrum, between 1800 and 2935 Å, is McAllister's Atlas [60] (Fig. 3*a*).

Clearly, attempts to explain quantitatively the solar spectrum in this spectral range would be of great interest: the continuous absorption coefficient in this spectral range is so great that the radiation (and, in particular, the spectral line radiation) emerges from photospheric levels considerably higher than those where the lines in the usual spectral region are emitted. By studying these lines one would get more information on the

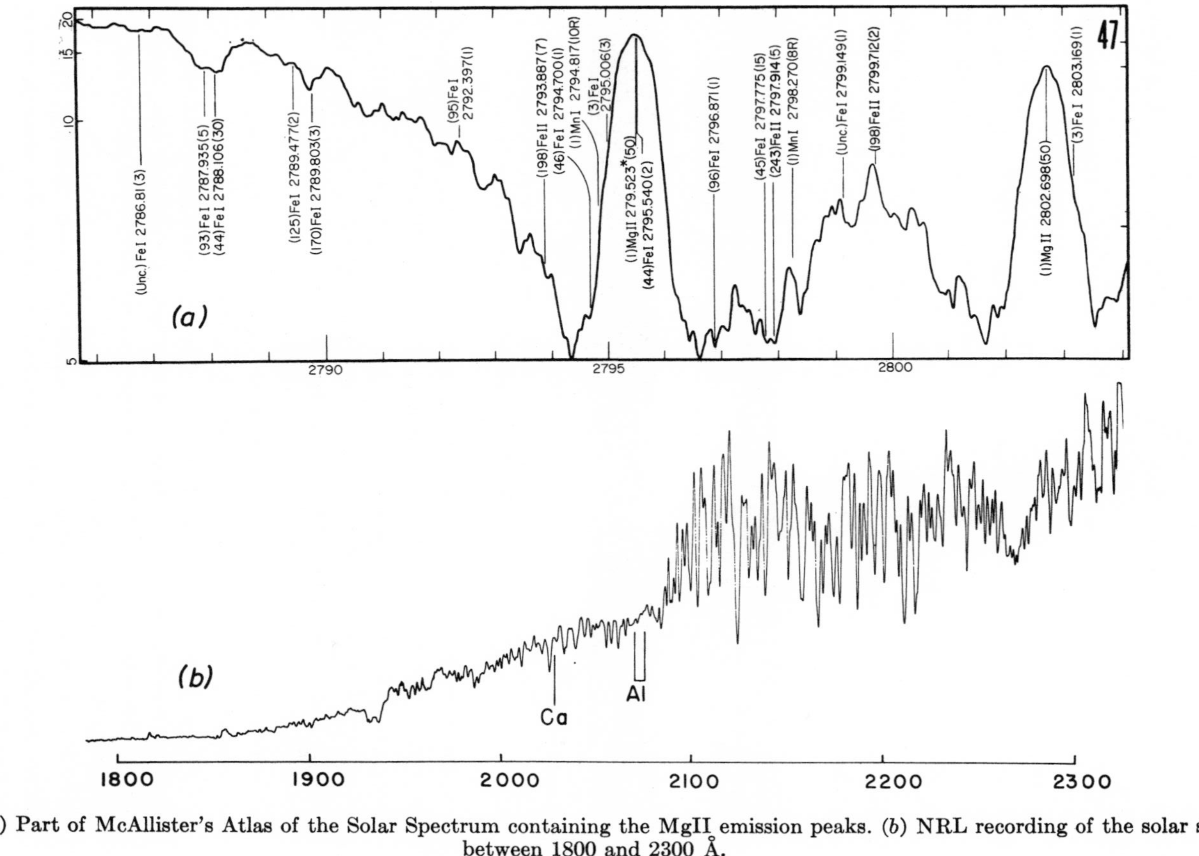

Fig. 3. (*a*) Part of McAllister's Atlas of the Solar Spectrum containing the MgII emission peaks. (*b*) NRL recording of the solar spectrum between 1800 and 2300 Å.

transition region to the chromosphere, where dissipation of mechanical energy starts being of some importance, and where the curious oscillations of the solar atmosphere described by Leighton and Noyes [58, 59, 69], and Evans and Michard *et al.* [33, 64] have been observed.

More direct information about the transition region to the chromosphere is given by the spectral region between 1000 and 2000 Å. Splendid observations of this region, virtually free of scattered light, were made with a double-dispersion grating spectrograph from an Aerobee-hi rocket flown on 19 April 1960 [20]. The spectral resolving power was about 1 Å. Later, Garrett, Purcell, and Tousey (see p. 35 of Tousey [84]) obtained new spectra between 1200 and 2000 Å, also with a double dispersion spectrograph. The resolution was 0.2 Å.

Recordings giving absolute spectral intensities in this spectral region have been published [20]. From these one reads that the solar radiation temperature* T_R obtains a minimum value of 4700° at $\lambda = 1400$ Å. This

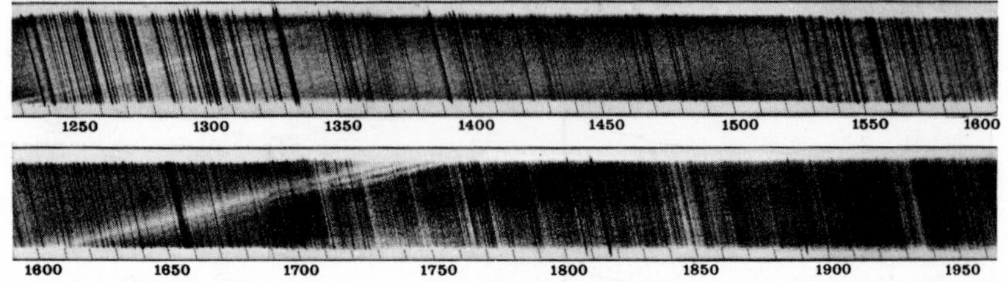

FIG. 4. Solar spectrum from 1200–2000 Å, recorded with 0.2 Å resolution by NRL, 22 August 1962 (Tousey [84]).

reflects the low-chromospheric temperature inversion: the continuous absorption coefficient in the photosphere increases with decreasing wavelength so that radiation at shorter and shorter wavelength is emitted from higher and higher solar layers. De Jager [49] has shown that these observations are compatible with a photospheric model in which a minimum temperature of 4500° is obtained at an optical depth τ_0 $(= \tau_{5000\,\text{Å}}) \equiv 0.02$. This is in good agreement with an earlier finding of Pagel [71], based on an investigation of an infrared multiplet of Fe Fraunhofer lines.

A similar conclusion may be drawn from the observation that the solar spectral lines occur as absorption lines above about 1520 Å, and occur as emission lines below 1900 Å (Fig. 4). The wavelength where absorption and emission lines are about equally numerous may be taken as 1800 Å.

Assuming local thermodynamical equilibrium and knowing that the continuous absorption coefficient increases monotonically toward shorter wavelengths it is immediately clear that the spectral lines must occur in

* Following the astrophysical convention the radiation temperature $T_R(\lambda)$ at a certain wavelength is the temperature of a blackbody of the sun's size that would emit the observed amount of radiation at the wavelength λ.

emission below a certain wavelength. It could be shown [49] that the observations are compatible with the above-mentioned results ($T_{\text{kin}} = 4500°$ at $\tau_0 = 0.02$). These conclusions are further confirmed by the observed limb brightening of the continuous spectrum below 1500 Å; for longer wavelengths, the sun still shows limb darkening.

2.3. Prospects for the Future

(*a*) It is easy to enumerate the many interesting spectral features in the region 2000–3000 Å which are now sufficiently accurately observed to be available for a theoretical discussion: see Tousey's review [84].

(*b*) A discussion of total spectral line intensities or equivalent widths in the region <2000 Å may appear to be most fruitful for an understanding of the problems of the transition region. The line profiles would be extremely useful to that aim but cannot yet be used: we therefore await future observations with a spectral resolving power ≤ 0.05 Å.

(*c*) The source function in this spectral region is strongly temperature-dependent (for a blackbody dB/dT increased strongly with decreasing wavelength). Hence observations in this spectral region refer mainly to the hot regions, and thus offer a nice opportunity to investigate the temperature inhomogeneities of the photosphere.

3. The Chromosphere and the Transition to the Corona

3.1. Structure and Problems of the Chromosphere

The structure of the chromosphere and the transition region to the corona is completely determined by the processes of the dissipation of mechanical energy and the subsequent loss of this dissipated energy (by radiation or conduction). At the top of the photosphere the mechanical energy flux is about 10^8 ergs/cm^2/sec^1; at the top of the chromosphere it is reduced to only about 10^6; at the basis of the corona it is about 10^5 ergs/cm^2/sec^1. If there was no mechanical energy flux in the sun, there would be no chromosphere or corona, and the sun would have a thin atmosphere with a "limb temperature" of about 3400°. The differences between the mechanical fluxes in the nonmagnetic and magnetic solar regions, and the different ways of dissipating this energy in these various regions, determine the structure of the chromosphere in its nonmagnetic quiet regions, in the magnetic parts of the "quiet" regions (the chromospheric mottling and network), and in the disturbed regions (the *faculae*, or *plages*).

When observed through an Hα filter or a spectroheliograph, the spicules are clearly visible at the sun's limb and also, but less easy, on the disc. This makes clear that the chromosphere is constituted of two different kinds of elements. Many spectral observations point to the same conclusion.

No doubts exist about the high chromospheric structures ($h > 5000$–7000 km). There the spicules are individually visible and protrude into the corona. Since the spicules emit Hα and the other low excitation lines, they must consist of elements of fairly cool gas, penetrating into the hot corona. Their temperature is estimated to be about 20,000° (to within a factor of the order $\frac{1}{2}$ ...4); the coronal temperature is close to 10^6°K.

Neither is there any dispute about the low chromosphere: the temperature is fairly low, perhaps slowly increasing from the solar limb value (4500°K) up to a value of the order of 10^4°K at 1000 km. It also seems that in these parts the spicular structure does not yet occur.

The real difficulty is connected with the middle chromosphere ($1000 < h < 5000$ km); see also Figure 5. It is here that the spicules seem to originate; it seems that they exist already as low as 1000 or 2000 km above the photosphere [45, 63]. The problem is, however, whether the spicules have their temperature of about 2.10^4°K already at that low level, or whether they have a low temperature in the middle chromosphere.

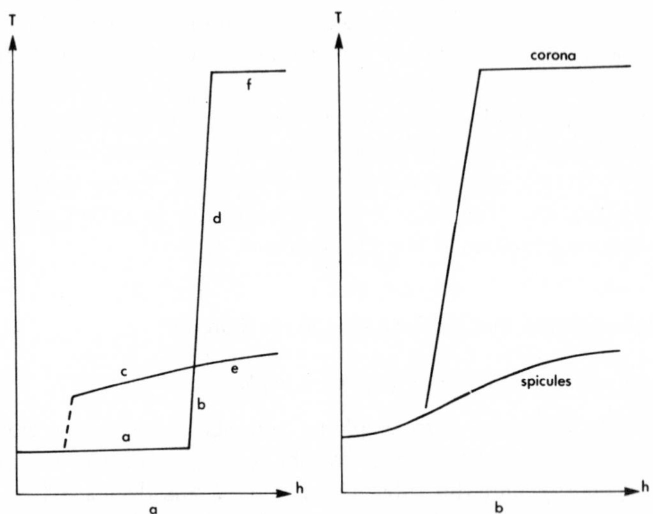

FIG. 5. Schematic representation of temperatures in the chromosphere.

Here, two contradicting models have been proposed in the course of the last ten years. The Thomas-Athay model [4] suggested that the spicular temperature varied along the track *a*, *b*, *e* in Figure 5*a*, and that the temperature of interspicular matter varied along *c*, *d*, *f*, whereas the Woltjer-de Jager model assumed *c*, *e* for the spicules and *a*, *b*, *d*, *f* for the interspicular matter [45, 90].

That the spicules cannot have the very low temperature indicated by the track *a* in Figure 5*a*, is evident from the following: (*i*) spicules observed on the disc [7, 13] occupy not more than 10 or 20 per cent of the middle chromosphere; (*ii*) the radio brightness temperature of the sun at mm waves (these waves are emitted by the middle chromosphere) is as low as 6000°K so that the average middle chromosphere must have a temperature of that order; and (*iii*) high excitation emission and absorption (like that of the infrared He line at 10 830 Å) is also bound to a relatively small volume of the chromosphere.

On the other hand, there are some indications that the fairly high temperatures like those shown by the track *c*, *e* of Figure 5*a* do not occur either. In fact, when all deduced temperatures of the low and middle chromosphere are plotted, there does not seem to be a considerable, or even a real, temperature difference between the two kinds of middle-

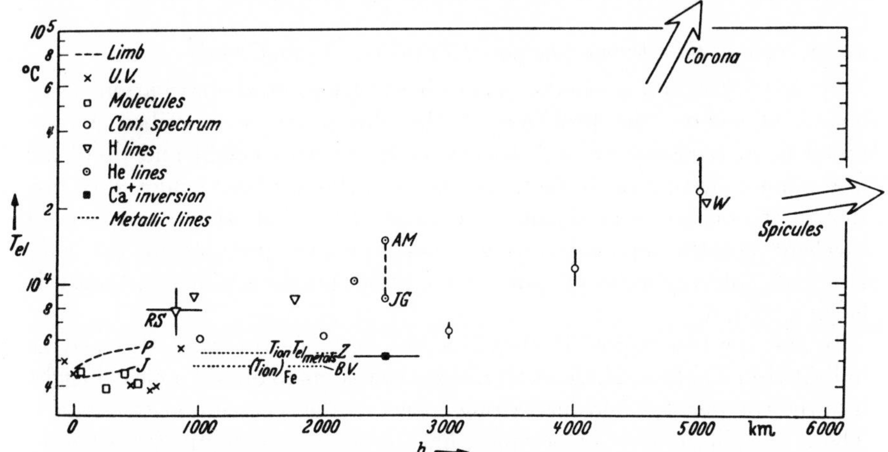

FIG. 6. Temperature determinations in the chromosphere (de Jager [45]).

chromospheric elements (Fig. 6), but that the temperature of the whole of the emitting elements seems to increase slowly from low values to sometimes 10^4°K at heights near 10,000 km.

Hence, the real problem is whether the middle chromosphere does really consist of cool *and* hotter chromospheric gases or whether there is perhaps only one kind of *chromospheric* element between which the hot coronal gas occurs. This fairly revolutionary suggestion has been put forward by Namba [66] in a paper that perhaps did not obtain the attention it deserves. He could show that the spicules are rather cool, and, on the basis of observations of Hiei (see [66]), that the whole chromospheric emission above 1000 or 2000 km comes from the spicules. Thus he derived a chromospheric model, essentially like the one schematically shown in Figure 5*b*.

Similar considerations, and furthermore the observation made at one solar eclipse (R. G. Athay and W. O. Roberts [94]) that the maximum of coronal line emission of λ 7892 of FeXI occurs below 10,000 km and that, in fact, the true height of the maximum could not be detected, have led Zirin and Dietz [92] to the same suggestion: the rapid transition from chromospheric to coronal temperatures should occur already near 2000 km so that the temperature variation in the chromosphere would be as shown in Figure 5*b*. The suggestion of Namba, supported by Zirin and Dietz is an interesting one, which may solve quite a number of problems.

On the basis of this suggestion there would no longer be any physical difference between the middle and the high chromosphere; the only difference would be an apparent one, based on the appearance of the chromosphere at the sun's limb: the spicules originate about at 1000 to 2000 km; many spicules extend up to 7000 km; and this suggests a homogeneous chromosphere; above that height spicules are individually visible.

3.2. Spectra of the Chromosphere and Transition to the Corona

We have to examine whether solar ultraviolet spectral observations have helped in solving the problems of the chromosphere described above: problems of temperature and density variation with height and problems of the inhomogeneities. In fact, regrettably little has been achieved so far, though the observers need not be reproached for that; they have secured excellent spectra and interesting monochromatic pictures of the sun. However, interpretation of most of the observations is difficult; theory is lagging behind.

In the spectral region 1500–200 Å the best spectra were obtained as indicated in Table 1. These observations enable us to obtain a clear insight into the complicated and interesting aspect of the spectrum in this region. The spectrum consists of emission lines only, characteristic for a gas in

TABLE 1

λ in Å	Reference	Date	Resolving Power in Å	Instrument
500–1550	[20]	19 April 1960	1	Photographic; double-dispersion
1200–2000	[79]	22 August 1962	0.2	Photographic, double-dispersion
250–1300	[40]	29 January 1960	2	Photoelectric, recording + telemetry
60–315	[41]	19 January 1960		
170–335	[85]	22 August 1962	0.3	Photographic
255–600	[39]	23 August 1961	1.5	Photoelectric recording
170–400	[8]	30 September 1961	1.5	Photoelectric recording
idem	[68]	Several months after 7 March 1962	1.5	Photoelectric recording in OSO I

which the source function increases outward. The lines cover a very wide range of excitation conditions, ranging from lines of neutral atoms of low ionization potentials like the Si I lines around 1400 Å, via lines of neutral atoms of high ionization and/or excitation potentials like the C I and N I lines, and like the famous Ly α line at 1216 Å, to lines from highly ionized atoms like the S VI lines near 950 Å, the O VI lines near 1100 Å, the lines of Ne VIII near 780 Å, those of Mg X near 615 Å. Lines of very highly ionized atoms in the short-wavelength end (like Ne VII at 465, Si XII at 500, Mg IX at 369, Fe XVI at 335, and Fe XV at 283 Å, and other similar lines) are already of coronal origin. Further interesting features in this spectral range are the lines of the Lyman series of hydrogen. Of this series eleven lines have been detected. The Lyman continuum has also been observed both photoelectrically and photographically. Of neutral He the resonance line at 584 Å and the 1^1S-3^1P line at 537 Å have also been observed with about one-ninth the intensity of the first. Five or six of the members of the Lyman series of ionized helium have been detected, as well as the Lyman continuum at 228 Å of ionized helium, and the first member of the Balmer series of ionized helium (1640 Å). (For a detailed description of the spectrum, see Tousey's review [84].)

The lines originate from the chromosphere, but those with high ionization or excitation potential come from the transition region chromosphere-

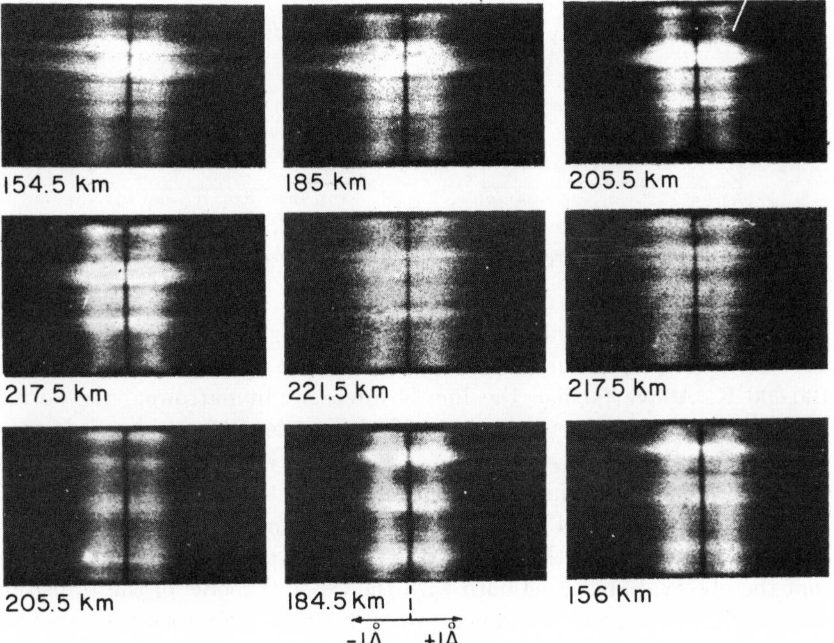

FIG. 7. Profiles of Ly α, observed by NRL 19 April 1961.

corona. Indeed the application of simple non-LTE ionization formulas [45] shows that in order to be present in the spectrum the O VI lines need temperatures of about 2.6×10^5°K. Lyman α needs lower temperatures; first estimates based on the measured intensities [3, 43] yielded temperatures of the order of 20,000–50,000°K. The interesting profile, with its central broad self-reversal of solar origin (Figs. 7 and 8), has been discussed by Morton and Widing [65], who found that the central part of the quiet-sun profile observed 22 August 1962 can be explained with an electron temperature of 50,000°K [65, 84]. Similarly, the profile of Ly β can be described by a kinetic temperature of 52,000° [42]. These temperatures are no longer representative of the chromosphere but rather of the transition

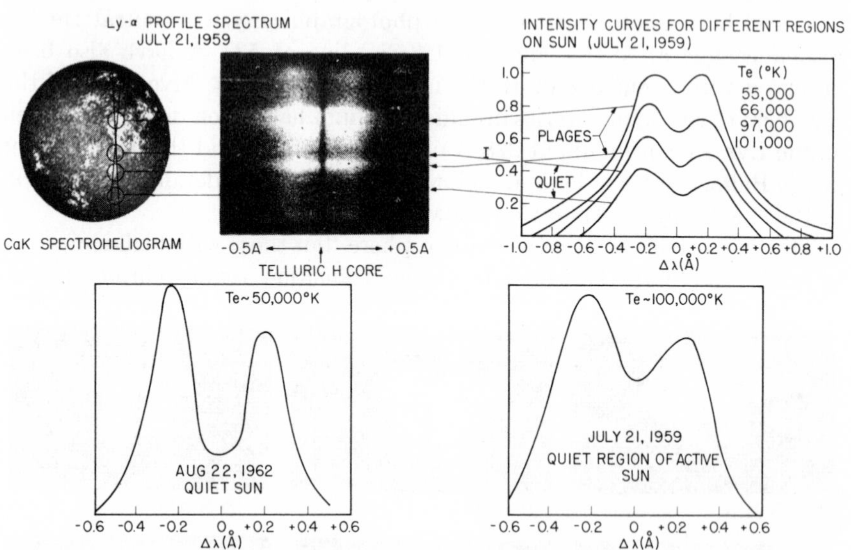

FIG. 8. Theoretical interpretation of the observed Ly α profiles (Tousey [84]).

region to the corona. Quiet regions of the active sun have less self-reversal; the electron temperature necessary to explain these profiles is about 100,000°K. Above faculae the line is intenser but narrower; the corresponding electron temperature is less by some ten thousands of degrees.

Allen [1] was the first to make a preliminary attempt to explain the observed intensities of lines emitted by the transition region. His work was hampered by the lack of absolute line intensity measurements, and by the lack of f-values. Nevertheless his investigation allowed him to conclude that the observations agree both with the Oster II model of the transition region and with a coronal temperature of 8.10^5°K. The work was repeated in more detail by Pottasch [76] who derived a method for deducing solar chemical abundances from the observed intensities; the problem of the deviations from LTE could be overcome by an ingenious procedure. Nor is his method, however, watertight, and what are needed may be listed as follows:

(*a*) Reliable wavelength predictions and identifications (cf., for example, [73]); (*b*) reliable line intensities; and (*c*) *f*-values: such information should allow the theorist to exploit to their full extent the splendid spectra hitherto obtained, and to do justice to the exciting work done by the observers. From the observational side, moreoever, one would desire (*a*) spectra with so high a resolving power that line profiles can be determined for a line profile, and even a line width is an important piece of information and allows a much easier deduction of the physical parameters of the source than is possible on the basis of total line intensities, (*b*) many more spectra of well-selected regions of the disc. They will allow us to determine the variation of the physical parameters like T, N_e, turbulent velocity component, etc., as a function of height and to intercompare these results for the various solar features. This would enable one to investigate the wonderful no-man's-land between the low chromosphere and the corona and to see what happens to the mechanical energy flux in these structures. Our ignorance of what really happens to the energy flux and its role for chromospheric and coronal heating could thus be removed in an empirical way. In order that this information can be derived sufficiently reliably one would need a spatial resolving power corresponding to about 5000 km on the disc—10–15″.

4. X-Rays from the Quiet Corona

4.1. Structure and Dynamics of the Quiet Corona

Seldom is the corona completely free of any sign of activity, and even if this is the case there is still a difference in structure between the quiet corona as it occurs during sunspot maximum and the quiet minimum corona.

There is one unique specimen of the quiet minimum corona: the one observed during the eclipse of 30 June 1954 (Fig. 8). At that time only one very small prominence was visible at the sun's limb; no spots had been observed for 8 days preceding and 12 days following the eclipse. This corona showed a remarkable symmetry with, as its main features, the oblated equatorial belt and the polar plumes, which are clear indicators of the corona's magnetic field.

The active corona (Fig. 9) is characterized by its rays which may extend up to many solar radii distance from the solar center; sometimes these rays are so numerous that they occult the polar plumes and make the corona

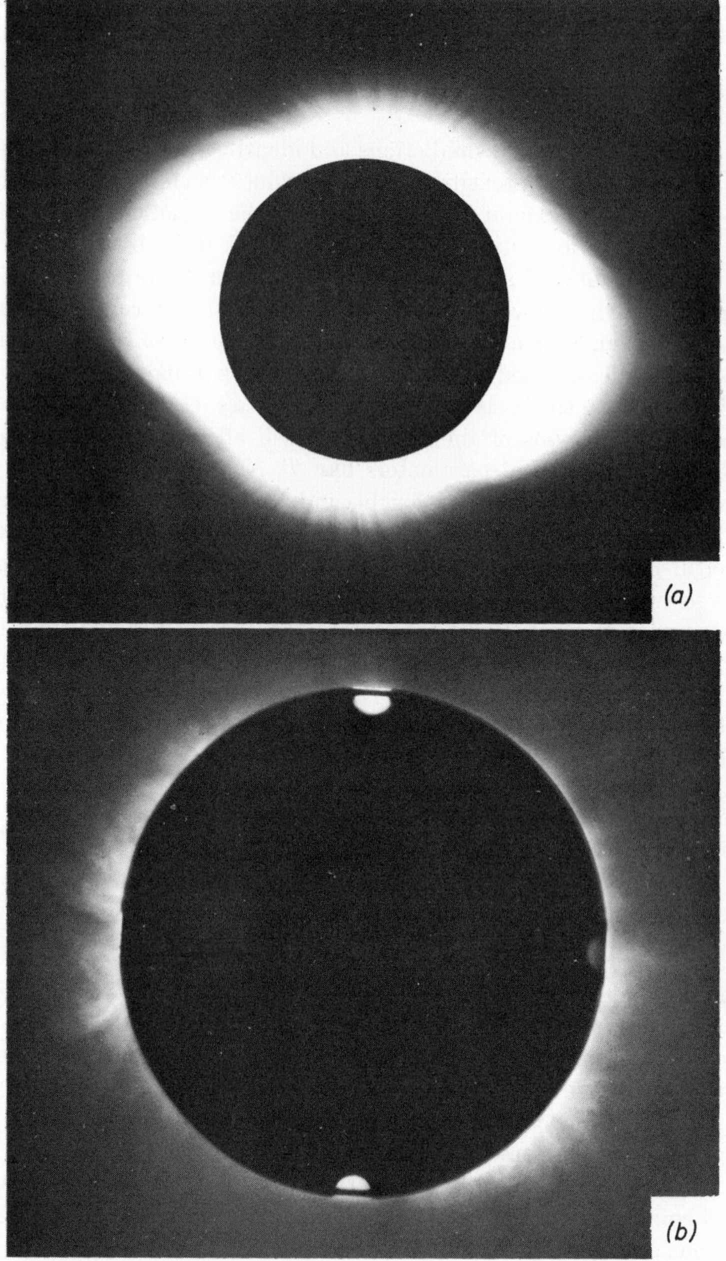

FIG. 9. (a) Solar corona photographed at the eclipse of 30 June 1954 by Å. Wallenquist, Uppsala. (b) Active corona, photographed in light of the 5303 Å line of Fe XI at Pic du Midi Observatory.

appear more or less spherical. The coronal light consists of three components:

L-corona: A line spectrum emitted by a completely ionized plasma ($T \approx 10^6$°K); because all coronal lines are due to a recombinationlike process the intensity of the *L*-corona depends on $N_eN_i \sim N_e^2$, and hence decreases rapidly with increasing distance to the sun.

K-corona: Light scattered by the free electrons of the above-mentioned coronal plasma; the intensity, proportional to N_e, decreases less rapidly than that of the *L*-corona. The light is polarized and does not contain Fraunhofer lines because of the high velocity of the electrons.

F-corona: Sunlight scattered by dust particles in the line of sight but at relatively great distances to the sun ($> 4\ R_\odot$). The spectrum is identical to that of the sun and contains Fraunhofer lines.

By investigating the polarization and the depths of the Fraunhofer lines, the *K*- and *F*- components can be separated, and this allows the determination of the coronal electron densities N_e/cm^3. Figure 10 gives these curves for four cases; the differences appear to be quite pronounced.

Before turning to a description of the X-ray spectrum of the quiet corona, we review some coronal problems; they were topical before the IGY and are not completely solved yet although we see the problems sharper now than ten years ago:

(*a*) *The Coronal Temperature.* Because of the high thermal conductivity of this very hot plasma, the corona is virtually isothermal up to a great distance to the sun. There is some dispute about the value of this temperature. Two ideas are strongly divergent:

(*i*) The corona has a relatively low kinetic temperature (Elwert, Lüst, de Jager and Kuperus, Seaton, Waldmeier) thought to be about 8×10^5°K. This value is derived from radio observations, coronal ionization, X-rays. It is realized, of course, that the observed widths of coronal emission lines give kinetic temperatures about one million degrees higher than those derived from coronal ionization, but Lüst and Seaton explain this by the assumption of random or systematic small-scale gas motions with a velocity of some tens of km/sec. Seaton [81] gives the following comparison (Table 2) between the "Doppler temperatures" T_D derived from widths of emission

TABLE 2

	T_D	T_e
Fe X	1.7–1.8 × 10^6°K	0.5 × 10^6°K
Fe XIV	2.4–2.6 × 10^6°K	1.1 × 10^6°K
Fe VI	—	1.6 × 10^6°K
Ca XV	3.5–4.0 × 10^6°K	2.5 × 10^6°K

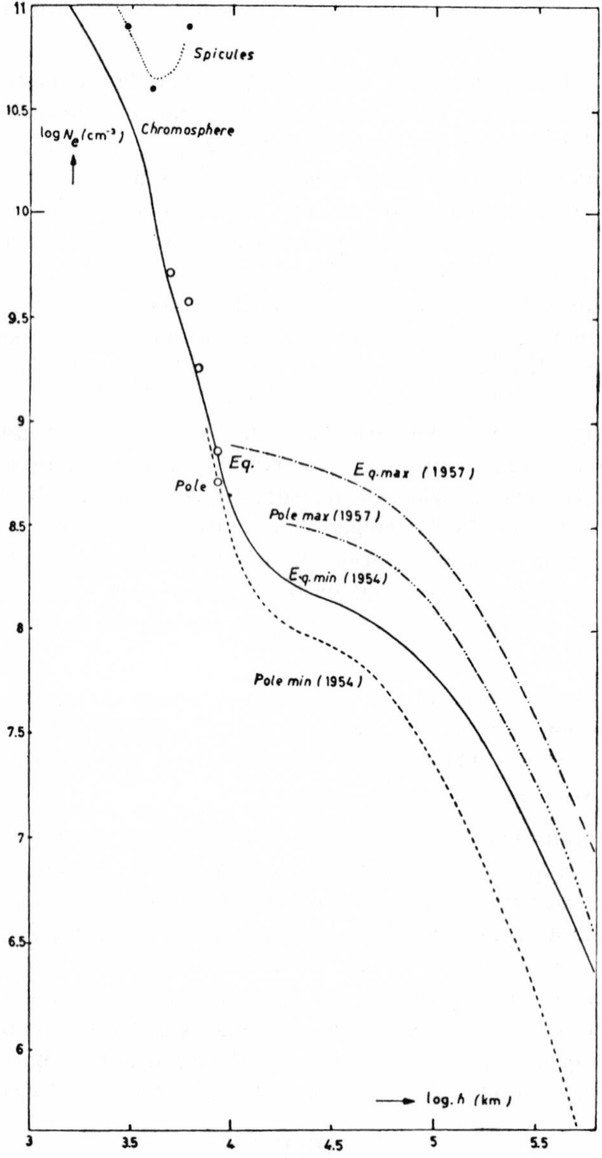

FIG. 10. Variation of the electron density with height for the equatorial maximum and minimum corona, and the polar maximum and minimum corona.

lines, and the (kinetic) electron temperatures deduced from the ratio of line intensities on the basis of a non-LTE ionization theory. At $T = 10^6$°K, the mean velocity of the electrons is 6000 km/sec, that of the Fe-ions is only 20 km/sec. Because the velocities add quadratically, the addition of random "turbulent" velocities of about 60 km/sec would, hence, only affect the ion motions and would double the "temperature" derived from the line widths, and would not influence the degree of ionization.

(*ii*) The other assumption is that the coronal kinetic temperature is really of the order 2×10^6°K (Billings, Zirin, and essentially the Boulder and Sacramento Peak groups). On the basis of this picture the low electron temperature still needs explaining. A possible explanation was given by Neupert [67] on the basis of the solar wind hypothesis: suppose that the coronal (and chromospheric) matter streams out. At a certain level the electron temperature increases discontinuously from chromospheric values up to a value of 2.5×10^6°K. There is, however, a time lag in the ionization, which is of the order of some tens of seconds, and depends moreover on the degree of ionization. The consequence is that at the bottom of the corona the ionization temperature is still low and that it increases in a range of sometimes 10^4 km to higher values (Fig. 11). This hypothesis could be verified if it could be shown observationally that a range of ionization temperatures occurs in the solar corona (which is the case) and that the highest temperatures occur at the greatest heights (which has not yet been shown). But observations of intensities at radio wavelengths, also those referring to the high coronal levels, indicate low electron temperatures; and this makes this latter suggestion somewhat doubtful.

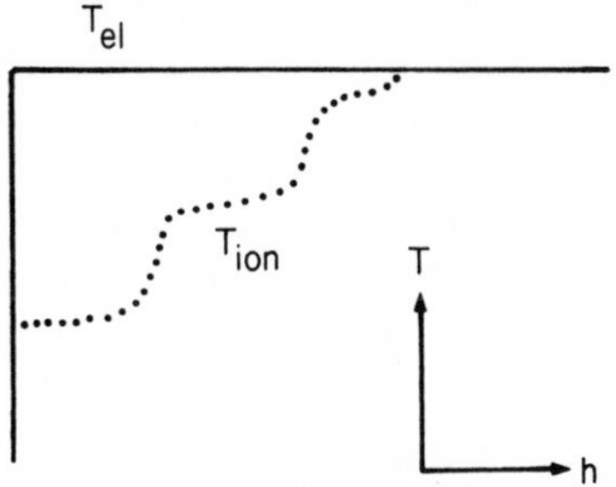

FIG. 11. Influence of solar wind on the coronal ionization temperatures (suggestion of W. Neupert).

(*b*) *Coronal Inhomogeneities.* Is the corona homogeneous or inhomogeneous? There are different ways of approach:

(*i*) Is the occurrence of ions of different degrees of ionization compatible with one coronal temperature? The observations show that lines of different degrees of ionization of the same element occur simultaneously and apparently at the same place at the limb. Current ideas (e.g., Seaton [81]) that these lines should then be emitted by different elements of gas, in the line of sight, and that it would be impossible for them to be emitted by the same gas are not confirmed by the investigation of Athay and Hyder [5] who considered coronal ionization by a two-step collision process, via the excitation of a metastable level; see Table 3, which gives the percentage of ions in that particular state of ionization. On the basis of this theory it is fairly well possible that the corona is thermally homogeneous with an electron temperature of the order of 8×10^5°K.

TABLE 3

	$T_{el} = 6 \times 10^{5}$°K	$T_{el} = 8 \times 10^{5}$°K
Fe X	0.35	0.06
XI	0.27	0.16
XII	0.12	0.25
XIII	0.04	0.34
XIV	2×10^{-3}	0.16
XV	8×10^{-4}	0.03

(*ii*) The obvious difficulty is that observations in the optical spectral region show the corona beyond the limb and that, hence, the line of sight passes through a considerable length of coronal gas. Still Dollfus [21] claims that the existence of one monochromatic emission in one point of the corona precludes that of another line. Each element of gas should, therefore, have one sharply defined ionization temperature. The hotter structures should surround but not penetrate the cooler ones.

(*iii*) One may also look at the chromosphere underneath. This part of the sun is clearly inhomogeneous, also in the quiet regions, and shows the features listed in Table 4.

The chromospheric network consists of coarse mottles; these, in turn seem to show a structure of fine mottles. The magnetic field of the network and the mottles seems to be 5 gauss. Because of the magnetic field, the mechanical energy flux will be different, presumably greater in the mottles than in the quiet nonmagnetic parts of the corona, but according to Osterbrock [70] such a flux in the magnetic parts would be reflected before reaching the corona. Kuperus [57], on the other hand, assuming heating by nonmagnetic shock waves finds it possible to explain that the corona above the magnetic regions has five times the density of the quiet corona, and a temperature that is some 50 per cent higher. From these points of view one could expect the very low corona to show a pattern like that of the mottles, but the problem is how this pattern would be smoothed in the higher corona by thermal conduction and what the role of the magnetic field is in this

TABLE 4

Element	Characteristic Length in km	Lifetime	Reference
Chromospheric network	25,000–50,000	Days	[44]
Coarse mottles	2000–8000	20 hours	[44, 61]
Fine mottles	1000	10–18 min	[7, 13]

respect. In conclusion we may state that the problem of the coronal inhomogeneities is still completely open.

4.2. Theory and Observations of X-Rays from the Quiet Corona

There are three components to the radiation of the corona: the continuum radiation consisting of a free-free component (mainly free-free transitions of electrons in the field of protons), a free-bound component (recombinations of electrons with the heavy ions of the coronal plasma), and the line emissions. Some of the emission lines are due to a deexcitation of an upper level populated by recombination; the greater part, however, is the result of direct excitation by electron impacts.

Since all the emissions are proportional to $N_e N_i$ and because in this highly ionized plasma N_i is proportional to N_e, the intensity of the coronal emissions is proportional to N_e^2. As in the corona N_e decreases outward with a scale height of about 5.10^4 km, the X-ray emission intensity should decrease outward with a scale height of about 2.5×10^4 km; i.e., the intensity would decrease to 0.01 of the limb value over a distance of a little more than 10^5 km.

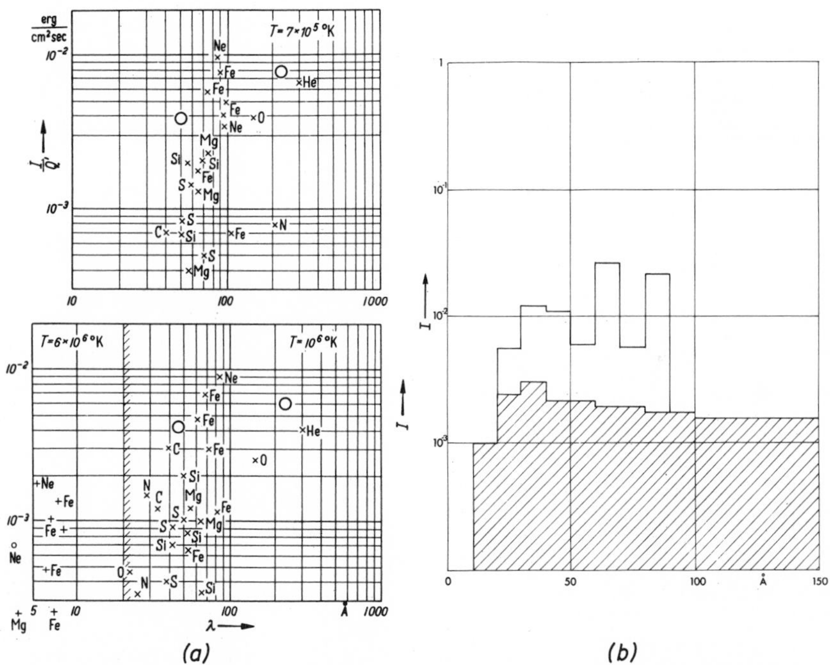

FIG. 12. (*a*) Spectrum of the corona for temperatures of 7×10^5, 10^6, and 6×10^6 °K (left part of lower figure). Lines are shown by crosses, series continua by circles. The ordinate gives the intensity at the earth's distance divided by an uncertainty factor Q' (G. Elwert [25]). (*b*) Comparison of computed continuous and line intensities (respectively shaded and not shaded) after Elwert's computations for $T = 10^6$ °K.

The detailed computations, which were made with great care by Elwert [23–29] still involve a number of uncertainties: most ionic levels have not yet been measured and their excitation and ionization energies had to be computed either by assuming the ion hydrogenlike or by extrapolation of isoelectronic sequences. Further uncertain factors are the probability of

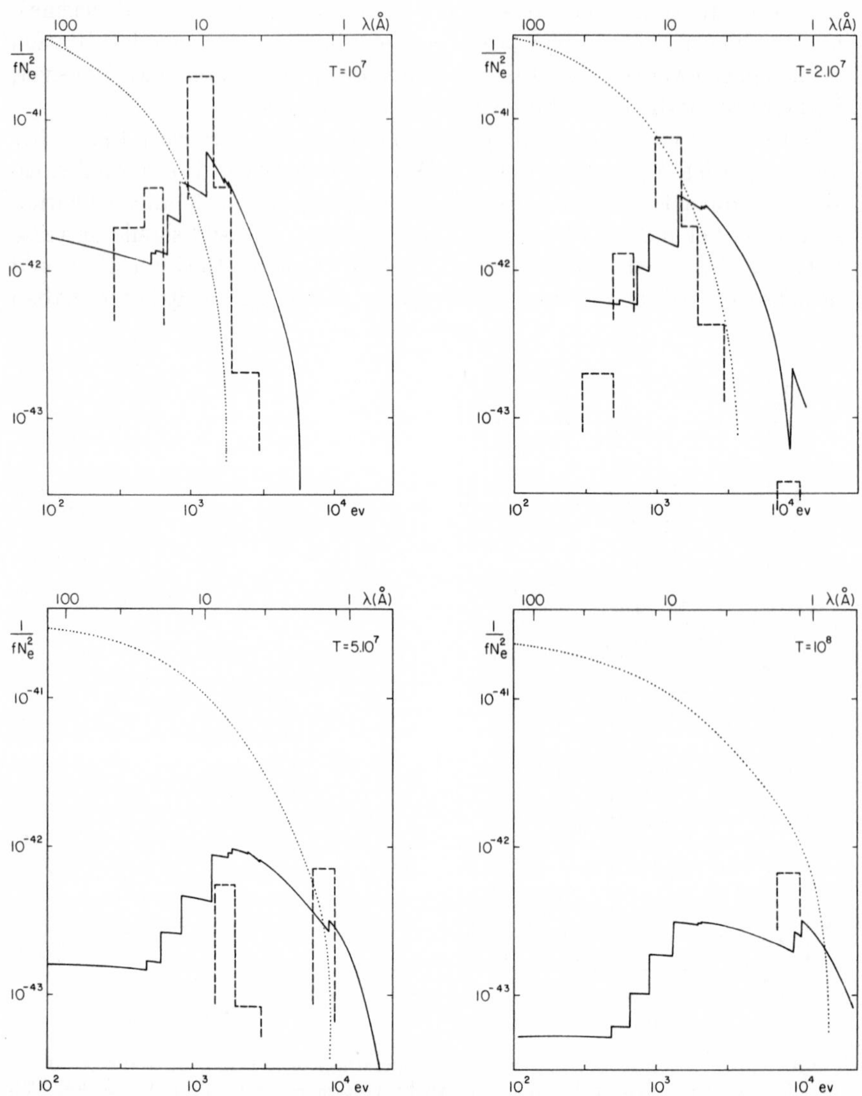

Fig. 13. Computed X-ray radiation for temperatures ranging between 10^7 till 10^{8}°K (after Kawabata [52]). Dotted lines: free-free transitions; solid lines: free-bound transitions; dashed lines: Line emissions summed up in discrete energy intervals.

recombination to excited states and the probability of direct excitation by electron impact. Furthermore, the fine structure of the lines could not be taken into account. Notwithstanding these uncertainties Elwert's computations were remarkably consistent with later observations. Elwert made his predictions for temperatures of 7.10^5, 10^6, and 6.10^6°K. Later Kawabata extended them to values of 10^7, 2.10^7, 5.10^7, and 10^8°K. One feature of the results is that the maximum wavelength of emission shifts to shorter wavelengths for increasing temperatures; another feature is that,

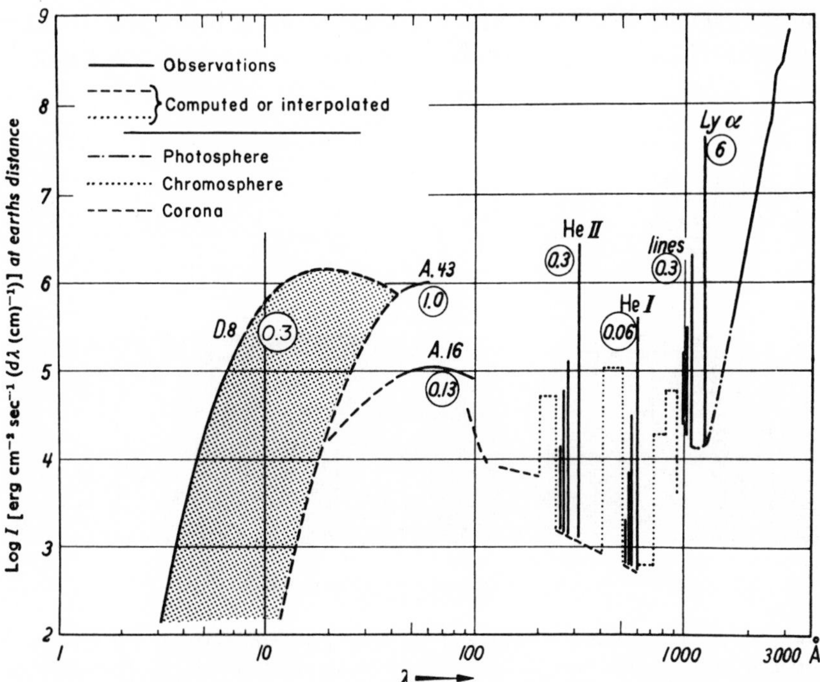

FIG. 14. Intensities as determined in the ultraviolet and X-ray spectrum of the sun during and around the IGY. Total flux emitted in the various groups of lines or under the solid curves is indicated in circles (ergs/cm²/sec). Curve A16 is more or less representative for quiet maximum corona; curve A43 for the active maximum corona; D8 for flare activity (from *Handbuch der Physik*, **52**, 264, 1959).

in any case for low temperatures, line emissions are predicted to be much more important than the continuous emission. For $T \approx 10^6$°K their ratio is of the order of ten. Figure 12 shows Elwert's results; Figure 13 those of Kawabata.

From these Elwert predicted an integrated X-ray flux of 0.03 Q erg/cm²/sec during sunspot minimum, 0.4 Q erg/cm²/sec during sunspot maximum (Q is an uncertainty factor of the order 2 to 4). These values are roughly in agreement with observations; during sunspot minimum Friedman [34] observed 0.13 erg/cm²/sec, during maximum he found values ranging from 0.4 to 1 erg/cm²/sec.

Around the IGY one was thus able to establish roughly the shape of the coronal spectrum shown in Figure 14. Later it appeared possible to observe the individual line radiations. The detailed X-ray spectrum of the quiet corona could only be measured after 1960. Figure 15 shows the spectrum between 160 and 62 Å as observed by Hinteregger [40, 41]. Very probably the little peaks and humps in the curve correspond to certain emission lines. For a correct comparison one has, however, to take into account that the observations were taken with a spectral resolving power of 2 Å. If the intensities of all lines in the predicted spectrum are smeared out over 2 Å,

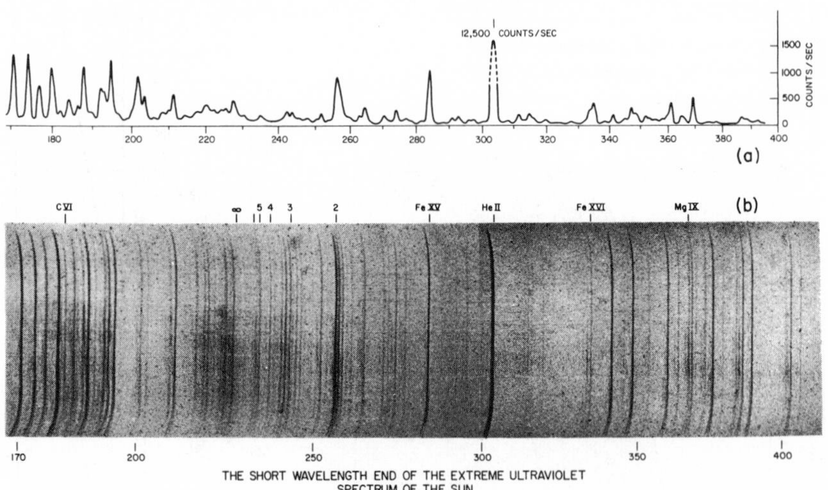

FIG. 15. (*a*) Photoelectric recording of the solar spectrum between 180 and 400 Å obtained with a rocketborne photoelectric recording spectrograph. (*b*) Photograph of the same spectral region, 22 August 1962 by NRL. (Tousey, p. 39 of [84].)

one obtains the result shown in Figure 16 (after Elwert). Taking into account our ignorance of the fine structure of the lines, the result agrees qualitatively with the observations.

More recently (1963) spectral line observations were made with a better spectral resolving power (see Tousey [84] appendix). Hinteregger *et al.* flew an Aerobee-hi rocket with the ARDC scanning grazing-incidence monochromator. Scanning was done between 315 and 55 Å with a scanning speed of 2 Å/sec; the detector had a LiF photocathode, which is blind for $\lambda > 1100$ Å, and this reduces greatly the influence of straylight (Ly α); furthermore the LiF cathode has a greater quantum efficiency for shorter wavelengths than ordinary tungsten. The instrumental profile had a width of 0.35 Å at 55 Å; lines could be detected down to 65 Å. The intensity drop

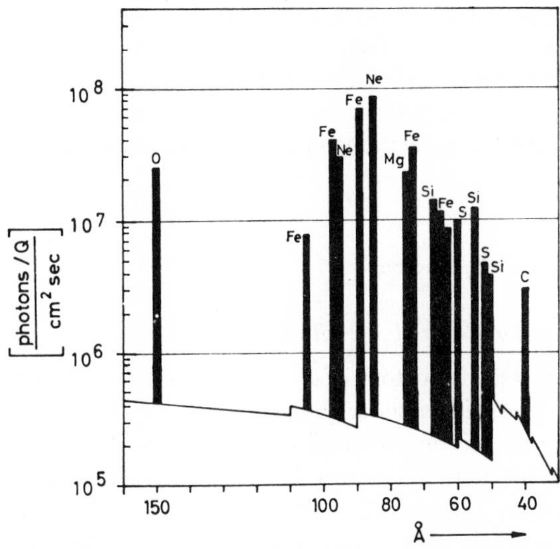

FIG. 16. Predicted quiet coronal spectrum between 150 and 30 Å (Elwert [30]). Fine structure has been neglected; lines were smeared out over 2 Å.

at 170 Å, observed earlier, appears to be real. On 10 May 1963 Austin, Purcell, and Tousey flew the NRL grazing-incidence spectrograph with a new diffraction grazing with increased speed. Lines could be detected down to 44 Å. In the summer of 1963 Friedman, Blake, Chubb, and coworkers flew a crystal spectrometer in a rocket and were able to detect many lines down to a wavelength of 13 Å; a preliminary investigation of the spectrum did not show traces of a continuous spectrum.

4.3. Future Observations

For a quantitative interpretation of the observations, it is necessary not only to dispose of line intensities but also of profiles of well-identified lines. A determination of the half-widths of the lines in the disc center and beyond the limb would enable one to see whether the lines in front of the disc have the same width as those at the limb. According to certain theories this should not be the case, and the limb lines should be broadened by a motion field with velocity components tangential to the surface. Such a determination could perhaps help to solve the problem of the coronal temperatures.

It would be very useful if the intensities of certain lines, all belonging to the same multiplet, could be determined with good precision ($\pm$ 10 per cent) across the disc and beyond the limb. Such a determination would enable one to determine curves of growth for various values of $\cos\theta$ (θ is the angle between the normal to the surface and the direction to the observer) and observationally to determine the amount of self-absorption in the lines, which would open the way to a thorough astrophysical treatment of the problem of coronal line formation. A further step would then be the determination of abundances of chemical elements in the corona. Finally, a very exciting achievement would be the determination of the Zeeman splitting of coronal lines, enabling one the measurements of coronal magnetic field.

5. The Coronal Activity Regions

5.1. Problems of the Coronal Activity Centers

The complicated life history of a coronal center of activity need not be discussed here (see Kiepenheuer [54] and de Jager [46]). A coronal activity center (CA) is the coronal extension of a photospheric or chromospheric plage (facular field); the structure is very complicated, and it is approximated by certain models, like the Waldmeier-Müller model [87]. As compared to normal coronal values a coronal CA has a greater density. From radio observations one obtains a densification factor of approximately 5 to 10; from K-coronameter observations the densification is 2 to 5. This need not be a contradiction: it may be that a coronal CA consists of two parts: a broad base where the density is only 2 to 5 times the normal coronal value, and a central part where it reaches its greatest density. Furthermore the enhancement of density seems to be greater at the basis of the CA than in higher levels (Fig. 17), and this also may be a reason for the difference between radio results (which apply to low levels) and coronameter results (applying to higher levels).

From a discussion of one activity center, observed by many different observational techniques, Christiansen *et al.* [16] derived the results shown and compared with other determinations in Figure 17. As compared with the normal corona the density is about 10 times greater at the basis, it is 5 times greater higher up. Further, also the temperature seems to be higher, but only slightly so (about 50 per cent).

The theoretical explanation of the shape of the coronal activity centers and of their physical parameters has not made much progress so far. Certainly the structure of an activity center is for an important part determined by its magnetic field; the latter is of the order of about 50 gauss; at their borderline the CA's have fields of the order of 10 gauss. In this connection we should immediately add that the chromospheric mottling consists of structures with essentially the same physical parameters (T; N_e) as the faculae [96]; only their magnetic field (about 5 gauss) seems somewhat smaller, curiously enough. It would not be surprising if the magnetic fields would eventually turn out to be of the same order; and in that case the problem of the theoretical explanation will be essentially the same for the mottling and the faculae.

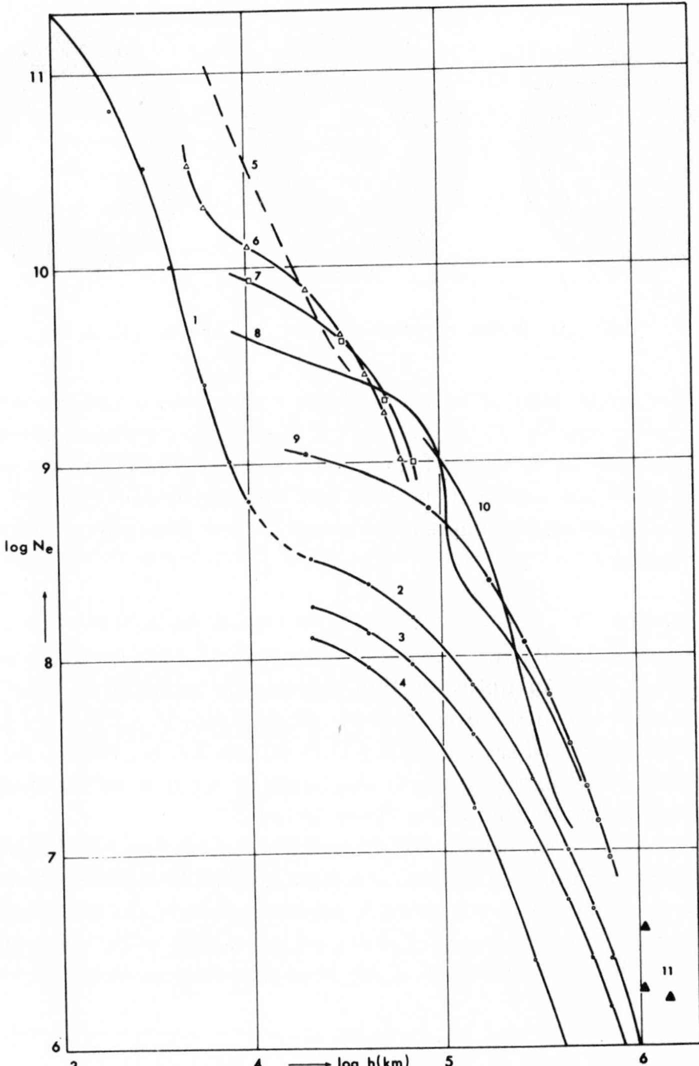

Fig. 17. Comparison of the electron density and temperature variation in the quiet corona and in an activity center (Kuperus [57]).

Osterbrock [70], assuming $B = 200$ gauss, computed the generation of mechanical energy in the solar convection layer and its dissipation and reflection. The mechanical energy flux appears to be fully reflected downward, already at heights below 2000 km, hence leaving no energy for the heating of chromospheric mottles and the corona. Kuperus [57] assumed a smaller field than Osterbrock, but such that the energy generated is still higher than for the quiet corona, and such that at the same time the waves

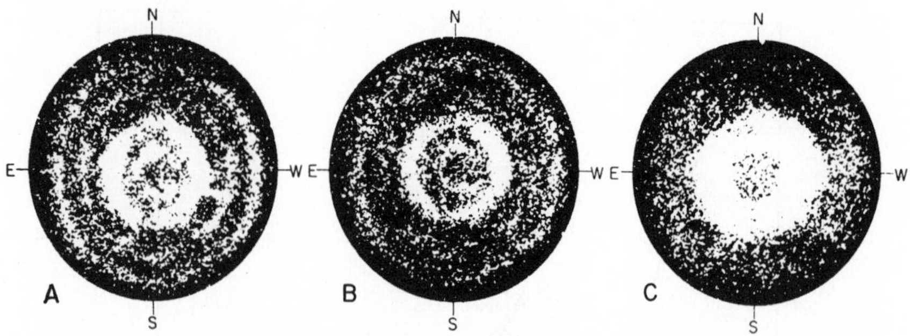

FIG. 18. Pinhole pictures of the sun (Blake *et al.* [9]).

have still the character of sound or shock waves (which are less reflected than magnetic waves). He thus found it possible to predict electron densities about four times those of the quiet corona, and of electron temperatures about 50 per cent higher. Although this agreement with the observations seems promising one should await a three-dimensional discussion of this problem.

5.2. Monochromatic X-Ray Images from Coronal Activity Regions

The electron density in the coronal CA's is two to ten times that of the quiet corona. For an optically thin corona the intensity of the X-ray radiation observed in the disc center is proportional to $\int N_e^2\, dh \approx \frac{1}{2} N_e^2 \mathcal{H}$, where $\mathcal{H}$ is the coronal scale height, which is $1\frac{1}{2}$ to 2 times that of the quiet corona. Hence the expected X-ray radiation in the disc center should be four to hundred times that of the quiet corona.

This result was confirmed by observations made by Friedman *et al.* [35], using the simplest possible technique, a pinhole camera. During the exposure the camera was subjected to a rotation of about 120° around the optical axis of the camera (Fig. 18); still a careful reduction appeared possible [9]; it showed that the X-ray intensity maxima nicely correspond

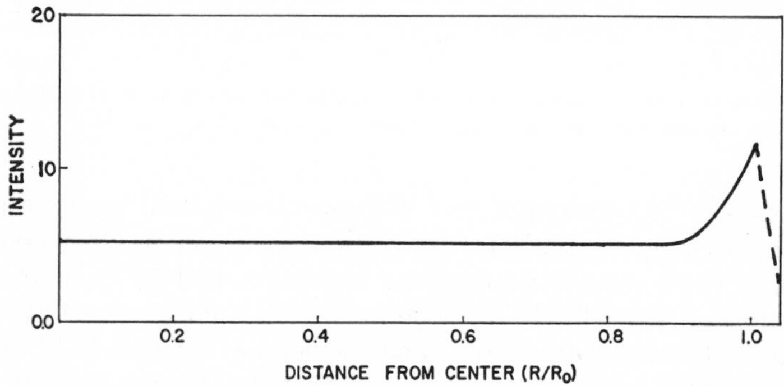

FIG. 19. Observed center-limb variation of the solar X-ray radiation (Blake *et al.* [9]).

in location to the chromospheric faculae, and that their radiation intensity ranges between 34 and 108 times the coronal background intensity; the average value is about 55. This would correspond to an electron density of about seven to twelve time (average: eight) that of the quiet corona:

$$\tfrac{1}{2}(N_e)_{\mathrm{CA}}{}^2\cdot\mathcal{H}_{\mathrm{CA}} = \tfrac{1}{2}(34 \text{ to } 108) \times (N_e)_c{}^2\mathcal{H}_c, \qquad \text{with} \quad \mathcal{H}_{\mathrm{CA}} = 1\tfrac{1}{2}\mathcal{H}_c.$$

Other pinhole pictures have been taken [9] showing essentially the same results.

All X-ray pictures show a clear limb brightening (Fig. 19) but this is obvious because the corona is optically thin for X-rays; it has been predicted by Elwert [26] (Fig. 20).

Other monochromatic heliograms of the corona before the disc were obtained in May, 1963 by the NRL group (Tousey [84] addendum). The observations were made with a concave grating spectrograph giving stigmatic solar images of 1.8-mm diameter, and a spatial resolving power of about 1′. Stray light was eliminated by having the light pass an unbacked Al film of 0.1 μ thick, supported on an 32 per cm mesh of 85 per cent transmittance. Images were obtained in the light of He II (303.78 Å; uniform disc with plages brightened), Fe XV and Fe XVI (284.2 and 335.4 Å respectively; disc hardly visible; plages strongly so). Observations were also obtained in a group of unidentified strong lines near 256 Å; these pictures show a bright ring and plages.

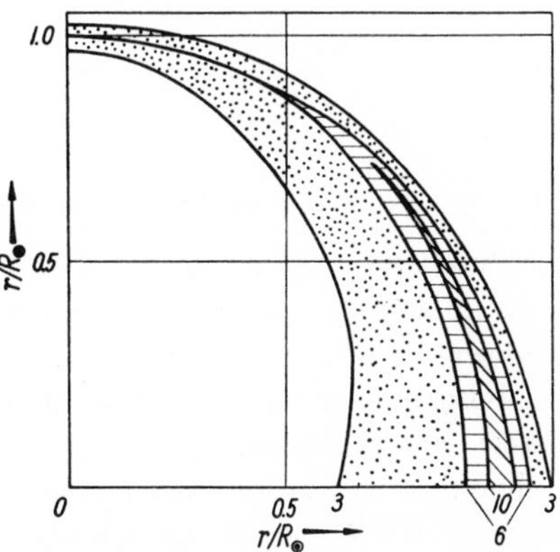

Fig. 20. Predicted X-ray intensity distribution over the disc (Elwert [28]).

It is simple to compare the X-ray observations with radio heliograms of the disc: these are also emitted by the corona. However, one cannot expect a one-to-one correspondence between the features and intensities in the two kinds of heliograms, because the X-ray intensities are roughly proportional to N_e^2, whereas the radio intensity depends in a more complicated way on N_e and T: the sun is opaque in dm radio waves, and an increase of the density will cause an increase in the monochromatic absorption coefficient so that the radiation will be emitted by higher layers where the temperature is higher. Because of these circumstances the emitted radio intensity I depends in an intricate way on N_e^2; generally $\log I_\lambda = f(\lambda) \log N_e$. The function $f(\lambda)$ is zero for $\lambda < 1$ cm and for $\lambda > 1$ meter, and is roughly equal to 2 only for 20 cm $\leq \lambda \leq$ 35 cm (Fig. 21). So there will be the greatest chance of similarity between X-ray and radio pictures of the sun for radio wavelengths between 20 and 35 cm.

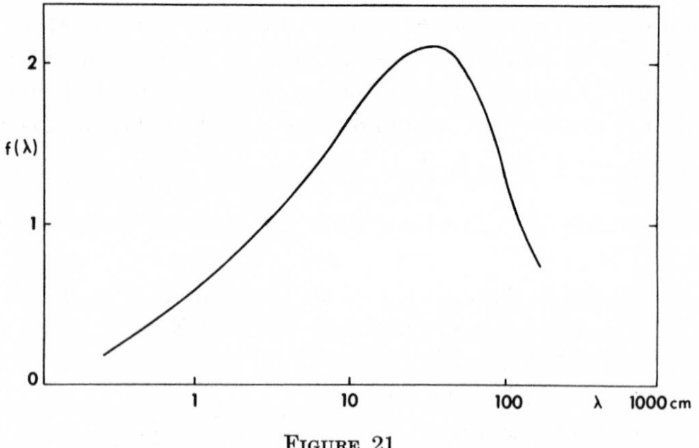

FIGURE 21

5.3. Spectral Observations of Coronal Activity Regions

"Pure" spectral observations of coronal activity regions have not yet been made: the spectra obtained were always integrated disc spectra and contained the quiet coronal and CA radiation; furthermore the spectral resolving power has been low up to quite recently; hence one could not detect spectral lines.

The first restriction may not be very serious; one can always attempt to subtract the quiet corona intensity, and this subtraction is simplified by the fact that a considerable part of the radiation is emitted at short wavelengths (≤ 30 Å) where the normal coronal radiation is weak: as a result of the slightly higher temperature of the coronal CA, its radiation is harder than that of the quiet corona. In fact, at least 75 per cent of the radiation for $\lambda < 60$ Å came from CA's [9].

The other restriction (the lack of sufficient spectral resolution in the observations) is more serious. It is true that Elwert predicted that the short wavelength end of the coronal spectrum would be virtually continuous and free of lines for $\lambda < 40$ Å. However, the recent NRL crystal spectrometer observations of the quiet corona showed lines in the coronal spectrum down to 13 Å; the continuous radiation seemed practically absent. This apparent discrepancy between theory and observation of the quiet corona should be solved before one can correctly interpret coronal spectral observations taken with a small resolving power.

The main characteristics of the active coronal spectrum — (*a*) the greater emission intensity and (*b*) the hardening of the spectrum — were discovered by Friedman *et al.* [37] and Byram *et al.* [14, 15]. Later observations by Mandel'stam *et al.* [62] for $\lambda < 10$ Å confirmed the dependence of the total radiation intensity and of the color temperature ($\equiv$ the temperature a blackbody should have to present a spectrum with, in the

TABLE 5

Date	$\int_0^{10\,Å} I\,d\lambda$ (ergs/cm²/sec at earth's distance)	T_{color} (°K)	5303 Å Fe XIV (Arbitrary Units)	
21 August 1959	$7.2\text{–}3.1 \times 10^{-4}$	4.5×10^{6}	71	
19–20 August 1960	$7\text{–}8 \times 10^{-4}$	3×10^{6}	91	88
1–2 December 1960	2.5×10^{-4}	2×10^{6}	51	47
15 February 1961	4×10^{-4}	1.5×10^{6}	65	

relevant wavelength region, the same shape as the observed curve) on the integrated limb intensity of the line Fe XIV 5303 Å (this line is enhanced in optical coronal activity regions), Table 5. (T_{color} has nothing to do with the kinetic temperature of the gas, it is only a parameter to describe the shape of the spectral intensity as a function of the wavelength and this parameter is useless and misleading, should the spectrum appear to be a line spectrum. However, very often one may expect: $dT_{col}/dT_{kin} > 0$.)

Further observations were made in 1962 with the Ariel satellite. The measurements were made in the range <15 Å; spectral discrimination was made by means of a photon counter, which has in this wavelength region a limited resolving power (e.g., at 10 Å the resolving power is about 2 Å). Pounds, Willmore *et al.* [78] communicate results from two observations of the slowly varying component of the solar radiation in Table 6.

TABLE 6

Two Ariel Observations [78]

		27 April	3 May
T_{color} ($\times 10^{6}$°K)	13–11 Å	1.4	1.3
	11–9 Å	1.6	1.4
	9–7 Å	1.7	1.4
Flux (erg/cm²/sec)	8–14 Å	3×10^{-3}	—
	<8 Å	1.3×10^{-4}	—
T_{el} ($\times 10^{6}$°K)	<8 Å	2.2	—
	<12 Å	1.7	—
$\int N_e^2\,dV$ (per cm³)		3×10^{48}	—

The electron temperature T_{el} and the value of $\int N_e^2 \, dV$ were deduced from the measured intensities with the aid of Elwert's theoretical computations. If we assume for the coronal CA a cylindrical form, with exponentially decreasing density, with a scale height of 10^5 km, and, following Blake *et al.* [9] a radius of 5×10^4 km, one obtains for the basis layer of the CA: $N_e = 2 \times 10^9/\text{cm}^3$, which is about six to eight times the quiet coronal value. This result is in agreement with the determinations quoted earlier.

5.4. Future Observations

(*a*) There is a need for monochromatic pictures in lines of strongly different origin so as to be able to investigate the excitation conditions in coronal activity centers. (*b*) An essential problem is that of the coronal structure above the magnetic network. If the coronal heating mechanism is equal to or similar in and above the facular regions and in and above the chromospheric network, then the corona seen in the disc center should show a similar, or the same fine structure as the upper chromosphere. Or does the great conductivity of the corona produce a smoothing of the inhomogeneities, so that the corona would be homogeneous, even in the case of inhomogeneous heating? What is the role of the magnetic field in this connection?

The answer to these questions will be found as soon as it appears possible to obtain monochromatic coronal images with a resolving power comparable to size of the coarse chromospheric mottling — 5000–10,000 km, (i.e., 10″). We are touching here upon one of the most important problems of the corona, the solution of which will be of the greatest importance for the further progress of solar research. Lastly (*c*), it will be highly necessary to obtain detailed spectra, with high resolution in the short wavelength end of the coronal spectrum. The determination of line widths in coronal CA's will enable one to arrive at a less ambiguous determination of their temperatures.

6. X-Ray Emission from Solar Flares

6.1. The Problem of Solar Flares

A flare is a sudden and short-lived brightening of a small part of the disc. In the visual spectral region the emission is monochromatic; a weak continuum with an intensity of some percents of the continuous spectrum is sometimes observed, but only in important flares. Some of the main properties:

(*a*) Location: flares occur mostly in the neighborhood of sunspots, mostly in magnetically complex groups; they seem to favor the region where the longitudinal magnetic field strength component is zero.

(*b*) Occurrence: their occurrence is correlated to changes in the area and/or in the magnetic field strength of the spot group.

(*c*) Physical parameters: from spectral studies the kinetic temperature and electron density of the optically visible flare could be determined; one finds: log $N_e \approx 13.5/\text{cm}^3$; log $T_{el} \approx 4$ to 5, closer to 4, °K.

The amount of matter contributing to the visible flare is small: the total geometrical thickness of the matter emitting Hα light seems to be of the order of 10 to some tens of km. Hence, because of lack of resolving power a flare looks homogeneous, but apparently it must be a very inhomogeneous structure consisting of a number of knotlike or filamentary structures.

(*d*) Height of appearance: some of the flares appearing at the sun's limb have a certain elevation and can sometimes be seen detached from the chromosphere. These flares are clearly coronal structures. The greater part of the other flares seem to have relationship to the chromosphere. However, since most flares do not show Hα self-reversal, their top must occur at least at heights of about 5000 km above the photosphere. Some flares seem to occur below about 3000 km: these show no central emission and only the wings are visible: these are the so-called moustaches; the larger ones are called Ellerman bombs.

(*e*) The hot counterpart of a flare: the cm and dm radio waves emitted during a flare, as well as the hard component of the X-ray spectrum emitted at that occasion, indicate the occurrence of hot regions, simultaneously with the flares. The temperature of these regions is between 10^6 and 10^7°K, sometimes even higher. From radio observations the electron density seems to be about $10^{10}/\text{cm}^3$; the emitting regions seem fairly small (1′ to 3′) [38]. The location of these hot clouds with respect to the flares is not clear. Certainly they must be coronal features, but it is not correct to identify them with the sporadic coronal condensations which have longer lifetimes.

(*f*) Mechanism: no acceptable theory has as yet been given to explain the flare mechanism; even the source of the energy is unknown. The often quoted hypothesis of their magnetic origin does not seem correct. The available magnetic energy in the vicinity of a flare is mostly quite insufficient to account for the flare energy output [48].

6.2. Quasi-Thermal X-Ray Emission Associated with Flares

There appear to be two components in the X-ray emission associated with flares. The first, treated here, is called thermal because the radiation is due to atomic transistions in a gas with a well-defined kinetic temperature; the adjective quasi is used because the gas is not in local thermodynamic equilibrium.

The cool optical flare does not contribute to this radiation; its temperature is too low. The hot coronal source of the radio flare must certainly also be the source for the quasi-thermal X-rays. During some flares hard

X-rays have been observed; the emission lasted for a time comparable to the lifetime of the flare and the emission time of the cm or dm radio waves.

With a scintillation counter Chubb *et al.* [17, 18] observed the short wavelength tail spectrum (20–60 kev) of flare associated emission on 31 August 1959, and found it describable by a color temperature of 1.2×10^8°K. The emission was observable for at least 6 min. The electron temperature corresponding to this high color temperature should still be determined, as well as the other physical conditions necessary to have a gas-emitting radiation with that characteristic.

Yefremov *et al.* [91] observed the solar radiation in the wavelength region between 1.4 and 110 Å by means of open multipliers with interchangeable filters, and found it to consist of two components: one is emitted

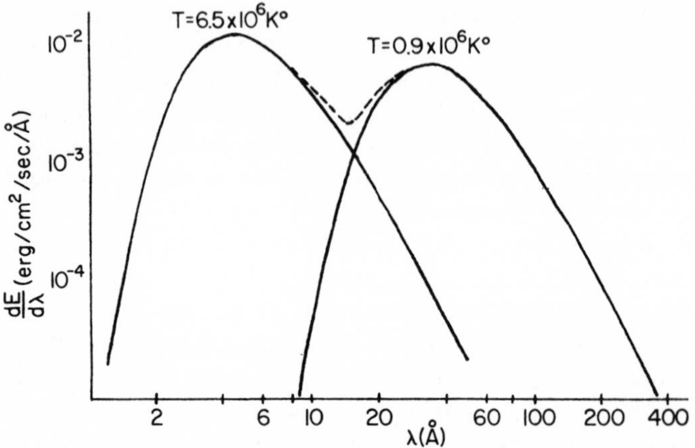

Fig. 22. Suggested intensity distribution in the solar X-ray spectrum (Yefremov *et al.* [91]).

by the quiet corona and has a color temperature of 0.9×10^6 °K; the other component occurs during flares and has a color temperature of 6.5×10^6°K (Fig. 22).

The U.K. Ariel satellite observed several flare spectra in the wavelength region 2–15 Å with the aid of a proportional counter, with a time resolution of 25 sec to 1 min [77, 78]. The X-ray flare of 3 May 1962 was of the "simple" type. It started at 06.45 UT and had in its maximum phase the following color temperatures (Fig. 23).

Wavelength	13–11	11–9	9–7	7–5 Å
T_c	2	2.2	2.7	3.8×10^6 °K

For this flare $\int N_e^2\, dV = 6 \times 10^{47}/\text{cm}^3$. The general characteristics of the

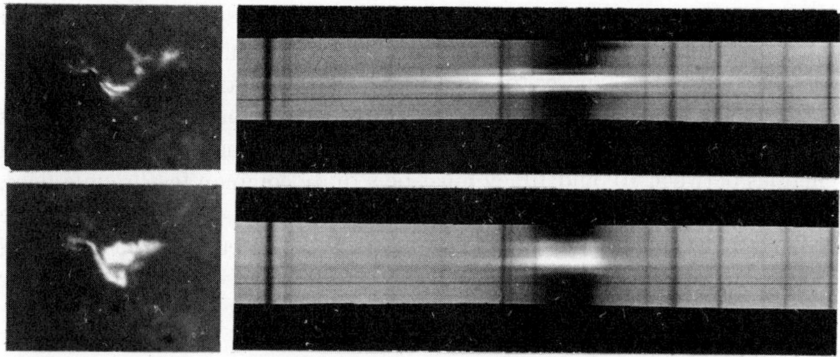

FIG. 23. Left: Two Hα filtergrams of the 3^+ flare of 31 August 1956, obtained by A. B. Severny at the Crimean Observatory: during ascending phase of flare activity (upper), during flash phase (lower). Right: Hα spectra taken almost simultaneously with the left-hand filtergrams at the Utrecht observatory by the author.

"simple" flare spectrum is that of a gradual hardening and intensification of the spectrum during the growth phase of the flare. The flare of 27 April 1962 developed slowly with a short "flash" of imp. 3 or 3+; at that moment a short burst of X-rays was observed, apparently due to a nonthermal source.

We conclude that X-ray observations confirm the existence of "hot" components of a flare. The location and structure of this component is still unknown. Theoretically one may expect a gas cloud with temperature of several 10^6°K to expand and nearly explosively leave the sun, shooting a blast wave into interplanetary space, unless being held near the sun by a magnetic field.

6.3. Nonthermal Radiation Bursts from Flares

Bursts of hard X-rays (10^4 to 10^6 ev) with durations ranging from some seconds to one or two minutes at maximum have been observed on several occasions [17, 18, 75, 77, 78, 86, 89]. These short-lasting bursts show the following properties:

(*a*) They occur mostly during the flash phases of flares. In this connection we remark that the flash phase tends to coincide with the acceleration of particles to high speeds; during a flare-flash, radio observations show (*i*) the emission of the Type III bursts, due to electrons with velocities between $0.2c$ and $0.9c$, and (*ii*) the start of Type II bursts, excited either by a proton-jet or by the wake of a shock front moving with $v \approx 1500$ km/sec.

(*b*) The X-ray bursts are correlated with cm radio bursts. These bursts occur in large activity centers, in particular when the flare "touches" the penumbras of sunspots.

(*c*) The energies of these bursts are of the order 10^4–10^6 ev, so that they must be due either to bremsstrahlung by electrons moving with velocities of 60,000–280,000 km/sec or to synchrotron radiation of magnetically trapped electrons. Similar velocities are observed for the electrons that produce Type III radio bursts, so that the acceleration of electrons with energies between 10^4 and 10^6 ev must be a quite common feature in a flare. However, electrons that excite Type III bursts can generally not excite X-ray bursts and vice versa, since X-rays are produced by bremsstrahlung of electrons shot downward and braked in the dense parts of the solar

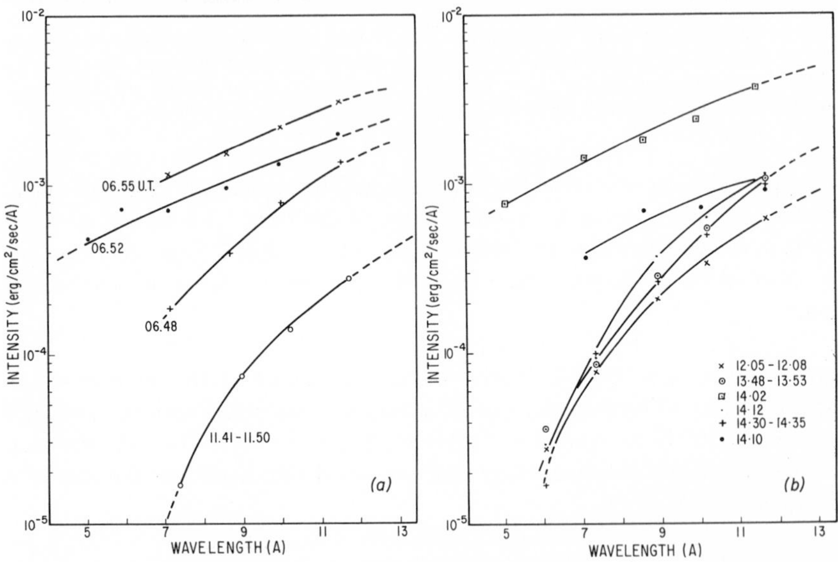

FIG. 24. (*a*) Development of solar X-ray intensities for an imp. 2 flare on 3 May 1962: compared with the quiet sun spectrum observed the same day; Ariel satellite observations. (*b*) X-ray spectrum observed by the Ariel satellite for the imp. 2 flare of 27 April 1962 (Pounds *et al.* [78]).

photosphere or trapped in the low corona, and Type III bursts are emitted by plasma oscillations in the corona excited by upward-going electrons; the latter are not braked because their mean free path is much longer than the scale height of the corona (for an exception to this rule see Section 6.4 and Fig. 28). It is indeed remarkable that Type III bursts with $v \leq 60{,}000$ km/sec do not occur: for velocities about equal this value the mean free path will be of the same order as the coronal scale height, so that these slower electrons do not reach very far.

(*d*) A characteristic and well-studied example is the burst observed during the flash of the flare of 27 April 1962, at 14.12 UT (Figs. 24 and 25).

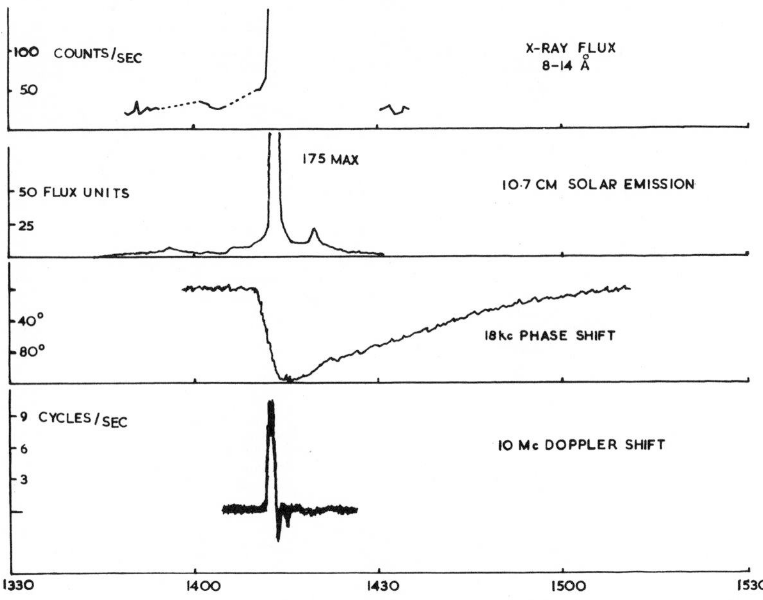

FIG. 25. X-ray flux between 8 and 14 Å, compared with other features, for the imp. 2 flare of 27 April 1963.

The relevant data are:

Measured burst intensity, 10^{-2} erg/cm^2/sec at earth's distance.

Total X-ray emission from sun (assumed isotropic), 2 to 7 $\times$ 10^{25} erg/sec.

Energy of electron stream (assume photon production efficiency of 5×10^{-5}), 5×10^{29} erg/sec.

Total emission (suppose duration 160 sec), 8×10^{31} ergs in 160 seconds: 10^{39} electrons involved; volume with $N_e = 10^{13}$/cm^3, $(5 \times 10^3$ km$)^3$; volume with $N_e = 10^{10}$/cm^3, $(5 \times 10^4$ km$)^3$.

This latter value is of the same order of the chromospheric mesh width. We thus conclude that in order to emit the X-ray burst of 27 April 1963 a volume of gas with $N_e = 10^{10}$/cm^3 and containing $(5 \times 10^4)^3$ km^3 should be involved and accelerated to energies of 50 kev (120,000 km/sec). This is an astonishingly vast volume and a huge amount of energy. Where is the theory that will explain all this?

6.4. A Model of the Flare Event

The succession of events and their interconnection may be shown by some schematic pictures, presented by the author in 1962 at the Washington COSPAR Symposium (see also [48]). The basic concept is the one put

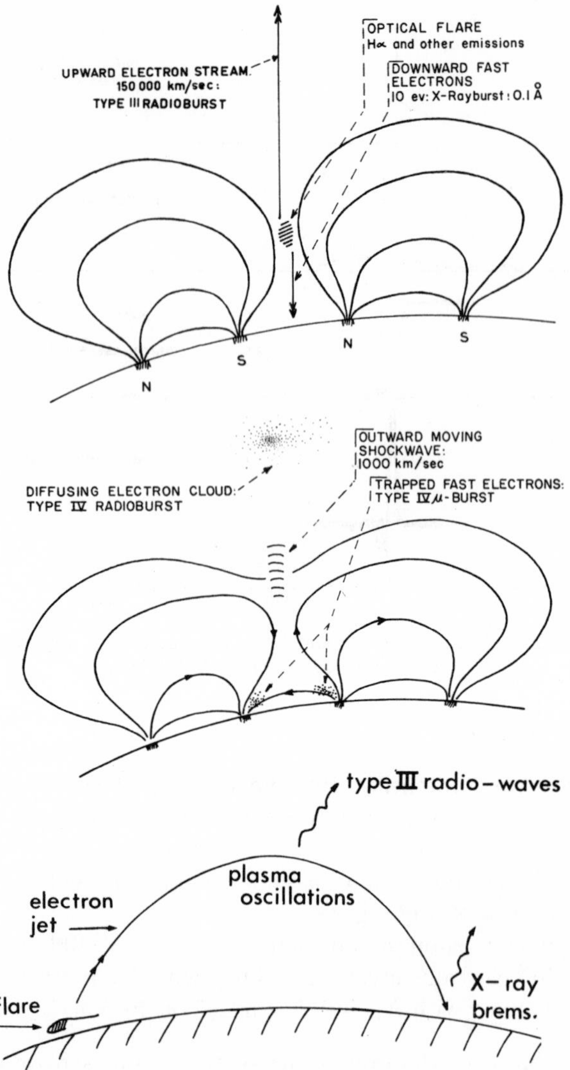

FIG. 26. Top: two bipolar spot groups approaching each other. Middle: processes in first phase. Bottom: excitation of Type III radio waves and X-ray bremsstrahlung by one electron jet (after Anderson and Winckler). See text.

forward first by Dungey [22] and Sweet [83] of two bipolar spot groups between which, upon mutual approach, a flare may originate.

(*a*) Figure 26, top: Two bipolar spotgroups, each with their own system of field lines approach each other. The field is strong in the photosphere, much weaker in the corona and chromosphere. Still, even in the corona, the magnetic energy greatly exceeds the kinetic energy of matter, and coronal matter moves with the moving field. The matter in between cannot be penetrated by the field lines and essentially behaves as a diamagnetic body. It is compressed. Some sort of instability arises, perhaps of the kind described by Severny [82] or Kiepenheuer [54], leading to a sudden collapselike compression of matter: the optical flare.

In this very early stage local accelerating electric fields may originate; they are not longer than 10 or 100 m; their field strengths may amount to 10^5 v or even 10^6 v. The fields directed in one way may accelerate electrons downward where they are braked in the denser parts of the photosphere or trapped in the low corona and produce X-ray bremsstrahlung bursts or synchrotron bursts in the energy range 10^5 ev ($\approx$0.1 Å).

Other fields, in other parts of the flare, may be directed upward and produce jets of electrons with velocities around 150,000 km/sec; these may excite coronal matter to plasma oscillations: the Type III bursts. These clouds are detected up to 2 and $2.5R_{\odot}$ above the photosphere; there they have an extension of about one solar radius [32].

(*b*) Figure 26, middle: The processes occurring in the first phase give rise to several secondary phenomena. (*1*) The compression which leads to the flare is the source of a hydromagnetic shock wave; behind the shock front matter propagates outward with an initial speed of the order of 1500 km/sec, decreasing at greater distances to the source, to some hundreds of km/sec. (*2*) The electrostatic interaction between the outgoing electrons and the remainder of the (at a certain moment slightly positively charged) sun may cause the Type V radio bursts. (*3*) As Dungey has shown, the compression phenomenon may lead to a local rearrangement of the field: the outermost lines of force of the two bipolar magnetic systems may break and join with those of the other system. In this way the two, initially independent, systems may partly combine to one. So, systems of lines of force may originate which are capable of trapping part of the outgoing electrons. These electrons bounce back and forward and receive further acceleration during their motion to and fro. The innermost system of trapped electrons may be the source of the Type IV-cm or IV-dm radio bursts. The diameter of the Type IV source is still small at this stage. Kundu and Firor [56] find that at 340 MHz the apparent diameter is smaller than 4′, the source is situated lower than 40,000 km. Boischot and Pick–Gutmann [12] find that the first phase of the Type IV event has a diameter of 6′ to 10′.

This picture is certainly not a final one but serves only to indicate a possible explanation of the various flare associated observations. If it would appear possible to obtain X-ray pictures with a sufficient spatial resolving power we would have a powerful method at hand to check the suggested flare mechanisms in the various stages of the flare. So one would recommend for future investigations:

1. *Quasi-thermal radiation*: the location and extension of the source, in relation with the topology of the flare, the sunspots, and the faculae region; observations should be obtained for different flares, at different positions at the sun's limb and beyond the limb.

2. *The nonthermal bursts*: here the main problems are: location, fine structure in time, fine structure in place. We recall that the Type III radio bursts are often composed of clouds of single bursts, each lasting for about 1 sec. If the X-ray bursts were due to a similar kind of accelerated electron jets, but moving downward, the fine structure should be detectable. However, (as Schatzman remarked at the 1963 Utrecht Symposium), such downward-shot electrons could still be trapped in the magnetic field pattern, and stay there longer, maybe for some seconds (the exact lifetime of such trapped particles depends greatly on the local field strength and density). All these considerations are reasons to look for the fine structure of the nonthermal X-ray bursts. In this connection we should also recall that many radio bursts have durations of down to $0^s.1$ or $0^s.2$ [95]. What would be the statistics of durations of X-ray bursts?

Another related problem was put forward (K. A. Anderson and J. R. Winckler [93]): on some occasions it might occur that an upward electron jet is guided down to the photosphere by a magnetic field. Such a jet would emit Type III bursts when going through the high corona, and X-ray bursts when being braked in the dense layers (Fig. 26, bottom).

The general conclusion is that, for a thorough study of the flare-associated radiation, simultaneous X-ray and radio heliographs of high spatial resolving power (10″) are extremely desirable. Simultaneous determination of the radio and X-ray spectrum is also required. We consider these as the most important program elements for heliophysics over the next ten years.

Acknowledgment

Many thanks are due to Dr. R. Tousey for placing a number of reproductions of the fine N.R.L. spectra at my disposal.

References

1. C. W. Allen, Solar ultraviolet and X-ray line emission, *Congrès et Coll. Liège*, **20,** 241 (1961).
2. R. G. Athay and R. N. Thomas, The thermodynamic state of the outer solar atmosphere. IV. Self-absorption and the population of the second quantum level, *Astrophys. J. Suppl.* **1,** 491 (1955).
3. R. G. Athay and R. N. Thomas, Lyman-alpha and the structure of the solar chromosphere, *Astrophys. J.*, **124,** 586 (1956).
4. R. G. Athay and R. N. Thomas, The numbers and motions of solar spicules, *Astrophys. J.*, **125,** 804 (1957).

5. R. G. Athay and C. L. Hyder, Coronal ionization by two-step collision processes, *Astrophys. J.*, **137,** 21 (1963).
6. J. Bahng and M. Schwarzschild, The temperature fluctuations in the solar granulation, *Astrophys. J.*, **134,** 337 (1961).
7. J. M. Beckers, Study of the undisturbed chromosphere from H-alpha disk filtergrams with particular reference to the identification of spicules, *Astrophys. J.*, **138,** 648 (1963).
8. W. E. Behring, H. C. McAllister, and W. A. Rense, Ultraviolet emission lines in the solar spectrum, *Astrophys. J.*, **127,** 676 (1958).
9. R. L. Blake, T. A. Chubb, H. Friedman, and A. Unzicker, Interpretation of X-ray photographs of the sun, *Astrophys. J.*, **137,** 3 (1963).
10. K. H. Böhm, Die Temperaturschichtung der Sonnenatmosphäre im nicht grauen Strahlungsgleichgewicht, *Z. Astrophys.*, **34,** 182 (1954).
11. K. H. Böhm, Zum Deutung der Mitte-Rand variation der Fraunhofer-Linien, *Z. Astrophys.*, **36,** 295 (1955).
12. A. Boischot and M. Pick-Gutmann, Structure of the type IV radioburst and its relation with solar cosmic rays, *J. Phys. Soc. Japan*, **17,** Suppl. A II, 203 (1962).
13. A. Bruzek, Über die Spiculen auf der Sonnenscheibe, *Z. Astrophys.*, **47,** 191 (1959).
14. E. T. Byram, T. Chubb, and H. Friedman, The contribution of solar X-ray to *E* layer ionization, *Phys. Rev.*, **92,** 1066 (1953).
15. E. T. Byram, T. Chubb, and H. Friedman, Solar X-ray emission, *Phys. Rev.*, **96,** 860 (1954).
16. W. N. Christiansen *et al.*, A study of a solar active region using combined optical and radio techniques, *Ann. Astrophys.*, **23,** 75 (1960).
17. T. A. Chubb, H. Friedman, and R. W. Kreplin, Measurements made of high-energy X-rays accompanying three class 2+ solar flares, *J. Geophys. Res.*, **65,** 1831 (1960).
18. T. A. Chubb, H. Friedman, and R. W. Kreplin, X-ray emission accompanying solar flares and non-flare sunspot maximum conditions, *Space Research*, H. Kallmann-Bijl (ed.), 695 (North-Holland Publishing Co., 1960).
19. L. Delbouille, L. Neven, and G. Roland, First results obtained with the double pass solar spectrograph at the Jungfraujoch, Switzerland, *J. Quant. Spectrosc. Radiat. Transfer*, **3,** 189 (1963).
20. C. R. Detwiler, J. D. Purcell, and R. Tousey, The extreme ultraviolet spectrum of the sun, *Congrès et Coll. Liège*, **20,** 254 (1961).
21. A. Dollfus, Propriétés des emissions monochromatiques de la couronne solaire, *C. R. Acad. Sci.*, **255,** 3369 (1962).
22. J. W. Dungey, The neutral point discharge theory of solar flares: A reply to Cowling's criticism, I.A.U. Symposium No. 6, 135 (1958).
23. G. Elwert, Das kontinuierliche Emissionsspektrum der Sonnenkorona im fernen Ultraviolet und bei weichen Röntgenstrahlen, *Z. Naturforsch. 7a*, 202 (1952).
24. G. Elwert, Über die Ionisations und Rekombinationsprozesse in einem Plasma und die Ionisationsformel der Sonnenkorona, *Z. Naturforsch. 7a*, 432 (1952).
25. G. Elwert, Die weiche Röntgenstrahlung der ungestörten Sonnenkorona, *Z. Naturforsch. 9a*, 637 (1954).
26. G. Elwert, Röntgenstrahlung koronaler Kondensationen, *Z. Astrophys.*, **41,** 67 (1956).
27. G. Elwert, Das Ionisationsgleichgewicht der Sonnenkorona und die Entstehung der gelben Koronalinie, *Z. Astrophys.*, **44,** 112 (1958).
28. G. Elwert, Die Verteilung der Röntgenstrahlung der Sonnenkorona über die emittierende Fläche und die Restintensität bei totalen Sonnenfinsternissen, *J. Atm. Terr. Phys.*, **12,** 187 (1958).
29. G. Elwert, Theory of X-ray emission of the sun, *J. Geophys. Res.*, **66,** 391 (1961).
30. G. Elwert, Comparison between theory and measurements of the X-ray emission of the sun, *Proc. Int'l Conf. The Ionosphere*, A. C. Strickland (ed.), 57 (Inst. Phys. & Phys. Soc., London, 1963).
31. G. Elwert, *Space Sci. Rev.*, **4** (in preparation).
32. W. C. Erickson, High resolution studies of type III solar emission at 11.4 meter wavelength, *J. Geophys. Res.*, **68,** 3169 (1963).

33. J. Evans and R. Michard, Observational study of macroscopic inhomogeneities in the solar atmosphere. II. Brightness fluctuations in Fraunhofer lines and the continuum; III. Vertical oscillatory motions in the solar photosphere, *Astrophys. J.*, **136,** 487, 493 (1962).
34. H. Friedman, Rocket observations of the ionosphere; *Proc. IRE*, **47,** 272 (1959).
35. H. Friedman *et al.*, I. X-ray and ultraviolet measurements during the eclipse of October 12, 1958; II. X-ray solar disk photograph, *Congrès et Coll. Liège*, **20,** 228 (1961).
36. H. Friedman, Rocket spectroscopy, *In*: *Space Science*, D. P. LeGalley (ed.), 549 (John Wiley & Sons, 1963); and H. Friedman, Ultraviolet and X-rays from the sun, *In*: *Annual Review of Astronomy and Astrophysics I*, L. Goldberg (ed.), 59 (Ann. Revs., Inc., Palo Alto, 1963).
37. H. Friedman, S. W. Lichtman, and E. T. Byram, Measurement of solar X-rays and extreme ultraviolet light by photon counters, *J. Opt. Soc. Amer.*, **41,** 292 (1951).
38. O. Hachenberg, Detection and observation of solar emission in the range of centimeter waves, *Varenna Summer Course*, **12,** 217 (1960).
39. L. A. Hall, K. R. Damon, and H. E. Hinteregger, Solar extreme ultraviolet photon flux measurements in the upper atmosphere of August 1961, *Space Research III*, 745 (North-Holland Publishing Co., 1963).
40. H. E. Hinteregger, Interplanetary ionization by solar extreme ultraviolet radiation, *Astrophys. J.*, **132,** 801 (1960).
41. H. E. Hinteregger, Preliminary data on solar extreme ultraviolet radiation in the upper atmosphere, *J. Geophys. Res.*, **66,** 2367 (1961).
42. L. Houziaux, Discussion remark at Colloquium on The Solar Spectrum (Utrecht, 1963).
43. C. de Jager, The distribution of Lyman-alpha radiation over the solar disc, *Solar Eclipses and the Ionosphere*, 174 (Pergamon Press, 1956).
44. C. de Jager, The interpretation of hydrogen spectroheliograms, *Bull. Astron. Obs. Neth.*, **13,** 133 (1957).
45. C. de Jager, Structure and dynamics of the solar atmosphere, *Handbuch der Physik*, **52,** 80 (1959).
46. C. de Jager, The development of a solar centre of activity, *Vistas in Astronomy*, **4,** A. Beer (ed.), 473 (Pergamon Press, 1961).
47. C. de Jager, The temperature fluctuations in the solar photosphere, *Comm. Astrophys. Inst. Univ. Brussels, No. A4* (1962). See also: R. W. J. Heintze, H. Hubenet, and C. de Jager, A reference model of the solar photosphere and low chromosphere, *Bull. Astron. Inst. Neth.*, **17** (in press).
48. C. de Jager, The sun as a source of interplanetary gas, *Space Sci. Rev.*, **1,** 487 (1962).
49. C. de Jager, The temperature minimum in the upper solar photosphere, *Bull. Astron. Obs. Neth.*, **17,** 209 (1963).
50. C. de Jager and L. Neven, The *C* multiplet at 10700 Å in the solar spectrum, (paper presented at Liège Symposium on Infrared Spectra of Celestial Bodies, 1963).
51. V. P. Kachalov and A. V. Yakovleva, The ultraviolet solar spectrum in the region, 2470–3100 Å, *Izv. Crimean Astrophys. Obs.*, **27,** 5 (1962).
52. K. Kawabata, The relationship between post-burst increases of solar microwave radiation and sudden ionospheric disturbances, *Ionos. Res. Report Japan*, **14,** 405 (1960).
53. K. O. Kiepenheuer, Über die Verdichtung der Koronamaterie, *Z. Astrophys.*, **48,** 290 (1959).
54. K. O. Kiepenheuer, The optical phenomena forming a solar center of activity, *Varenna Summer Course*, **12,** 39 (1960).
55. M. R. Kundu, Centimeter-wave radio and X-ray emission from the sun, *Space Sci. Rev.*, **2,** 438 (1963).
56. M. R. Kundu and J. W. Firor, Interferometric studies of solar bursts of continuum radiation on 340 and 87 Mc/s, *Astrophys. J.*, **134,** 389 (1962).
57. M. Kupurus, The acoustic energy flux of the sun and the heating of the corona, (Thesis, in preparation, Utrecht, 1965).

58. R. B. LEIGHTON, Discussion remark concerning "Review on granulation observational studies," *I.A.U. Symposium No. 12*, 321 (1961).
59. R. B. LEIGHTON, R. W. NOYES, AND G. W. SIMON, Velocity fields in the solar atmosphere. I. Preliminary report, *Astrophys. J.*, **135**, 474 (1962).
60. H. C. MCALLISTER, A preliminary photometric atlas of the solar ultraviolet spectrum from 1800 to 2965 Angströms (Univ. of Colorado, Boulder, 1960).
61. C. J. MACRIS, Studies on the flocculi of the solar chromosphere. Part I. Lifetime of the flocculi, *Mem. Soc. Astron. Ital.*, **33**, 85 (1962).
62. S. MANDEL'STAM *et al.*, Measurements of solar X-ray radiation, *Space Research III*, 822 (North-Holland Publishing Co., 1963).
63. R. MICHARD, La raie H-alpha dans la chromosphère, *Ann. Astrophys.*, **22**, 547 (1959).
64. R. MICHARD *et al.*, Etude statistique des fluctuations locales de brillance et de vitesse dans la photosphère, *Ann. Astrophys.*, **25**, 279 (1962).
65. D. C. MORTON and K. G. WIDING, The solar Lyman-alpha emission line, *Astrophys. J.*, **133**, 596 (1961).
66. O. NAMBA, Note on the structure of the solar chromosphere with some remarks on the Athay-Thomas spicule model, *Proc. Kon. Ned. Akad. Wetensch., Ser. B*, **64**, 715 (1961).
67. W. M. NEUPERT, Emission of extreme ultraviolet radiation from solar centers of activity, *Space Research IV* (in press, 1964).
68. W. M. NEUPERT, W. E. BEHRING, AND J. C. LINDSAY, The solar spectrum from 50 to 400 Å, *Space Research IV* (in press, 1964).
69. R. W. NOYES AND R. B. LEIGHTON, Velocity fields in the solar atmosphere. II. The oscillatory field, *Astrophys. J.*, **138**, 631 (1963).
70. D. E. OSTERBROCK, The heating of the solar chromosphere, plages, and corona by magnetohydrodynamic waves, *Astrophys. J.*, **134**, 347 (1961).
71. B. E. J. PAGEL, A model atmosphere for the solar limb based on continuum observations, *Mon. Not. Roy. Astron. Soc.*, **116**, 608 (1956).
72. B. E. J. PAGEL, Ultraviolet emission from the sun, *Planet. Space Sci.*, **11**, 333 (1963).
73. C. PECKER AND F. ROHRLICH, Identification des raies permises dans le spectre ultra-violet solaire, *Congrès et Coll. Liège*, **20**, 265 (1961).
74. J.-C. PECKER, La prédiction du spectre ultraviolet des étoiles et du soleil, *Congrès et Coll. Liège*, **20**, 487 (1961).
75. L. E. PETERSON AND J. R. WINCKLER, Gamma-ray burst from a solar flare, *J. Geophys. Res.*, **64**, 697 (1959).
76. S. R. POTTASCH, The lower corona: Interpretation of the ultraviolet spectrum, *Astrophys. J.*, **137**, 945 (1963).
77. K. A. POUNDS AND A. P. WILLMORE, Instrumentation of satellite UK 1 for obtaining low resolution solar X-ray spectra, *Space Research III*, 1195 (North-Holland Publishing Co., 1963).
78. K. A. POUNDS AND A. P. WILLMORE; P. J. BOWEN, K. NORMAN, AND P. W. SANFORD, Measurements of the solar spectrum in the wave-length band 4–14 Å, *Proc. Roy. Soc., Ser. A*, (in press, 1964).
79. J. D. PURCELL, D. L. GARRETT, AND R. TOUSEY, Solar spectra from 3500 to 2200 Å at 30 mÅ resolution, *Space Research III*, 781 (North-Holland Publishing Co., 1963).
80. J. RÖSCH, Continuum studies of granulation, *Trans. I.A.U.*, **11B**, 197 (1962).
81. M. J. SEATON, The temperature of the solar corona, *The Observatory*, **82**, 11 (1962).
82. A. B. SEVERNY, The appearance of flares in neutral points of the solar magnetic field and the pinch-effect, *Izv. Crimean Astrophys. Obs.*, **20**, 22 (1958).
83. P. A. SWEET, The neutral point theory of solar flares, *I.A.U. Symposium No. 6*, 123 (1958).
84. R. TOUSEY, The extreme ultraviolet spectrum of the sun, *Space Sci. Rev.*, **2**, 3 (1963).
85. R. TOUSEY, W. E. AUSTIN, J. D. PURCELL, AND K. G. WIDING, Solar emission lines in the region 168 Å to 1000 Å, *Space Research III*, 772 (North-Holland Publishing Co., 1963).
86. J. I. VETTE AND F. G. CASAL, High Energy Röntgen-rays during solar flares, *Phys. Rev. Letters*, **6**, 334 (1961).

87. M. Waldmeier and H. Müller, Die Sonnenstrahlung im Gebiet von $\lambda = 10$ cm, *Z. Astrophys.*, **27,** 58 (1950).
88. W. A. White, Solar X-rays: Slow variations and transient events, *Space Research IV* (in press, 1964).
89. J. R. Winckler, T. C. May, and A. J. Masley, Observation of a solar Bremsstrahlung burst of 1926 UT, August 11, 1960, *J. Geophys. Res.*, **66,** 316 (1961).
90. L. Woltjer, A photometric investigation of the spicules and the structure of the chromosphere, *Bull. Astron. Obs. Neth.*, **12,** 165 (1954).
91. A. I. Yefremov, A. L. Podmosensky, and O. A. Yefremov, Investigations of solar X-rays and Lyman-alpha radiation on August 19–20, 1960, *Space Research III*, 843 (North-Holland Publishing Co., 1963).
92. H. Zirin and R. D. Dietz, The structure of the solar chromosphere. I. A picture based on extreme ultraviolet, millimeter and λ10830 data, *Astrophys. J.*, **138,** 664 (1963).

References added in proof:

93. K. A. Anderson and J. R. Winckler, Solar flare X-ray burst on 28 September 1961, *Space Research III*, 839 (North-Holland Publishing Co., 1963).
94. R. G. Athay and W. O. Roberts, Coronal line intensities at the Khartoum eclipse, *Astrophys. J.*, **121,** 231 (1955).
95. T. de Groot, Spectra of short-lived transients in solar noise at 400 Mc/s, *I.A.U. Symposium*, **9,** 245 (1948).
96. O. Namba, The profile of the infrared He I line in solar faculae, *Bull. Astron. Inst. Neth.*, **17,** 93 (1963).

CHAPTER 2

SOLAR FLARES*

M. A. Ellison and J. H. Reid

1. Introduction

It was in 1923 that George Ellery Hale retired from the directorship of the Mount Wilson Observatory. During the next ten years he built and perfected, in the garden of his home in Pasadena, the first spectrohelioscope. The instrument itself and many of its applications to the study of solar activity are described in four delightful papers which appeared in the *Astrophysical Journal* [27], the journal which he himself had founded.

A brilliant flare occurred on the sun a few days after the new instrument had been brought into use and it was followed by a great magnetic storm. This sequence of events impressed upon Hale the importance of establishing a chain of such instruments round the world so that the sun's hydrogen atmosphere could be kept under continuous observation. From his initiative has sprung the solar patrol as we know it today along with many new and exciting developments in our knowledge of solar–terrestrial relations. We also recognise the great contribution made by Bernard Lyot in developing the narrow-band filter and in applying it to solar cinematography.

Important flares emit X-rays, ultraviolet light, emission lines in the visible regions, radio waves, and particles having a wide range of energies. The geophysical effects of these radiations are of such great interest that a continuous survey of solar activity at its point of origin has become of paramount importance. During the International Geophysical Year such a patrol was successfully organized for the first time by Y. Öhman [39]; uniform standards for film characteristics and photometric procedures were laid down by W. O. Roberts and his IAU Committee [39] and the whole plan was successfully carried through by the world-wide cooperation of

* Professor Ellison had written part of this paper prior to his untimely death: I have endeavored to finish it in the form which he had outlined. J. H. R.

solar astronomers. The sun was kept under observation for about 95 per cent of possible hours.

2. Flare Statistics

Contributing to the solar patrol were some 19 cinematographic stations that photographed the sun in Hα light at intervals varying between ½–5 minutes (Fig. 1). There were also about 30 stations which made visual

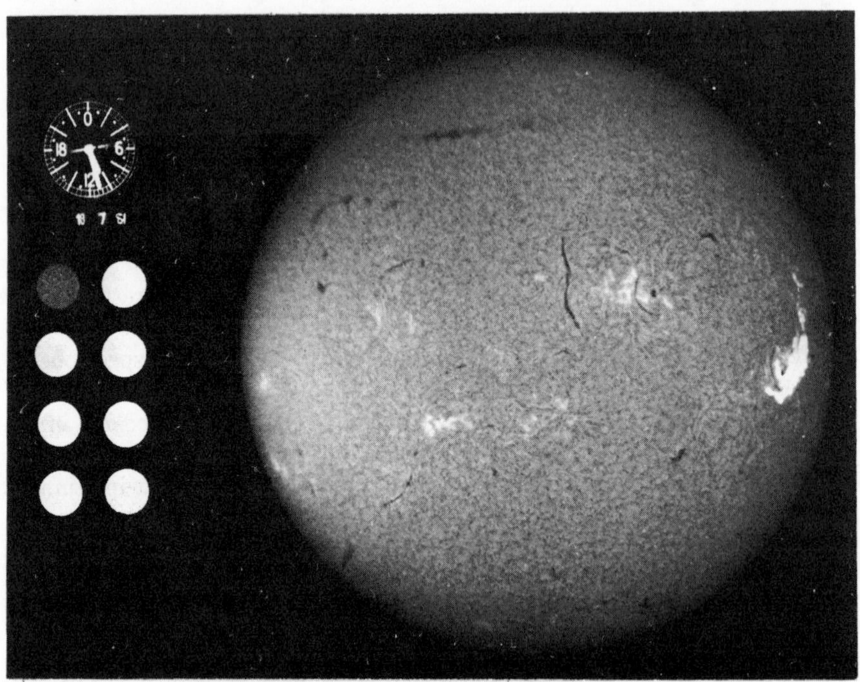

FIG. 1. Cape heliograph exposure, 18 July 1961, 10^h 27^m 13^s, showing a Class 3^+ flare in operation. Normal sky orientation.

observations at fixed hours, mostly with spectrohelioscopes or with Lyot filters, while others took Hα spectroheliograms at varying intervals.

All the flare observations (26,400 in number) made by every station during the IGY arrived at the Data Centers and appeared eventually in the *Quarterly Bulletin for Solar Activity*. Multiple and often incomplete observations of the same flare are difficult to interpret. Geophysicists will, therefore, find it valuable to refer to the *McMath-Hulbert Working Lists of Flares* for the years 1957–1960. Here we have [10] expert compilations by Helen W. Dodson and E. Ruth Hedeman giving the best mean evaluation of all the particulars such as position, importance, duration, etc., for each recorded flare. During the IGY, for example, there were 6762 flares rated Class $\geqslant 1$ and full details of each are given.

The same authors have studied [9] the homogeneity of the flare observations made at the above mentioned stations (*a*) in relation to longitude and (*b*) cinematographic *versus* visual. They found that, although the flare patrol was gratifyingly complete and uniform (mean value 95 per cent of possible hours), approximately twice as many flares $\geqslant 1$ were reported per hour from 05^h to 16^h UT as during the remainder of the Universal Day, and this strong dependence upon longitude existed in the flare data for each month of the IGY. The cinematographic stations failed to confirm this very high rate of flare occurrence for 05^h to 16^h UT. It was noted that in these longitudes visual stations predominated, and that these constituted the main source of the inhomogeneity in the reported flare data. Many visual stations were evidently reporting as Class 1, or greater, flares which would have been rated as subflares by the cinematographic stations. Near the time of solar maximum, May to July 1958, the cinematographic patrol stations were reporting 0.3 flare ($\geqslant 1$) per hour of observation. Some visual stations reported figures close to this mean value but others were grossly in excess. In the future it should be one of the main duties of the World Data Center C at Meudon, which throughout the IGY was responsible for the collection and analysis of flare data, to pick out such stations that for one reason or another persistently exaggerate their ratings of flare importance and to request them to investigate the causes of these systematic discrepancies.

Following the recommendations adopted by the IAU in 1955, the *importance* class of a flare should be based primarily upon the area of the emission filaments at the time of their maximum brightness [56]. The measured (i.e., projected) area is the quantity which has to be recorded (in terms of the unit 1 square degree at the disc center), but the importance must be determined from the *corrected* area.

The relationship to be adopted between the importance class and corrected area was given as shown in Table 1.

TABLE 1

Importance Class		Corrected Area	
Subflares	1^-	<100 m*	<2.06 sq degrees
Flares	1	100–250	2.06–5.15
	2	250–600	5.15–12.4
	3	600–1200	12.4–24.7
	3^+	>1200	>24.7

* Millionths of the visible hemisphere: 1 sq degree = 48.5 millionths.

Since a flare at some distance from the center of the hemisphere is reduced in area by foreshortening, it was recommended that a correction factor should be applied to the measured area in order to obtain the corrected area. Ideally, what we wish to know is the area which the flare would have if it could have been observed at the center of the disc, i.e., from vertically above. This involves a knowledge of how the foreshortening of a flare depends on its angular distance (h) from the disc center. If a flare were a plane horizontal surface, the foreshortening factor would be simply sec h, and most observers, following the IAU recommendations [56], have been in the habit of using the sec h function out to distances (h) of about 65° from the disc center; thereafter it leads to serious errors. However, a statistical treatment [3] shows a nonuniform distribution of flares in any given importance class with distance from the center. This evidently arises from the inadequacy of the sec h correction for areas, since flares of any given class should be equally likely in all longitudes. In individual cases errors have arisen from the fact that a few stations based their estimates of importance upon the measured areas rather than upon the corrected areas, as recommended [9].

By the application of statistical methods and a computer, Constance Warwick [54] has compiled a list of flares with normalized values of importance and area. This list irons out the systematic differences of importance recorded by different stations and gives an importance rating for the IGY flares that is independent of the position of the flare upon the solar disc. By the use of such methods it should be possible to derive a more realistic empirical relation between the corrected area and the measured area for all angular distances (h) from the center of the disc. However, we should note that, since flares differ greatly in structure and vertical extent, such methods, while they may be statistically valid, may yet give corrected areas (and importances) that are wide of the mark in individual cases.

3. Flare Observations

Some of the heliographs at patrol stations were provided with means for standardizing the individual photographs for light intensity [15], and it has thus been possible to derive numerous light curves in Hα for outstanding flares [16, 40, 47]. Similarly, line-width development curves, plotted from measures made with the line shifter of a spectrohelioscope [33], have provided valuable information about the times of start, maximum, and end of flares, as well as indicating the rapidity of the flash phase.

The Hα flash of radiation is the most fundamental feature of the whole flare mechanism [12]. I have often been asked how the flash phase is defined. For its recognition quantitative measures of line width or central intensity of the Hα line are needed. Figure 2 shows some outstanding examples for those great flares which have accelerated high-energy (>1

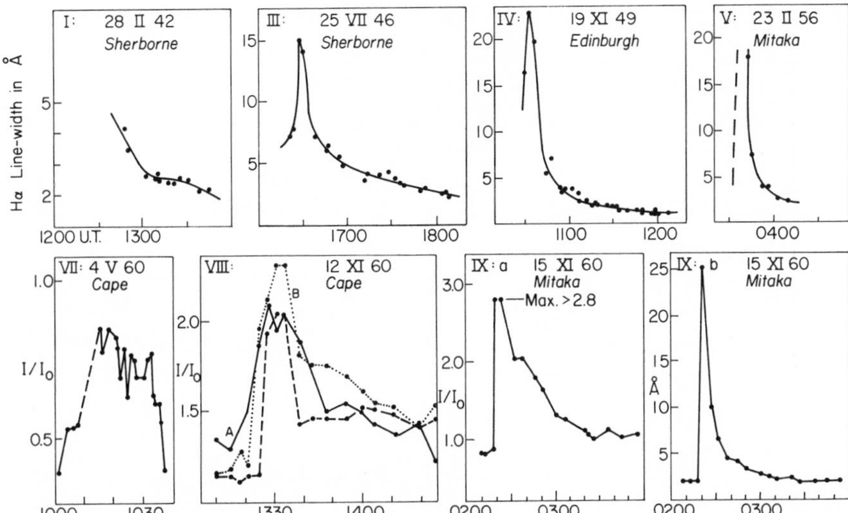

FIG. 2. Light curves (VII, VIII, and IXa) and line-width development curves in Hα (I, III, IV, V, and IXb) for flares which have generated cosmic-ray increases recorded at ground level on the earth.

Bev) protons to the earth. In these cases it can be seen that the Hα line width and central intensity rise to their maximum values (~20 Å and 3 X continuum, respectively) in times of the order of 2–3 minutes. Frequently, the flare is observed to be in progress for 15–30 minutes, as a few small areas of lesser brightness, before the sudden extension and turbulence of the flash begins. The duration of maximum is probably momentary even though the total duration of the flare may be many hours.

Figure 3 illustrates the profile of the flare Hα line near the time of maximum brightness. Here XY is the visibility range, or effective line width, and AB/BI is the central intensity expressed as a fraction of the local continuum. In order to follow the flash phase, one or both of these quantities must be measured at 1-min intervals: they may be derived from spectral profiles if sufficient spectra are available, or more conveniently from visual measures made with a spectrohelioscope. The central intensity may also be deduced from calibrated filtergrams.

The Hβ line and the higher members of the Balmer series show profiles similar to that for Hα, differing only in intensity and line width, and showing a normal Balmer decrement. During the flash phase, however, the Balmer decrement becomes quite anomalous. This extraordinary change may be illustrated by the figures of Table 2 which refer to the flare of 1960 September 2. They were obtained by Elske v.P. Smith from spectra taken with the universal spectrograph at Sacramento Peak [48]. They show the central intensities and line widths from Hα to Hζ before, during and after the flash.

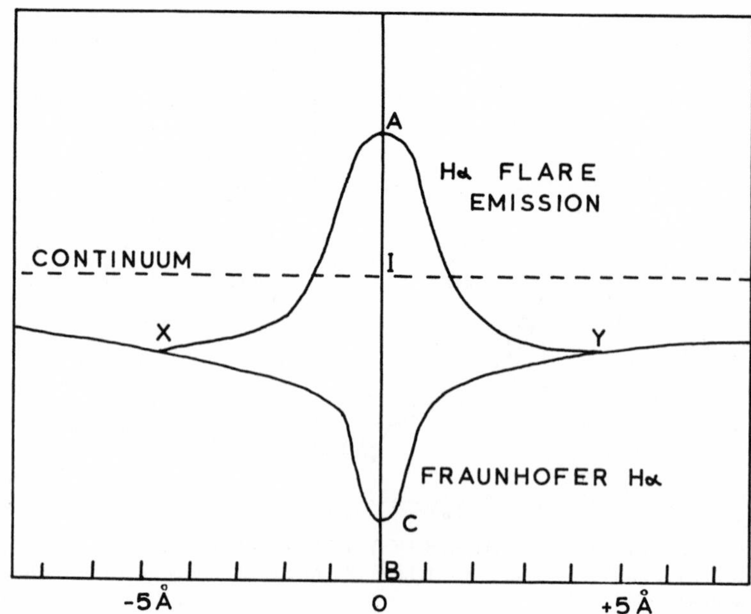

FIG. 3. Profile of the flare Hα line near the time of flare maximum. XAY is the emission profile; XCY is the normal Fraunhofer profile; I is the level of the continuous spectrum just beyond the wings of the hydrogen line; XY is the visibility range, or the effective line width; AB/BI is the central intensity of the flare expressed as a fraction of the local continuum.

It is evident from these measures that during the flash phase the central intensities are approximately the same for the first six members of the series, and likewise the line widths; whereas before and after the flash phase there is a well-marked decrement from Hα to Hζ.

During the few minutes of the flash phase, immensely rapid extensions (~1000 km/sec) of the emission filaments are often observed [19]. To what extent these velocities represent actual movements of matter is still an unsettled question. Great turbulence of this kind may well be the cause of the sudden widening of the hydrogen lines but the Stark effect due to a sudden increase of ion density also appears to be in operation. The important point to note is that these high velocities are confined to the flash phase: once the light curve has passed its peak, the bright filaments settle down into a quiescent state of decreasing luminosity and separate slowly over a period of several hours with velocities that never exceed ~3 km/sec [21].

Athay and Moreton [1] have examined the flash phase (called by them the "explosive" phase) with high time resolution (one photograph every 10 sec): they have brought to light the occurrence of high-speed "influences" radiating outward from these flashes at speeds ~1500 km/sec. These expanding shock waves, or whatever they may be, can be observed to

TABLE 2

	Time h	m	s	Hα	Hβ	Hγ	Hδ	Hε	Hζ	
Central intensities	23	01	20	0.52	0.46	0.34	0.36	—	0.24	Before flash
in terms of the local	23	04	53	1.91	2.25	2.11	2.05	1.80	2.26	During flash
continuum	23	19	56	0.92	0.82	0.65	0.58	—	0.35	After flash
Line width in angstroms	23	01	20	1.8	0.8	0.4	0.3	—	—	Before flash
	23	04	53	18	17	14.5	15.8	13	14	During flash
	23	19	56	4.3	2.8	3.5	2.2	—	—	After flash

activate prominences situated in the corona at great distances round the bulge, covering almost an entire hemisphere.

It is clear from all this evidence that the flash phase of a flare is something new in astrophysics. Most present-day theories regard the flare as a process in which energy that has been slowly stored up in a chromospheric magnetic field is suddenly released through instability in the plasma, being converted into radiation, both wave and particle. How is this energy stored and what gives rise to its catastrophic release? These are problems of plasma physics which will be considered later.

Once the flash phase is over, the bright flare filaments remain almost stationary both horizontally and vertically, apparently anchored in the magnetic field. But many secondary phenomena associated with the flare occur in the vicinity and show high velocities [11, 38] ~100–500 km/sec. These are the flare surges and "sprays," the blow-off filaments, and the coronal loop prominences. Many of these have been studied by Smith and Booton as they appear on the Sacramento Peak patrol films [49]. Since they all appear unusually bright compared with normal prominences when seen against the dark sky background, they have often been confused with the Hα flare itself which is at a lower level.

The shapes of flares and the location of their bright filaments in relation to the sunspots within an active region have been the subject of studies on the Cape heliograph films [19–21]. First, consider the great 3^+ flares, those which have been associated with strong outbursts of Type IV radio emission and have also generated high-energy (>1 Bev) protons that have been detected by their secondary effects at ground level on the earth within some 5–30 minutes of the flash of the flare. It has been found [20] that: (*a*) These flares occur over large *E*- or *F*-type spot groups which contain complex magnetic field distributions (γ or $\beta\gamma$) and high field strengths (~3000 gauss) in some of the umbrae. The spots of opposite polarity are closely juxtaposed, usually within the same penumbra. (*b*) There are *two* flare emission filaments; these cross the group and run parallel to one another. (*c*) The two filaments also lie parallel to the magnetic axis of the group, that is the line which separates the N polar umbrae from the S polar umbrae within the group. (*d*) One of the emission filaments crosses and obscures the strongest N poles and the other obscures the main S poles. This seems to mean that high-energy particles are most easily accelerated when the flare occurs in a region of strong magnetic fields.

These findings have been generalized by Avignon *et al.* who have studied the shapes and positions of flares [2] that have given rise to streams of cosmic-ray protons of lower energy (~10–400 Mev). These particles occur much more frequently than those which produce effects at ground level, they cause strong ionization of the *D*-layer in polar regions and give rise to polar cap absorption (PCA) effects. The authors find that the majority of the PCA flares are characterized in shape and position by what they call "configuration A": this is essentially that described by Ellison, McKenna and Reid [20] as characterizing the high-energy proton flares.

Martres and Pick [35] have also investigated the shapes and locations of flares which have emitted strong radio noise outbursts of Type IV (continuum emission). In 36 cases of flares which generated centimeter-wave outbursts, 32 of them covered up at least part of the penumbrae and umbrae of the underlying spots. The moment at which a bright flare filament passed over a spot umbrae was also the time at which the radio outburst was recorded.

In 22 cases of flares which generated strong meter-wave outbursts 17 lay along the course of a plage filament (dark) and 4 had the above-mentioned "configuration A." It is now generally believed that Type IV radio noise is caused by the synchrotron emission of high-energy electrons spiraling in a coronal magnetic field [6]. These particles originate in the region of the flare discharge. The whole phenomenon evidently requires the occurrence of the flare in a region where there is a strong magnetic field, i.e., directly over a sunspot umbra.

These results seem to be in conflict with the evidence of Severny [44], who finds that flares usually occur at the neutral points in the active region magnetic fields. For those special flares we have been discussing this seems to be very unlikely: their locations at heights of $\sim$30,000 km directly over sunspot umbrae having measured field strengths of $\sim$3000 gauss suggests that they avoid neutral points or lines and occur in regions of the strongest fields.

Of course there is conflicting evidence about the effect of a flare on the magnetic field of the active region in which it occurs. Severny [44, 45], as mentioned above, has made many isogauss plots of the active region fields before and after important flares. He finds that in almost all cases the flare begins where a neutral point seems to exist and where there is also a sufficiently large magnetic field gradient. Evans [23] has also reported large changes over the whole magnetic field of an active center at the time of a 1^+ flare.

On the other hand, Howard and Babcock [29] and Michard *et al.* [37] were unable to detect any significant changes in the magnetic field configuration as the result of a flare. It should be remembered that all these magnetic measures refer to fields at the photospheric level and not to the region, some 30,000 km higher up, where the flares occur.

Ellison *et al.* [17–19] have sought for visible changes at the chromospheric level brought about by magnetic field disturbances. From numerous studies of the film records of the Hα striation patterns in the vicinity of major flares, they find that in all cases where the flares are associated with outbursts of Type IV (continuum) radio emission the striation patterns are temporarily destroyed, at, or within a few minutes of, the time of peak intensity of the flare. Since they believe these patterns are maintained in their peculiar alignment by the action of weak magnetic fields in the chromosphere, they take the observed changes as an indication of the destruction or reorientation of the magnetic field of the region due to the flare process. More recently Reid [42, 43] has found that the bright streaks and mottles in the striation pattern decrease in intensity to the level of the dark spaces between them, this gives the impression of the formation of a dark halo around the flare region—the flare "nimbus." He found that this nimbus is more horseshoe-shaped than oval, and was some 300,000 × 400,000 km in extent. The two legs of the horseshoe lie down either side of the magnetic axis of the spot group.

The alignment of the striation pattern is due to weak magnetic fields on the perimeter of the flare region. Reid [42, 43] also investigated the position and intensity distribution of the plage regions before and after major flares. He found that there were very definite changes in both the positions of the plages and in the intensity distribution within them following the flare. These changes he has ascribed to the flare process, and he tentatively links the nimbus changes with the Type IV radio emission.

4. Flare Spectra and Theories

The energy released by a solar flare is an important quantity, since we cannot, as yet, investigate directly the magnetic fields in which we believe the energy is stored until such a time as it is triggered off to produce the flare. The emission filaments of the greatest flares are always located above the umbrae of sunspots which have complex magnetic fields [20]. It has been possible [22] to derive the energy radiated by a 3^+ flare at optical wavelengths from (*a*) the profiles of emission lines; (*b*) the white light continuum.

(*a*) The highest measured value for the total radiation from the Hα line profile at maximum for five flares (three 3^+, one 3, and one 2) was 1.08×10^{27} ergs/sec [14]. The contribution from the other members of the Balmer series is difficult to estimate with accuracy owing to the lack of observations and the anomalous Balmer decrement [30, 50]; this varies from flare to flare due to self-absorption and Stark broadening and is quite unlike the decrement for solar prominences. A rough estimate gives an energy output for the series as 15 times that for Hα. Other emission lines, numbering about 400, are mainly Fe and Fe I [46]. These have their absorption lines filled in or are in weak emission about the continuum level, and their contribution may be taken to be about 10 times that of Hα. If we assume that an energy output equal to one-half of the value at the time of flare maximum is maintained for one hour we have:

$$\text{Total energy radiated in emission lines} = 0.54 \times 10^{27} \times 25 \times 3600$$
$$= 5 \times 10^{31} \text{ ergs}$$

(*b*) The energy contributed by the enhancement of the white light continuum may be derived from the Sherborne and Edinburgh spectra [12, 13] which showed an increase of the continuum brightness ~10 per cent in association with two 3^+ flares (1946 July 25 and 1949 November 19). It is assumed that the enhancement extends over the whole spectrum, duration is ~10 minutes, and area one-fifth that of the flare, whence

Total radiation emitted by enhanced continuum $= 154 \times 4.2 \times 10^7 \times 2 \times 10^{19} \times 600$

$= 8 \times 10^{31}$ ergs

where 1540 cal/cm²/sec is the normal rate of emission for all wavelengths from the solar surface.

From (*a*) and (*b*) a value of $\sim 10^{32}$ ergs is evidently the total radiation in the emission lines plus continuum. This will be a lower limit since the emission lines lying outside the visible have been neglected. The value of $\sim 10^{32}$ ergs is in good agreement with the estimate of Parker [41] for the flare of 1956 February 23, and it represents about one-thirtieth of the energy radiated by the whole sun in one second. In fact, the total optical emission of a 3^+ flare is greater than the total energy content of the solar atmosphere above the photosphere. If we take the volume of a 3^+ flare as $\sim 10^{29}$ cm³ (an upper limit for such flares) then the total energy released in the flare region is at least 10^3 ergs/cm³, which is about a hundred to a thousand times greater than the energy density of an equivalent nonflare region of the chromosphere.

The essential problems of the flare mechanism are to discover in what form this energy is stored and how its release is triggered off. It seems that the most probable form of storage is in the local magnetic field, and if this is so, then $H^2/8\pi$ is $\sim 10^3$ ergs/cm³, and we require the destruction of a field of approximately 150 gauss.

In Severny's theory [44, 45] the essential feature is the instability of the plasma in an active region when the magnetic energy $(H^2/8\pi)$ greatly exceeds the thermal energy density (Nkt). A pinch effect develops near a neutral point, and compression and contraction of the plasma takes place in a matter of seconds. Temperatures of the order of 5–10 million degrees may then develop in a thin layer, perhaps only 10 km thick. The compression is eventually stopped by the development of a shock wave, and expansion then follows in the region behind the shock wave. The fine structure of the "moustaches" in the early stage spectra are attributed to these turbulent regions, and in observational support of his "pinch" mechanism, his magnetic plots have shown that flares begin at or near neutral points, that there are high magnetic field gradients in the region, and that the flare produces a large reduction and redistribution of the isogauss pattern. The reasons for triggering off the reaction when $H^2/8\pi \gg Nkt$ are not at all clear.

A more detailed study of the slow storage and catastrophic release of energy in flares has been made by Gold and Hoyle [25]. They show that the necessary magnetic energy can be stored in twisted bundles of lines of force. The sudden release of the energy occurs when two such bundles, having opposite senses of twist, come into contact. The period of coalescence and energy release is of the order of 100 seconds, but from the theory one would expect to observe only a single flare filament where the two bundles of lines of force make contact. In fact, for the great flares [20] there are two bright filaments, parallel to one another and to the magnetic axis of the spot group. It would seem that more extensive observations of the various aspects of flares and a more thorough understanding of plasma physics are still required before a more accurate theory of the flare mechanism can be propounded.

To be successful the theory must account for all the characteristic observational features, including (1) the slow buildup of energy densities, some hundreds of times the normal thermal values, within a limited volume; (2) the catastrophic release of energy during the flash phase; (3) the location of the bright flare filaments in relation to the sunspots; (4) the emission of X-rays and the generation of the various types of radio noise emission in their correct sequence; (5) the acceleration of protons and electrons to high energies.

5. Physical Processes and the Results of the Plasma Discharge

A physical model of the flare process has been suggested by Wild [55] in which he attempts to explain qualitatively the various physical phenomena that follow the plasma discharge (Fig. 4). He assumes that the flare is initiated in a neutral plane between two spot groups, as envisaged in several electromagnetic theories of flares. The plasma instability triggers off a Fermi mechanism which causes the immediate ejection of a shower of relativistic electrons; these generate the Type III and Type V radio bursts above the disturbance, the microwave early burst, and the hard X-rays burst below and around the flash region. At the same time a magnetohydrodynamic shock conveying ions and electrons passes upward from the center at a speed of 1000 km/sec. The shock front is identified with the source of the Type II burst.

The interaction of the shock front and the various particles accelerated by the magnetic perturbations within the ejected cloud traveling behind it leads to the emission of the Type IV radiation and to the acceleration of the high-energy protons, whose secondary emissions are detectable at ground level on the earth. Under some conditions the efflux of the plasma will be of sufficient energy to carry the magnetic field of the region away from the sun to yield the Type IV-B component of radio emission, which

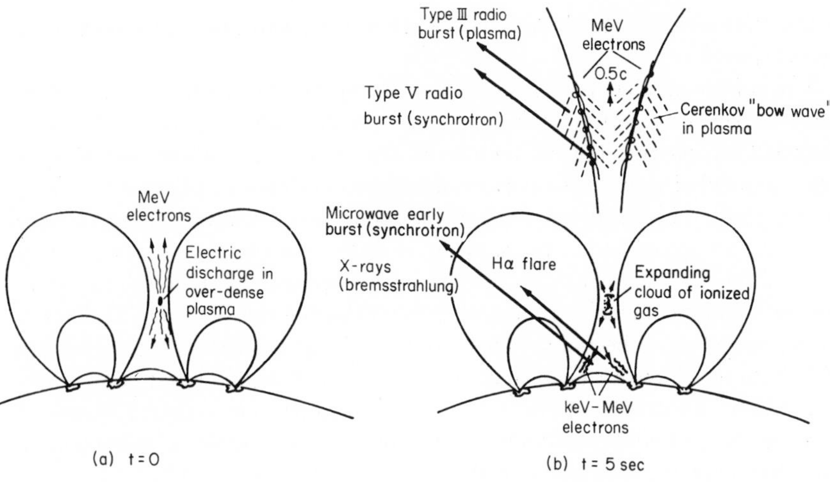

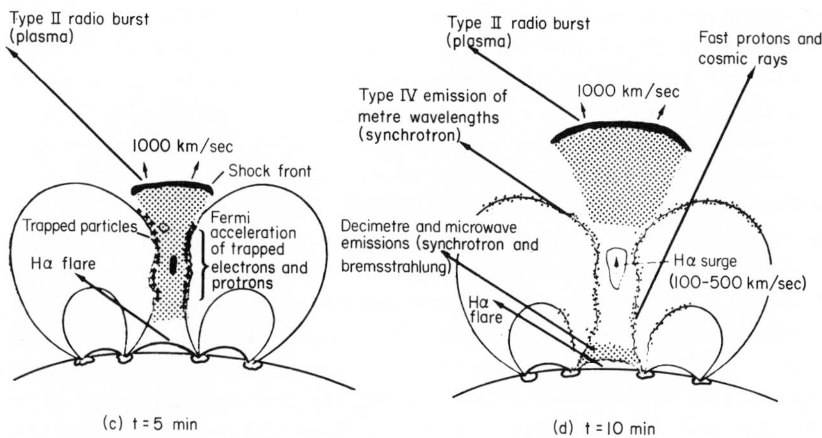

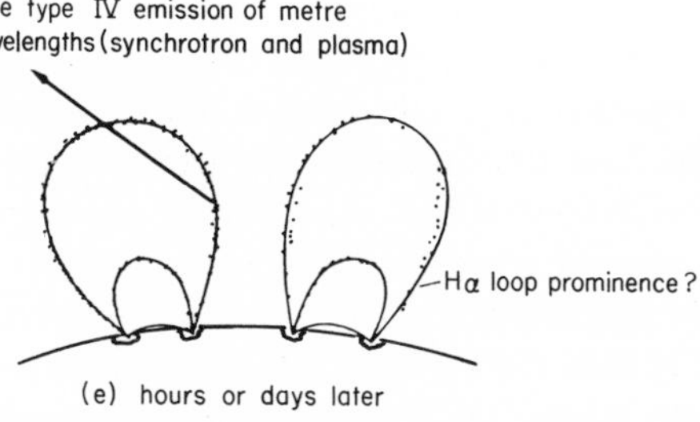

FIG. 4. A time sequence of diagrams illustrating a possible model by which radio and other manifestations of a major flare may be interpreted. Courtesy of J. P. Wild [55].

is the "classical" type discovered by Boischot, who also investigated its properties [5].

The initial acceleration of electrons during the flash phase of the flare leads to the production of X-rays. From a statistical analysis of events recorded during the first six months of the IGY, Hachenberg and Kruger [26] concluded that SID's occur only when centimeter radiation (3.2 cm) is detected. This appears to indicate that the bremsstrahlung X-rays (1–10 Å) are generated at the same level as the centimeter radiation. They suggest this is 2000–6000 km above the photosphere, but Kundu [31], who reaches similar conclusions, suggests a height in the range 15,000–30,000 km which seems more probable. This would be in agreement with the findings of Constance Warwick [53] that limb flares below 15,000 km do not generate SID's. Fokker [24] also found a close association between bursts of ionizing X-rays and centimeter radiation in his studies of geomagnetic solar flare effects (crochets) and the microwave bursts.

Simultaneous to the X-ray emission there are the Type III and Type V bursts. The Type III bursts are characterized by a "fast" drift in the frequency of maximum intensity from high to low frequencies at a rate of approximately 20 Mc/sec/sec. These events occur in groups near the start of flares and subflares, and they have a duration of about 10 minutes. Their polarization is either random or partially circular or elliptical. The Type V emission is a short continuum burst lasting only a few minutes at most, and is probably due to synchrotron radiation. Following comes the Type II bursts; these are characterized by a "slow" drift from high to low frequencies at a rate of approximately 0.25 Mc/sec/sec. The Type II events occur in the post-maximum phase of certain important flares, they last for about ten minutes, and generally have random polarization.

Uchida [52] has suggested that the Type II and Type III bursts, though having a common radiation mechanism, may have distinctly different excitors. The Type III being produced by the free streaming motion of individual high-velocity particles, while the Type II bursts could be due to plasma oscillations caused by a hydrodynamic shock, perhaps through charge separation at the shock front. Maxwell and Thompson [36] find, whatever the generating mechanism, that the regions of origin of individual plasma frequencies are at much greater heights in the solar atmosphere than would be expected from conventional models of electron density. Their data suggest that the initiating disturbances are being propagated outward along coronal streamers, which may be aligned along lines of force extending outward from the flare. The electron densities in these streamers would be about ten times the normal Baumbach–Allen values.

After the Type II slow drift bursts, a broad-banded continuum emission, which may last from several minutes to hours and whose dynamic spectrum is featureless, may be observed. This is the Type IV continuum emission. It begins during the flash phase of the flare, as observed optically in Hα

light, and reaches a maximum intensity some 20–30 minutes later. Radio astronomers now consider that at least three phases of Type IV radiation can be distinguished, and these have been summarized by Kundu and Smerd [32] as shown in Table 3.

Type IV-B is the "classical" Type IV discovered by Boischot and which Boischot and Pick [7] suggest is produced by synchrotron radiation from a source of relativistic electrons ejected by the flare and spiraling in a magnetic field. Denisse [8] has suggested that the Type IV-C emission could be explained by a plasma Čerenkov mechanism, where the high-energy electrons ejected at the beginning of the flare are trapped near the sun. They slowly diffuse into the coronal streamers and excite longitudinal plasma waves. These, in turn, transfer their energy to electromagnetic waves capable of propagation outward through the solar atmosphere. In theory, such wave coupling would take place at an altitude where the critical frequency approaches close to the wave frequency, so the emission would be expected to originate in the low corona, as has been observed.

Type IV-A emission is an extension of the Type IV bursts at decimeter and microwave (centimeter) bands. Takakura and Kai [51] consider the decimeter emission, not as a high-frequency component of the meter wave emission, but as a separate radiation. Hachenberg and Kruger [26] interpret the centimeter continuum radiation as a quasi-thermal one generated by free-free transitions. They consider its occurrence indicates the presence of a cloud of superthermal electrons in the flare plasma.

Ellison *et al.* [17–19] found a close relation between the Type IV-B emission and the flare nimbus phenomenon. Reid [43] has suggested that, when the efflux of plasma from the flare region is of sufficient energy to carry the local magnetic field away from the sun to yield the Type IV-B emission, then the magnetic energy withdrawn from the active region may result in the bright chromospheric mottles returning to the level of the normal undisturbed chromospheric intensity, with a consequent disappearance of any form of coherent striation pattern. When the magnetic field is ejected to its greatest extent, when the Type IV-B source become stationary at a distance of several solar radii from the flare, the effect at the chromospheric level should be at a maximum, and this is about the time, some 20–30 minutes after flare maximum, when the nimbus is most conspicuous.

Another indication of magnetic fields above flare regions is given by the development of coronal loops after some large flares at the limb. In the case of the flare of 1960 May 4 [20] a magnificent system of coronal loop prominences developed after the flare had almost completely faded. At full development the height of their bright tops was 24,000 km, but as they decayed their height increased over the next hour to 57,000 km. Hansen and Gordon [28] studied five limb flares on 13 October 1958 and concluded that either the general shape of the magnetic field above an active region is

TABLE 3

	IV-A	IV-B	IV-C
Spectral range	10,000 to ~250 Mc/sec	~250 to 25 Mc/sec	~1000 to 25 Mc/sec (the upper frequency limit is uncertain)
Beginning	At or near flare start	Uusually within minutes of a Type II burst; after flare maximum.	Following a IV-B
Duration	Several tens of minutes	Several tens of minutes	Hours (possibly days)
Polarization	Partially circular	Partially circular	Strongly circular
Location	In bright region, near flame	Well away (up to several solar radii) from the flare after initial movement.	Closer to flare (a fraction of a solar radius) than IV-B.
Movement	Not appreciable	Early, large-scale movement away from flare at speeds of several 1000 km/sec.	None
Source size	Small (<5′ arc)	Large (~10′ arc)	Small (a few minutes of arc)
Directivity	Little	Little	Strong toward the center

unaltered by flare events, or the magnetic field was restored to its preflare configuration in the course of 2–3 hours. The latter conclusion is in accord with the occurrence of homologous flares. They also found that the over-all shape of the limb flares strongly suggested the lower section of a giant loop in the solar atmosphere with a height of about 100,000 km.

Something about the behavior of the magnetic fields of an active region can be deduced from a study of the particle emissions from flares. These can be divided into three classes of different energies: (*a*) the high-energy (>1-Bev) protons which produce secondary cosmic-ray events at ground level (GLE). (*b*) protons of lower energy (10–400 Mev) which are responsible for the ionospheric polar cap absorption effects (PCA). (*c*) clouds of particles with low energies (<1 Mev) which generate geomagnetic storms and auroral displays.

It is these plasma clouds which draw out into interplanetary space some part of the magnetic field of sunspots, thereby creating radial magnetic fields which expand outward and frequently envelop the earth. When such clouds are ejected from the sunspot region, the ends of the magnetic lines of force remain anchored at the sun, while the loops continue to thread the ejected material. A magnetic bottle is thus formed. Its lines of force are approximately in the plane of the ecliptic, and the solar rotation bends these radial fields convex toward the West. The concept of a magnetic bottle is necessary to provide a working hypothesis for the transmission of high-energy (>1-Bev) protons from flare outbursts to the earth, where they produce cosmic-ray effects at ground level. If the earth is in such a bottle, then:

(*a*) If a major flare occurs in the active region within the neck of the bottle, there will be already in existence direct trajectories, consisting of lines of force, along which the high-energy particles can spiral from the flare to the region of the earth's field. At the earth the particles will appear to arrive from the west of the sun-earth line, and this has been deduced from the records of some of the earlier solar cosmic-ray events by McCracken and Palmeira [34].

(*b*) Energetic particles do not travel in straight lines but are guided in helical trajectories around the lines of force. Thus there is a much greater probability of high-energy protons reaching the earth from a flare which occurs in the western hemisphere of the sun (see Fig. 5). In general Class 3 and 3^+ flares are distributed quite uniformly across the disc in longitude and Bell [4], who studied the longitude distribution of 580 flares of importance 2^+ or greater, found that exactly half occurred to the east of the central meridian and half of them to the west.

(*c*) When the earth is inside a magnetic bottle it will be shielded from the influx of galactic cosmic rays, and there may be a reduction (the Forbush decrease) of as much as 30 per cent in the low-energy flux (1–10

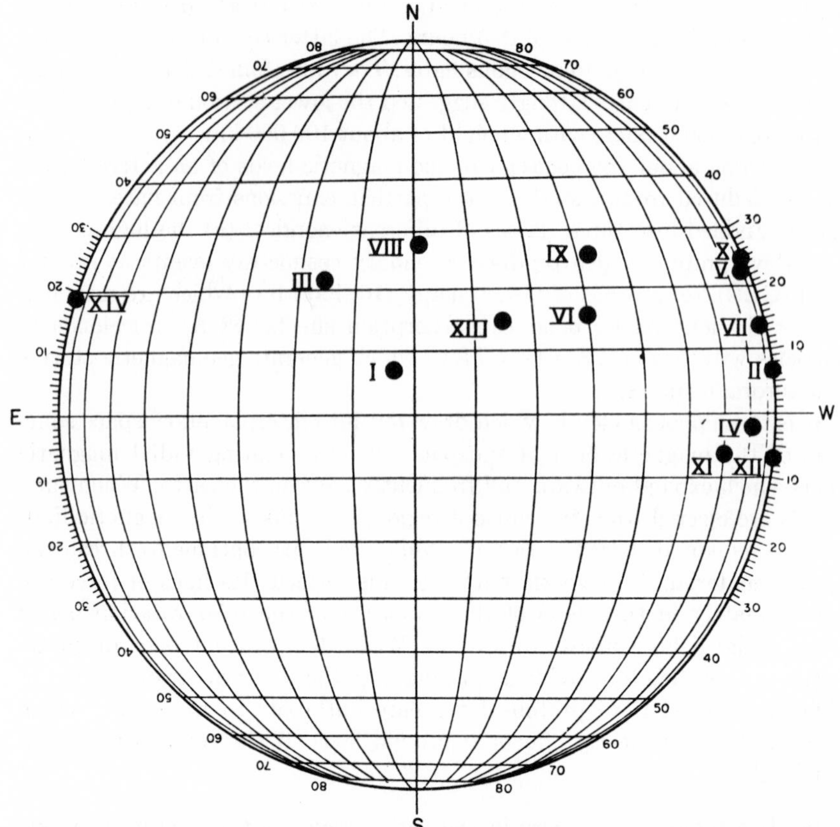

Fig. 5. Heliographic coordinates of the 14 flares which have generated high-energy (>1 Bev) protons recorded on the earth by their secondary effects at ground level (GLE). Note the predominance of western positions. These flares occurred on I 1942 February 28, II 1942 March 7, III 1946 July 25, IV 1949 November 19, V 1956 February 23, VI 1959 July 16, VII 1960 May 4, VIII 1960 November 12, IX 1960 November 15, X 1960 November 20, XI 1961 July 18, XII 1961 July 20, XIII 1956 August 31, and XIV 1960 September 3.

Bev) of the galactic component. The onset of this decrease coincides with the arrival of the geomagnetic storm particles at the earth.

The recovery period for the galactic component of cosmic rays to its normal level extends over some 5–10 days and this suggests that the life of the magnetic bottle with its guiding lines of force for high-energy solar particles is of the same order.

The 1961 July event [21] is a very good illustration of the formation of a magnetic bottle. A complex magnetic sunspot group developed rapidly after its passage in from the east limb on 7 July. The first major flare (Class 3) occurred on the 11th and a second (Class 3$^+$) on the 12th when the spot group was 22° east of the central meridian. No high-energy particles from either of these flares reached the earth, but the flare on the 12th ejected a cloud of low-energy particles. These reached the earth 25 hours after the flare, generating a sudden commencement geomagnetic storm, and a simultaneous Forbush decrease of the galactic component of cosmic-ray intensity occurred. The earth was now enveloped in a magnetic bottle and the high-energy protons from the next two major flares in the group, a 3^+ on the 18th and another 3^+ on the 20th, found ready-made and easy trajectories to the earth, arriving some 35 minutes and 20 minutes respectively after the causative flare.

During the International Years of the Quiet Sun it may be possible to examine isolated events, or groups of events, without the ambiguity which exists when the level of solar activity is high. It is to be hoped that an intensive study of such occurrences will give us a greater insight into the flare process and the resulting conditions in interplanetary space.

References

1. R. G. Athay and G. E. Moreton, Impulsive phenomena of the solar atmosphere, 1: Some optical events associated with flares showing explosive phase, *Astrophys. J.*, **133,** 935 (1961).
2. Y. Avignon, M.-J. Martres-Tropé, and M. Pick-Gutmann, Identification d'une classe d'éruptions chromosphériques responsables des absorptions ionosphériques polaires, *C. R. Acad. Sci.*, **256,** 2112 (1963).
3. M. C. Ballario, Studio statistico sulle dimensioni dei brillamenti cromosferici in radiazione di idrogeno osservati ad Arcetri, Capri Sevzia, Hawaii, McMath, Mitaka, USNRL, *Mem. Soc. Astron. Ital.*, **31,** 329 (1960).
4. B. Bell, Major flares and geomagnetic activity, *Smithsonian Contrib. Astrophys.*, **5,** 69 (1961).
5. A. Boischot, Etude du rayonnement radioélectrique solaire sur 169 Mhz, à l'aide d'un grand interféromètre à réseau, *Ann. Astrophys.*, **21,** 273 (1958).
6. A. Boischot and J. F. Denisse, Les émissions de type IV et l'origine des rayons cosmiques associés aux éruptions chromosphériques, *C. R. Acad. Sci.*, **245,** 2194 (1957).
7. A. Boischot and M. Pick, Structure of the Type IV radio burst and its relation with solar cosmic rays, *J. Phys. Soc. Japan*, **17,** Suppl. A-II, 203 (1962).
8. J. F. Denisse, Les phénomènes radioélectriques solaires et leur interpretation physique, *U.R.S.I. XIIIth General Assembly*, 7 p. (1960).
9. H. W. Dodson and E. R. Hedeman, Survey of the number of solar flares observed during the International Geophysical Year, *J. Geophys. Res.*, **65,** 123 (1960).
10. H. W. Dodson and E. R. Hedeman, Flare index for each day of IGY based on McMath-Hulbert Observatory working list of IGY flares; McMath-Hulbert Observatory working list of flares and daily flare index for IGC-1959; McMath-Hulbert Observatory working list of flares and daily flare index for 1960, *IGY Solar Activity Rept. Nos.* **14, 15,** and **18,** (High Altitude Observatory, Boulder, 1961–1962).
11. M. A. Ellison, Some studies of the motions of hydrogen flocculi by Doppler displacements of the Hα line, *Mon. Not. Roy. Astron. Soc.*, **102,** 11 (1942).
12. M. A. Ellison, Visual and spectrographic observations of a great solar flare, 1946 July 25, *Mon. Not. Roy. Astron. Soc.*, **106,** 500 (1946).
13. M. A. Ellison and M. Conway, The solar flare of 1949 November 19, *The Observatory*, **70,** 77 (1950).

14. M. A. Ellison, A photometric survey of solar flares, plages and prominences in Hα light, *Pub. Roy. Obs. Edinburgh,* **1,** 75 (1952).
15. M. A. Ellison, The Lyot Hα heliograph at the Cape of Good Hope, *Nature,* **182,** 624 (1958).
16. M. A. Ellison, S. M. P. McKenna, and J. H. Reid, Cape Lyot heliograph results, 1: Light-curves of 30 solar flares in relation to sudden ionospheric disturbances, *Dunsink Obs. Pub.,* **1,** 1 (1960).
17. M. A. Ellison, S. M. P. McKenna, and J. H. Reid, Cape Lyot heliograph results, 2: The 3+ flare of 1960 June 1 and its influence on the Hα striation pattern, *Dunsink Obs. Pub.,* **1,** 37 (1960).
18. M. A. Ellison, S. M. P. McKenna, and J. H. Reid, The flare of 1960 April 1, *The Observatory,* **80,** 149 (1960).
19. M. A. Ellison, S. M. P. McKenna, and J. H. Reid, Flares associated with the 1960 November event and the flare nimbus phenomenon, *Mon. Not. Roy. Astron. Soc.,* **122,** 496 (1961).
20. M. A. Ellison. S. M. P. McKenna, and J. H. Reid, Cosmic ray flares: A description and discussion of the ten great solar flares which have generated cosmic rays recorded at ground level, *Dunsink Obs. Pub.,* **1,** 51 (1961).
21. M. A. Ellison, S. M. P. McKenna, and J. H. Reid, Cosmic ray flares associated with the July 1961 event., *Mon. Not. Roy. Astron. Soc.,* **124,** 263 (1962).
22. M. A. Ellison, Energy release in solar flares, *Q. J. Roy. Astron. Soc.,* **4,** 62 (1963).
23. J. W. Evans, Flare-associated magnetic activity in the sun [Abstract], *Astron. J.,* **64,** 330 (1959).
24. A. D. Fokker, The relation between geomagnetic solar flare effects and solar microwave outburts, *Bull. Astron. Inst. Neth.,* **16,** 311 (1962).
25. T. Gold and F. Hoyle, On the origin of solar flares, *Mon. Not. Roy. Astron. Soc.,* **120,** 89 (1960).
26. O. Hachenberg and A. Krüger, The correlation of bursts of solar radio emission in the centimetre range with flares and sudden ionospheric disturbances, *J. Atmos. Terr. Phys.,* **17,** 20 (1959).
27. G. E. Hale, The spectrohelioscope and its work, Parts I–IV, *Astrophys. J.,* **70,** 265 (1929); **71,** 73 (1930); **73,** 379 (1931); **74,** 214 (1931).
28. R. Hansen and D. Gordon, The limb flares of October 13, 1958, *Publs. Astron. Soc. Pacific,* **72,** 194 (1960).
29. R. Howard and H. W. Babcock, Magnetic fields associated with the solar flare of July 16, 1959, *Astrophys. J.,* **132,** 218 (1960).
30. J. T. Jefferies, E. v.P. Smith, and H. J. Smith, The flare of September 18, 1957, *Astrophys. J.,* **129,** 146 (1959).
31. M. R. Kundu, Some relations between centimeter-wave radio bursts and solar cosmic rays and X-rays, *J. Phys. Soc. Japan,* **17,** Suppl. A-II, 259 (1962).
32. M. R. Kundu and S. F. Smerd, *Info. Bull. Solar Radio Observatories No.* **11** (1962).
33. J. Kvíčala, F. Hřebik, V. Letfus, J. Olmr, Z. Švestka, and L. Křivsky, List of flares observed at Ondřejov Observatory during the IGY, *Czech. Akad. Ved. Astron. Ustav. Publ. No.* **43** (1960).
34. K. G. McCracken and R. A. R. Palmeira, Comparison of solar cosmic rays injection including July 17, 1959 and May 4, 1960, *J. Geophys. Res.,* **65,** 2673 (1960).
35. M.-J. Martres-Tropé and M. Pick, Caractères propres aux éruptions chromosphériques associées à des émissions radioélectriques, *Ann. Astrophys.,* **25,** 293 (1962).
36. A. Maxwell and A. R. Thompson, Spectral observations of solar radio bursts, 2: Slow-drift bursts and coronal streamers, *Astrophys. J.,* **135,** 138 (1962).
37. R. Michard, Z. Mouradian, and M. Semel, Champs magnétiques dans un centre d'activité solaire avant et pendant une éruption, *Ann. Astrophys.,* **24,** 54 (1961).
38. H. W. Newton, Characteristic radial motions of Hα absorption markings seen with bright eruptions on the sun's disc, *Mon. Not. Roy. Astron. Soc.,* **102,** 2 (1942).
39. Y. Ohman, Solar activity [Instruction manual] *Annuals of the IGY,* **5,** 247 (1958).
40. M. B. Ophir and N. E. Steshenko, Photometry of solar flares, *Izv. Crimean Astrophys. Obs.,* **25,** 134 (1961).

41. E. N. PARKER, Acceleration of cosmic rays in solar flares, *Phys. Rev.*, **107**, 830 (1957).
42 J. H. REID, Hydrogen plage regions and great solar flares, *The Observatory*, **83**, 40 (1963).
43. J. H. REID, Cape Lyot heliograph results, 3: A study of regions where important solar flares occur, *Dunsink Obs. Pub.*, **1**, 91 (1963).
44. A. B. SEVERNY, The appearance of flares in neutral points of the solar magnetic field and the pinch effect, *Izv. Crimean Astrophys. Obs.*, **20**, 22 (1958).
45. A. B. SEVERNY, Investigations of magnetic fields related to flares on the sun, *Izv. Crimean Astrophys. Obs.*, **22**, 12 (1960).
46. A. B. SEVERNY, N. V. STECHENKO, AND V. L. KHOKHLOVA, The spectroscopy of solar flares with echelette gratings, *Astron. Zh.*, **37**, 23 (1960); Translation: *Sov. Astron.—AJ*, **4**, 19 (1960).
47. E. F. SHAPOSHNIKOVA AND M. B. OPHIR, Development of chromospheric flares according to observations in 1957, *Izv. Crimean Astrophys. Obs.*, **21**, 112 (1959).
48. E. v.P. SMITH, Spectrum of the flare of September 2, 1960, *Astrophys, J.*, **137**, 580 (1963).
49. H. J. SMITH AND W. D. BOOTON, A study of Sacramento Peak flares, 4: Filament disappearances, flare sprays, and loop prominences, *GRD Research Note No.* **58** (AFCRL-472(IV), Geophys. Res. Directorate, Bedford, Mass., 1962).
50. Z. SVESTKA, Hydrogen spectrum of the flare of July 30, 1958, *Bull. Astron. Inst. Czech.*, **11**, 167 (1960).
51. T. TAKAKURA AND K. KAI, Spectra of solar radio Type IV bursts, *Publs. Astron. Soc. Japan*, **13**, 94 (1961).
52. Y. UCHIDA, On the exciters of Type II and III solar radio bursts, *J. Physics. Soc. Japan*, **17**, Suppl. A-II, 234 (1962).
53. C. S. WARWICK, Flare height and association with SID's, *Astrophys. J.*, **121**, 385 (1955).
54. C. S. WARWICK, The National Bureau of Standards list of IGY flares with normalized values of importance and area, *IGY Solar Activity Rept. No.* **17** (High Altitude Observatory, Boulder, 1962).
55. J. P. WILD, The radio emission from solar flares, *J. Phys. Soc. Japan*, **17**, Suppl. A-II, 249 (1962).
56. Working Group on Flare Classification, Report of the . . ., *Trans. Intn'l Astron. Un.*, **9**, 146 (1955).

CHAPTER 3

SOLAR RADIO EMISSIONS

S. F. Smerd

1. Solar Radio Astronomy before the IGY [44, 68]

At the beginning of the IGY in 1957 the sun had been observed fairly regularly, and at a number of points in the radio spectrum, for some ten years; these years included a maximum (1947) and a minimum (1954) of solar activity (Fig. 1). Good progress had been made in this relatively short time. The broad classes of radio emissions from the sun were well established: the quiet-sun component, the slowly varying component at microwavelengths, and bursts right through the observed wavelength ranges.

Radio studies of the quiet sun had proved fruitful, yet somewhat disappointing. They had confirmed the high kinetic temperature of the corona, the small, if any, general magnetic field of the sun, the rapid transition from chromosphere to corona, and the latter's oblate shape and lower electron density near the last sunspot minimum. They had not uncovered new features on the sun, nor had it been possible to derive the physical state of the chromosphere and corona without recourse to optically determined electron density or temperature.

This situation has not changed significantly to the present time. Let me suggest two reasons to account for some of these limitations: (1) The resolving power of radio telescopes is inherently poor. (2) The information contained in brightness distributions (resolution permitting) across the sun is not sufficient to derive unambiguous particle and field distributions with height in the sun's atmosphere. The second reason may be the more basic.

Radio maps of the sun at 21-cm and 60-cm wavelengths are shown in Figure 2; both were obtained from several months' observations with interferometers near the last sunspot minimum. They confirmed the predicted limb brightening, at least in the equatorial regions, but gave a

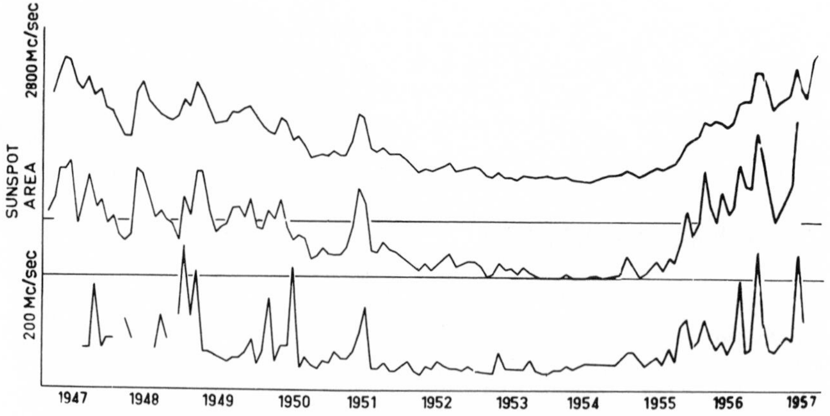

FIG. 1. Solar radio emission and sunspot area, 1947–1957.

smoothed version of the sharply peaked predicted distributions. That this smoothing may be entirely due to incomplete resolution is illustrated in Figure 3. The struggle for higher resolution continues unabated.

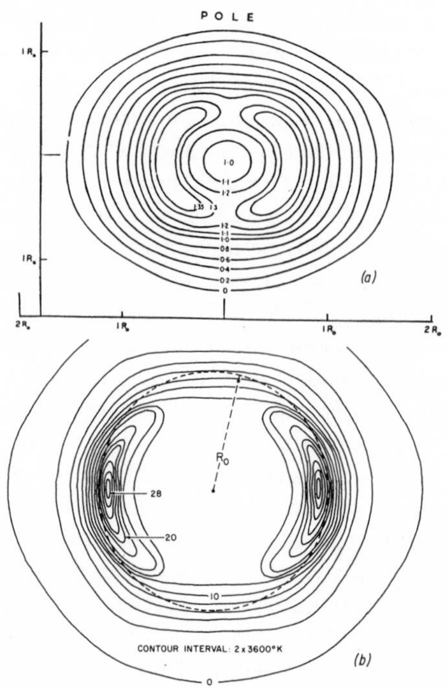

FIG. 2. Quiet-sun brightness distribution from fan beam observations in a number of directions by (*a*) O'Brien and Tardberg-Hanssen [41] (1955) at 60-cm wavelength. (*b*) Christiansen and Warburton [9] (1955) at 21-cm wavelength.

The same interference techniques were applied to studies of microwave bright regions on the sun. The resolution, at the best, was about 3′ arc but only in one direction. Eclipse observations had earlier demonstrated that the slowly varying component was the cumulative effect of bright regions on the sun. These, the radio plages, were found to overlie sunspots and other longer lived, slowly varying manifestations of solar activity like hydrogen and other plages. Partial circular polarization was detected at 10-cm wavelength.

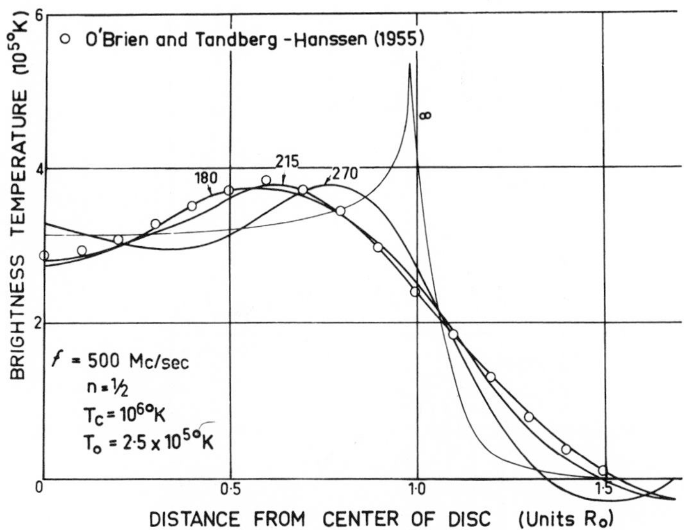

FIG. 3. A comparison of predicted and observed, equatorial brightness distributions on the sun. The number on the curves give the greatest spacing in multiples of the wavelength of a two-aerial, variable-spacing interferometer; the curves were computed by convolution of the predicted distribution with the corresponding aerial beam.

Their over-all effect, the slow rise and fall in the flux from the sun as a whole, closely duplicated the course of the sunspot area. Indeed, this close correlation was used to define the quiet-sun level as the residual flux at zero sunspot area.

Radio plages were thought to be thermal emission from dense hot regions above sunspot magnetic fields.

From their earliest chance discovery, by British radar stations in 1942, radio bursts and storms have proved a most spectacular manifestation of violent solar activity. The observed fluctuations, ten-thousandfold and more, in the flux from the whole sun and brightness temperatures up to a million times the coronal background temperature were unsuspected from previous solar observations. It was soon found that the number of bursts, their variety and variability, and the burst intensity relative to the base

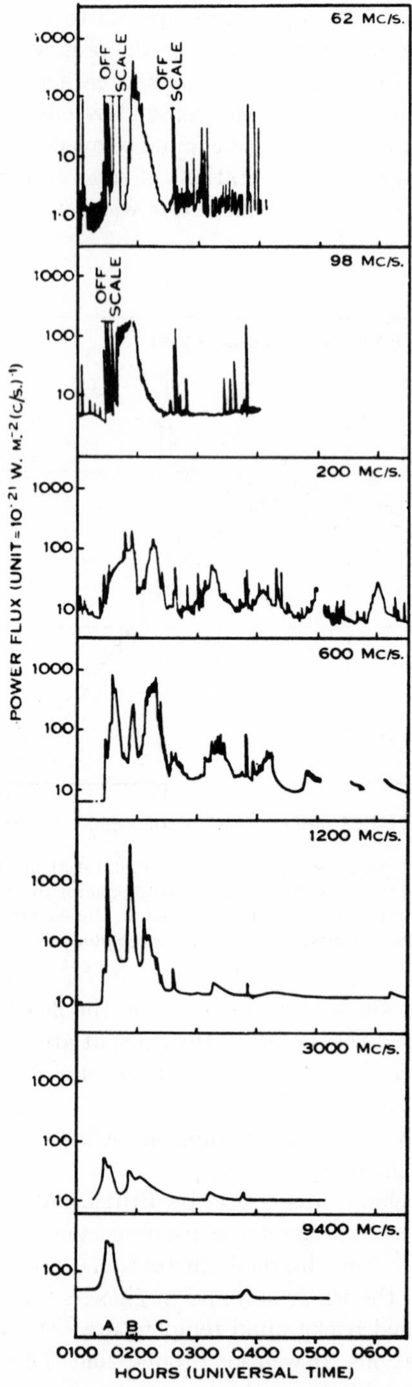

Fig. 4. The large outburst of 17 February 1950 at several wavelengths in the range 3 cm–5 m (Christiansen *et al.*[7]).

level decreased with decreasing wavelength (Fig. 4). Also, some of the earliest outbursts recorded at meter wavelengths had already suggested a systematic delay in onset with wavelength (Fig. 5). This delayed onset was a feature in the first and later series of dynamic spectra where it showed as a frequency drift with time of broad spectral features.

Two types of drifting bursts were recognized at meter wavelengths: the slow-drift Type II burst and the fast-drift Type III burst. On the hypothesis that the radiation originated near the plasma level and with the use of a standard model of coronal densities, observed drift rates suggested the outward rush of burst sources at about 500 km/sec for the Type

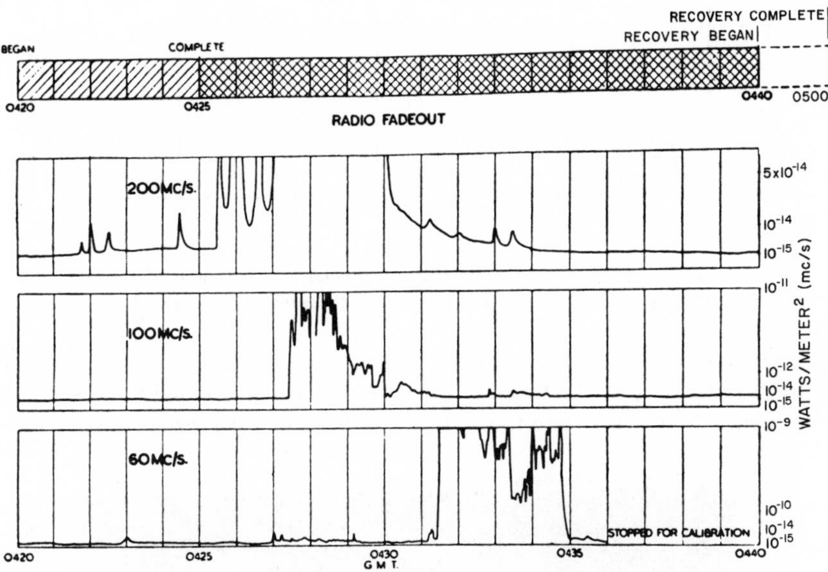

Fig. 5. The delay in the onset of the large outburst of 8 March 1947 in the wavelength range 1.5–5 m (Payne-Scott *et al.* [43]).

II burst and about 30,000 km/sec for the Type III burst. Even the slower velocity was faster than any movement on the sun known from optical observations. When the two bursts were compounded in the same event, their time separation and drift rates hinted at a common origin of the slow and fast burst sources (Fig. 6).

The "plasma hypothesis" received a boost with the discovery of harmonic structure in drift bursts: sometimes a fundamental spectrum repeated itself at twice the frequency (Fig. 7). Drifting bursts were thenceforth attributed to radiation from plasma waves.

A nondrifting, narrow-band, and short-lived burst was also found in large numbers in the dynamic spectra. It was labeled the Type I or storm burst and tended to be associated with wide-band enhancements of the general background. Such circularly polarized radio storms were known to

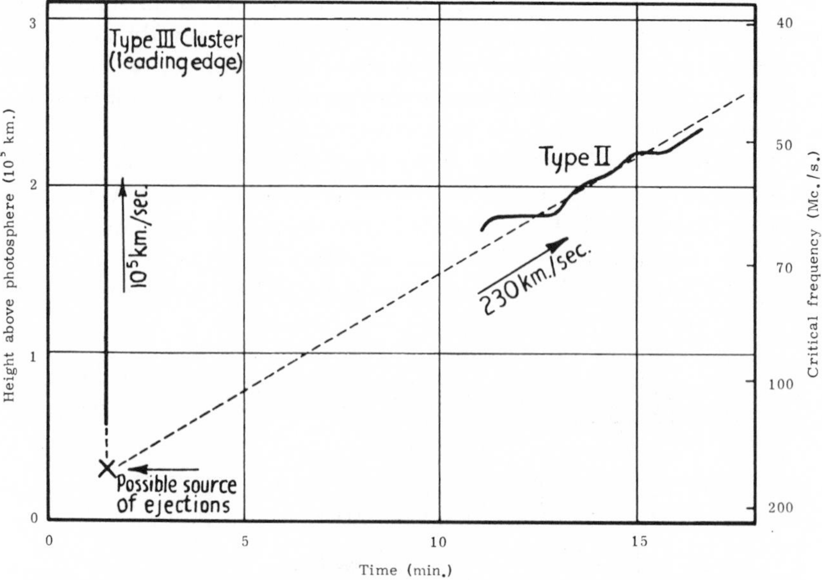

FIG. 6. A plot of the derived motions from spectral observations of a compound Type III Type II event at 0336 UT on 1 September 1952 (Wild *et al.* [73]).

persist for days and to be most intense near central meridian passage. Storm radiation, unlike those of the drifting bursts, seemed to be strongly beamed. The storms were found to be associated with large sunspots, and

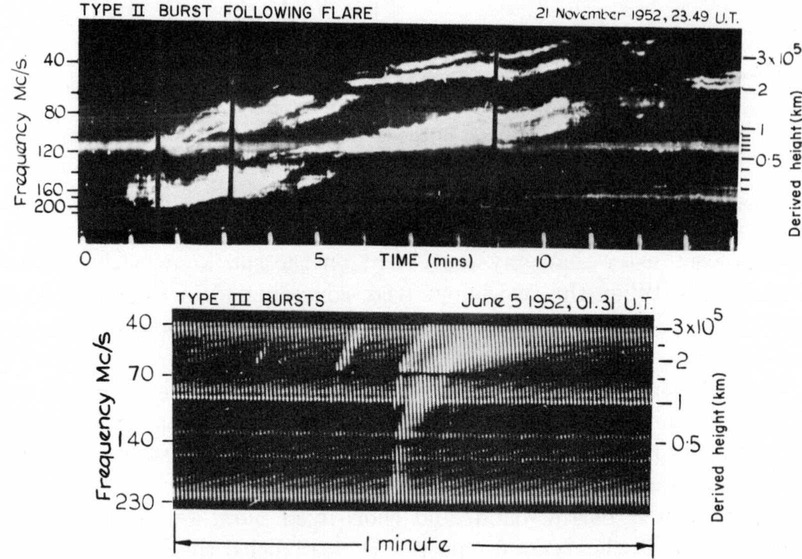

FIG. 7. Harmonic structure in spectral Type II and Type III bursts (Wild *et al.* [69, 72]).

at 3-meter wavelength were found to move across the disc faster than the spots themselves. This placed the storm source at a practically constant height of several hundred thousand kilometers.

The previous result was obtained with a rapidly phase-swept 2-aerial

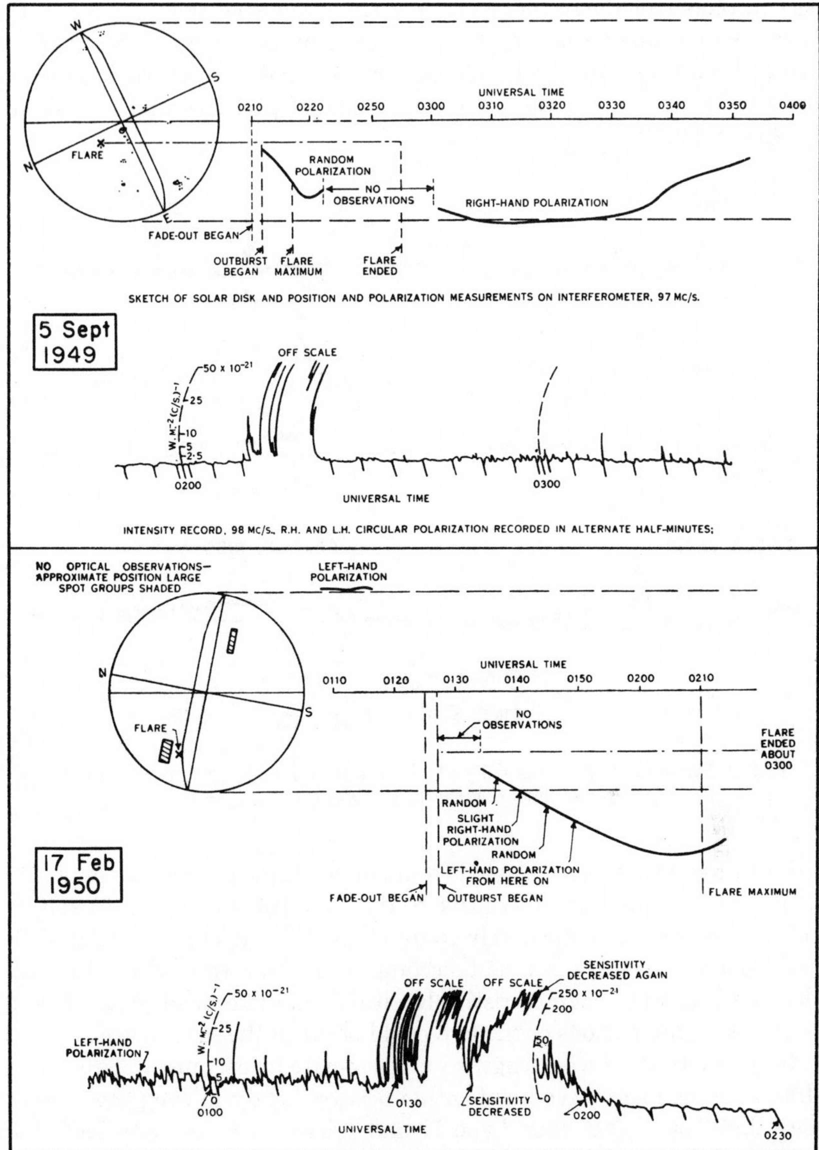

FIG. 8. Intensity, polarization, and position of the large outbursts on 5 September 1949 and 17 February 1950 at a wavelength of 3 meters (Payne-Scott and Little [42]).

interferometer which was also used to observe large-scale and fast movement of the sources of some large outbursts. Characteristically, an outward movement at speeds of up to 3000 km/sec was followed by a slower return to near the flare position (Fig. 8). The polarization changed from random in the first few minutes to circular. It is not possible to separate the various spectral phases of the outbursts from single frequency traces. Some of the observed movement was perhaps that of Type II sources. However, on current knowledge, the prolonged movements and late return to near the flare were probably the earliest observations of positions and movements of Type IV bursts.

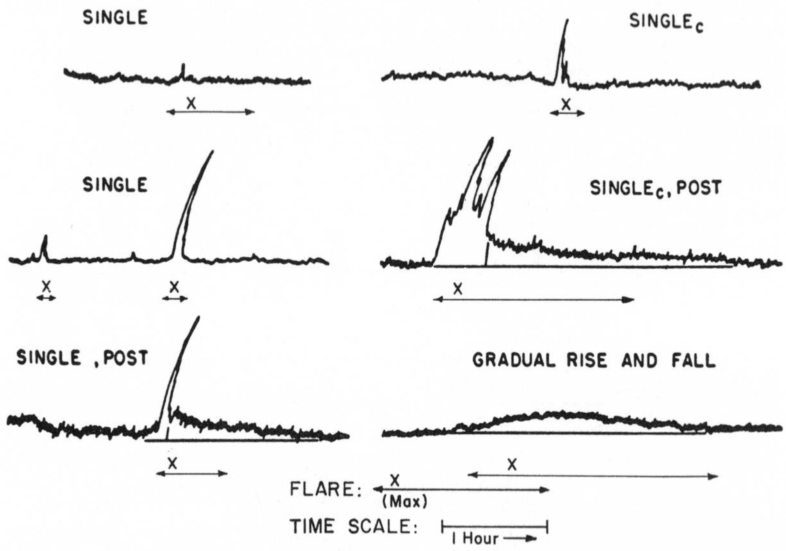

Fig. 9. Burst types recognized by Covington at a wavelength of 10.7 cm and their association with flares (Dodson *et al.* [15]).

Microwave bursts were classed from single frequency records only. The burst types were mainly descriptive of the recorded traces (Fig. 9) and did not lend themselves immediately to deriving the physical properties of the burst sources. However, it had become clear that transient microwave enhancements were characteristically either burstlike or of gradual onset and decay; combinations of the two could occur in the same event.

Many bursts at all wavelengths were associated with optical flares. Type III and simple microwave bursts often occurred early in even the smallest detectable flares. The rarer Type II and microwave outbursts tended to occur around the maximum of larger flares.

Some radio storms were known to follow large flares and outbursts; however, most storms were not obviously flare-initiated.

The previously established connection between some large flares and geomagnetic storms a day or two later was extended to radio outbursts; the Type II burst was thought to provide evidence for the progress outward through the corona of the hypothetical magnetic-storm cloud.

Of other geophysical disturbances that were previously known to be flare associated, the ionospheric communication fadeout was shown to be well correlated with microwave bursts (Fig. 10).

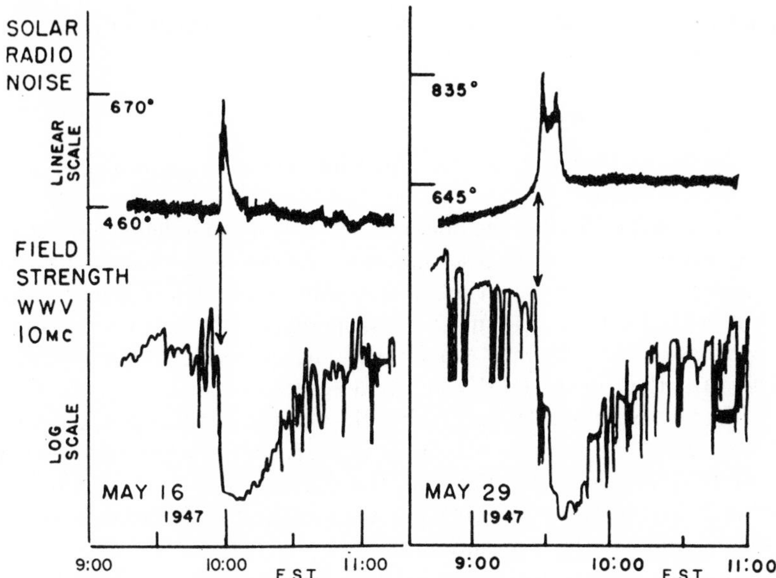

Fig. 10. Two selected 10.7-cm bursts whose onset coincided with that of a communication fade out at 10 Mc/sec (Covington [11]).

This then in broad outline was the position of solar radio astronomy at the beginning of the IGY. There were some clear requirements for future observations: higher resolution and resolution in two dimensions at all wavelengths; an extension of spectral observations to the microwaves and toward the ionospheric, long-wavelength cutoff; polarization measurements with high-resolution telescopes and a 24-hour radio flare coverage. Some specific problems could be formulated and were awaiting solution: the size, structure, and polarization of radio plages; a check on the plasma hypothesis for the drifting bursts which predicted successively higher coronal source levels with increasing wavelength, and detailed comparisons of the timing and structure of the flare event in all its solar and terrestrial manifestations. The importance of radio studies in the search for the basic nature of solar flares had already clearly emerged.

2. The Present State of Solar Radio Astronomy

During and since the IGY many of the observational requirements have been met, answers have been found to some specific questions, and new discoveries have helped to clarify existing problems while posing new ones. Most progress has come from research planned and executed independently in a number of research institutes of many countries. At the same time one can cite specific IGY contributions: a very much improved flare patrol at optical and radio wavelengths and of geophysical effects, warning of imminent activity, and the rapid dissemination of the results of world-wide observations.

2.1 The Quiet Sun [6]

During the IGY and for a few years after, the sun was probably never free of active regions.

We found earlier that at the microwavelengths we can define a quiet-sun level by extrapolation to zero sunspot area. At the meter wavelengths the flux remains for weeks at a time at a nearly constant low level between sharply peaked excursions during active periods. This again allows us to define a base level. Thus we can form a quiet-sun spectrum even during active years; that for the IGY is shown in Figure 11.

The flux during the IGY was higher than at the last sunspot minimum, as it was also at the previous maximum in 1947. On the very limited experience of $1\frac{1}{2}$ solar cycles the flux from the sun increases from minimum to maximum. The increase is compatible with an increase in coronal electron density as proposed by van de Hulst.

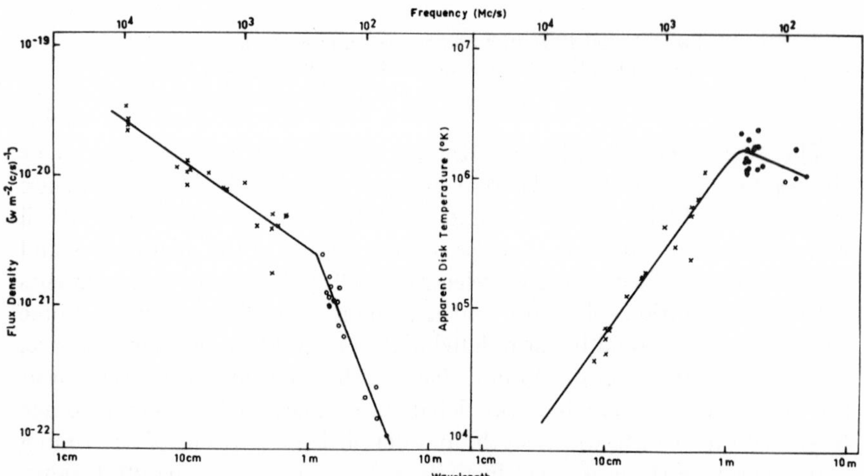

Fig. 11. Quiet-sun spectrum for the IGY period: X, points by extrapolation to zero sunspot activity; O, the constant level in the absence of activity (Smerd [54]).

An attempt was made in 1958 [36], and again during an eclipse in 1959 [30], to determine the brightness distribution across the quiet sun at 21-cm wavelength. The Christiansen crossed-grating interferometer was used both as a pencil beam of width about 3′ arc and the N-S arm of the instrument as a narrower fan beam. The combined results suggest that the shape of the sun was essentially the same oval shape with limb-darkening in the polar regions and limb-brightening in the equatorial regions as that observed at sunspot minimum (Fig. 2*b*). The brightness, however, was twice as high.

A very similar result was obtained by Swarup [56] with the Stanford pencil beam at 9.1-cm wavelength during a period of low solar activity in July and August, 1960. The brightness was about $\frac{4}{3}$ times that at the last sunspot minimum.

Waldmeier [63] has linked the spherical maximum corona with a high latitude (about 70°) of the polar prominence zone and with a reversal in the polar magnetic field. The latter was observed in mid-1957 for the Southern Hemisphere and late in 1958 for the Northern Hemisphere.

The radio evidence indicating an oblate coronal shape at that time does not support this explanation.

2.2 The Slowly Varying Component and Radio Plages [6]

The strong correlation between the microwave flux from the whole sun and sunspot number (the sunspot areas, which usually show better correlation, were not available) is demonstrated for the IGY period in Figure 12. Straight lines drawn though the scattered points give the base level at zero sunspot number and the slowly varying component from their slopes; the spectrum of the latter is given in Figure 13. The most notable feature of the spectrum is the peak near 10-cm wavelength.

Other properties can be inferred from auto- and cross-correlations of microwave flux densities and sunspot number; such correlograms, again for the IGY, with time lags of ±60 days or more than two solar rotations are reproduced in Figure 14. They suggest [54]:

(*a*) That the microwave flux at the short decimeter wavelengths is an excellent monitor of long-lived, slowly varying solar activity.

(*b*) That the previous-rotation dependence and longevity decrease with wavelength in the range 30 cm to 3 cm; they are similar to those of sunspots near 10-cm wavelength.

(*c*) That the correlation between microwave flux and sunspot number is not likely to be improved by assuming that one depends on varying previous-rotation amounts of the other; the latter method was used by Piddington and Davies [48] in determining quiet-sun and slowly varying component levels.

Two-dimensional studies with pencil beam interferometers at 21 cm and 9.1 cm, one-dimensional high-resolution interferometry in the wavelength

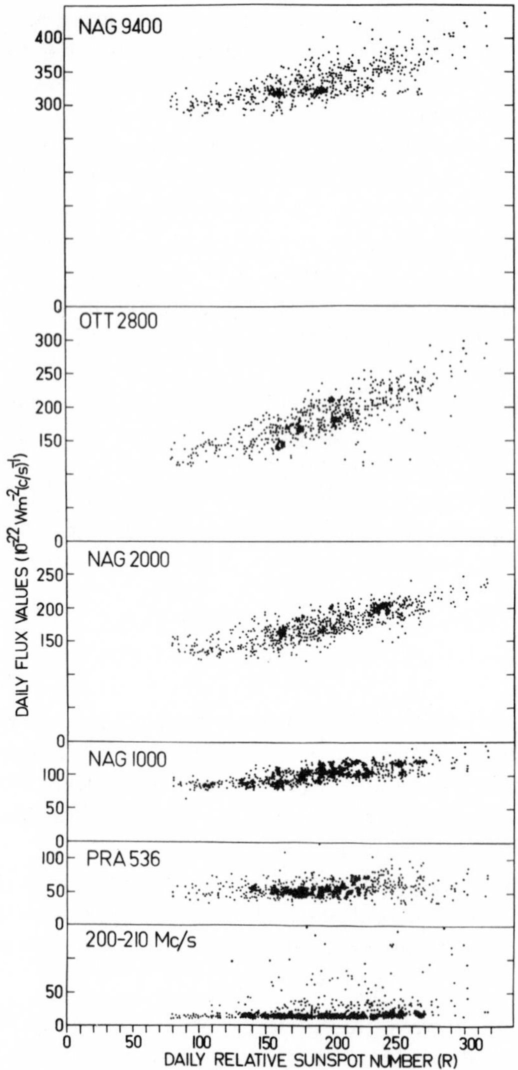

FIG. 12. The relation between the flux density at several radio wavelengths and the sunspot number for the IGY period (Smerd [54]).

range of 3 cm to 1.8 m, and eclipse observations together yielded a fairly consistent, but still incompletely resolved, picture for the source region of radio plages.

Basically, the source region is deduced to be an overdense tube extending near radially outward from localized magnetic fields in the photosphere through the chromospheric hydrogen and calcium plages. The size of the tube seems to remain about that of the optical plages (several minutes of

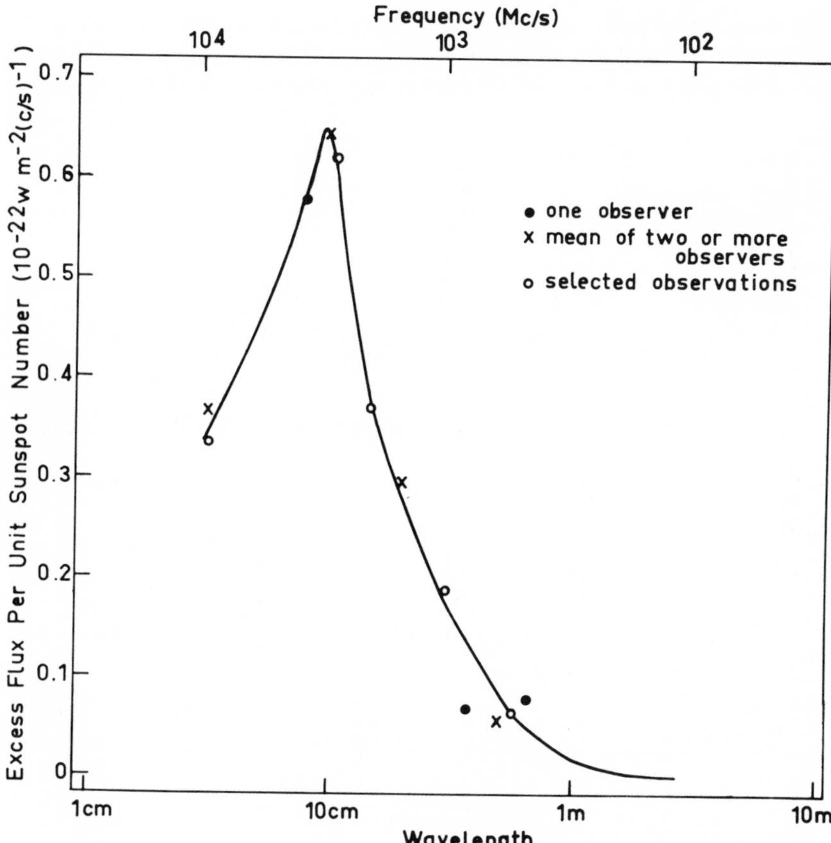

FIG. 13. The spectrum for the slowly varying component during the IGY period. The selected observations (shown thus, O) are those of Figure 12 (Smerd [54]).

arc) for several ten thousand kilometers into the corona; there is evidence for a widening to some 10′ arc above a height of about 10^5 kilometers.

In a strong radio plage the temperature might rise steeply to 10^{6}°K near 10^4 km, reach a maximum of 2–4 $\times$ 10^{6}°K at 2–3 $\times$ 10^4 km, the average height of a 10-cm plage, and decrease gradually to some 10^{6}°K at 1.5 $\times$ 10^5 km where 1.8-m plages are sometimes detected. Such temperature distributions are similar to those derived for the transition region and inner corona in general. There is, however, no sure radio evidence to decide whether the temperature inside a particular plage region is higher or lower than that of the surrounding corona. The observed brightness temperatures supported a thermal interpretation of the radio plage radiation.

I applied such an interpretation, neglecting magnetic fields, to a selected plage region observed late in 1957 at four observatories: Nançay 178 cm, Sydney 21 cm, Toyokawa 7.5 cm, Washington 88 cm. Two spectra, those of brightness temperature and height of emission, were used to derive the electron density and temperature through the plage region. It was the first such determination from radio observations. The result is shown in Figure

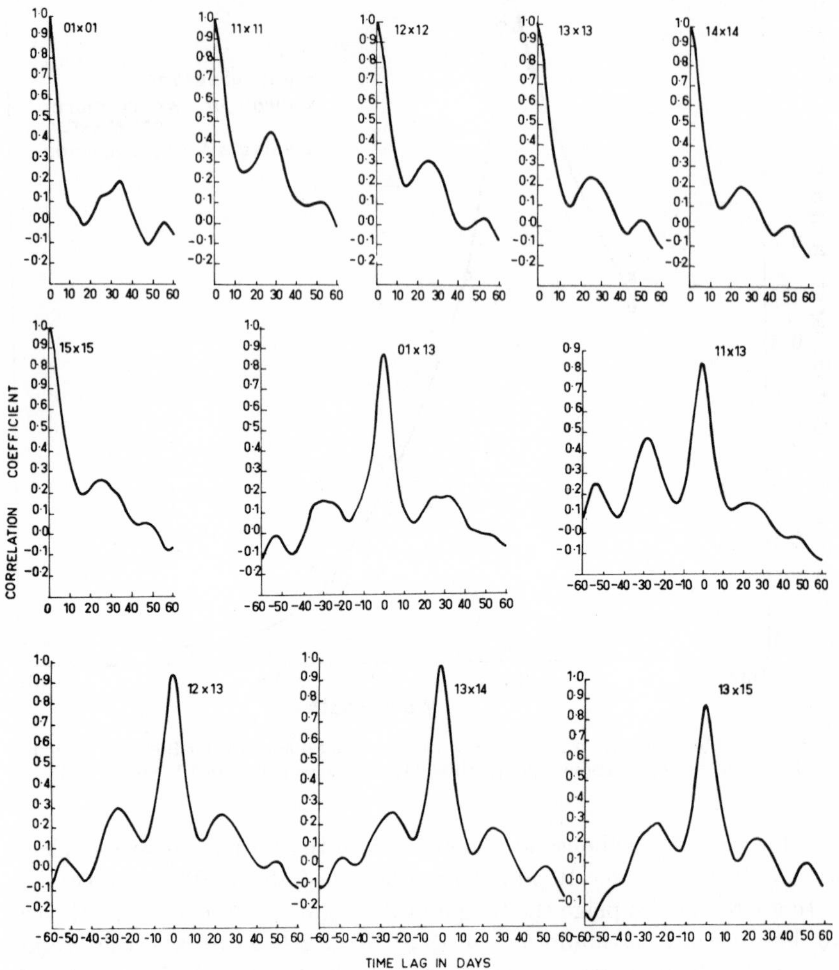

FIG. 14. Auto- and cross-correlations over ±60 days for the following daily indices of slow solar activity: sunspot number (01), flux density at a wavelength of 30 cm (11), 15 cm (12), 10.7 cm (13), 8 cm (14), 3.2 cm (15). (The radio data are from Nagoya 1000, 2000, 3750, 9400 Mc/sec and Ottawa 2800 Mc/sec observations.) The time lag in the correlograms refers to the second index in the notation $a \times b$ (Smerd [54]).

15. Magnetic fields in the lower reaches were indicated by the observed polarization at the shortest wavelength. However, if the actual plage spectra were those used in the analysis (through only 4 points and with inaccurately known heights) then the density and temperature in the plage

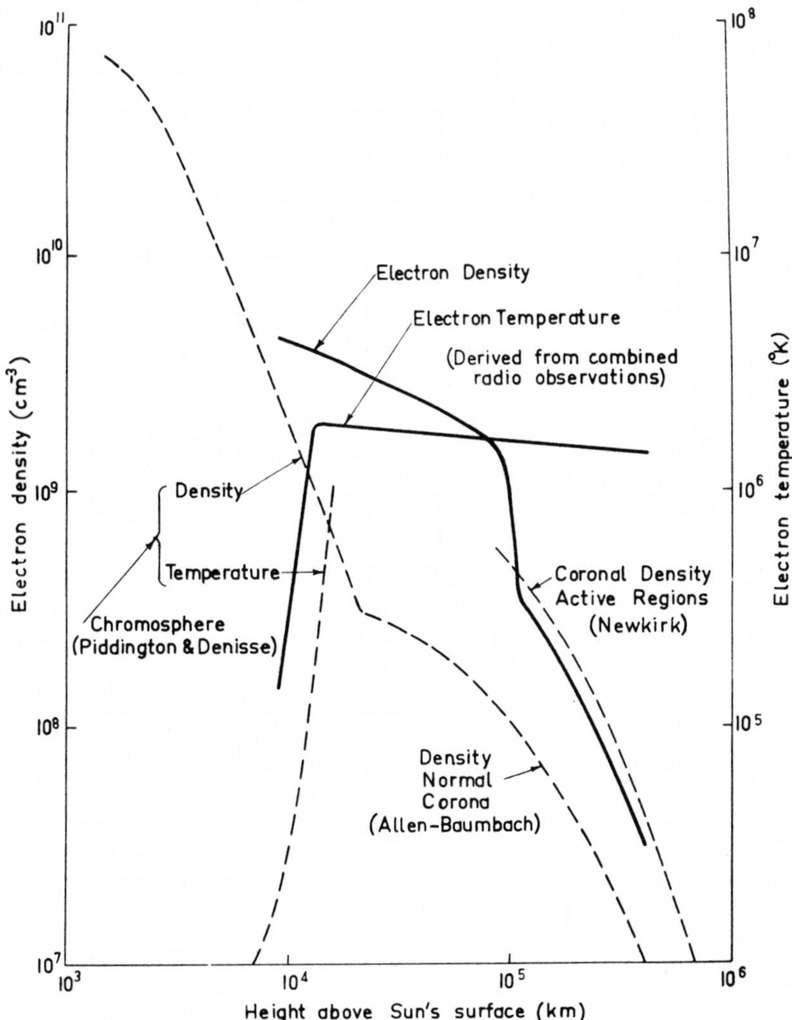

FIG. 15. The distribution of electron density and temperature with height in a selected plage region; the latter was observed in the wavelength 7.5 to 178 cm by American, Australian, French, and Japanese radio astronomers (Christiansen *et al.* [8]).

region were as shown in the figure, except that the density at the lowest heights is likely to be overestimated.

Observations in the range 3–10 cm wavelengths with one-dimensional resolution of 1′ to 2′ arc have shown structure within radio plages. Characteristically, some plages have a bright and strongly polarized core centered on a sunspot and a diffuse randomly polarized halo centered on the optical plage. The bright core seems to fade as the radio plage ages. The polarized radiation corresponds to the extraordinary mode. High-resolution observations at the longer wavelength of 21 cm no longer reveals a bright core. Magnetic-field effects seem to dominate at the short wavelength where the plage polarization is found to increase steadily: about 10 per cent at 10 cm and 30 per cent at 3 cm; the core may be more highly polarized.

The thermal theory of radio plages received a jolt with the discovery of a peak in the flux spectrum of strong radio plages. This is evident in the statistical IGY spectrum (Fig. 13) and has been found in individual plages by Russian and Japanese observers and in cooperative studies at Nagoya (3.2, 7.5 cm), Ottawa (10.7 cm), Stanford (9.1 cm), and Sydney (21 cm). Piddington [47] had shown in 1951 that thermal emission from a hot plasma could not decrease at the short wavelengths unless strong refraction or strong magnetic fields were important at the source. The latter were invoked by Ginzburg and Zheleznyakov [22], who showed that the peak in the spectrum may be due to additional opacity caused by resonance absorption at the low harmonics of the gyrofrequency. This interpretation was used by Kakinuma and Swarup [29] to find model plage regions which could account for both the peaked flux and the steadily rising polarization spectra; they inferred magnetic fields of about 600 gauss at 2×10^4 km and about 250 gauss at 4×10^4 km above the photosphere.

The gyroresonance effects highlight the fundamental role played by strong magnetic fields in active centers on the sun. A knowledge of the structure and the fields in plage regions is important because it seems to be these same regions from which X-ray and corpuscular radiations emanate and where the explosions occur which initiate the widespread manifestations of solar flares.

2.3 Bursts and Storms [76]

(*a*) *Meter Waves.* The plasma hypothesis for the *drifting bursts* has been tested by observations with a swept-frequency interferometer in the range 40–70 Mc/sec (4.3 to 7.5 m). The height of individual burst sources were indeed found to increase with wavelength, a result which directly confirmed that the disturbances moved outward through the corona [65, 74]. This finding is in strong support of the plasma hypothesis. The observed movement led to the revised and faster speeds of some 10^3 km/sec for Type II bursts and about 0.4c for Type III bursts. It also suggested coronal densities about 10 times those of the undisturbed corona (Fig. 16). The burst sources are therefore inferred to move out along coronal streamers.

Some of the directional observations of Type II bursts, in particular, allowed the separate identification of fundamental and harmonic positions (Fig. 17) [55]. At a given wavelength the harmonic was found to lie inside the fundamental, i.e., quite opposite to what was predicted by a simple application of the plasma hypothesis. The anomalous positions can be explained if the harmonic is emitted towards the sun and observed only after reflection and refraction much lower in the corona. Such preferential backward emission follows naturally from a theory of burst generation by Ginzburg and Zheleznyakov [21]. In this theory fast electron streams are invoked to set up plasma waves in the corona; these waves are then supposed to be converted to electromagnetic radiation through scattering on

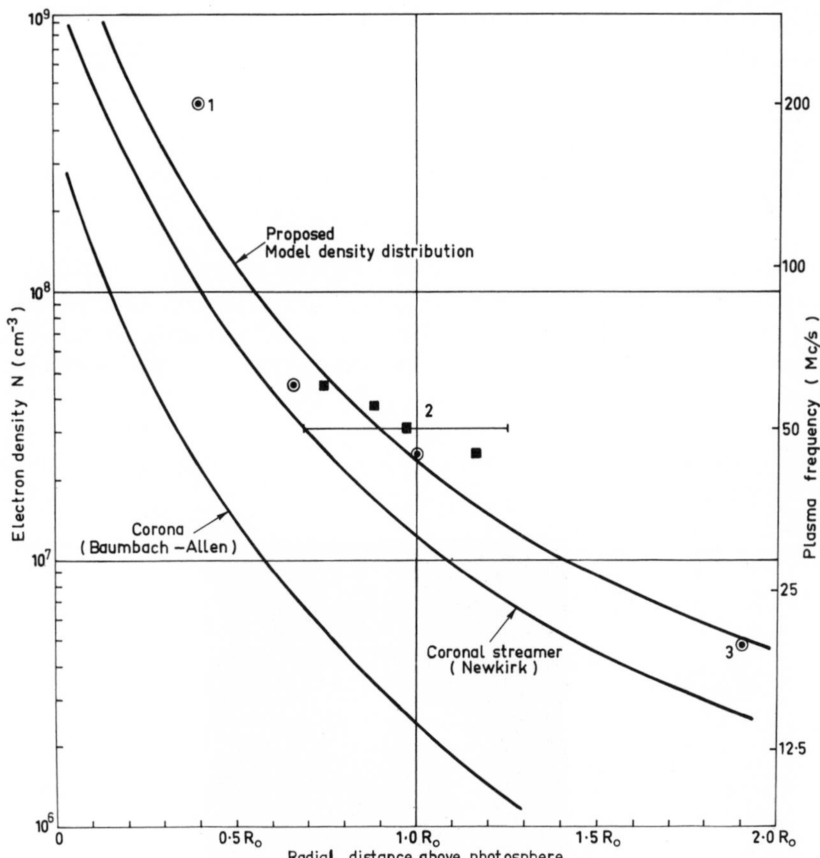

FIG. 16. Electron densities in the corona and source positions of Type II (shown thus, ■) and Type III (shown thus, ⊙) bursts. The points are from: 1. Morimoto (1961) at 200 Mc/sec (1.5 m); 2. ⊙ Wild, Sheridan, and Neylan at 45, 60 Mc/sec [74], ■ Weiss (1963), 45–60 Mc/sec (5–6.7 m). 3. Shain and Higgins (1959) at 19 Mc/sec (15.8 m). The bar represents the probable errors in the Type II points (Weiss [65]).

plasma fluctuations. Rayleigh scattering on the random ion-fluctuations account for the forward emission at the fundamental frequency; "combination" scattering on electron density ripples, themselves plasma waves, explains the preferential backward emission of the harmonic at twice that frequency. The backward to forward emission ratio increases with electron

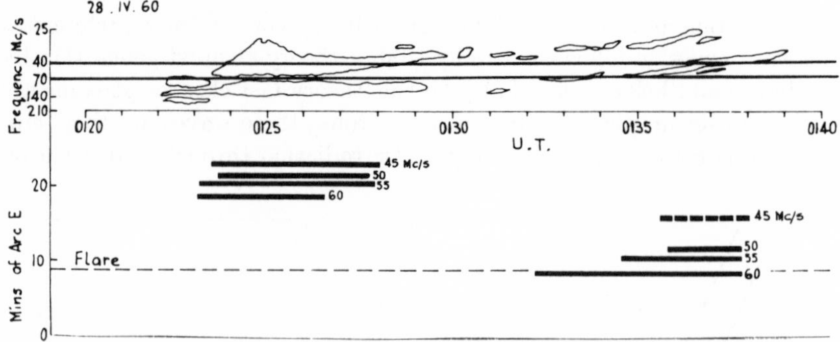

FIG. 17. The dynamic spectrum and E–W positions of a Type II burst recorded on 28 April 1960. The early positions refer to the fundamental band (Smerd *et al.* [55]).

speed. Hence one is led to the idea that Type II sources may be the slow carriers of very fast electrons; some support for this inference comes from the observation of "herringbone" structure in some Type II bursts [49]. Thus an observation which at first seemed to contradict the plasma hypothesis has possibly given evidence in its favor; the hypothesis is now, however, linked with preferential backward emission of the harmonic and with scattering as the conversion mechanism from longitudinal to transverse waves.

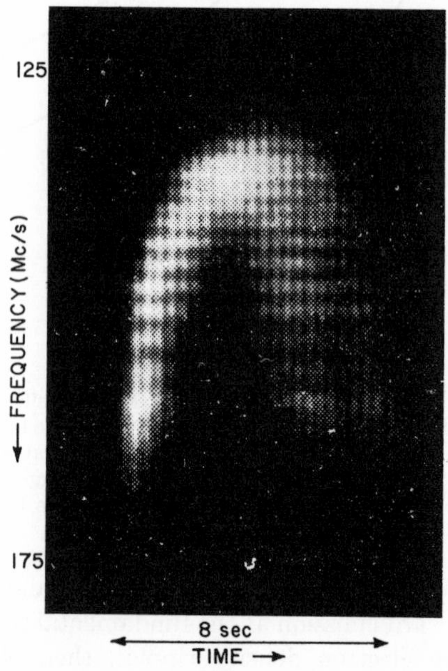

FIG. 18. An inverted-*U* burst recorded at Fort Davis on 29 November 1956 (Maxwell and Swarup [38]).

There is now evidence for multiple Type II bursts [65] whose sources begin at slightly different times and move in different directions with different speeds. If, as is commonly believed, the disturbances are magnetohydrodynamic shock waves, then the initial explosions appear to be multiple and the surrounding magnetic fields highly complex.

The relative positions of Type III bursts, where recognition of harmonic structure is more difficult, are inconclusive; there is a suggestion of both forward and backward emission of the harmonic, perhaps signifying that the Type III electrons are slower than the Type II electrons. However, Type III electrons move unencumbered by heavy ions. In some cases the source continues at undiminished speed as far as observation permits ($f \sim 5$ Mc/sec), while in others the source turns off its outward path, culminating at times in a complete reversal of the outward movement as shown by the inverted-*U* burst (Fig. 18). The curved paths are taken as evidence for magnetic guiding of Type III electrons.

Occasionally a Type III burst, particularly one near the limb, is closely followed for about a minute by a wide-band continuum at the low frequencies (<150 Mc/sec); this has been labeled the Type V burst (see Fig. 19). Its position and polarization are similar to those of the parent Type III

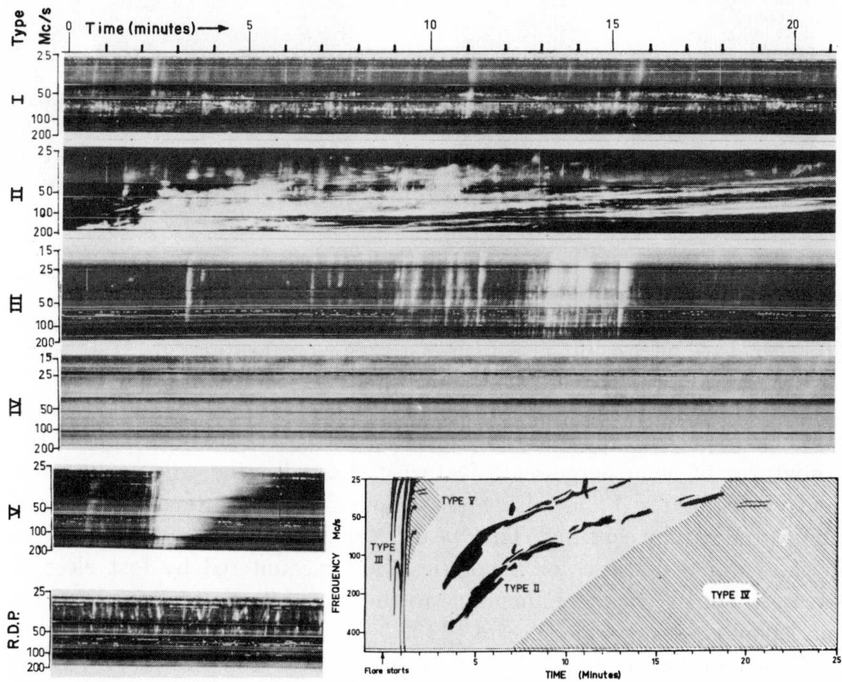

FIG. 19. Examples of the dynamic spectra for the five main types recognized at meter wavelengths. The inset is an idealized sketch of a complete flare event as discussed in Section 3.

burst. Because of the lack of spectral features it was first interpreted as synchrotron radiation from the Type III electrons gyrating in a magnetic field; energies of 2 Mev and a magnetic field of 1.5 gauss were required. However, the early interpretation is untenable if the electrons move, as is likely, in a drawn-out helix, because then the electron speed (practically c at those energies) should also be the Type III velocity; this is not observed. Gyrosynchrotron radiation and plasma waves remain as possible generating mechanisms for Type V bursts.

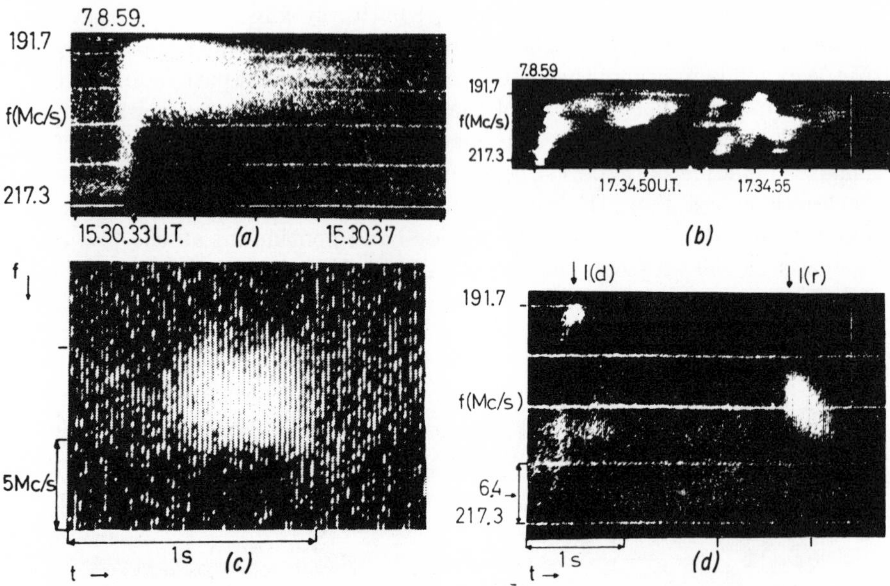

FIG. 20. Fine structure in Type I and Type III bursts from high-resolution spectra recorded near 200 Mc/sec (1.5 m) at Oslo. (*a*) A miniature III-V event of 4 seconds total duration. (*b*) Blobby structure in Type III bursts. (*c*) A nondrifting Type I burst. (*d*) Forward and reverse drift Type I bursts in close succession (Elgaroy [17]).

Fine structure in Type III and Type I bursts has been revealed by high-resolution spectroscopy (Fig. 20). The fine-structure features appear like miniatures of some large-scale features: sharp leading edges with well-defined drift rates, blobs with and without forward or reverse drift, and diffuse and patchy continua. They bear fascinating evidence of irregularities in the coronal densities or magnetic fields encountered by fast electron streams. They seem to be amenable to the same interpretations as are the corresponding large-scale spectra [17].

High-resolution spectra of Type I bursts near 200 Mc/sec reveal an elementary burst lasting but a fraction of a second and a few megacycles wide. About half these bursts show no frequency drift, while of the remainder similar numbers exhibit forward and reverse drifts. Their positions were found to be scattered over the same region as was occupied by the general enhancement, the Type I continuum [27]. This source size, 5′–10′, increases with wavelength. The polarization of bursts and continuum is usually the same; it corresponds in most, but by no means all, cases to that of the ordinary mode when associated with the leader of the associated sunspot group. This evidence is certainly compatible with a continuum due to a superposition of many bursts or, alternatively, with the bursts as fleeting glimpses of the continuum [20]. However, occasional differences between the polarization of bursts and continuum and the existence of fine structure features such as band splitting [17] suggest that Type I bursts and continuum are separate phenomena, though closely related.

The average apparent height of the storms increases somewhat with wavelength but often seems to lie below the plasma levels derived from the drifting bursts, a phenomenon possibly due to refraction.

Much of the evidence favors an origin in plasma waves. In one such interpretation [13] the plasma waves are excited by downstreaming electrons; once again, after conversion to electromagnetic radiation, the disturbance is seen as the reflected image of the storm source. However, an origin in gyrosynchrotron radiation cannot be discounted at present especially since Ginzburg and Zheleznyakov [22] have shown that this mechanism too can account for the observed directivity and polarization.

We found earlier that radio storms often followed outbursts. We also noted the prolonged movement and accompanying change to circular polarization which had been observed late in some outbursts at 3-m wavelength. It was left to Boischot [4] to establish, again by one-dimensional interferometry, this time at 169 Mc/sec (1.78 m), the definitive features of a new phase in an outburst which he called the Type IV. The enhancement appeared quite smooth, lasted for tens of minutes, and was of large angular size ($\approx 10'$); its chief characteristics were an early outward movement, for several solar radii at a time, at speeds of about 1000 km/sec and a late, slow return to near the flare region. Partial circular polarization was measured; on the leading-spot identification the radiation was of the extraordinary mode. Boischot and Denisse [5] proposed that these bursts were synchrotron radiation from vast numbers of 3-Mev electrons in fields of 1 gauss.

The spectral observers [25, 39, 75] extended the Type IV classification to all flare-associated continua in the range 40–600 Mc/sec (50 cm–7.5 m); the term continuum is used to denote a prolonged, wide-band, relatively smooth enhancement. In this process the early definitive characteristic of large-scale fast movement was lost. Eventually the term Type IV was appended to all flare-associated continua anywhere in the observed wavelength range.

Monique Pick [46] distinguished two phases in the meter-wavelength Type IV burst; these could occur individually or together. The first phase, the original Boischot Type IV, could occur anywhere on the sun's disc and tended to be associated with the larger of the more frequent microwave Type IV's. The second phase which was restricted to the central region of the sun continued for hours in a smaller source region low in the corona; it was peculiar to the meter wavelengths. A continuation for days of the meter-wave continuum with, perhaps, gradually increasing number of storm bursts was considered distinct from Type I storms and called a continuum storm. The second phase and the continuum storm were found to be circularly polarized; on the leading-spot identification the radiation is of the ordinary mode.

Weiss [66] has probably taken the analysis of the meter-wave Type IV as far as the observations of the current cycle permit, and his conclusions largely confirm those of Pick. He distinguishes a moving Type IV which is identical with the original Boischot Type IV; ("moving" is here used to denote movement in position at one frequency). He finds that the first part (the moving Type IV burst) has probably never been observed at or above 200 Mc/sec (1.5 m). This short-wave limit for the synchrotron radiation is important in estimates of electron energy and magnetic-field strengths responsible for the emission. He finds that the second phase (the stationary Type IV burst) often begins with a Type II-like drift rate; subsequently the intensity and polarization increase to reach their maximum values after about one-half hour. Weiss extends the meaning of the stationary event to cover continuum storms. The known properties of the stationary component agree so well with those of the Type I continuum that the two may well be identical.

The Type IV continuum is the rarest meter-wave activity and dominates the energy output in a large outburst. Whatever the generating mechanism, it is evidence for emission from very large numbers of energetic electrons.

(*b*) *Microwaves.* Perhaps the most important observational development has been the extension of solar spectroscopy to the microwave spectrum: Harvard and Michigan observed through the meter range and up to about 600 Mc/sec (50 cm); later they added a range of about 2000–4000 Mc/sec (7.5–15 cm). The Convair-Caltech spectrograph covered the range 500–950 Mc/sec (32–60 cm).

Two kinds of drifting bursts were discovered with the latter: a variety of fast-drift burst (Fig. 21*b*) with drift rates in excess of 100 Mc/sec/sec and the intermediate-drift burst (Fig. 21*c*) with drift rates from 10–50 Mc/sec/sec. The fast-drift bursts, about 20 per cent of them showing reverse drift, often occur during Type III activity. However, they are not in general a short-wave extension of Type III bursts. The intermediate-drift bursts occur in groups usually within a major event, presumably of Type IV. Forward and reverse drift bursts in the same frequency range may at times give rise to a criss-cross pattern. The origin of these bursts is unknown; if it is similar to that of Type II and III bursts, i.e., if the plasma hypothesis ap-

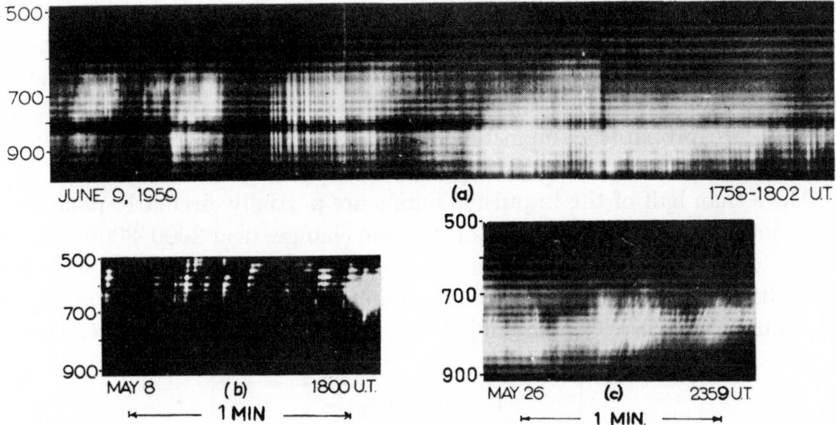

Fig. 21. Dynamic spectra at the decimeter wavelengths. The horizontal stripes are instrumental. (*a*) Fine structure in Type IV event. (*b*) Fast-drift bursts. (*c*) Intermediate-drift bursts (Young *et al.* [77]).

plies, all derived velocities are much less than those for Type III bursts. A direct investigation of possible source movements will need observations of very high angular resolution.

The characteristic structure in a Type-IV event is a closely spaced striation which merges into or is superposed on a continuum (Fig. 21*a*). This structure is usually intensity-modulated with periods of the order of minutes. The striae can extend to 4000 Mc/sec [61] and similar structure has been observed in meter-wave Type IV bursts.

The single-frequency classification of microwave bursts was strengthened when Covington and Harvey [12] found a two-pronged distribution in the scatter of burst intensity against duration. The two basic burst types, other than the outburst, or Type IV, are: the *impulsive burst* of short duration and intense, and the *gradual burst*, prolonged and weak. The latter encompasses [76] the gradual rise and fall, the postburst increase and the precursor. They are probably due to bremsstrahlung from thermal sources.

Most bursts at the short wavelengths are impulsive. Hachenberg and Wallis [24] found the shape of the burst spectra compatible with emission from a thermal plasma. However, the brightness of impulsive bursts is often in the range 10^7–10^{9}°K which seems to preclude an origin in thermal bremsstrahlung. Takakura [58] has explained impulsive-burst radiation as gyroradiation from intermediate-energy electrons and in rather high magnetic fields of $\sim$1000 gauss. Since then, the close association (e.g., Fig. 22) which has been established [1, 32] between microwave and X-ray bursts suggests that electrons of the same source gyrating in the same magnetic fields may be able to explain both. An interpretation of the X-ray emission seems to require electron energies up to 100 Mev, much higher than those invoked by Takakura in his interpretation of impulsive bursts. However, fewer electrons of higher energy and gyrating in smaller magnetic fields could also explain the nonthermal portion of impulsive bursts and at the same time account for the hard X-radiation. Both X-ray and microwave spectra are probably compatible with nonthermal high-energy electrons injected into a hot thermal background.

More than half of the impulsive bursts are partially circularly polarized. Characteristically, the sense of polarization changes near 2000–3000 Mc/sec to the ordinary mode (assuming the leading-spot identification). This has been attributed to differential absorption of the two magnetoionic modes at the source [28, 58]. Cohen [10] claims that this cannot explain the occa-

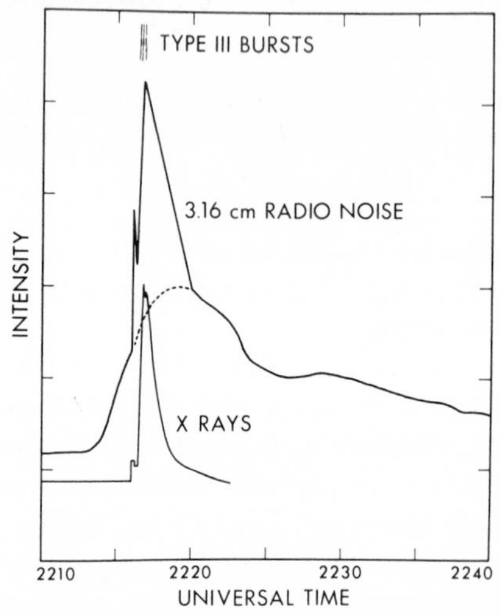

FIG. 22. Simultaneous radio and X-ray burst observed at the flash phase of a flare on 28 September 1961. (3-cm record from Tokyo; Anderson and Winckler [1].)

sional double reversal; he explains the polarization change as a propagation phenomenon.

There is evidence [54] that the meter-wave Type III, the decimeter, and the microwave impulsive bursts can occur together, but they seem to preserve their separate identity in the spectrum of the composite event (Fig. 23). Hence the observed polarization change may merely reflect opposite senses of polarization of the distinctive decimeter and microwave emissions. Indeed, the observations may be compatible with synchrotron radiation in the extraordinary mode for impulsive bursts and radiation in the ordinary mode from plasma waves for decimeter bursts (group of fast-drift bursts with or without continuum).

A microwave outburst or, more generally, a long, flare-associated continuum in the microwave range is now called a microwave Type IV; it has been observed up to 70,000 Mc/sec ($\approx$4 mm) (Edelson, see Thompson and Maxwell [61]). However, it is not clear yet whether the continua on centimeter and decimeter wavelengths are physically distinct. That they are is favored by the Japanese observers [59] on the basis of different durations and polarizations. Takakura suggests that two magnetic bulges may be created during an outburst. The cm-Type IV would then be associated with synchrotron emission from close above the leading spot, the m-Type IV

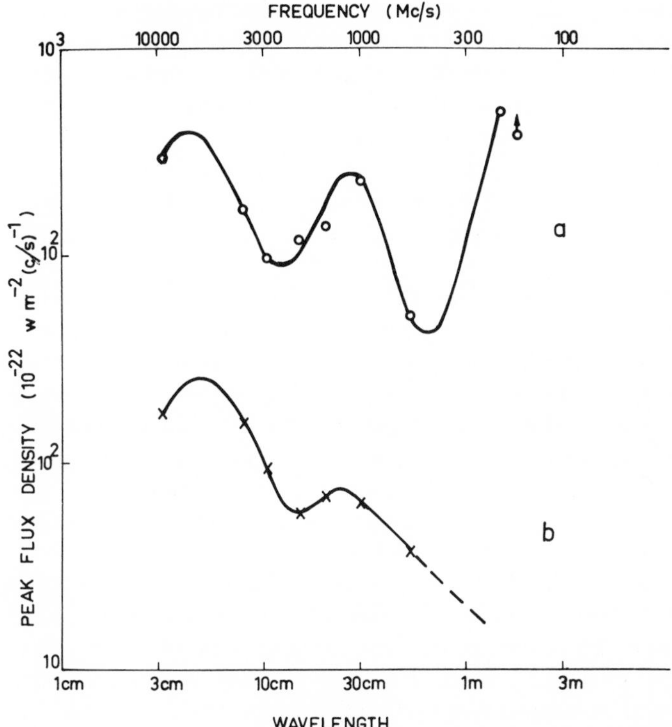

Fig. 23. (*a*) Average spectrum of Type III associated short microwave bursts during the IGY. (*b*) Average spectrum of similar microwave bursts during the IGY which were not accompanied by Type III bursts (Smerd [54]).

with synchrotron emission from the trapping region high in that bulge and a dm-Type IV from the trapping region low in the bulge above the following spot. On the other hand there may be no real distinction between centimeter and decimeter components: a change in polarization may, as has been proposed for the impulsive burst, be due to differential absorption, while much longer durations sometimes observed at the decimeter wavelengths may be due to a high-frequency extension of the "stationary" meter-wave Type IV [35].

Further observations are needed to resolve these questions; in particular, high-resolution position determinations should show whether there is this leading-following spot separation between the centimeter and decimeter emissions.

3. The Flare Event

We have found that all types of bursts and some storms are associated with flares. We therefore conclude this review by describing, along the line developed at the Cloudcroft and Kyoto Symposia, how the several types of bursts compound during different phases of a "complete" flare event; we mention briefly some of the accompanying solar and related terrestrial effects and possible unifying physical causes.

Synthetic radio spectra, as developed by Japanese workers (e.g., Takakura and Kai [60]), of such an event are shown in Figures 24*a* and 24*b*; the differences in the two versions are those discussed at the end of the preceding section.

(*a*) *Gradual Onset.* The radio event may start with a gradual burst at the microwavelengths (not evident in Fig. 24), and it may accompany a similar rise in the Hα-flare. These glowlike emissions are electromagnetic only and probably thermal. They could be the result of compression in a coronal condensation caused, perhaps, by local excess magnetic pressure ($H^2/8\pi > NkT$). This phase, which occasionally contributes the whole flare, may be accompanied by a gradual ionospheric fadeout.

(*b*) *Flash phase.* The next phase in the radio flare is characterized by its sudden onset and by the brevity and repetition of some of its components: meter-wave Type III bursts, (with or without an associated short continuum of Type V), microwave fast-drift bursts, and the microwave impulsive burst. These bursts coincide in time with the flash phase [19] or explosive phase [2] of the Hα-flare; we have earlier found them to be linked with streams of fast ($\approx 10^5$ km/sec) electrons. The observations then suggest repeated ejections outwards into the corona, and into the denser regions below, of large numbers of intermediate energy ($\lesssim$100-kev) electrons. Each discharge takes place in a second or less, with only seconds between successive ones. This time scale seems to preclude acceleration by the Fermi or some similar process; rather does it imply the catastrophic type of energy release envisaged in several proposals for the partial ($\approx$150 gauss [18]) and temporary destruction of the magnetic field [23, 51, 57]. Severny proposed the pinch effect (for which we need $H^2/8\pi \gg NkT$) to explain the catastrophic event and linked this plasma instability with steep magnetic-field gradients around neutral points. Some support for the pinch effect comes from the repetitive nature of the discharge inferred from the regular, repetition of some Type III bursts.

Optically the flare flash is accompanied by surges and other eruptions.

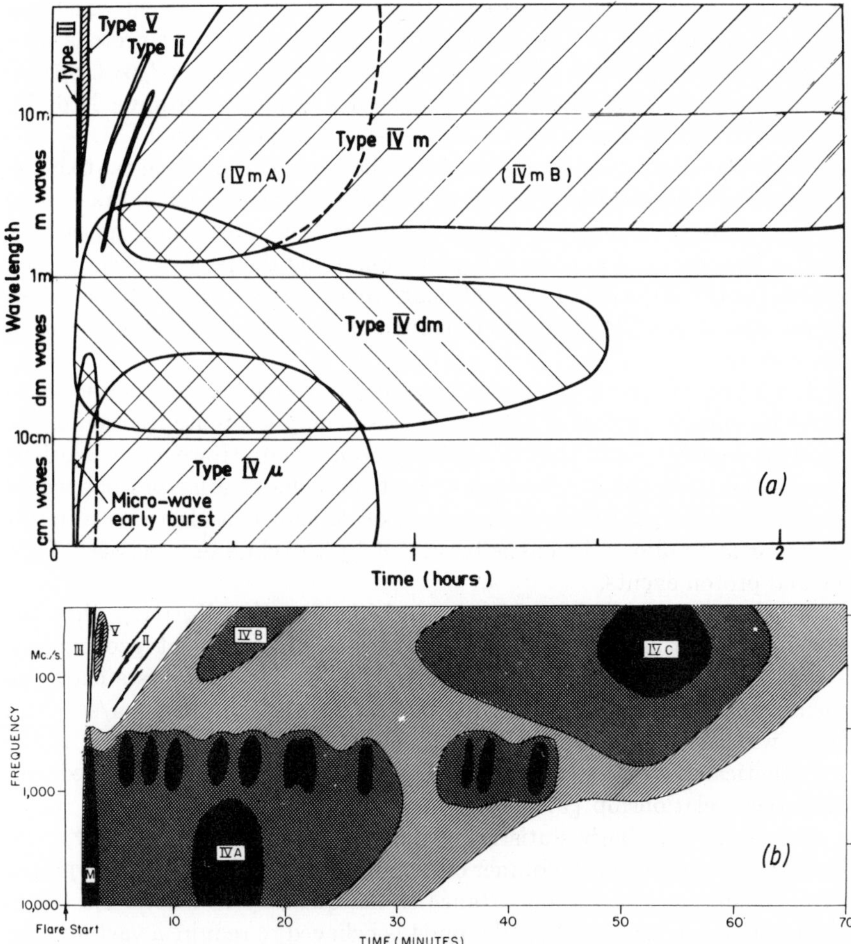

FIG. 24. Synthetic radio spectra of a complete flare event. Both were devised soon after the Kyoto Symposium of 1961. Model (*a*) appears in a summarizing paper in the Proceedings of the Kyoto Symposium (Wild [71]); model (*b*) differs slightly by suggesting that the dm-continuum is the long-wavelength extension of the cm-continuum in the early stages and perhaps a short-wavelength extension of the m-continuum in the later stages. Superimposed on such continua are a number of discrete bursts, with drift-band fine structure, which is peculiar to the dm-range (Kundu and Smerd [35]).

An X-ray burst (Fig. 22) and a sudden, ionospheric fadeout (Fig. 10) at that time depend on and correlate with the microwave impulsive burst.

Most flares are small ($\leqslant 1$ importance) and develop no further.

(*c*) *The Type IV and Proton Events.* In a large radio flare the next phase, significantly associated with complex sunspot fields [3], is dominated by the prolonged, intense wide-band emissions of the Type IV event. It occurs in the postmaximum phase of some large flares, specially when these cover the umbrae of large sunspots [16]. It is the Type IV event which has emerged as the best of known indicators of observable solar protons with energies from 10 Mev to, very rarely, several Bev [3, 14, 26, 62, 64]. Special significance was found in the occurrence of a strong microwave Type IV burst both for the appearance of a meter-wave Type IV burst [31, 45, 46] and for solar proton emissions [34, 50]. These associations suggest that the early particle acceleration, for electrons and positive ions alike, takes place in the microwave-emission region. However, the occasional appearance high in the corona of a moving Type IV burst and the persistence of proton events for the duration of the stationary meter-wave Type IV burst or the continuum storm [34] indicate that further trapping and storage occur in the corona.

The Type IV event dominates the energy balance of large radio flares while its energy content of about 10^{24} ergs is only a minute fraction of the total flare energy, or of that in a solar proton event. However, a heuristic assumption that the acceleration of vast numbers of solar protons would surely be accompanied by the acceleration of sufficient electrons to result in important radio emissions is borne out by the close link between Type IV and proton events.

(*d*) *Geomagnetic storms.* More surprising was the discovery that the Type IV event is also the best indicator of an imminent geomagnetic storm a day or so later [40, 52, 53]. Ever since Type II bursts had been identified with an outward source movement at about 10^3 km/sec, this burst was thought to mark the early stages in the sun-earth travel of the hypothetical magnetic-storm cloud [67]. This inference was supported by a statistical relationship [37, 49].

The discovery, both statistically and individually, that the Type IV event was an essential forerunner of the geomagnetic storm was interpreted [70] as emphasizing the importance of the quantity of matter ejected in the plasma cloud since a Type IV burst is believed to require a vast number of intermediate energy electrons, while a Type II burst requires fewer but more energetic electrons. The role of the Type II shock fronts was then not clear. More recently, the significance of the Type II burst as a link with a geomagnetic activity was restored to some extent when it was found [3, 33] that the probability of a large magnetic storm was considerably enhanced if the Type IV burst was preceded by a Type II burst. We thus infer that plasma clouds emitted from flares produce geomagnetic storms only when the number of particles contained in the cloud is very great and when the cloud advances behind a shock front.

We may conclude by summarizing the role of plasma streams and shock fronts. We have found that the *compound burst* (Type III-Type II) implied a common origin for the "fast" Type III electrons and the "slow" Type II plasma streams or shock waves. Athay and Moreton [2] have obtained optical evidence for similar matter or shock waves issuing (though tangentially) from the flare explosion at Type II speeds. Thus, by origin, the Type II burst belongs to the flash phase.

We have invoked such shock fronts and the mass transport of plasma accompanying them to account for several observed phenomena:

1. To explain the acceleration of the electrons that radiate Type IV emission and the protons observed in a "proton event."

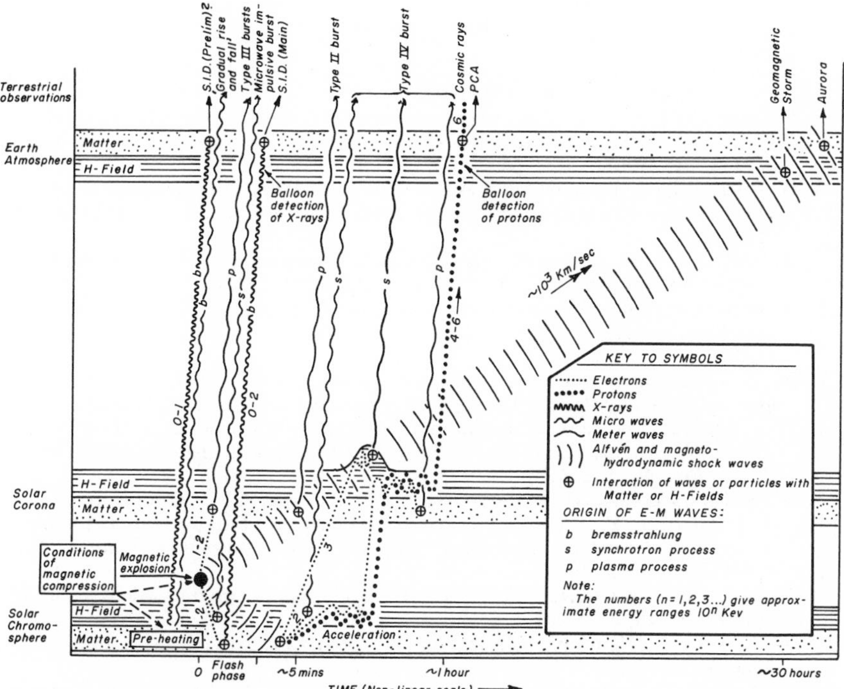

FIG. 25. A schematic diagram to illustrate possible origins of the radio, X-ray, and corpuscular radiations emitted in great solar flares (Wild *et al.* [76]).

2. To cause the dragging out of the magnetic field lines implied by the moving Type IV burst.
3. To give rise to the propagation through interplanetary space of the plasma cloud responsible for the geomagnetic storm.

The above picture of a flare event, its different phases of radio emission and the relations and associations between the various electromagnetic and particle radiations is illustrated in Figure 25 which is reproduced from Wild, Smerd, and Weiss [76]. The ideas outlined and illustrated here are necessarily tentative and incomplete. There is need for further observational evidence. No doubt much of this will come from observations of the renewed activity in the next solar cycle with the instruments now being planned.

ACKNOWLEDGMENT

The author would like to thank Dr. J. P. Wild of the CSIRO Radiophysics Laboratory for his critical reading of the manuscript.

REFERENCES

1. K. A. ANDERSON AND J. R. WINCKLER, Solar flare X-ray burst on September 28, 1961, *J. Geophys. Res.*, **67**, 4103 (1962).
2. R. G. ATHAY AND G. E. MORETON, Impulsive phenomena of the solar atmosphere, I—Some optical events associated with flares showing explosive phase, *Astrophys. J.*, **133**, 935 (1961).
3. B. BELL, Solar radio bursts of spectral type-II and IV: their relations to optical phenomena and to geomagnetic activity, *Smithsonian Contribs. Astrophys.*, **5**, 239 (1963).
4. A. BOISCHOT, Caractères d'un type d'émission hertzienne associé à certaines éruptions chromosphériques, *C. R. Acad. Sci.*, **244**, 1326 (1957).
5. A. BOISCHOT AND J. F. DENISSE, Les émissions de type IV et l'origine des rayons cosmiques associés aux éruptions chromosphériques, *C. R. Acad. Sci.*, **245**, 2194 (1957).
6. W. N. CHRISTIANSEN, The quiet and quasi-quiet sun, Proceedings of the XIV-th General Assembly, URSI, Tokyo, 9–20 September 1963 (to be published).
7. W. N. CHRISTIANSEN, J. V. HINDMAN, A. G. LITTLE, R. PAYNE-SCOTT, D. E. YABSLEY, AND C. W. ALLEN, Radio observations of two large solar disturbances, *Austral. J. Sci. Res.*, **4**, 51 (1951).
8. W. N. CHRISTIANSEN, D. S. MATHEWSON, J. L. PAWSEY, S. F. SMERD, A. BOISCHOT, J. F. DENISSE, P. SIMON, T. KAKINUMA, H. DODSON-PRINCE, AND J. FIROR, A study of a solar active region using combined optical and radio techniques, *Ann. Astrophys.*, **23**, 75 (1960).
9. W. N. CHRISTIANSEN AND J. A. WARBURTON, The sun in two dimensions at 21 cm, *Observatory*, **75**, 9 (1955).
10. M. H. COHEN, Microwave polarization and coronal magnetic fields, *Astrophys. J.*, **133**, 978 (1961).
11. A. E. COVINGTON, Solar radio astronomy, *J. Roy. Astron. Soc.*, **51**, 298 (Canada, 1957).
12. A. E. COVINGTON AND G. A. HARVEY, Impulsive and long-enduring sudden enhancements of solar radio emission at 10 centimeter wavelength, *J. Roy. Astron. Soc.*, **52**, 161 (Canada, 1958).
13. J. F. DENISSE, Les phenomènes radioélectriques solaires et leur interpretation physique, 13th Gen. Assembly URSI, London (1960); English translation: *NASA, Tech. Transl. F-72* (1961); and Une interpretation des orages radioélectriques solaires, *Info. Bull. S.R.O.E., No.* **4,** 3 (1960).
14. J. F. DENISSE, A. BOISCHOT, AND M. PICK-GUTMANN, Propriétés des éruptions chromosphériques associées à la production de rayons cosmiques par le soleil, *Space Research*, H. K. Kallmann-Bijl (ed.), 637 (North-Holland Publishing Co., 1960).
15. H. W. DODSON, E. R. HEDEMAN, AND A. E. COVINGTON, Solar flares and associated 2800 Mc/sec (10.7 cm) radiation, *Astrophys. J.*, **119**, 541 (1954).
16. H. DODSON-PRINCE, Characteristics of flares associated with Polar cap absorption, *Trans. Intern. Astron. Union (Proceedings 1961)*, **11B**, 474 (Academic Press, 1962).
17. Ø. ELGAROY, High resolution spectrometry of enhanced solar radio emission, *Astrophysica Norvegica*, **7**, 123 (1961).

18. M. A. Ellison, Energy release in solar flares, *J. Roy. Astron. Soc.*, **4,** 62 (1963).
19. M. A. Ellison, Characteristic properties of chromospheric flares, *Mon. Not. Roy. Astron. Soc.*, **109,** 3 (1949).
20. A. D. Fokker, Studies of enhanced solar radio emission at frequencies near 200 MHz, Doctoral Thesis, Univ. of Leiden, Leiden, Netherlands, 1960.
21. V. L. Ginzburg and V. V. Zheleznyakov, On the possible mechanisms of sporadic solar radio emission (radiation in an isotropic plasma), *Astron. Zh.*, **35,** 694 (1958); English translation *Soviet Astronomy, A. J.*, **2,** 653 (1958).
22. V. L. Ginzburg and V. V. Zheleznyakov, Non-coherent mechanisms of sporadic solar radio emission in the case of a magneto-active coronal plasma, *Astron. Zh.*, **38,** 3 (1961); English translation *Soviet Astronomy, A. J.*, **5,** 1 (1961).
23. T. Gold and F. Hoyle, On the origin of solar flares, *Mon. Not. Roy. Astron. Soc.*, **120,** 89 (1960).
24. O. Hachenberg and G. Wallis, Das Spektrum der Bursts der Radio-frequenzstrahlung der Sonne im cm-Wellenbereich, *Z. Astrophys.* ,**52,** 42 (1961).
25. F. T. Haddock, Introduction to radio astronomy, *Proc. IRE*, **46,** 3 (1958).
26. Y. Hakura and T. Goh, Pre-SC polar cap ionospheric blackout and type IV solar radio outburst, *J. Radio Res. Lab., Japan*, **6,** 635 (1959).
27. K. Kai, Some characteristics of type I burst, *Publ. Astron. Soc. Japan*, **14,** 1 (1962).
28. T. Kakinuma, Polarization of solar radio bursts at microwave frequencies I, *Proc. Res. Inst. Atmospherics, Nagoya Univ.*, **5,** 71 (1958).
29. T. Kakinuma and G. Swarup, A model for the sources of the slowly-varying component of microwave solar radiation, *Astrophys. J.*, **136,** 975 (1962).
30. T. Krishnan and N. R. Labrum, The radio brightness distribution on the sun at 21 cm from combined eclipse and pencil-beam observations, *Austral. J. Phys.*, **14,** 403 (1961).
31. M. R. Kundu, Structures et propriétés des sources d'activité solaire sur ondes centimétriques, *Ann. Astrophys.*, **22,** 1 (1959); Some studies on the occurrence of type IV solar bursts of continuum radiation, *Astrophys. J.*, **134,** 96 (1961).
32. M. R. Kundu, Bursts of centimeter-wave emission and the region of origin of X-rays from solar flares, *J. Geophys. Res.*, **66,** 4308 (1961).
33. M. R. Kundu, The nature of type IV solar radio bursts, *J. Phys. Soc. Japan*, **17,** Suppl. A-II, 215 (1962).
34. M. R. Kundu and F. T. Haddock, A relation between solar radio emission and polar cap absorption of cosmic noise, *Nature*, **186,** 610 (1960).
35. M. R. Kundu and S. F. Smerd, Note on type-IV emission, *Info. Bull. Solar Radio Observatories No.* **11,** 4 (1962).
36. N. R. Labrum, The radio brightness of the quiet sun at 21 cm wavelength near sunspot maximum, *Austral. J. Phys.*, **13,** 700 (1960).
37. A. Maxwell, A. R. Thompson, and G. Garmire, The association of solar radio bursts with auroral streams, *Planet. Space Sci.*, **1,** 325 (1959).
38. A. Maxwell and G. Swarup, A new spectral characteristic in solar radio emission, *Nature*, **181,** 36 (1958).
39. A. Maxwell, G. Swarup, and A. R. Thompson, The radio spectrum of solar activity, *Proc. IRE*, **46,** 142 (1958).
40. D. J. McLean, Solar radio emission of spectral type IV and its association with geomagnetic storms, *Austral. J. Phys.*, **12,** 404 (1959).
41. P. A. O'Brien and E. Tandberg-Hanssen, Distribution of radio-frequency brightness across the solar disk at a wavelength of 60 cm, *Observatory*, **75,** 11 (1955).
42. R. Payne-Scott and A. G. Little, The position and movement on the solar disk of sources of radiation at a frequency of 97 Mc/s, III—Outbursts, *Austral. J. Sci. Res.*, **5,** 32 (1952).
43. R. Payne-Scott, D. E. Yabsley, and J. G. Bolton, Relative times of arrival of bursts of solar noise on different radio frequencies, *Nature*, **160,** 256 (1947).
44. J. L. Pawsey and S. F. Smerd, Solar radio emission, *The Sun*, G. P. Kuiper (ed.), Chap. 7 (Univ. Chicago Press, 1953).
45. M. Pick-Gutmann, Sur la structure des types IV, les orages continuum, *C. R. Acad. Sci.*, **250,** 2127 (1960).

46. M. Pick-Gutmann, Evolution des émissions radioélectriques solaires de type IV et leur relation avec d'autres phenomènes solaires et géophysiques, *Ann. Astrophys.*, **24,** 183 (1961).
47. J. H. Piddington, The origin of galactic radio-frequency radiation, *Mon. Not. Roy. Astron. Soc.*, **111,** 45 (1951).
48. J. H. Piddington and R. D. Davies, Thermal radio emission from the sun and the source of coronal heating, *Mon. Not. Roy. Astron. Soc.*, **113,** 582 (1953).
49. J. A. Roberts, Solar radio bursts of spectral type II, *Austral. J. Phys.*, **12,** 327 (1959).
50. K. Sakurai and H. Maeda, A relation between solar radio emission and low-energy solar cosmic rays, *J. Geophys. Res.*, **66,** 1966 (1961).
51. A. B. Severny, Solar flares as a pinch effect, *Trans. Intn'l Astron. Union* (*Proceedings 1958*), **10,** 647 (Cambridge Univ. Press, 1960).
52. P. Simon, Les eruptions chromosphériques associées aux sursuats radioélectriques de type IV effets ionosphériques et géomagnetiques, *Ann. Astrophys.*, **23,** 102 (1960).
53. K. Sinno and Y. Hakura, On the relation of solar eruptions to geomagnetic and ionospheric disturbances, II—On the types of solar radio outbursts, *Rept. Ionos. Res. Japan*, **12,** 296 (1958).
54. S. F. Smerd, Solar radio emission during the International Geophysical Year, *Annals of the IGY* (in press).
55. S. F. Smerd, J. P. Wild, and K. V. Sheridan, On the relative position and origin of harmonics in the spectra of solar radio bursts of spectral types II and III, *Austral. J. Phys.*, **15,** 180 (1962).
56. G. Swarup, Studies of solar microwave emission using a highly directional antenna, *Scientific Report No. 13*, Radioscience Laboratory Standard Electronics Laboratories, Stanford University, 1961.
57. P. A. Sweet, The neutral point theory of solar flares, *Intn'l Astron. Union Symposium No. 6, Stockholm, 1956*, B. Lehnert (ed.), 123 (Cambridge Univ. Press, 1958).
58. T. Takakura, Synchrotron radiation from intermediate energy electrons in helical orbits and solar radio bursts at microwave frequencies, *Publ. Astron. Soc. Japan*, **12,** 352 (1960).
59. T. Takakura, Solar radio outbursts and acceleration of electrons, *J. Phys. Soc. Japan*, **17,** Suppl. A-II, 243 (1962).
60. T. Takakura and K. Kai, Spectra of solar radio type IV bursts, *Publ. Astron. Soc. Japan*, **13,** 94 (1961).
61. A. R. Thompson and A. Maxwell, Spectral observations of solar radio bursts, III—Continuum bursts, *Astrophys. J.*, **136,** 546 (1962).
62. A. R. Thompson and A. Maxwell, Solar radio bursts and low energy cosmic rays, *Nature*, **185,** 89 (1960).
63. M. Waldmeier, Zirkulation and Magnetfeld der Solaren Polarzone, *Z. Astrophys.*, **49,** 176 (1960).
64. C. S. Warwick and M. W. Haurwitz, A study of solar activity associated with polar-cap absorption, *J. Geophys. Res.*, **67,** 1317 (1962).
65. A. A. Weiss, The positions and movements of the sources of solar radio bursts of spectral type II, *Austral. J. Phys.*, **16,** 240 (1963).
66. A. A. Weiss, The type IV solar radio burst at metre wavelengths, *Austral. J. Phys.*, **16,** 526 (1963).
67. J. P. Wild, Observations of the spectrum of high-intensity solar radiation at metre wavelengths, II—Outbursts, *Austral. J. Sci. Res.*, **3,** 399 (1950).
68. J. P. Wild, Observational radio astronomy, *Adv. in Electronics and Electron Physics*, **7,** 299 (1955).
69. J. P. Wild, Radio observations of solar flares, *Trans. Intn'l Astron. Union* (*Proceedings 1955*), **9,** 661 (Cambridge Univ. Press, 1957).
70. J. P. Wild, Solar radio spectroscopy, *Rend. Scuola Intern. Fis., Corso XII*, 296 (1960).
71. J. P. Wild, The radio emission from solar flares, *J. Phys. Soc. Japan*, **17,** Suppl. A-II, 249 (1962).
72. J. P. Wild, J. D. Murray, and W. C. Rowe, Harmonics in the spectra of solar radio disturbances, *Austral. J. Phys.*, **7,** 439 (1954).

73. J. P. WILD, J. A. ROBERTS, AND J. D. MURRAY, Radio evidence of the ejection of very fast particles from the sun, *Nature*, **173,** 532 (1954).
74. J. P. WILD, K. V. SHERIDAN, AND A. A. NEYLAN, An investigation of the speed of the solar disturbances responsible for type III radio bursts, *Austral. J. Phys.*, **12,** 369 (1959).
75. J. P. WILD, K. V. SHERIDAN, AND G. H. TRENT, The transverse motions of the sources of solar radio bursts, *Paris Symposium on Radio Astronomy*, R. N. Bracewell (ed.) (Stanford Univ. Press, 1959).
76. J. P. WILD, S. F. SMERD, AND A. A. WEISS, Solar bursts, *Annual Review of Astronomy and Astrophysics*, **1,** 291 (1963).
77. C. W. YOUNG, C. L. SPENCER, G. E. MORETON, AND J. A. ROBERTS, A preliminary study of the dynamic spectra of solar radio bursts in the frequency range 500–950 Mc/S, *Astrophys. J.*, **133,** 243 (1961).

CHAPTER 4

CORONAL EXPANSION AND SOLAR CORPUSCULAR RADIATION

E. N. Parker

1. The Existence of Solar Corpuscular Radiation

The elusive phenomenon of solar corpuscular radiation has been under study since the beginning of the century. But until space vehicles became available a few years ago, the solar corpuscular radiation could be known only through its indirect effects, and so there was wide diversity of opinion concerning its nature and origin. Evidence for the existence of such radiation had its first substantial beginnings with the pioneering work of Störmer [49] on the aurora. Störmer showed that much of the latitude behavior and curtainlike forms of the aurora could be accounted for if it were assumed that sprays of monoenergetic particles with energies of the order of several Mev were emitted from the sun and propagated in straight lines to the magnetic dipole field of earth. Störmer's well-known calculations of the charged particle motion in the geomagnetic field illustrated how the auroral forms might come about. It has become evident in the last few decades that the aurora cannot be so produced because charged particles with enough energy to behave in the geomagnetic field as imagined by Störmer would penetrate much more deeply into the terrestrial atmosphere than is observed. The present value of Störmer's work, so far as solar corpuscular radiation is concerned, lies in his calling attention to the particle nature of the aurora and to the possibility of particle emission from the sun. (It has become evident in the past few years that the outer boundary of the geomagnetic field lies so far out [14, 22, 26, 48] that the energetic particles in the aurora are probably not the same particles as are emitted by the sun but are excited only by the solar particles in some indirect way.)

The next major step toward present concepts of solar corpuscular radiation had to do with geomagnetic activity and the magnetic storm phenomenon. Lindemann suggested that the geomagnetic storm was the result of neutral clouds or streams of ionized hydrogen shot out of the sun at the time of a solar flare. Following this, Chapman and Ferraro [16–19] worked out several examples of the dynamical interaction of ionized hydrogen with the geomagnetic field and demonstrated the soundness of the idea. Their pioneering work has served as the foundation of all subsequent developments in the theory of the geomagnetic storm, which are centered upon the idea that the geomagnetic storm, and geomagnetic activity in general, are the result of the impact of interplanetary plasma clouds against the geomagnetic field (see discussion and references in Parker [40]).

Forbush showed that the intensity of the galactic cosmic rays varies over the 11-year (or 22-year) cycle of solar activity [24]. Cosmic-ray intensity tends to be higher when solar activity is low rather than when it is high. Forbush also pointed out the tendency for the galactic cosmic-ray intensity to decline in general association with the geomagnetic storm. With the development of the neutron monitor [45] which apprehended cosmic-ray protons in the low-energy range of a few Gev, these variations were large enough to study in some detail. Simpson [46] was able to show that the variations were of extraterrestrial origin and evidently the work of the solar corpuscular radiation. It became clear that the active sun and the associated corpuscular radiation were in some way able partially to exclude galactic cosmic rays from the vicinity of earth. Variations in cosmic-ray intensity became then a means for studying interplanetary conditions (see discussion and review in Simpson [47]). A great variety of models, such as a plasma cloud carrying a small-scale disordered magnetic field [30] were considered (see references and discussion in Parker [41]). The important point here is that solar corpuscular radiation turns up again as the perpetrator of an observable effect in the terrestrial environment.

For several centuries it has been known that the gaseous tails of comets tend to point straight away from the sun irrespective of the direction of orbital motion of the comet around the sun. The classical explanation was always radiation pressure. However about twenty years ago the analysis of the acceleration of the visible inhomogeneities in the tail of the comet [52] began to make it clear that the outward pressure on the gas in the comet tail must be enormous. Biermann [2–4], pointed out that radiation pressure was inadequate by a large factor and that the only tenable assumption was solar corpuscular radiation. Biermann's realization of the role of solar corpuscular radiation in comet tail behavior was of particular importance because it made clear in a striking manner that solar corpuscular radiation is evidently emitted in *all directions* from the sun at *all times* (see further discussion in Stumpff [50] and Lüst [27]). It made it clear that solar corpuscular radiation is not a special property of active regions and flares on the sun, but is a general and continuing property of the quiet, as well as the active, sun.

There are a number of means by which the velocity of propagation of the solar corpuscular radiation has been estimated. (*a*) The one- or two-day delay of the geomagnetic storm and the cosmic-ray decrease after a large flare on the sun shows clearly that the velocity of propagation is something of the order of 1000–2000 km/sec from the very active sun. (*b*) If it is assumed that plages on the central meridian of the sun are associated with slight enhancements in the quiet-day corpuscular radiation emitted in the direction of earth, then the delay of the small increases in geomagnetic activity suggests quiet-day propagation velocities of 150–400 km/sec [29, 31, 32], with the lower velocities being more prevalent during years of sunspot minimum. (*c*) Comet tail acceleration reflects clearly the variations in the strength of the solar corpuscular radiation with the level of solar activity. Biermann has pointed out that the gaseous comet tails seem always to lie within about 3° of the radial direction from the sun, which when combined with a typical transverse orbital velocity of, say, 30 km/sec gives a corpuscular velocity which is about 500 km/sec.

So far as we are aware, there are no methods for estimating the density of the solar corpuscular radiation indirectly. Early attempts to deduce the interplanetary electron density from observations of the polarized component of the zodiacal light [1, 23] and from free particle models of comet tail interaction [4] gave quiet-day values of the order of 500/cm^3 at the orbit of earth. Blackwell [7–9] pointed out however that the density must be much lower, less than 100/cm^3, and that the polarized component of the zodiacal light was scattered principally by dust grains rather than electrons. Then Blackwell and Ingham [10] suggested that the density was of the order of 300/cm^3 at the peak of a strong outburst from the sun, based on a supposed brightening of the zodiacal light at that time. It was pointed out by Parker [40] that the effect of the outburst on the geomagnetic field suggested a maximum density of more like 30/cm^3.

Recent direct observation in space shows the continuing presence of solar corpuscular radiation [25, 44]. The quiet-day velocity is 300–600 km/sec (about 1 kev per proton) and the density is 2–20 protons/cm^3 [11–13, 33]. The observations show clearly that the intensity of the solar corpuscular radiation may fluctuate rapidly at times, even on what would otherwise be considered a quiet day. There are as yet no certain direct quantitative measurements of the typical enhanced solar corpuscular radiation, so that we can only speculate that it may reach a maximum of 30/cm^3.

2. The Origin of Solar Corpuscular Radiation

A variety of interesting ideas about the origin of solar corpuscular radiation at the sun have been proposed over the years. Many authors have looked to the plage as the origin of much of the corpuscular emission and others have favored the more violent solar flare. Some have considered the sunspot with its intense magnetic fields and great store of energy and constant change. Many workers believe that the origin of kilovolt solar corpuscular radiation is closely associated with the energetic (1 Mev–10 Gev) particles emitted from so many solar flares. Very little has been worked out quantitatively, but it is evident that most of the ideas have centered around the magnetic field as a major factor in catapulting the corpuscular radiation into space. Perhaps the most clear-cut of these ideas is the well-known "melon seed" model put forth by Schluter [43].

It has been our own view that the solar corpuscular radiation may have a somewhat less special origin than has generally been imagined. This view stems from Biermann's demonstration of the continuing nature of the solar corpuscular radiation, and Chapman's theoretical studies of the thermal conductivity of the solar corona suggest where to start looking for its origin. Chapman pointed out that the thermal conductivity of the ionized hydrogen, of which the corona is composed, is extremely large ($6 \times 10^{-7} T^{5/2}$ ergs/cm sec°K) and therefore the coronal temperature (some 10^6°K) must extend far into space [15]. He pointed out that, except perhaps in the lowest portions of the corona, radiation losses may be neglected compared to the energy transported by thermal conduction. Then assuming that the corona is static, and more or less symmetric about the sun, he showed that the temperature declines outward only very slowly, like $1/r^{2/7}$. This would mean that the temperature of the corona at the orbit of earth is about 0.2 what it is at the sun: 10^6°K at the sun would imply 2×10^5°K at the orbit of earth. The density of the corona at the orbit of earth proved to be 10–100 atoms/cm^3 on the basis of this model. Now there may be other means of energy transport besides thermal conduction available, so that we do not take seriously the $1/r^{2/7}$ temperature dependence of this particular model. The great importance of Chapman's calculation lies in its demonstration that, unless some powerful mechanism inhibits the outward extension of coronal temperature, the temperature must extend far into interplanetary space. (There has been some concern that transverse magnetic fields might seriously inhibit the conduction of thermal energy in the radial direction outward from the sun. The reentrant nature of some of the filaments over active regions strongly suggests the existence of strong inhibition there. However, apart from some active regions, the general radial configuration of corona streamers and striations suggests that there may be little or no inhibition to an outward conduction of heat throughout most of the solar corona.)

The continuing nature of the solar corpuscular radiation and enormous extent of the coronal temperature and density into space suggested to us that the ordinary hydrodynamic properties of the solar corona might be a fruitful field of investigation. The first step was to show that the solar gravitational field, no matter how tightly it may bind the lower corona to the sun, is not able to contain the more distant portions of the corona. One way to see this is to note that the gravitational potential decreases outward like $1/r$, but there is no evident way in which the temperature can be made to decline so rapidly. Hence, sufficiently far from the sun the thermal energy of the gas exceeds the gravitational energy and the gas should be free to escape. Consequently, it is necessary to abandon the traditional idea of a static corona and admit the possibility of continual expansion. We must turn from the hydrostatic barometric equation to the hydrodynamic equation. (Some have been concerned as to whether the hydrodynamic equation is applicable to the solar corona. The traditional treatment of the corona has centered on the ideal of individually moving particles which may evaporate freely into space. But the mean free path in the corona is small compared to the scale height: far out from the sun in interplanetary space there is the interesting possibility, if the temperature is high enough, that the mean free path may be relatively long [36]. However, the weak magnetic fields, and their associated hose and mirror instabilities, maintain the pressure in an approximately isotropic state and rather closely confine the motions of each individual ion and electron; the effect is much the same as a high collision rate, so that the usual hydrodynamic equation is a valid approximation for the over-all large-scale motion of the gas.)

It is sufficient for present purposes to consider the simple case of a solar corona with spherical symmetry about the center of the sun and composed solely of ionized hydrogen. Then for steady conditions the outward velocity $v(r)$, the numbers of ions/cm^3 $N(r)$, and the temperature $T(r)$ are related by the familiar equation

$$v\frac{dv}{dr} = -\frac{1}{NM}\frac{d}{dr}2NkT - \frac{GM_{\odot}}{r^2} \tag{1}$$

where M is the mass of a hydrogen atom. Conservation of matter requires that

$$N(r)v(r)r^2 = N_0v_0a^2 \tag{2}$$

where $r = a$ is the reference level, taken for convenience to lie in the lower corona where $N(a) = N_0$, $v(a) = v_0$. Solution of the hydrodynamic equation for the simple case of an isothermal corona $T = T_0$ showed immediately that the corona not only expands, but that it expands with supersonic velocities of several hundred km/sec [35]. Subsequent solution with an outward decline of $T(r)$ given by the polytrope relation

$$T(r) = T_0\left[\frac{N(r)}{N_0}\right]^{\alpha-1}$$

showed that the supersonic expansion is not critically dependent on the form of $T(r)$ nor on the value of T_0 [37]. Recent theoretical investigations [42] of the solar corona with the assumption that $T(r)$ is determined by the heat flow equation show that, within the idealizations contained in the equations, the corona must expand supersonically for all coronal T_0. (To what extent energy may be supplied to the outer corona in addition to thermal conduction [34] as a consequence of the dissipation of hydromagnetic waves, etc., is still open; hence the heat flow equation probably represents a minimum energy supply.) The expansion of the solar corona to give the supersonic solar wind appears to be an ordinary and unavoidable consequence of the hot, tightly bound corona and the cold interstellar void; this topic is considered in Section 4.

Finally, since the integration of the hydrodynamic equations proceeds along the stream lines, the results are essentially independent of whether the corona is composed of many radial striations and filaments or whether it is more or less homogeneous. The basic properties of the equations are the same in all cases, predicting several hundred km/sec at the orbit of earth when the coronal temperature is of the order of 10^6°K; thus here we may as well consider the original isothermal coronal model because the computations are simpler.

Investigation showed that the gravitationally bound stellar corona has the general property of being nearly static at its base and expanding with a velocity that increases monotonically outward to values of several hundred km/sec, i.e., considerably in excess of the rms thermal velocity at the base of the corona. It is evident at once that the "solar corpuscular radiation," postulated to account for so many geophysical effects, is probably the manifestation of this coronal expansion. The velocity requirements of 200–2000 km/sec are just those predicted from the observed coronal temperatures of 0.5–3 $\times$ 10^6°K. The hydrodynamic origin suggests that some such term as the "solar wind" might be more appropriate than "solar corpuscular radiation."

3. Physics of Coronal Expansion

The physics behind the formal mathematics of the expansion of the solar corona can be understood on the basis of an analogy by Clauser [20]: that the gravitational field of the sun plays the same role in coronal expansion as the throat in a deLaval nozzle. If we look into the similarity of the two types, we note that in both cases the gas attains supersonic velocity while passing from a high pressure into a vacuum due to constriction in the flow. To see this directly note that the equation for conservation of mass for steady flow through a nozzle of cross section $A(r)$ is

$$N(r)v(r)A(r) = N_0v_0A_0 \tag{3}$$

The decrease in $A(r)$ as the gas moves into the throat requires a corresponding increase in the flow velocity $v(r)$, and in this way the throat causes $v(r)$ to increase up to the speed of sound. Beyond the throat the nozzle flares out and the velocity of the gas increases above the speed of sound as it expands into the vacuum. It is important to note that the gas can be made to decelerate, rather than accelerate, after reaching the speed of sound in the throat only if the nozzle does not open into a near vacuum. Only a suitably high back pressure at the exhaust end will force the gas back down to subsonic velocities.

Equation 2 is the equation for conservation of mass in the solar corona. In this case $N(r)$ decreases rapidly with height in the corona because of the strong solar gravitational field. Consequently $v(r)$ must increase rapidly with height to maintain the net flow of matter, with the result that the velocity reaches the speed of sound at a distance of a few solar radii. Beyond that point the velocity increases further as a consequence of expansion into the vacuum of interstellar space, just as in the nozzle [4].

As would be expected from the existence of the analogy of coronal expansion to expansion through a nozzle, the hydrodynamic equations for the corona possess a critical point across which passes the solution of physical interest for expansion into a vacuum. The critical point may be demonstrated by using Equation 2 to eliminate $N(r)$ from Equation 1. The result is

$$\frac{dv}{dr}\left(v - \frac{2kT}{Mv}\right) = -\frac{2kr^2}{M}\frac{d}{dr}\left(\frac{T}{r^2}\right) - \frac{GM\odot}{r^2}. \tag{4}$$

The critical point is the point (r_c, v_c) at which the right-hand side of this equation and the coefficient of dv/dr both vanish. Equating the right-hand side to zero leads to an expression that yields r_c as soon as the function $T(r)$ is specified. The temperature at the critical point $T(r_c)$ follows immediately. The velocity v_c at the critical point follows from the coefficient of dv/dr as $v_c^2 = 2kT(r_c)/M$. The critical point corresponds to the point at which the fluid velocity becomes supersonic. For expansion through a nozzle the critical point lies in or near the throat. For the expanding corona it defines the position of the fictitious "gravitational throat."

For the simple case of an isothermal corona, which typifies the phenomenon of coronal expansion, the critical point has coordinates

$$r_c = \frac{GM\odot M}{4kT_0}, \qquad v_c^2 = \frac{2kT_0}{M} \tag{5}$$

Requiring that the integral of Equation 4 pass through the critical point leads to the solution

$$\frac{v^2}{v_c^2} - \ln\frac{v^2}{v_c^2} = -3 + 4\ln\frac{2v_c^2 r}{w^2 a} + \frac{2w^2 a}{v_c^2 r}$$

where $w^2 = GM\odot/a$. It is readily seen that at large r, the velocity increases as $2v_c[\ln (r/a)]^{1/2}$. The velocity at the reference level $r = a$ is given by

$$\frac{v_0^2}{v_c^2} - \ln \frac{v_0^2}{v_c^2} = -3 + 4 \ln \frac{2v_c^2}{w^2} + \frac{2w^2}{v_c^2}$$

The mass loss to the sun is $4\pi N_0 v_0 a^2$, which is determined by the velocity v_0 in the low corona. Numerically we have $v_c = 1.3 \times 10^4 T_c^{1/2}$ cm/sec and $w^2 = 1.9 \times 10^{15}$ cm/sec. At the orbit of earth we have very roughly that $v \cong 5 \times 10^4 T_0^{1/2}$ cm/sec. As a specific example note that a coronal temperature of $T_0 = 1.0 \times 10^6$°K yields $v_0 = 0.7$ km/sec at the base of the corona ($a \cong 7 \times 10^{10}$ cm, $N_0 \cong 2 \times 10^8$ atoms/cm³). The mass loss to the sun is 1.5×10^{12} gm/sec or about $10^{-4} M_\odot$ in the 5×10^9 years that the sun has existed. The rms thermal velocity is 150 km/sec and the gravitational escape velocity is $2^{1/2} w \cong 600$ km/sec. The critical point lies at $r_c = 4 \times 10^{11}$ cm $\cong 6R_\odot$, where the expansion velocity is 120 km/sec. The velocity at the orbit of earth is about 500 km/sec, and the density is about 7 atoms/cm³. A lower temperature of 0.75×10^6°K yields 400 km/sec and 1 cm³. Velocity as a function of radial distance from the sun is plotted in Figure 1 for several values of T_0. Note that for the higher temperatures of 3 and 4×10^6°K the expansion velocity exceeds 10^3 km/sec. The solar

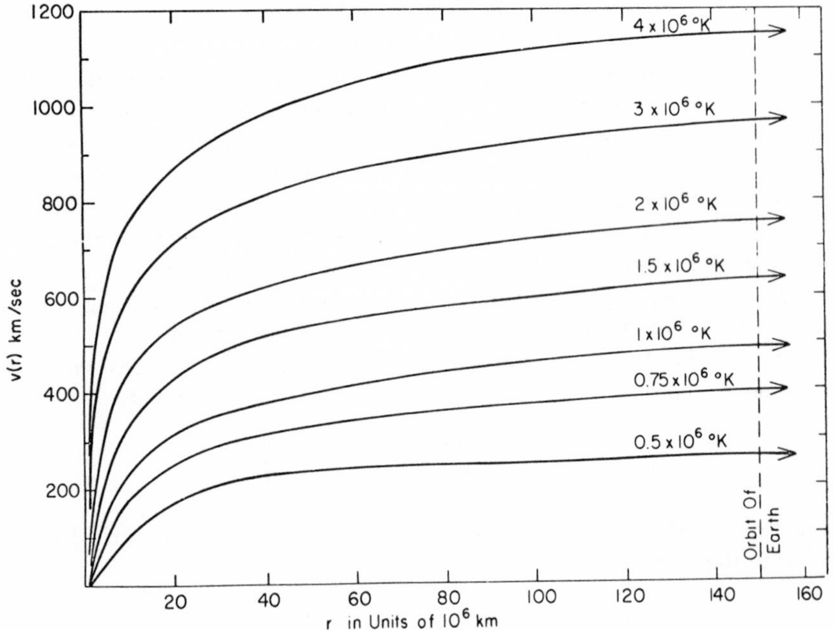

FIG. 1. A plot of the radial expansion velocity of an isothermal corona as a function of distance from the sun (measured in units of 10^6 km) for various values of the coronal temperature T_0.

wind from this simple 1×10^6°K model falls near the middle of the velocity and density ranges observed in space. It is evident that the observed variation of coronal temperature with time and with position around the sun must lead to marked variations in the solar wind velocity and density with time and in different directions from the sun. (See such reviews as van de Hulst [51], Billings [5, 6], and Lüst *et al.* [28] for a discussion of the observational determination of the temperature of the solar corona; the 10^6°K employed in the present discussion has been chosen as a representative mean value suggested by the several methods of observational determination.)

One interesting feature of the expanding corona is the enormous rate of decrease of the density of the solar wind with declining coronal temperature. The velocity of the solar wind varies approximately as $T_c^{1/2}$, as we would expect, but the density varies much more rapidly. For instance a uniform coronal temperature of 2×10^6°K gives a wind velocity of 700 km/sec and a density of more than 10^2/cm^3 at the orbit of earth. The density is up by about a factor of 15 from what it was for 1×10^6°K. Obviously the density of the solar wind at the orbit of earth cannot be predicted from the temperature of the corona at the sun unless that temperature is known rather precisely. One can fit the old indirect density estimates of 10^2/cm^3 or more at the orbit of earth, as well as the new direct measurements in space of 2–20/cm^3 with temperatures within the observational range of 0.5–3×10^6°K.

The distance to which the solar wind extends outward into interstellar space has been estimated to be somewhere in the range of 10–10^3 A.U. depending upon what assumptions are made for the interstellar pressure [38]. One expects a shock transition at the outer boundary of the solar wind across which the velocity drops down to something of the order of 10^2 km/sec.

4. Supersonic Expansion Solutions

Whether a corona must expand supersonically or whether there is some subsonic or even static solution of the momentum equation is intimately connected to the existence and role of the critical point [35–37]. The general topology of the solutions of Equation 4 in the rv-plane is illustrated in Figure 2 for temperature distributions $T(r)$ which decline gradually with increasing r. The existence of the critical point depends upon the existence of a zero of the right-hand side of Equation 4. To determine sufficient conditions for the existence of the critical point, and to demonstrate the implications of its existence, we state the essence of an argument presented more formally and in greater detail elsewhere [42].

The first term on the right hand side of Equation 4 is positive because T/r^2 declines with increasing r. It is obvious that in a sufficiently strong

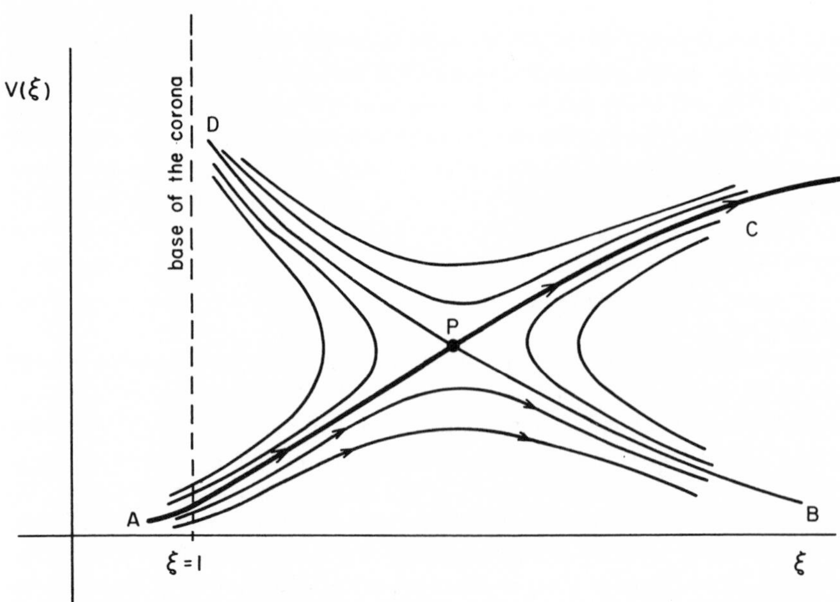

FIG. 2. Sketch of the topology of the solutions $v(r)$ of the momentum equation 4 when $T(r)$ declines less rapidly than $1/r$. The critical point is labeled P. The heavy line represents the solution of physical interest for expansion of corona into a vacuum.

gravitational field the second term on the right-hand side is of larger magnitude than the first, at least near the sun. The second term is obviously negative: hence the right-hand side is negative near the sun.

If the temperature declines less rapidly than $1/r$, then as r becomes large the first term on the right-hand side must eventually become larger in magnitude than the second term; the right-hand side must become positive. Hence it possesses a zero. It follows that if the temperature declines outward less rapidly than $1/r$ for a suitable finite distance, the critical point exists.

The next step is to note that the plasma arriving at the critical point has positive enthalpy; i.e., the total enthalpy per atom is of the order of kT,

$$\frac{1}{2}Mv^2 + 5kT - \frac{GM_\odot M}{r} = O(kT)$$

on any solution passing near the critical point. This is easily proved because, in some sufficiently small neighborhood of the critical point, $T(r)$ may be represented accurately by *constant*$/r^\gamma$, where $\gamma < 1$. Now conservation of the energy flux in the flow requires that this energy convected past the critical point must be transported on to $r = \infty$. The energy cannot be transported as thermal energy, and hence must be transported as kinetic energy of the bulk motion. To show that the energy cannot be transported to $r = \infty$ as thermal energy, note that the temperature at $r = \infty$ would have to be comparable with the temperature T at the critical point. But this could be the case only if the gas did not expand much beyond the critical point, and implies that the gas pressure $2NkT$ at $r = \infty$ is comparable with the gas pressure at the critical point in the corona. Such enormous gas pressures do not exist at $r = \infty$ (interstellar space). Q.E.D. Hence the energy can be transported only as bulk motion, which must be comparable with the thermal velocity at the critical point, and hence highly supersonic far beyond the critical point. It is evident from Figure 2 that there is only one solution with this property: the curve APC passing straight across the critical point. Altogether, then, conservation of energy leads to the conclusion that (*a*) when the gas pressure at infinity is negligible, and (*b*) when a critical point exists, then we must choose the solution which passes straight across the critical point to supersonic velocity at large r.

The final question is whether $T(r)$ may increase more or less rapidly than $1/r$. In a static coronal without radiation loss the temperature would decline as in Chapman's model, viz., $T(r) \propto 1/r^{2/7}$. A sufficiently vigorous radiative loss to the corona could cause the temperature to decline arbitrarily rapidly, i.e., much faster than $1/r$; so could some hypothetical transverse magnetic field as a consequence of the enormous reduction of thermal conductivity in the directions across the lines of force. A static corona might then be the result. But in the sun the magnetic lines of force, as outlined by the coronal streamers, appear to be largely radial and to connect each element of volume of the corona with the supposed heat source at its base. Little inhibition of heat flow to any point in the corona is expected. Further, the solar corona is sufficiently tenuous that radiation losses are unimportant compared to thermal conduction in the *extended outer* corona. Thus, altogether, the ordinary heat flow equation should apply in the extended corona and the energy flux F,

$$F = -r^2\kappa \frac{dT}{dr} + Nvr^2\left(\frac{1}{2}Mv^2 + 5kT - \frac{GM_\odot M}{r}\right)$$

ergs/sec sterad, is independent of r.

Under these circumstances $F > 0$ and $T(r)$ declines less rapidly than $1/r$ at large r. Assume first that for a given coronal density N_0, the total outward energy flux F does not decrease when the coronal temperature T_0 is increased, and keep this in mind until later. Then recall that the mass efflux declines extremely rapidly with declining T_0, something like $\exp(-A/T_0)$ where A is a suitable constant. This is the case for both subsonic and supersonic solutions of the momentum equation. On the other hand, the energy flux by thermal conduction $O[\kappa(T_0)aT_0]$ declines only as fast as $T_0^{7/2}$. Mass efflux can be made arbitrarily small compared to the thermal conduction flux by choosing T_0 sufficiently small. Since $\frac{1}{2}Mv^2$ and $5kT$ do not increase enormously as the coronal temperature declines, the convection term in square brackets in the expression for F can be made arbitrarily small compared to the heat flow term $r^2\kappa dT/dr$. Thus in the limit of small T_0

$$F \cong -r^2\kappa \frac{dT}{dr}$$

from which it follows that $T \propto 1/r^{2/7}$ and $F = \frac{2}{7}\kappa(T_0)aT_0 > 0$. Thus F is nonvanishing and T declines less rapidly than $1/r$ for a sufficiently small coronal temperature. Hence the corona must expand to supersonic velocity if the temperature is sufficiently low. But if $F > 0$ and the expansion is supersonic for low T_0, then, as assumed at the outset, we must have $F > 0$ and supersonic expansion for higher temperatures. Q.E.D. It has been shown, then, that if radiation losses are neglected in the extended outer corona, the energy flux to infinity is nonvanishing, the wind velocity is supersonic, and the coronal temperature declines less rapidly than $1/r$. The momentum and heat flow equations possess no alternative solutions. (N.b. This is a discussion of the formal mathematical properties of the momentum and heat flow equation for a corona of fully ionized gas; the fact that these equations may not be physically correct for a corona of arbitrarily low temperature is irrelevant.)

5. Quiet-Day Interplanetary Magnetic Fields

The expansion of the solar corona carries with it the general solar magnetic field of 1 gauss as a consequence of the high electrical conductivity of the coronal gas [35, 36]. If the sun did not rotate, the result of the radial expansion of the corona would be to stretch out the magnetic lines of force in the radial direction, giving a magnetic field which declines outward as

$$B_r(r) = B_0\left(\frac{a}{r}\right)^2$$

The sense of the radial field in any direction from the sun would be determined by the sense of the field B_0 at the base of the corona in that direction. The rotation of the sun, with a period of about 25 days, has little or no effect on the radial motion of the coronal gas, but it introduces a pronounced spiral in the magnetic field configuration. In the equatorial plane of the sun there results the azimuthal component

$$B_\varphi(r) \cong B_0 \frac{a\Omega}{v}\frac{a}{r}$$

in addition to the radial component, where v is the solar wind velocity and

Ω is the angular velocity of the sun. The lines of force form an Archimedes spiral, $r \cong (v/\Omega)(\varphi - \varphi_0)$. The observed quiet-day solar wind velocities of 400–600 km/sec imply that the lines of force at the orbit of earth are inclined about 45° to the radial direction. A field of 1 gauss at the sun leads to about 3×10^{-5} gauss at the orbit of earth, a value which seems to be in agreement with the observations of Mariner II [21]. Except in the low corona the magnetic energy density appears to be small compared to the kinetic energy of the gas, so that the reaction of the magnetic field on the coronal gas can be neglected (not that it is negligible under every circumstance) in a first rough approximation when considering the gross radial expansion of the solar corona. In particular, observations of coronal streamers indicate that the field tends to channel the solar wind, or corpuscular radiation, toward the solar equatorial plane at times of sunspot minimum. It is also evident that the magnetic field plays a role in isolating and preserving the observed filamentary structure of the corona for some distance into space.

When the observed variations of coronal temperature with solar latitude and longitude are considered, leading to a solar wind velocity v at large distance from the sun which varies considerably around the sun, it is evident that in the actual case the idealized Archimedes spirals discussed here must become considerably distorted and entangled.

6. Enhanced Solar Corpuscular Radiation

Thus far the discussion has dealt with the quiet-day solar corpuscular radiation. When the sun is particularly active, with one or more large flares, the velocity of the corpuscular radiation may rise to 1000–2000 km/sec. The density may rise to perhaps $30/\text{cm}^3$ or more at the orbit of earth (see discussion in Parker [40]) for periods of a few hours. Calculations [38] would seem to suggest that this enhanced solar corpuscular radiation, like the quiet-day radiation, is accounted for in a straightforward manner by the hydrodynamic expansion of the enhanced corona, whose temperature is observed to rise to three or four times 10^6°K, and higher, at such times. The expansion velocity of a region of the solar corona at 4×10^6°K reaches about 1150 km/sec, and the density may be $10^2/\text{cm}^3$ at the orbit of earth which would seem to fill all the requirements for the enhanced corpuscular radiation. We cannot absolutely rule out the possibility of other dynamical mechanisms contributing to the enhanced radiation, of course, but we do not know at the present time what they might be.

A sudden increase at the sun in the rate of coronal expansion will lead to an overtaking of the slower solar wind or corpuscular radiation ahead by the more recent and faster wind behind. Consequently the enhanced solar corpuscular radiation from an enhanced coronal region tends to scoop up the quiet-day wind ahead like a snowplow and build up a blast wave with a shock transition at its head. The hydrodynamic behavior of the blast wave can be computed under certain idealized circumstances to show how its velocity and density vary with time and distance from the sun [38]. The cosmic-ray effects of the magnetic fields carried in the blast wave can be shown to resemble the observed Forbush-type decreases [38, 41], the principal effect being a general sweeping back of cosmic rays by the advancing front.

References

1. A Behr and H. Siedentopf, Untersuchungen über Zodiakallicht und Gegenschein nach lichtelektrischen Messungen auf dem Jungfraujoch, *Z. Astrophys.*, **32,** 19 (1953).
2. L. Biermann, Kometenschweift und solare Korpuskularstrahlung, *Z. Astrophys.*, **29,** 274 (1951).
3. L. Biermann, Uber den Schweif des Kometen Halley in Jahre 1910; *Z. Naturforsch.*, **7a,** 127 (1952).
4. L. Biermann, Solar corpuscular radiation and the interplanetary gas, *Observatory*, **77**(898), 109 (1957).
5. D. E. Billings, Distribution of matter with temperature in the emission corona, *Astrophys. J.*, **130**(3), 961 (1959).
6. D. E. Billings and C. G. Lilliequist, Coronal temperature gradient and the solar wind, *Astrophys. J.*, **137,** 16 (1963).
7. D. E. Blackwell, The zodiacal light and its interpretation, *Endeavour*, **19**(73), 4 (1960).
8. D. E. Blackwell, Interplanetary electron densities, *J. Geophys. Res.*, **65**(8), 2476 (1960).
9. D. E. Blackwell, The zodiacal light, *Sci. Amer.*, **203**(1), 54 (1960).
10. D. E. Blackwell and M. F. Ingham, Observations of the zodiacal light from a very high altitude station, *Mon. Not. Roy. Astron. Soc.*, **122,** 113 (1961).
11. A. Bonetti, H. S. Bridge, A. J. Lazarus, E. F. Lyon, B. Rossi, and F. Scherb, Explorer X plasma measurements, *Space Research III*, 540 (North-Holland Publishing Co., 1963).
12. A. Bonetti, H. S. Bridge, A, J. Lazarus, B. Rossi, and F. Scherb, Explorer 10 plasma measurements, *J. Geophys. Res.* **68**(13), 4017 (1963).
13. H. S. Bridge, C. Dilworth, A. J. Lazarus, E. F. Lyon, B. Rossi, and F. Scherb, Direct observations of the interplanetary medium, *J. Phys. Soc. Japan*, **17**, Suppl. A-II, 553 (1962).
14. L. J. Cahill, Jr., and P. G. Amazeen, Termination of the earth's magnetic field during the period September 11–14, 1961 [Abstract], *J. Geophys. Res.*, **67**(9), 3547 (1962).
15. S. Chapman, Notes on the solar corona and the terrestrial ionosphere, *Smithsonian Contrib. Astrophys.*, **2**(1), 1 (1957).
16. S. Chapman and V. C. A. Ferraro, A new theory on magnetic storms, *Terr. Mag. Atmos. Elec.*, **35,** 77, 171 (1931).
17. S. Chapman and V. C. A. Ferraro, A new theory on magnetic storms, *Terr. Mag. Atmos. Elec.*, **37,** 147, 421 (1932).
18. S. Chapman and V. C. A. Ferraro, A new theory on magnetic storms, *Terr. Mag. Atmos. Elec.*, **38,** 79 (1933).
19. S. Chapman and V. C. A. Ferraro, The theory of the first phase of a geomagnetic storm, *Terr. Mag. Atmos. Elec.*, **45,** 245 (1940).
20. F. H. Clauser (1960) (unpublished).

21. P. J. Coleman, Jr., L. Davis, Jr., E. J. Smith, and C. P. Sonett, The mission of Mariner II: Preliminary observations: Interplanetary magnetic fields, *Science* **138**(3545), 1099 (1962).
22. S. Dolginov and N. Pushkin, *Pravda*, 15 July 1959.
23. H. Elsasser, Die räumliche Verteilung der Zodiakallichtmaterie, *Z. Astrophys.*, **33,** 274 (1954).
24. S. E. Forbush, World-wide cosmic-ray variations, 1937–1952, *J. Geophys. Res.*, **59**(4), 525 (1954).
25. K. I. Gringauz, V. V. Bezrukikh, V. D. Ozerov, and R. E. Rybchinskii, A study of interplanetary ionized gas, energetic electrons and solar corpuscular radiation using the three-electrode charged particle traps on the second Soviet cosmic rocket, *Dok. Akad. Nauk SSSR*, **131,** 1301 1960 (Translation in: *Soviet Physics*, **5,** 361 1960).
26. J. P. Heppner, J. D. Stolarik, I. R. Shapiro, and J. C. Cain, Project Vanguard magnetic field instrumentation and measurements, *Space Research*, 982 (North-Holland Publishing Co., 1960).
27. R. Lüst, Aktivität von Kometenschweifen in Perioden geomagnetischer Ruhe, *Z. Astrophys.*, **51,** 163 (1961).
28. R. Lüst, F. Meyer, E. Trefftz, and L. Biermann, Remarks about the temperature of the solar corona, *The Solar Corona*, J. W. Evans (ed.) 21 (Academic Press, 1963).
29. O. N. Mitropolskaya, Some results of statistical treatment of geomagnetic disturbances of the declining branch of solar activity, *Astron. Zh.*, **36,** 224 (1959); Translation: *Soviet Astronomy—AJ*, **3,** 228 (1959).
30. P. Morrison, Solar origin of cosmic ray variations, *Phys. Rev.*, **101,** 1397 (1956).
31. E. R. Mustel, Statistical effects due to the connection between flocculi and geomagnetic disturbances, *Astron. Zh.*, **36,** 215 (1959): Translation: *Soviet Astronomy—AJ*, **3,** 221 (1959).
32. E. R. Mustel and O. N. Mitropolskaya, On certain statistical effects in the problem of the origin of geomagnetic disturbances, *Observatory*, **79,** 15 (1959).
33. M. Neugebauer and C. W. Snyder, The mission of Mariner II: preliminary observations: solar plasma experiment, *Science*, **138**(3545), 1095 (1962).
34. L. M. Noble and F. L. Scarf, Conductive heating of the solar corona. I, *Astrophys. J.*, **138,** 1169 (1963).
35. E. N. Parker, Dynamics of the interplanetary gas and magnetic fields, *Astrophys. J.*, **128**, 664 (1958).
36. E. N. Parker, Dynamical instability in an anisotropic ionized gas of low density, *Phys. Rev.*, **109,** 1874 (1958).
37. E. N. Parker, The hydrodynamic theory of solar corpuscular radiation and stellar winds, *Astrophys. J.*, **132**(3), 821 (1960).
38. E. N. Parker, Sudden expansion of the corona following a large solar flare and the attendant magnetic field and cosmic-ray effects, *Astrophys. J.*, **133**(3), 1014 (1961).
39. E. N. Parker, The stellar-wind regions, *Astrophys. J.*, **134**(1), 20 (1961).
40. E. N. Parker, Dynamics of the geomagnetic storm, *Space Sci. Revs.*, **1**(1), 62 (1962).
41. E. N. Parker, *Interplanetary Dynamical Processes* (Interscience, 1963).
42. E. N. Parker, Dynamical properties of stellar coronas and stellar winds, I Integration of the momentum equation, *Astrophys. J.*, **139** 72 (1964); II Integration of the heat flow equation, *Astrophys. J.*, **139,** 93 (1964).
43. A Schluter, Dynamic des Plasmas I Grundgleichungen, Plasma in gekreuzten Feldern, *Z. Naturforsch.*, **5a,** 72 (1950).
44. I. S. Shklovskii, V. I. Moroz, and V. G. Kurt, The nature of the earth's third radiation belt, *Astron. Zh.*, **37**(5), 931 1960 (Translation in: *Soviet Astron.-AJ*, **4**(5), 871 1961).
45. J. A. Simpson, The neutrons from the nucleonic component as an indicator of primary intensities, *Phys. Rev.*, **81,** 895 (1951); neutrons produced in the atmosphere by the cosmic radiation, *Phys. Rev.*, **83,** 1175 (1951).
46. J. A. Simpson, Cosmic-radiation intensity-time variations and their origin. III. The origin of the 27-day variations, *Phys. Rev.*, **94,** 426 (1954).

47. J. A. Simpson, Variations of solar origin in the primary cosmic radiation, *Astrophys. J. Suppl.*, **4**(44), 378 (1960).
48. C. P. Sonett, D. L. Judge, and J. M. Kelso, Evidence concerning instabilities of the distant geomagnetic field, Pioneer I, *J. Geophys. Res.*, **64**(8), 941 (1959).
49. C. Störmer, *The Polar Aurora* (Clarendon Press, 1955).
50. P. Stumpff, Zur Korrelation zwischen dem Auftreten von Kometenshweifen des Typ I und der solaren Korpuskularstrahlung, *Astron. Nachr.*, **286,** 87 (1956).
51. H. C. van de Hulst, The chromosphere and the corona, *The Sun*, G. P. Kuiper (ed.) 207 (The Solar System, **1,** University of Chicago Press, 1953).
52. K. Wurm, *Mitt. Sternw. Hamburg-Bergedorf*, **8**(51) (1943).

CHAPTER 5

HIGH-ENERGY SOLAR PARTICLE EVENTS

J. G. Roederer

High-energy solar particles are produced in association with great solar outbursts. We have a chain of processes by means of which these particles are picked out of the chromosphere's environment, injected into a certain acceleration mechanism, kept there for a sufficient time in order to gain high enough energy, and then ejected into the interplanetary space. Violent hydromagnetic phenomena are responsible for these steps. A second chain of processes governs the propagation of the particles away from the sun, their scattering, and their trapping in huge extensions of interplanetary space. Magnetic fields, carried by solar plasma clouds or compressed in hydrodynamic shocks, are responsible for these processes.

Those high-energy particles destined to meet our planet travel through the earth's magnetosphere following complicated trajectories; the "optical" image of their initial angular distribution in space will result in a certain distribution over the earth's surface, which condenses into well-defined "bright" spots (impact zones) for a completely collimated beam of particles. Finally, they may end their journey precipitating into denser layers of the atmosphere. If their energy is high enough, they may trigger the development of a cascade of nuclear particles, a tiny fraction of which might then finally be detected at the earth's surface.

The above processes may be outlined under three categories. First, solar flare environment: (*a*) injection, (*b*) confinement, (*c*) acceleration, (*d*) release. Second, interplanetary space: (*a*) propagation, (*b*) scattering, (*c*) trapping. Third, earth environment: (*a*) geomagnetic deflection, (*b*) nucleon cascade. These three areas of interest will be discussed one by one in inverse order. Section 1 will deal with the problem of how to connect the unknown solar particle flux, energy spectrum, and angular distribution in space to measurements made on the earth's surface; Section 2 with experimental information about properties of high energy particle fluxes in space; and Section 3 with the flare acceleration mechanism itself.

1. Detection of Particles at Earth

Effect of the Atmosphere

1.1 One of the main experimental problems in the investigation of high-energy solar particle fluxes is the determination of the energy, or rigidity, spectrum and angular distribution of the particles in space and also their dependence on time. [Rather than energy, cosmic-ray physicists prefer to use rigidity ($P = mvc/ze$) because it is the magnitude which determines the motion of a charged particle in a magnetic field.] However, until recently most of the information on high-energy particles of solar origin came from cosmic-ray detectors (mainly neutron monitors) located at the earth's surface, under the absorbing atmosphere and inside the geomagnetic field, both inevitably altering all original characteristics of the solar particle flux.

Cosmic-ray neutron monitors are sensitive to the secondary components of the nucleon cascade, generated in nuclear interactions by the primary radiation, when it penetrates the earth's atmosphere. Normally these detectors register the continuous flux of secondary particles generated by galactic radiation. When an additional flux of solar particles impinges on the top of the atmosphere, an additional nucleon cascade develops, giving an increase ΔC in the counting rate of the monitor. Figure 1 is a classical example for a big counting rate increase in connection with a solar particle flux emitted by a flare on 23 February 1956 [35]. This counting rate increase is thus the primary source of information available.

The characteristics of the nucleon cascade generated by a solar particle flux is quite different from that produced by the galactic radiation, because of the difference in their primary spectra. Indeed, the differential primary rigidity spectrum of galactic cosmic rays is approximately of the form $j(P)dP = KP^{-\gamma}dP$ with $\gamma \simeq 2.3$ (for the exact shape see McDonald and Webber [32]), whereas for the high-energy solar particle spectrum, which can also be approximated by a power law (Section 2.12), γ has a value of 6–7. Therefore, solar particle fluxes have steep, "soft" spectra, which will give rise only to a weak, quickly absorbed nucleon cascade. Very frequently the primary solar particle spectrum is so soft that the nucleon cascade cannot propagate down to the earth's surface, giving no detectable effect for neutron monitors; such soft solar particle fluxes are detectable only by balloon, rocket, or satelliteborne equipment, or indirectly as Polar Cap Absorption events in riometers. For a detectable increase at a sea level, high latitude neutron monitor, a minimum rigidity of 1 Gv (450 Mev) is required for primary protons.

1.2 The difference between nucleon cascades generated by galactic and solar particles, respectively, is of importance for the interpretation of neutron monitor data. Because neutron monitors are not all at the same altitude (the same atmospheric depth), their counting rates have to be normalized in order to furnish intercomparable values. This is usually done by taking into account the roughly exponential dependence of the normal counting rate on atmospheric depth (given by the mean atmospheric pressure p in gm/cm²): $C(p) = C_0 \exp(-p/L)$. L is the absorption length ($\simeq$140 gm/cm² for neutron monitors at middle latitudes [9]). This exponential expression enables one to normalize counting rates of different detectors

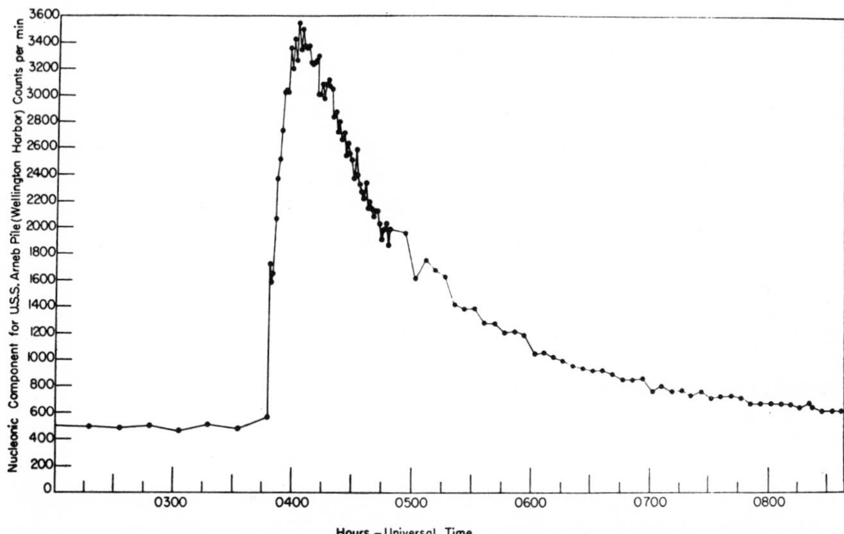

FIG. 1. Nucleonic component intensity vs. time (neutron monitor aboard *U.S.S. Arneb*, Wellington Harbor, New Zealand) at time of 23 February 1956 flare; one-minute intervals between 0348 and 0445 UT. From Meyer *et al.* [35].

to the same level (say, $p_0 = 1000$ gm/cm²). However, L depends on the primary spectrum, i.e., on the exponent γ [45]. In particular, a soft solar particle spectrum will lead to a smaller L-value (faster absorption). If one wants to compare solar particle increases registered at different stations, it is then necessary to make a correct normalization, using the proper L-value for the additional radiation. McCracken [29] has suggested a normalization method which takes this into account.

Once one has obtained the normalized counting rate increases for different monitors, one has to link these measured increases ΔC with the unknown increase $\delta j(P)$ of the primary spectrum. This relation is provided by an integral transformation, given by the so-called "coupling functions" [9] $W_\lambda(P)$, which relate the relative counting rate variation $\Delta C/C$, registered by a neutron monitor located at a geomagnetic rigidity cutoff P_λ [44], with the relative variation $\delta j(P)/j(P)$ of the primary spectrum:

$$\frac{\Delta C}{C} = \int_{P_\lambda}^{\infty} \frac{\delta j(P)}{j(P)} W_\lambda(P)\, dP \tag{1}$$

These coupling functions can be obtained empirically in the rigidity range 1–15 Gv [2, 60].

If we have an additional high-energy solar flux which at a certain instant of time has a differential rigidity spectrum $\delta j(P) = \delta K P^{-\gamma_S}$, the relative variation $\delta j(P)/j(P)$ of the primary spectrum would be

$$\frac{\delta j(P)}{j(P)} = \frac{\delta K P^{-\gamma_S}}{K P^{-2.3}} = \frac{\delta K}{K} P^{-(\gamma_S - 2.3)} \sim P^{-\gamma}$$

Taking the $\Delta C/C$ values (1) from many stations with different geomagnetic cutoff values, it is possible to determine the γ value through a best fit procedure, provided no changes in the geomagnetic cutoff values occurred at that time. The exponent of the solar particle spectrum $\delta j(P)$ would then be $\gamma_S = \gamma + 2.3$. [There is some confusion in the literature about the exponent of a solar particle spectrum, because sometimes it is not stated clearly enough, whether one has to deal with γ_S (the exponent of the actual spectrum), or with γ (the exponent of the relative variation spectrum).]

Effect of the Earth's Magnetic Field

1.3 The procedure described to obtain the exponent of a solar particle spectrum is applicable only if the solar flux is strictly isotropic in the outer space. If this is not the case, two detectors with the same geomagnetic cutoff rigidity need not show the same relative counting rate increase because they may be sampling solar particles arriving from different directions in space.

Thus we must consider the effect of the geomagnetic field on the motion of the solar particles. In the days of IGY/IGC, Firor's method [13] of "impact zones" was widely used to determine where particles from a fixed, known source will impinge. Using the centered dipole approximation, Firor determined the relation between the latitude of impact on earth, the longitudinal drift, and the angle between the direction of the particle at infinity and the equatorial place. The main result of these calculations is that for a given source of particles, with a given angular extension and for a given energy range, well-defined "impact zones" are found, corresponding to groups of particles which cross the equatorial plane 0, 1, 2, . . . times.

1.4 Firor's method (with a better approximation of the geomagnetic field) can be used straightforwardly if the position of the source of particles is known a priori. Several years ago it somehow seemed obvious that solar particles should come along the earth-sun line: however, in connection with the first great solar particle increases after IGY/IGC, it became clear that this was not the case (see, e.g., [28, 51]). Hence, the problem appeared in the inverse: to determine the source distribution outside the geomagnetic field, given the known intensity increase distribution at the earth's surface.

Several authors introduced the concept of "asymptotic direction of arrival" of a particle (see, e.g., [29]). It represents the direction at infinity of a (positively charged) particle with given rigidity, which impinges in a given direction on a given point of the earth's surface. McCracken [29] has systematically computed the asymptotic directions of arrival of primary particles for many operating cosmic-ray monitors over a wide rigidity interval and for several local zenith angles relevant to the cosmic-ray detectors. The Finch and Leaton sixth degree approximation of the geomagnetic field was used [12].

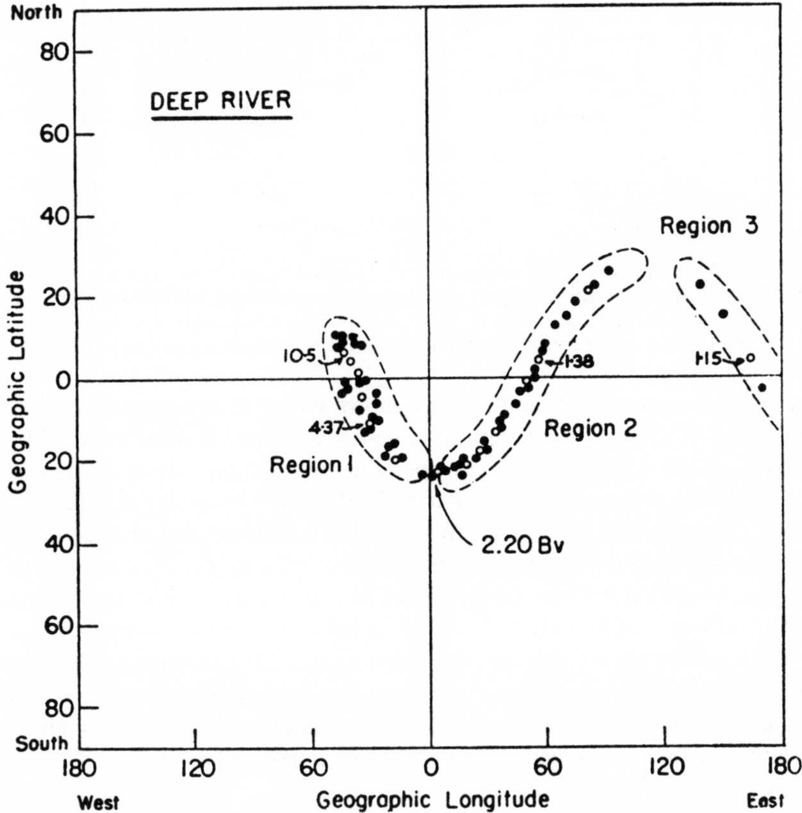

FIG. 2. Asymptotic directions of approach for particles arriving at Deep River, Canada, from the zenith (open circles) and at 32° to the zenith from the geomagnetic north south, east, and west (solid circles). The rigidities from right to left are: 1.15, 1.27, 1.38, 1.45, 1.60, 1.75, 1.88, 2.20, 3.15, 4.37, 5.74, 6.50, 7.73, and 10.5 Bv. From McCracken [29].

Looking at the results (Fig. 2), and considering how these asymptotic directions are lumped together, McCracken introduced the concept of "asymptotic cone of acceptance," which represents the solid angle in the celestial sphere into which a given neutron monitor is "looking," i.e., from which particles have to come in order to contribute significantly to the detector's counting rate. Averaging over a typical solar particle spectrum, and taking into account the monitor's sensitivity to different primary energies, McCracken computed the "mean asymptotic directions of viewing," i.e., the mean direction from which a given monitor samples a

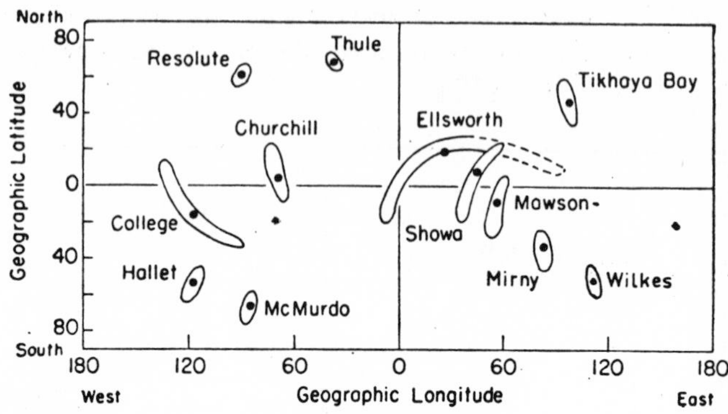

FIG. 3. Asymptotic cones of acceptance of 11 neutron monitors. The lines define the limits within which lie the asymptotic directions corresponding to rigidities between 1.0 and 5.74 Bv, zenith arrival angles of ±32°. Solid circle is the mean direction of viewing of the detector for a flare-type rigidity spectrum. From McCracken [29].

typical solar particle flux. Figure 3 shows cones of acceptance and mean directions of viewing for several cosmic-ray stations. With the use of these "maps" in the celestial sphere, it is possible in principle to trace iso-intensity contours of a given solar particle flux, leading to its angular distribution in space (Section 2.5). Recently, Webber [61] recalculated the asymptotic directions and mean directions of viewing for different types of solar particle spectra, following a different approach. In this paper, consideration is given to the influence of an external field like such produced by a ring current.

The introduction of this new representation, which one could call "cosmic ray optics in the geomagnetic field," was as important for a better understanding of space phenomena as the introduction of the two-dimensional B-L description of geomagnetically trapped particles [33].

2. The Particles in Interplanetary Space

General Features

2.1 One of the most striking characteristics of such particle ejections is that only very few big solar outbursts were actually followed by high-energy particle intensity increases at the earth. During the whole IGY, no high-energy solar particles were present in space, in spite of the occurrence of many great solar flares. Figure 4 shows the occasions when intensity increases were registered with neutron monitors: increases were detected only during the decreasing and increasing phases of the solar cycle.

Furthermore, an inspection of the behavior of the galactic cosmic-ray intensity preceding high-energy solar particle increases reveals that they occurred during the recovery phase of a Forbush decrease, i.e., during a general depression of the galactic cosmic-ray flux. [These considerations do not hold at all for low energy ($\lesssim$500 Mev) solar particles, such as those detected at, or above, the top of the atmosphere].

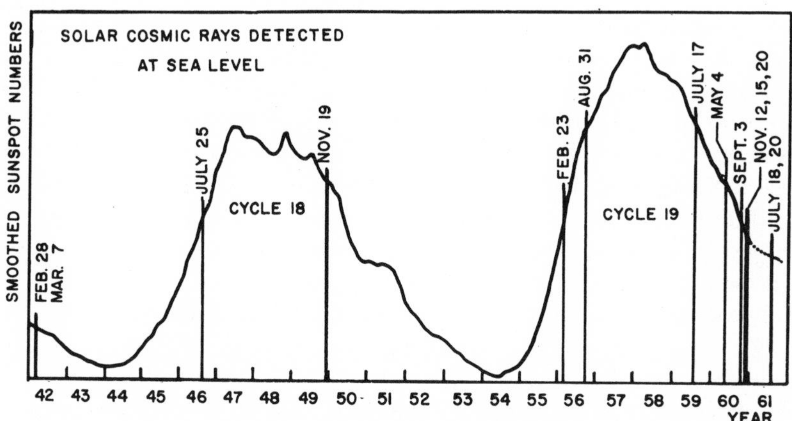

FIG. 4. Sunspot cycles 18 and 19 showing the dates of reported occurrences of high-energy particles from the sun. From Carmichael [7].

2.2 It is likely that all solar flares accompanied by radio noise outbursts over a wide band of frequencies (up to 10,000 Mc/sec) are evidence for particle acceleration at the sun (see e.g., [55]). However, apparently only a few of them were followed by high-energy particle increases at earth. This might be due to both a rate of high-energy particle production varying throughout solar cycle [56] and a strong influence of magnetic conditions dominant in space on particle guidance. The fact that solar particle increases are detected preferably shortly after the start of a Forbush decrease seems to indicate that propagation conditions are best behind a plasma cloud or a magnetic front responsible for the Forbush decrease mechanism (see, e.g., [19, 42, 49]).

2.3 Several attempts were made to determine whether at least very small neutron monitor increases tend to occur after major solar flares, which would not show up individually but would in a statistical analysis [1, 13, 15, 25, 57, 63]. In these papers, counting rates of several monitors were analyzed during a period of several hours, centered around the start of several previously selected solar flares. In some of the papers, data were corrected for other time variations which might otherwise mask any genuine effect. Considerations were given as to whether the detector was inside or outside the impact zones (corresponding to a source centered at the sun). No really convincing answer to the original question could be given. In any case, one can safely put an upper limit of less than 1 per cent to any eventual effect. This is very small compared to the intensity increases indicated in Figure 4, and therefore confirms the statements advanced in the previous paragraph.

Morphology of Solar Particle Increases

2.4 The morphology of a high-energy solar particle increase, as it is usually detected at earth (Fig. 1), has two characteristic features: a relatively short rising phase and a long-lasting intensity decay. The rising phase usually starts 10–30 minutes after the beginning of the optical flare. The transit, rise, and decay times vary from case to case. During the initial phase of rising intensity, detectors at different longitudes usually behave very differently (Fig. 5), indicating a marked anisotropy of the arriving radiation. For most of the cases, this anisotropic behavior vanishes during the decaying phase.

The existence of a finite rise time and a much longer decay time suggests the action of a scattering and a trapping mechanism in interplanetary space. Further, a rather long transit time indicates either the action of a "hold-back" mechanism at the sun or the existence of a rather tortuous propagation path from sun to earth, or both.

2.5 In considering the propagation of high-energy particles from sun to earth, we first examine the anisotropy during the rising phase of intensity, which was analyzed beautifully by McCracken [30]. Using the method of asymptotic cones of acceptance and mean directions of viewing (Section 1.4), McCracken analyzed the great solar flare increases of 4 May, 12 November, and 15 November 1960, concluding: (*a*) During the initial, rising phase of the increases of 4 May, 15 November, and the first stage of 12 November, particles were arriving from a direction 40–55° west of the sun-earth line, near the plane of the ecliptic (Fig. 6). (*b*) Particles did not arrive completely collimated, but had a rather wide angular distribution around the mean direction (Fig. 7*a* and *b*).

McCracken further found a striking correlation between the order of magnitude of the intensity rise time, the degree of anisotropy (or the existence of impact zones), and the position of the originating solar flare on the solar disc (Table 1) [31]. In summary, one can say: (*c*) Solar flares near the west limb of the sun tend to give rather strong collimated beams of fast rising intensity, whereas central or east-limb flares give poorly collimated, or even isotropic, slowly building up fluxes. To this we may add

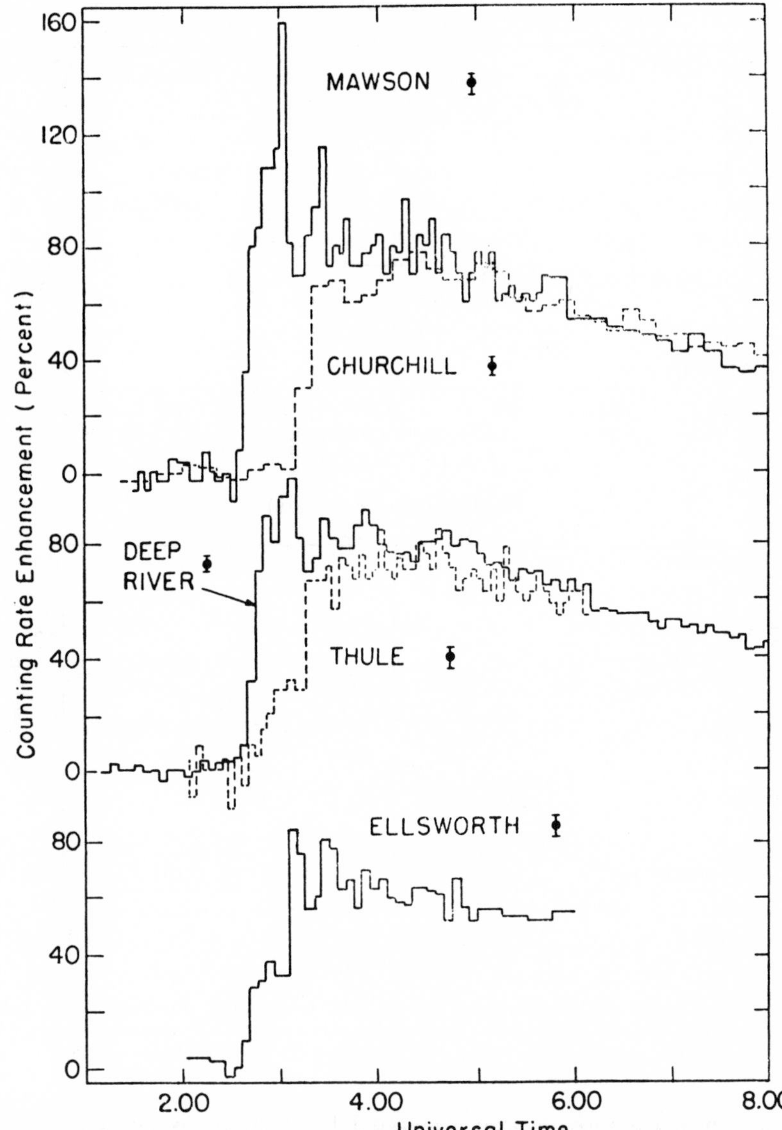

FIG. 5. Neutron intensity enhancements observed during flare effect of 15 November 1960. Enhancements are expressed relative to the intensities for the period 22 to 02 UT and have been corrected to the 1000 gm/cm² pressure level by the 2-attenuation-length correction method. From McCracken [30].

(already mentioned) that (*d*) high-energy solar flare particles were detected only during the recovery phase of a Forbush decrease.

2.6 Evidence (*a*) and (*d*) are a strong indication for a magnetic configu-

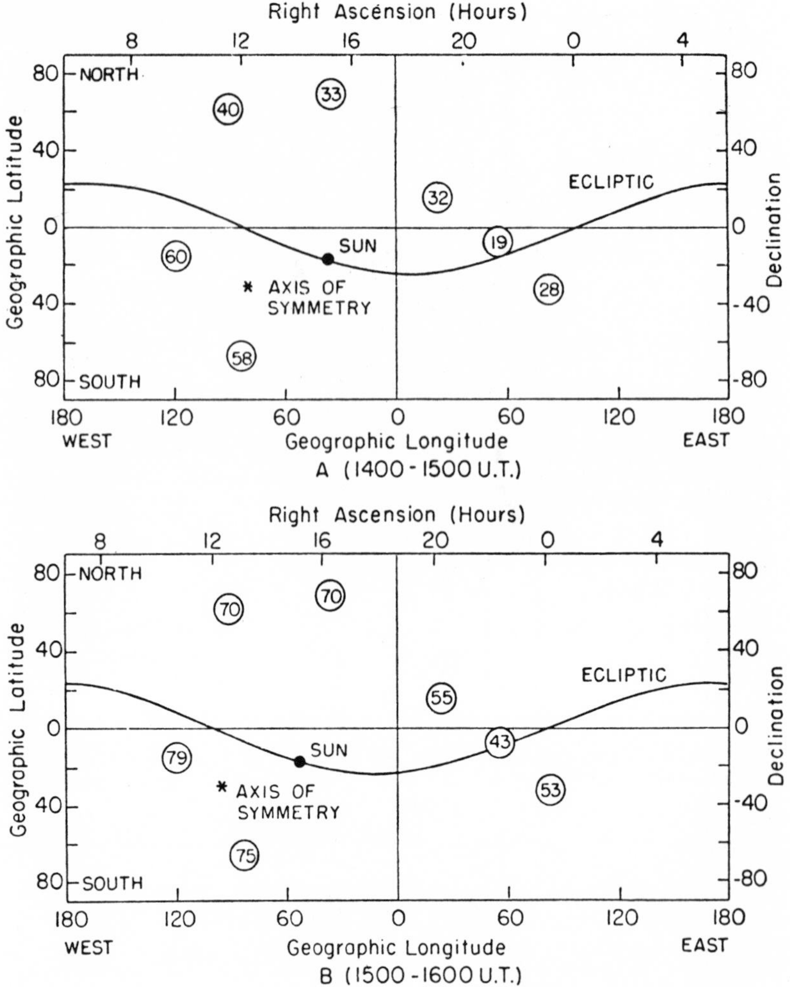

FIG. 6. A: Map of dependence of flux of solar origin upon direction during period 1400 to 1500 UT on 12 November. The direction about which the fluxes were symmetrical is shown. B: As above for the period 1500 to 1600 UT. From McCracken [30].

ration in space such as that suggested by Gold to be effective after a Forbush decrease [17–19]. According to Gold, a Forbush decrease is caused by the sweeping effect on galactic cosmic rays, of a magnetized plasma cloud ejected by the sun, which drags out radially lines of force of the original sunspot field, remaining connected with the sun for several days. These lines of force should be bent into a spiral form by the combined effect of solar rotation and steady solar wind outflow (the "garden hose effect"), thus serving as the guiding field for charged particles originating at the sun (Fig. 8). The general direction of arrival (40–55°W of the sun-earth

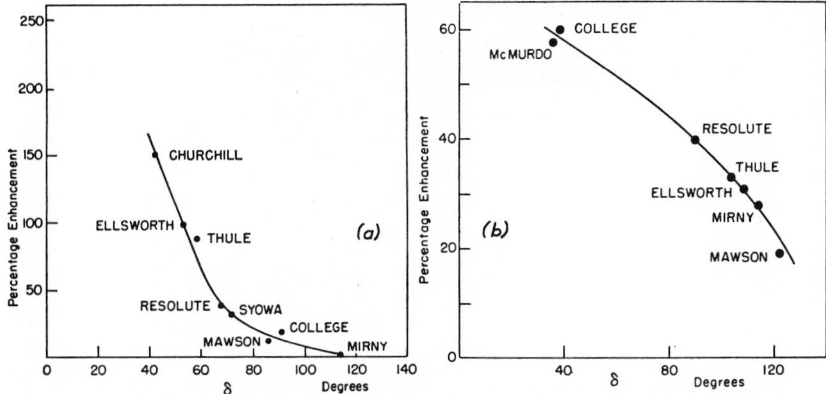

FIG. 7. (*a*) Dependence of counting-rate enhancement upon δ (angle in space between the particle's asymptotic direction and the axis of symmetry (Fig. 6)) for the period period 1045 to 1100 UT on 4 May 1960. (*b*) As above, 1400 to 1500 UT, 12 November 1960. From McCracken [30].

line) is in agreement with the direction predicted for the field lines at one astronomical unit, taking a solar wind velocity of about 500 km/sec.

McCracken considers Parker's model of a hydrodynamical blast wave [41] as equally able to provide particle guidance as observed. However, Parker's model (which for all times requires a steady solar wind with a radial, twisted field) should provide favorable conditions for particle guidance at any time, even prior to Forbush decreases. Furthermore, after

TABLE 1

Event	Time Scale	Position on Solar Disc	Impact Zones
May 4, 1960	1	90°W	Very marked*
Feb. 23, 1956	4	80°W	Marked*
Nov. 15, 1960	6	45°W	Very marked*
Nov. 19, 1949	6	70°W	Very marked*
Mar. 7, 1942	7	90°W	Marked
Feb. 28, 1942	13	4°E	Poorly defined
July 25, 1946	17	15°E	Not noticeable
Nov. 12, 1960	20	10°W	Poorly defined*
July 17, 1959	36	30°W	None*
Sept. 3, 1960	50	90°E	None
Aug. 31, 1956	..	15°E	...
Nov. 20, 1960	..	90°W	...
July 18, 1961	..	60°W	...
July 20, 1961	..	90°W	...

* Event for which a large number of observations are available and on which the greatest reliance can be placed. From McCracken [31].

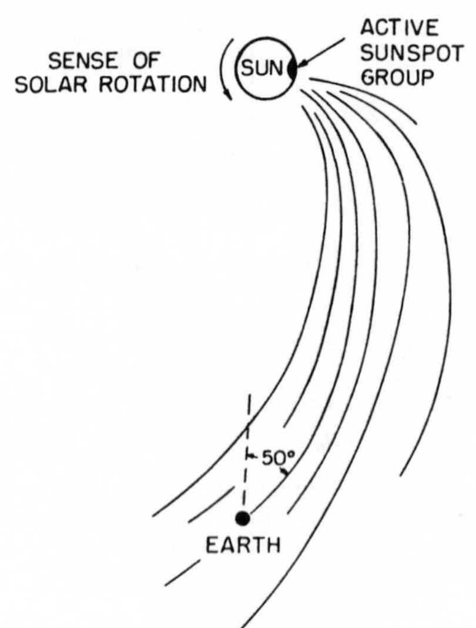

FIG. 8. Sketch of the working hypothesis for the magnetic field in the sun-earth region at a time when a large sunspot group is on the far western part of the solar disc. The projections of the lines of force into the ecliptic plane are shown. The lines of force are essentially parallel to this plane. From McCracken [31].

a Forbush decrease (i.e., behind a blast wave), the field configuration computed by Parker does not meet too well the requirement of lines of force twisted 40–55° at the earth's orbit.

2.7 Evidence (*c*)—correlation of rise time with heliographic position of the originating flare—is explained by the fact that field lines in space which pass through the earth environment are likely to be connected with the western side of the solar disc (see Fig. 8). Hence, if a flare near the western limb ejects high-energy particles, these will readily encounter the proper field lines to be guided to the earth. If, instead, a flare ejects particles near the east limb, only those particles will be guided to the earth which succeed in diffusing in the lower corona towards the proper (western) field lines. Taking into account the action of this diffusion mechanism, we then expect the rise times to be the longer, the farther away from the guiding field lines (the more towards the east) is the particle source. A beautiful example in favor of the existence of a magnetic configuration with spiral field lines is given by the solar flare increase of 20 November 1960 [7]. The flare occurred 23° behind the western limb of the sun; yet it was able to transfer high-energy particles to the earth. This evidently was provided by lines of force connected with the west limb, to which the flare particles were able to diffuse. All these results mentioned were found to hold statistically also for fluxes of very low energy solar protons, responsible for PCA events [38].

Taking into account the path of a particle from sun to earth along the curved lines of force, Carmichael [7] computed transit times for high-energy particles. The values are still 10–20 minutes less than measured transit times; this is an indication of the action of a "holding" mechanism at the sun, which suddenly releases particles after a time which Carmichael calls the "transit time anomaly."

2.8 To explain the experimental result (*b*), in particular for those cases (4 May 1960) in which the flare was very favorably situated with respect to the guiding field lines, a scattering mechanism acting well out in space has to be introduced. Otherwise, particles would come completely collimated in the field's direction, due to field line divergence, which would reduce particle pitch angles to zero (taking the adiabatic invariant $\sin^2 \alpha/B = \text{const}$, if $B \to 0$ then pitch angle $\alpha \to 0$). The only imaginable scattering mechanism, effective in interplanetary space, must be provided

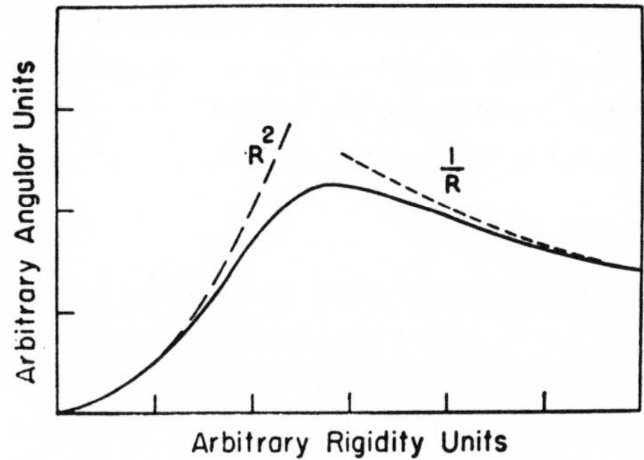

Fig. 9. Qualitative scattering angle-rigidity dependence. From McCracken [31].

by magnetic field irregularities. McCracken [31] discussed some qualitative features of such a mechanism, comparing the size of irregularities with the gyroradius of a charged particle. For low-energy particles, with gyroradii small compared to the radii of curvature of the field lines in the irregularities, the adiabatic invariants governing particle motions will hold all the time. The particles will thus "filter through" the irregularities following the field lines, without being scattered in pitch angle. Only their total path (and transit time) will be increased.

On the other hand, for a particle with a gyroradius comparable to the field line's radii of curvature, the adiabatic invariants will break down, and scattering will be most effective. Finally, for particles with a gyroradius large compared to the mean size of irregularities, scattering will be of decreasing importance with increasing energy. Figure 9 shows McCracken's sketch of the scattering angle-rigidity dependence. Although only a qualitative relation, it is of greatest importance for the better understanding of the process of particle guidance from sun to earth. Analyzing the increase of 4

May 1960, McCracken reached some qualitative conclusions about the size and the number of scattering regions along the lines of force.

This kind of scattering mechanism explains at once why, after a solar flare, detection of low-energy particles at high altitudes (with balloons, rockets, or satellites) or from ground with riometers is much more likely (see for instance [3, 64]). These particles could glide freely through magnetic irregularities in space even when high-energy particles would be scattered into all directions. Another possible explanation, mainly applicable to intense PCA proton fluxes, would be given by the effect of a very dense particle "cloud" with energy density high enough to open its way through field irregularities, by pushing away the magnetic lines of force [59].

On the other hand, the above mechanism leads to the prediction that the rigidity spectrum of solar high-energy particles, as measured in the earth's vicinity, need not be identical with the original spectrum as produced at the sun. Moreover, it is likely that the guiding and scattering mechanisms may introduce significant changes in the spectra of solar particles, in a similar way as the magnetic configuration in interplanetary space is continuously modulating the galactic cosmic-ray energy spectrum at its lower end, roughly in phase with solar activity.

The Trapping Mechanism

2.9 As to the mechanism of particle trapping in space, responsible for the long-lasting, isotropic, decaying phase of particle intensity: First of all the question arises as to whether a separate, independent trapping mechanism (e.g., magnetic mirroring) is needed, or whether it is sufficient to suppose a particle "hold back" in a diffusive medium (the same as the one causing scattering of the flux on its way to the earth). Gold's model, for instance, provides a natural trapping mechanism, completely independent of that of scattering, in the form of a "magnetic bottle" built up by the stretched-out field lines. Parker's model equally well provides an independent trapping mechanism in the form of a "magnetic wall" in the blast wave. On the other hand, one might suppose the existence of a region in space, extending from the lower corona out to some A.U., in which solar particles propagate diffusively (increasing phase) and leak out after reaching the outer boundary (decreasing phase). In this picture, there would be essentially only one mechanism responsible for both scattering and decay.

2.10 As to the experimental evidence about these possibilities: First of all, McCracken and Palmeira [28] found an almost constant relationship between rise and decay times of solar particle increases. This apparently suggests that the scattering mechanism is coupled, at least to a certain extent, with the trapping mechanism. However, a long rise time does not necessarily mean an enhanced scattering while particles are guided along the proper lines of force. In view of the description in Section 2.7, it rather means that a central or an east limb flare has ejected particles into a certain region of space (probably extending into space to the evening side of the earth), and that particles leaking out of this region and diffusing towards the proper western lines of force are the ones responsible for the slow increase measured at earth. For these central or eastern flare cases, complex diffusion processes which first take particles out of the initial trapping volume and then transfer them transversely to lines of force, very likely govern both the slow increase and the long-lasting decay of intensity at earth.

The solar particle increase of 12 November 1960 gave excellent evidence

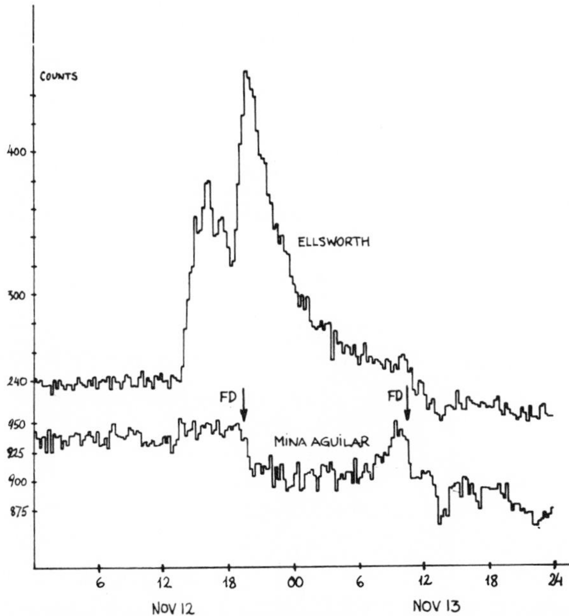

FIG. 10. Cosmic-ray intensity at Ellsworth (1-Gv cutoff) and Mina Aguilar (12-Gv cutoff) for 12 and 13 November 1960. From Roederer *et al.* [48].

for the action of a remarkably efficient, well-localized, trapping mechanism [48, 54]. Figure 10 shows the behavior of neutron monitor intensity at Ellsworth (sensitive to solar particles) in comparison with the intensity at Mina Aguilar (sensitive to high-energy galactic radiation only). At about 1930 UT, a Forbush decrease detected at Mina Aguilar and by all other low-latitude monitors, indicates the arrival of a magnetic front which sweeps away part of the galactic radiation. At almost the same time, the solar particle flux increases sharply, suddenly becoming isotropic. We take this as an indication that the detectors are now sampling the isotropic flux caught behind the sharp trapping boundary. Prior to the arrival of this boundary, the detectors were sampling those solar particles which managed to leak through the boundary and were brought to the proper lines of force (see preceding paragraph). The trapping mechanism is therefore very likely identical with that responsible for the Forbush decrease.

The next day (13 November) at 1021 UT, a second Forbush decrease occurred, linked to the arrival of the magnetized cloud expelled by the same solar flare which produced the high-energy particle flux. Roederer *et al.* [47] found that, in coincidence with this event, the high-energy solar particles suddenly disappeared completely. A similar effect was found for

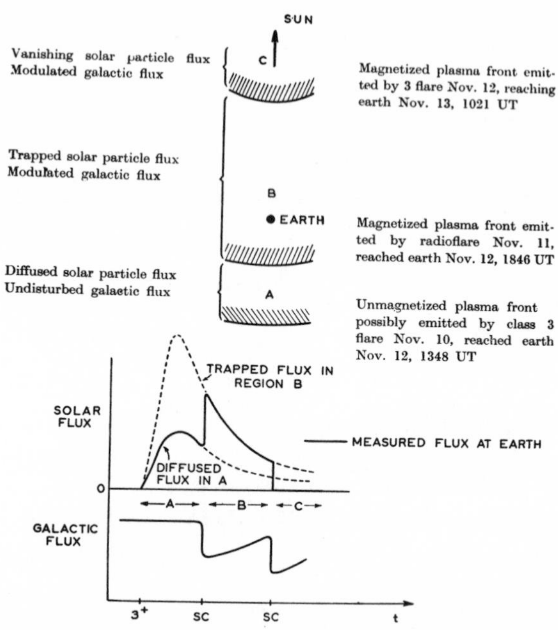

FIG. 11. Modulating fields in interplanetary space on 12 November, several hours after the flare, and intensity-time dependence for solar and galactic cosmic rays. From Roederer *et al.* [47].

the solar particle flux of 16–17 July 1959, which was swept away in coincidence with the Forbush decrease on 18 July [46]. We are here again in the presence of an extremely efficient, well-localized trapping mechanism, acting this time in the inverse way, i.e., keeping solar particles out of a certain region of space. A comprehensive picture on the trapping events of 12 November 1960 is given in Figure 11.

Such sharp variations in the high-energy solar particle flux could hardly be explained by a purely diffusive model—not even by one with a sharp boundary. They necessarily imply the existence of an independently acting, sharply localized trapping mechanism, associated either with a magnetic-bottle-type trapping, or with particle reflection at a magnetic front.

2.11 Trapping mechanism efficiency should be rigidity-dependent, just as is scattering efficiency. A proof of this might be given by the fact that the sweeping-out effect of the second magnetic front arriving 13 November 1960 was not seen in the low-energy particle flux detected by means of rockets [40]. In fact, this could be explained by supposing that low-energy particles did leak through the front into the second bottle. On the other hand, several PCA events were observed to break down in coincidence with the sudden commencement of a geomagnetic storm (arrival of solar plasma). These are examples in which the magnetic front was effective in sweeping out low-energy particles [39]. Direct evidence for particle trapping in this low energy region was provided by Injun I measurements [43]. Finally, Vogt's balloon measurements [58] revealed the existence of a persistent flux of solar protons in the range of 80–350 Mev, trapped for unusually long times.

There is evidence for the fact that the trapping efficiency of a magnetic front depends on the previous configuration of space into which it propagates. This trapping efficiency probably depends on how the two regions on both sides of the front are interconnected magnetically [49]. It follows, again, that the rigidity spectrum of a trapped particle flux (i.e., during the isotropic, decaying phase of a solar particle event) very likely differs from the original particle spectrum.

The time behavior during decay (which sometimes appears to be exponential, sometimes to follow a power law) should depend on both particle leakage and spatial expansion of the trapping region.

Energy Spectrum and Composition.

2.12 Although this review is limited to high-energy solar particles, some features of the low-energy tail of the solar particle spectrum are pertinent. In general, low-energy solar particles do not necessarily have to have the same characteristics as the high-energy flux, mainly because of different responses to the scattering and trapping mechanisms in space (Sections 2.8 and 2.11). However, they are relevant here for two main reasons: first, the most accurate solar particle spectrum and composition measurements were made in the range of some 70 to 1000 Mev; second, low-energy and high-energy solar particles belong, after all, to the same family of flare particles.

Let us first consider the energy or rigidity spectra of solar particles. In the high-energy range, estimates were possible during the decaying, isotropic stage of intensity, essentially following the method outlined in Section 1.2. Power law spectra were fitted reasonably well, leading to exponents γ of the order of 6–7 [26, 30, 48]. These figures are in agreement with indirect estimates obtained by radioisotope analysis of recovered satellite parts [24]. They also agree fairly well with spectra obtained by balloon measurements [8, 64]. A common feature of energy spectra of solar particle fluxes is their steepening with increasing time. This is a general indication for high-energy particles to escape more easily from the trapping region.

2.13 The most exhaustive analysis of solar particle energy spectra was very recently made by Freier and Webber [14]. For the first time, the three main energy domains covered by solar particle flux measurements were connected: between 1 and 15 Mev (riometer–PCA), from 70 to 500 Mev (balloons, rockets, and satellites), and above 500 Mev (neutron and meson monitors). Energy spectra estimated by means of the first and the third techniques are always strongly influenced by cutoff rigidity variations

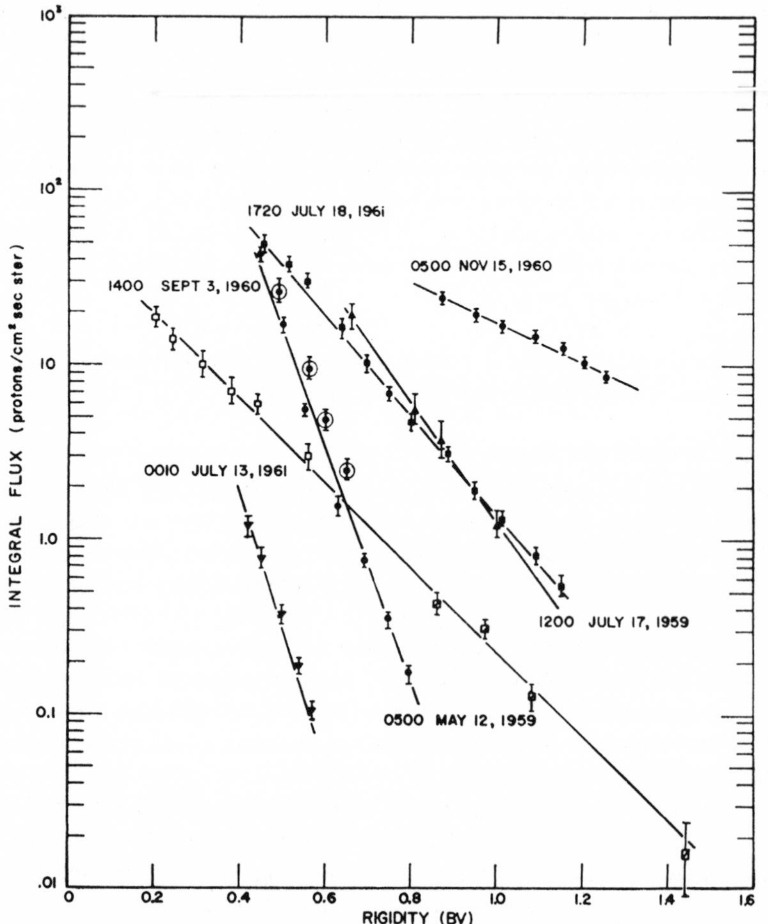

FIG. 12. Integral proton spectrums are shown as exponentials in rigidity at selected times for six different solar flares. Data points taken from counter ascents are shown as solid symbols; those taken with emulsions, as open symbols. From Freier and Webber [14].

during geomagnetic disturbances. The only direct energy measurements are obtained by the second technique. Freier and Webber carefully applied the powerful range-energy method to the results obtained from balloon ascent or descent measurements in the upper atmosphere. Figure 12 shows their results for several solar particle events, leading quite convincingly to exponential forms, rather than to power law spectra. These spectra seem to fit in absolute value well enough into the higher (neutron monitor) and lower (PCA) energy regions, provided proper corrections are introduced for the two latter regions in order to take into account shifts in the cutoff rigidities. Freier and Webber advance the hypothesis that solar particle rigidity spectra might be connected with the particle distribution in the plasma expelled simultaneously by the same flare. Taking into account their experimental results, they picture the high or middle energy particle

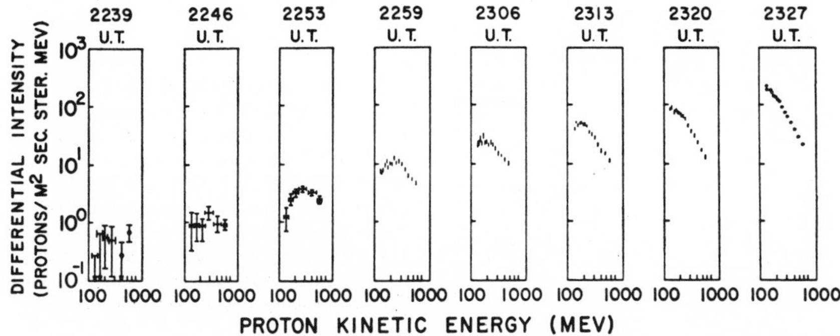

FIG. 13. Rise of the 28 September solar proton event; differential energy spectrums of the particle increases over galactic background are shown. These "snapshots" of the solar proton spectrum were recorded about 7 minutes apart and show that the spectral shape changed rapidly early in the event. From Bryant *et al.* [6].

spectrum as an upper tail of one and the same over-all spectrum of particles which includes the plasma at its lower end. However, the action of a strongly rigidity-dependent propagation mechanism for solar particles, necessarily imposes severe limitations to the significance of this hypothesis.

2.14 More direct information on intermediate energy spectra was provided by Explorer XII [6]. Figure 13 shows the building up of the proton energy spectrum during the initial phase of the 28 September 1961 solar outburst. The strong time dependence of the spectral form suggests a strong energy dependence of guiding and scattering mechanisms. Assuming a simple diffusion model, these authors were able to describe remarkably well the intensity-time dependence for different energy intervals during the whole isotropic phase (Fig. 14), securing reasonable values for the mean free path in accordance with estimates by McCracken (Section 2.8). Similar considerations of simple diffusion models were recently applied to the low-energy solar particle intensity-time dependence by Hofmann and Winckler

[21] and by Winckler and Bhavsar [65]. In the high-energy range, diffusion theory was applied by several authors [16, 27, 35].

However, whenever one deals with diffusion processes, one has to keep in mind that diffusion equations greatly smear out details of the physical processes involved, often leading to quite similar gross behavior for quite different operating conditions.

Finally, Bryant *et al.* [6] discovered a remarkable additional increase in the low-energy solar particle flux, in connection with the arrival of storm plasma at the satellite (Fig. 15). This effect (called by the authors "energetic storm particles event") is again evidence for how deeply the low-energy

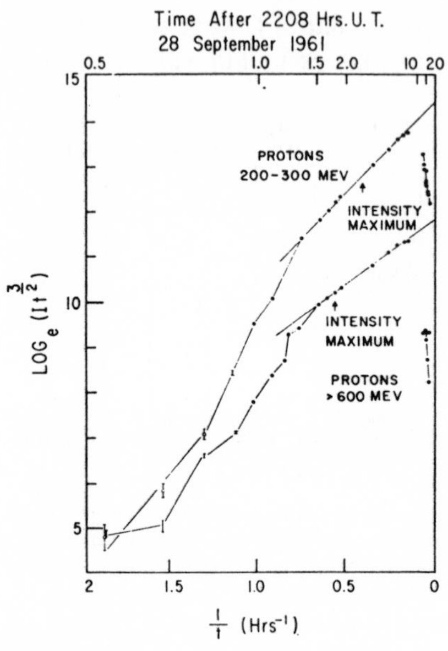

FIG. 14. Comparison of history of proton intensity with that predicted by diffusion theory. Ln (intensity $\times\ t^{3/2}$) is plotted against $1/t$ for protons with energy between 200 and 300 Mev and for protons >600 Mev. From 1.4 hours after the X-ray burst, when isotropy is established, to at least 7 hours after the X-ray burst, both components show close agreement with diffusion theory. From Bryant *et al.* [6].

particle flux can be modulated in energy by interplanetary magnetic perturbations.

2.15 As to the composition of solar particle fluxes: Fichtel and Guss [11] measured, with rocketborne nuclear emulsions, the relative abundances of light nuclei in the (medium energy) solar particle fluxes of 3 September, 12 November, and 15 November 1960: the CNO, B Be, and hydrogen nuclei occur in similar abundance as established by spectroscopic evidence of the sun's atmosphere. Different nuclei seem to have common rigidity spectra, although the shape varies from event to event. More data on the primary composition of the 15 November 1960 flare particles were recently published [4, 14, 66]. Freier and Webber establish that rigidity spectra of of solar protons and alpha-particles coincide in (exponential) shape at any time, although the spectral parameters change as a function of time,

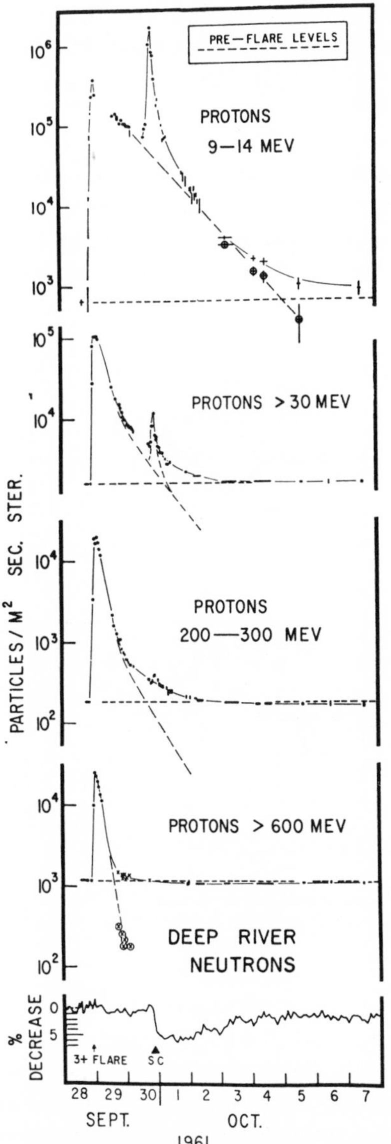

FIG. 15. Representative proton intensities between 28 September and 7 October 1961; decay of the solar proton event and arrival of the energetic storm particles late on 30 September are shown. The Deep River neutron monitor record is shown for comparison. From Bryant *et al.* [6].

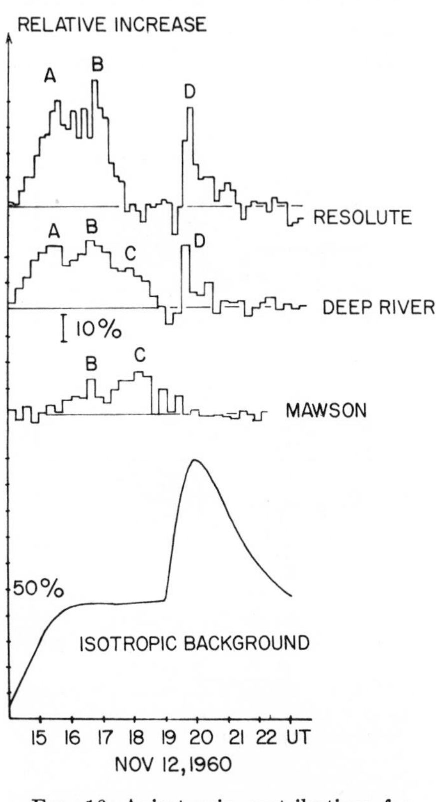

FIG. 16. Anisotropic contributions for 12 November 1960 at three different stations. From Roederer *et al.* [50].

and from flare to flare. The presence of high-energy solar electrons was detected in only one case (22 July 1961) [34]. The other events like the 3 September and 12 November 1960 flares failed to show measurable fluxes of electrons [10, 37].

Complexities

2.16 Although, in the propagation of high-energy particles from sun to earth, there is pretty good evidence for a series of common features, there are several events which do not fit well into the picture. Particles from solar outbursts which occurred 20 July and 28 September 1961 did arrive

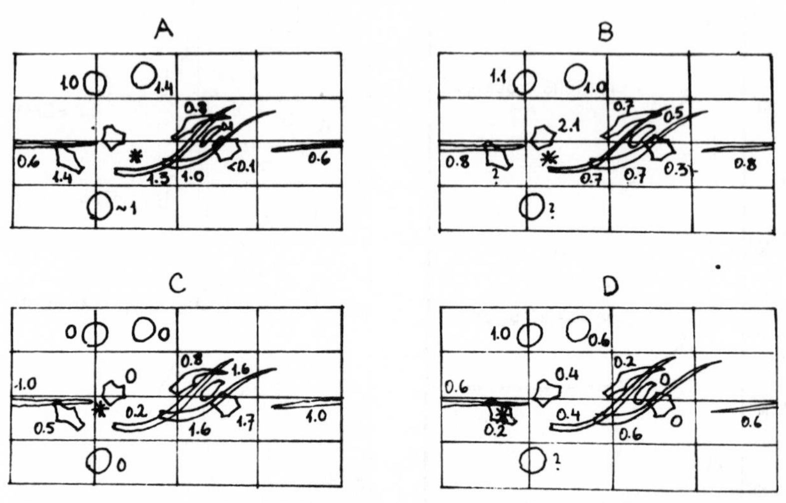

Fig. 17. Asymptotic cones of acceptance showing particle increases *A*, *B*, *C*, and *D* from Figure 16 (coordinates as in Fig. 6); numbers attached are relative intensities. From Roederer *et al.* [50].

from the "wrong" direction, i.e., from the *east* of the sun-earth line [6, 7]. A detailed analysis of the "fine structure" (small superimposed intensity variations) of several high energy solar particle increases [50] showed a rather complicated structure. Normalizing neutron monitor intensity increases to the common background of isotropic radiation, it was possible to "filter out" the purely anisotropic contribution for each detector. An example of the results obtained is given in Figure 16. This anisotropic contribution shows a rather complicated behavior, corresponding to particles which sometimes arrive from the antisun direction (Fig. 17). This was first observed by McCracken in the analysis of the 12 November 1960 event [30]. It is not clear whether these additional increases represent particle clouds bouncing back and forth in a trapping region, whether they are due to angular modulations of the existing flux of particles, or whether they correspond to additional, later emissions of particles by the sun.

2.17 Recent plasma measurements in interplanetary space with Mariner II [53] show a rather complicated filamentary or beam structure of the flow of plasma away from the sun. Such filamentary structure, in good agreement with coronal observations [23], probably imposes a filamentary structure on the interplanetary magnetic field, too, lumping lines of force together into beams of different intensity and curvature, rooted in the different active spots at the sun. Such a model of the interplanetary magnetic field would provide strong scattering for particles with gyroradii of the order of the mean diameter of a beam. It would be very important to know how this field configuration changes behind a magnetic front, in order to be able to infer guiding, scattering, and trapping conditions. More precise plasma and field measurements far out in space, during both quiet and disturbed conditions, are necessary for the establishment of a comprehensive and qualitative picture describing the propagation of high-energy particles from the sun to the earth. Only then we would be able to infer conclusively on the generation process, on the basis of measurements carried out in a region located one astronomical unit away from the source.

3. Solar Production of High-Energy Particles

Injection, Trapping, Acceleration, and Release

3.1 Four mechanisms are associated with the generation process of high-energy particles in the flare region: injection, confinement, acceleration, and release. Very little is known about these mechanisms; Type IV outbursts are probably the only direct evidence for the action of a particle (electron) acceleration process. Composition, energy spectrum and time dependence of high-energy solar particles, measured in the earth's vicinity, are only indirectly related to the original flux, because of the action of different modulation mechanisms in space (Section 2).

Several models for the flare mechanism have been advanced [20, 22, 23, 62]. With respect to particle acceleration to high energies, these give only more or less qualitative pictures.

Particle injection probably takes place by thermal heating of local plasma in the flare region. Ions and electrons at the high-velocity end of the thermal distribution are probably the particles picked up by the acceleration process. Injection by nuclear reactions could hardly furnish the estimated total number of high-energy particles, which, even after acceleration, might be as high as 10^{32}. If heating of local plasma constitutes the main injection mechanism, then the initial composition of particles to be accelerated should be that of the solar chromosphere. Considering the fact that the injected ions belong to the upper tail of the thermal spectrum, they very likely enter the acceleration process in a highly, if not completely, ionized state.

Particle confinement during acceleration must be provided by a proper magnetic field configuration in the flare region. It is so far impossible to say anything about the efficiency of such confining fields. The most one can do is to introduce an escape probability or, better, a mean confinement time T_c, which in general should be a decreasing function of energy.

Particle acceleration may be sustained by any of the following mechanisms (see, e.g., [9]): *(i)* acceleration by a statistical mechanism in highly turbulent fields; *(ii)* acceleration by magnetohydrodynamic waves; *(iii)* shock wave acceleration; *(iv)* betatron acceleration in strongly varying magnetic fields; *(v)* electric field acceleration. According to Dorman, the first three mechanisms seem reasonable, leading to reasonable values of the intervening parameters; they well might be acting simultaneously. Processes *(iv)* and *(v)* are considered by Dorman to be less plausible; processes *(i)*–*(iii)* essentially represent mechanisms of momentum transfer to a gas of particles trapped in the acceleration volume. Processes *(iv)* and *(v)* provide continuous acceleration, acting on particles according to their rigidity. These mechanisms might occur in a catastrophic form, whereas processes *(i)*–*(iii)* hardly could lead to considerable energies unless they act during a sufficiently long time.

Finally, particle release might take place according to one, or both, of the following alternatives: *(a)* breakdown of the acceleration mechanism; *(b)* breakdown of the confining field. There is good evidence (Section 2.7) for a quite abrupt release of particles.

Energy Spectrum After Acceleration

3.2 Some general quantitative considerations on acceleration mechanism were made by Dorman [9]. Consider a volume containing the particles under acceleration. The total number of particles in the total energy interval between E and $E + dE$, $N(E, t)dE$, contained in the acceleration volume is given by the equation

$$\frac{\partial N(E, t)}{\partial t} = -\frac{\partial}{\partial E}\left[N(E, t)\,\frac{dE}{dt}\right] - \frac{N(E, t)}{T_c} + q(E, t) \tag{2}$$

where T_c is the mean confinement time, $q(E, t)$ is the injection rate and dE/dt the acceleration rate for a given particle. The first term of the right member represents acceleration; the second term, particle escape; the third term, injection. We neglect nuclear interactions and ionization loss (in a first approximation, these could be included in T_c and dE/dt, respectively). For present considerations, consider only the acceleration of protons or other nuclei.

For simplicity, one supposes T_c to be energy- and time-independent.

For the injection rate, there should be an upper cutoff:

$$q(E, t) = 0 \qquad \text{for} \quad E > E_i$$

where the maximum injection energy E_i probably lies somewhere in the upper tail of the thermal spectrum (for the ions, we can safely take $E_i \approx$ rest energy). It can be shown that the acceleration rate is a function of the total energy for processes (*i*), (*ii*), and possibly (*iii*). To a good approximation, one can set

$$\frac{dE}{dt} = \frac{1}{T_a}E$$

The parameter T_a, which we may call the mean acceleration time, should in general be time-dependent. However, again for simplicity, we take it as constant during the whole acceleration process. We do the same with the injection rate.

We now can describe the two possible release mechanisms in the following way:

(*a*) breakdown of the acceleration:

$$T_a = \infty \qquad \text{for} \quad t \geq t_0 \qquad (t_0\text{: instant of release})$$

(*b*) breakdown of the confinement:

$$T_c = 0 \qquad \text{for} \quad t \geq t_0$$

If confinement time T_c is short with respect to the total duration t_0 of the accelerating process, a steady-state regime will be attained shortly after beginning. For such a steady state ($\partial N/\partial t = 0$), the solution of Equation 2 is:

$$N(E) = T_a E^{-(1+T_a/T_c)} \int_{\substack{\text{rest}\\\text{energy}}}^{E} q(E') E'^{T_a/T_c} dE'$$

As we are interested in high-energy particles only, $E > E_i$ (the maximum injection energy), and therefore:

$$N(E) = KE^{-\gamma} \qquad \text{with} \qquad \begin{cases} \gamma = 1 + T_a/T_c \\ \\ K = T_a \displaystyle\int_{\substack{\text{rest}\\\text{energy}}}^{E_i} q(E') E'^{T_a/T_c} dE' \end{cases}$$

Even dropping some of our limiting assumptions, the spectrum of accelerated particles will always retain a form close to a power law. (We have deduced a power law form for the total energy spectrum. For relativistic energies $v \approx c$, this also leads to a power law of the rigidity spectrum. Even for $v \simeq 0.5c$, the rigidity spectrum would be approximately a power law; however, in this case, the rigidity exponent is smaller than the energy exponent.) Notice that the steepness γ depends on the ratio of the acceleration time to the confinement time.

If at the time t_0 the acceleration mechanism breaks down suddenly, the total number of particles contained in the trapping volume will decrease exponentially after t_0.

$$N(E, t) = KE^{-\gamma} \exp\left(-\frac{t - t_0}{T_c}\right)$$

If, in turn, the confining mechanism breaks down suddenly, the particle flux in the volume will disappear at once.

The maximum energy available after release, is given by

$$E_{\max} = E_i \exp\left(\frac{t_0}{T_a}\right)$$

Dorman has used this expression to estimate the acceleration time for the 23 February 1956 solar outburst. He takes $E_{\max} \gtrsim 20$ Gev, $E_i = 1$ Gev and $t_0 \approx$ 5–10 minutes, getting $T_a \lesssim 500$ sec. Assuming that no change occurred to the spectrum of the particles on their way to the earth, we would obtain (taking $\gamma = 7$) a value $T_c \approx 80$ sec for the confinement time.

In Section 2.7 we mentioned the "transit time anomaly." Dorman supposes the long transit time just due to the finite duration of the acceleration process (containment time), of 5–10 minutes. If this were not the case, and if the whole acceleration took place in a time, say, an order of magnitude shorter, T_a would be of the order of 50 sec. This seems to be an extremely short acceleration time, incompatible with the order of magnitude estimated for the acceleration processes which might take place in the flare region [9].

3.3 For betatron or electric field acceleration processes (*iv*) or (*v*), one must rewrite Equation 2 in terms of rigidity rather than total energy. The acceleration rate dP/dt will be given by the electric field intensity. In case (*v*), the acceleration rate will be independent of the particle rigidity (and, hence, energy). To a first approximation, we can suppose

$$\frac{dP}{dt} = \alpha = \text{const}$$

($\alpha = c\mathcal{E}$; $\mathcal{E}$ is the mean electric field). In this case, Equation 2 reads

$$\frac{\partial N(P, t)}{\partial t} = -\alpha \frac{\partial N(P, t)}{\partial P} - \frac{N(P, t)}{T_c} + q(P, t) \tag{2'}$$

Again, for the late stage of acceleration ($t \approx t_0$), a steady-state regime will be attained, giving a solution

$$N(P) = \frac{1}{\alpha} \exp\left(-\frac{P}{\alpha T_c}\right) \cdot \int_0^P q(P') \exp\left(\frac{P'}{\alpha T_c}\right) dP'$$

If $P > P_i$ (maximum injection rigidity),

$$N(P) = K \exp\left(-\frac{P}{P_0}\right) \quad \text{with} \quad \begin{cases} P_0 = \alpha T_c \\ K = \dfrac{1}{\alpha} \displaystyle\int_0^{P_i} q(P') \exp\left(\frac{P'}{\alpha T_c}\right) dP' \end{cases}$$

We thus obtain an exponential rigidity spectrum, as found by Freier and Webber [14] for the particle flux in interplanetary space (Section 2.13). Taking a characteristic rigidity P_0 of the order of 150 Mv, and a maximum rigidity $P_{\max} = \alpha t_0 \approx 3$ Gv, we obtain, supposing $t_0 \approx 10$ minutes:

$$\alpha = 5.10^6 \text{ v/sec}$$

$$\mathcal{E} = \alpha/c = 1.6 \times 10^{-4} \text{ v/cm}$$

$$T_c = \frac{P_0}{\alpha} \approx 30 \text{ sec}$$

These are again quite plausible values for the different parameters. Actually, electric field values 2–3 orders of magnitude greater are still imaginable for a catastrophic process. This would lead to t_o and T_c values 2–3 orders of magnitude shorter. In this case, it would be necessary to suppose the action of a separate trapping mechanism in the lower corona, in order to explain the transit time anomaly (Section 2.7). Recently, Schatzman [52] described a shock wave acceleration mechanism (*iii*), which also leads to an exponential spectrum.

From the point of view of the values of characteristic parameters, all five proposed acceleration mechanisms seem plausible. To decide which is dominant, it is necessary to know exactly whether the spectrum of solar particles is a power law or an exponential form, before the particles undergo the complex processes of scattering and trapping in interplanetary space.

The above discussion does not apply to electrons. For these particles, bremsstrahlung and synchrotron radiation energy losses would become dominant processes at high energies, thus balancing out the acceleration rate. It is therefore unlikely that electrons could acquire high energies in a solar outburst (see Section 2.15). However, acceleration of electrons in a flare is an extremely important process, for it provides the only direct evidence for the action of an acceleration mechanism through the Type IV radio emissions.

Plasma Clouds and Particle Clouds

3.4 If Freier and Webber's suggestion—that high-energy solar protons and heavier nuclei constitute the upper tail of an over-all particle spectrum (which in its lower end includes solar plasma) (Section 2.13)—is true, we might imagine the action of only one acceleration process for both high-energy particles and plasma clouds. In other words, we could imagine a single mechanism catastrophically heating up local plasma; this plasma will probably then separate during the heating process into two quite distinct fractions. Above a critical value in the energy distribution, the electron temperature will tend to asymptotize to a certain limit determined by radiation loss, whereas the ion temperature could continue to increase freely by the effect of the acceleration process, thus leading to a "cloud" of high-energy ions. Below the critical energy, electrons will still be able to maintain a certain form of thermal quasi-equilibrium with the ions, thus constituting a "cloud" of genuine, hot plasma. A release process (or the breakdown of the acceleration process) might then liberate these two parts, ejecting them in the form of a high-energy particle flux and a high-velocity plasma cloud.

But, if high-energy solar particles remain trapped inside a plasma cloud, both ejected simultaneously by the same flare, their flux and energy would reduce to a vanishing level once this cloud and the corresponding "magnetic bottle" have expanded to the earth's orbit. However, high-energy solar particles, when detected at earth, are invariably found to be trapped in a "bottle" emitted at an earlier time than the particles. This means that solar particles, if initially formed and trapped in a plasma cloud, have to get out of their "home cloud" in the immediate vicinity of the sun. We can conclude that, in addition to whatever happens in the outer space, modulation mechanisms acting in the lower corona where the particle "cloud" energy density possibly exceeds the local magnetic field energy density, play a crucial role in the whole process of propagation.

Thus, one of the important aspects of the study of acceleration, ejection, and propagation of solar high-energy particles is that it may lead us to a general model for energetic particle production at the stars and their propagation through the stellar atmosphere out into interstellar space, as the initial stage in the process of generation of galactic cosmic radiation.

Acknowledgments

This review paper was conceived and written during a stay at the Laboratorio de Física Cósmica de Chacaltaya (Bolivia) and the Instituto Geofísico de Huancayo (Perú). The author wishes to express his gratitude to Professor Ismael Escobar and Ing. Alberto Giesecke for their kind hospitality and stimulating discussions. Reading of the manuscript and valuable critical remarks by Dr. T. Obayashi are greatly appreciated.

References

1. J. C. Anderson, R. L. Chasson, and K. Maeda, Characteristics of solar-flare cosmic rays during IGY, *J. Phys. Soc. Japan*, **17**, Suppl. A-II, 264 (1962).
2. R. J. Baduell, J. M. Cardoso, H. S. Ghielmetti, L. C. Marzulli, and J. G. Roederer, New determination of neutron monitor coupling functions, *Space Research III*, 700 (North-Holland Publishing Co., 1963).
3. D. K. Bailey and J. M. Harrington, A survey of polar cap absorption events (solar proton events) in the period 1952 through 1960, *J. Phys. Soc. Japan*, **17**, Suppl. A-II, 334 (1962).
4. S. Biswas, C. E. Fichtel, D. E. Guss, and C. J. Waddington, Hydrogen, helium, and heavy nuclei from the solar event on November 15, 1960, *J. Geophys. Res.*, **68**(10), 3109 (1963).
5. E. A. Brunberg and A. Dattner, Experimental determination of electron orbits in the field of a magnetic dipole, Part 2, *Tellus*, **5**, 269 (1953).
6. D. A. Bryant, T. L. Cline, V. D. Desai, and F. B. McDonald, Explorer 12 observations of solar cosmic rays and energetic storm particles after the solar flare of September 28, 1961, *J. Geophys. Res.*, **67**(13), 4983 (1962).
7. H. Carmichael, High-energy solar-particle events, *Space Sci. Revs.*, **1**(1), 28 (1962).
8. A. N. Charakhchyan, V. E. Tulinov, and T. N. Charakhchyan, The energy spectrum and time dependence of the intensity of solar cosmic ray protons in flares, *J. Phys. Soc. Japan*, **17**, Suppl. A-II, 365 (1962).
9. L. I. Dorman, *Cosmic Ray Variations* [*Variatsii Kosmicheskikh Luchey*] (State Publishing House for Technical and Theoretical Literature, Moscow, 1957; translation by Wright-Patterson Air Force Base Technical Documents Liaison Office.)
10. J. A. Earl, Cloud-chamber observations of solar cosmic rays over Minneapolis on September 4, 1960, *J. Geophys. Res.*, **67**(6), 2107 (1962).
11. C. E. Fichtel and D. E. Guss, Heavy nuclei in solar cosmic rays, *J. Phys. Soc. Japan*, **17**, Suppl. A-II, 321 (1962).
12. H. P. Finch and B. R. Leaton, The earth main magnetic field-epic 1955.0, *Mon. Notices Roy. Astron. Soc.*, Geophys. Suppl. No. 1, 314 (1957).
13. J. Firor, Cosmic radiation intensity-time variations and their origin, Part 4: Increases associated with solar flares, *Phys. Rev.*, **94**, 1017 (1954).
14. P. S. Freier and W. R. Webber, Exponential rigidity spectrums for solar-flare cosmic rays, *J. Geophys. Res.*, **68**(6), 1605 (1963).
15. H. S. Ghielmetti, J. C. Anderson, J. M. Cardoso, J. R. Manzano, J. G. Roederer, and O. R. Santochi, Solar flare effects on cosmic ray intensity, *Nuovo Cim.*, **15**, 87 (1960).
16. H. S. Ghielmetti, The spectrum and propagation of relativistic solar flare particles during July 17–18, 1959, *J. Geophys. Res.*, **66**(6), 1611 (1961).
17. T. Gold, Plasma and magnetic fields in the solar system, *J. Geophys. Res.*, **64**(11), 1665 (1959).
18. T. Gold, Emission from the sun, and transmission of radiation through the interplanetary space, *J. Phys. Soc. Japan*, **17**, Suppl. A-II, 607 (1962).
19. T. Gold, Magnetic storms, *Space Sci. Revs.*, **1**(1), 100 (1962).
20. T. Gold, (preprint) Lectures at the University of Buenos Aires.
21. D. J. Hofmann and J. R. Winckler, Simultaneous balloon observations at Fort Churchill and Minneapolis during the solar cosmic ray events of July 1961, *J. Geophys. Res.*, **68**(8), 2067 (1963).
22. C. de Jager, Structure and dynamics of the solar atmosphere, *Handbuch der Physik*, **52**, 221 (1959).
23. C. de Jager, The sun as a source of interplanetary gas, *Space Sci. Revs.*, **1**(3), 487 (1962).
24. J. E. Keith and A. L. Turkevich, Radioactivity induced in Discoverer 17 by solar-flare protons, *J. Geophys. Res.*, **67**(12), 4525 (1962).
25. Ye. V. Kolomeets, Small effects of solar flares and the energy spectrum of primary variation of cosmic rays, *Zh. Eksp. Teoret, Fiz.*, **36**(9) (1959) (Translation: *Soviet Physics-JETP*, **36**(9), 960 (1959).

26. J. A. Lockwood and M. A. Shea, Variations of the cosmic radiation in November 1960, *J. Geophys. Res.*, **66**(10), 3083 (1961).
27. R. Lüst and J. A. Simpson, Initial stages in the propagation of cosmic rays produced by solar flares, *Phys. Res.*, **108**(6), 1563 (1957).
28. K. G. McCracken and R. A. R. Palmeira, Comparison of solar cosmic rays injection including July 17, 1959 and May 4, 1960, *J. Geophys. Res.*, **65**(9), 2673 (1960).
29. K. G. McCracken, The cosmic-ray flare effect, 1. Some new methods of analysis, *J. Geophys. Res.*, **67**(2), 423 (1962).
30. K. G. McCracken, The cosmic-ray flare effect, 2. The flare effects of May 4, November 15, 1960, *J. Geophys. Res.*, **67**(2), 435 (1962).
31. K. G. McCracken, The cosmic-ray flare effect, 3. Deductions regarding the interplanetary magnetic field, *J. Geophys. Res.*, **67**(2), 447 (1962).
32. F. B. McDonald and W. R. Webber, "A study of the rigidity and charge dependence of primary cosmic ray temporal variations, *J. Phys. Soc. Japan*, **17,** Suppl. A-II, 428 (1962).
33. C. E. McIlwain, Coordinates for mapping the distributions of magnetically trapped particles, *J. Geophys. Res.*, **66**(11), 3681 (1961).
34. P. Meyer and R. Vogt, High-energy electrons of solar origin, *Phys. Rev. Letters*, **8**(10), 387 (1962).
35. P. Meyer, E. N. Parker, and J. A. Simpson, Solar cosmic rays of February, 1956 and their propagation through interplanetary space, *Phys. Rev.*, **104**(3), 768 (1956).
36. P. Meyer, Cosmic radiation and solar modulation (Chapter 6 of this volume).
37. E. P. Ney and W. A. Stein, Solar protons, alpha particles, and heavy nuclei in November 1960, *J. Geophys. Res.*, **67**(6), 2087 (1962).
38. T. Obayashi, Propagation of solar corpuscles and interplanetary magnetic fields, *J. Geophys. Res.*, **67**(5), 1717 (1962).
39. T. Obayashi, Some notes on cosmic radiations and magnetic fields measured by Pioneer V, *J. Geophys. Res.*, **67**(5), 2039 (1962).
40. K. W. Ogilvie, D. A. Bryant, and L. R. Davis, Rocket observations of solar protons during the November 1960 events, 1., *J. Geophys. Res.*, **67**(3), 929 (1962).
41. E. N. Parker, Sudden expansion of the corona following a large solar flare and the attendant magnetic field and cosmic-ray effects, *Astrophys. J.*, **133**(3), 1014 (1961).
42. E. N. Parker, Interplanetary dynamics and cosmic ray modulation, *J. Phys. Soc. Japan*, **17,** Suppl. A-II, 563 (1962).
43. G. F. Pieper, A. J. Zmuda, C. O. Bostrom, and B. J. O'Brien, Solar protons and magnetic storms in July 1961, *J. Geophys. Res.*, **67**(13), 4959 (1962).
44. J. J. Quenby and G. J. Wenk, Cosmic ray threshold rigidities and the earth's magnetic field, *Phil. Mag.*, **7**(81), 1457 (1962).
45. J. G. Roederer, Zur Theorie des Breiteneffektes der Nukleonenkomponente der Kosmischen Strahlen, *Z. Naturforsch.*, **9a,** 740 (1954).
46. J. G. Roederer, J. R. Manzano, and O. R. Santochi, On the superposition of cosmic ray modulation effects during the July 1959 storms, *IUGG Monograph No.* **7,** 44 (1960).
47. J. G. Roederer, J. R. Manzano, O. R. Santochi, N. Nerurkar, O. Troncoso, R. A. R. Palmeira, and G. Schwachheim, Cosmic ray modulating fields in interplanetary space during the November 1960 disturbances, *Space Research II*, 754 (North-Holland Publishing Co., 1961).
48. J. G. Roederer, J. R. Manzano, O. R. Santochi, N. Nerurkar, O. Troncoso, R. A. R. Palmeira, and G. Schwachheim, Cosmic ray phenomena during the November 1960 solar disturbances, *J. Geophys. Res.*, **66**(6), 1603 (1961).
49. J. G. Roederer, Acceleration and propagation of fast particles in interplanetary space, *Space Research III*, 518 (North-Holland Publishing Co., 1963).
50. J. G. Roederer, J. M. Cardoso, and H. S. Ghielmetti, On the fine structure of high energy solar particle injections, *Space Research IV* (North-Holland Publishing Co., 1964; in press).
51. O. R. Santochi, J. R. Manzano, and J. G. Roederer, Cosmic ray intensity increase on May 1, 1960, *Nuovo Cim.*, **17**(1), 119 (1960).

52. E. Schatzman, Energy and mass spectra of solar cosmic rays, *Space Research III*, 709 (North-Holland Publishing Co., 1963).
53. C. W. Snyder and M. Neugebauer, Interplanetary solar-wind measurements by Mariner II, *Space Research IV* (North-Holland Publishing Co., 1964; in press).
54. J. F. Steljes, H. Carmichael, and K. G. McCracken, Characteristics and fine structure of the large cosmic ray fluctuations in November 1960, *J. Geophys. Res.*, **66**(5), 1363 (1961).
55. T. Takakura, Solar radio outbursts and acceleration of electrons, *J. Phys. Soc. Japan*, **17**, Suppl. A-II, 243 (1962).
56. T. Takakura and M. Ono, Yearly variation in activities of outbursts at microwaves and flares during a solar cycle with special reference to unusual cosmic-ray increases, *J. Phys. Soc. Japan*, **17**, Suppl. A-II, 207 (1962).
57. L. C. Towle and J. A. Lockwood, Cosmic-ray increases associated with solar flares, *Phys. Rev.*, **113**(2), 641 (1959).
58. R. Vogt, Primary cosmic-ray and solar protons, *Phys. Rev.*, **125**(1), 366 (1962).
59. C. S. Warwick, Propagation of solar particles and the interplanerary magnetic field, *J. Geophys. Res.*, **67**(4), 1333 (1962).
60. W. R. Webber and J. J. Quenby, On the derivation of cosmic ray specific yield functions, *Phil. Mag.*, **4**, 654 (1959).
61. W. R. Webber, The motion of low-rigidity cosmic rays in the earth's magnetic field and the effects of external fields, *J. Geophys. Res.*, **68**(10), 3065 (1963).
62. J. P. Wild, The radio emission from solar flares, *J. Phys. Soc. Japan*, **17**, Suppl. A-II, 249 (1962).
63. B. G. Wilson and C. P. Nehra, Cosmic ray increases associated with solar flares, *J. Phys. Soc. Japan*, **17**, Suppl. A-II, 269 (1962).
64. J. R. Winckler, Geomagnetic and interplanetary effects on solar cosmic rays, *J. Phys. Soc. Japan*, **17**, Suppl. A-II, 353 (1962).
65. J. R. Winckler and P. D. Bhavsar, The time variations of solar cosmic rays during the September 3, 1960 event, *J. Geophys. Res.*, **68**(8), 2099 (1963).
66. H. Yagoda, Radiation studies in space with nuclear emulsion detectors, *Space Sci. Revs.*, **1**(2), 224 (1962).

CHAPTER 6

COSMIC RADIATION AND SOLAR MODULATION

Peter Meyer

Forbush's discovery that the intensity of cosmic radiation which reaches the earth is correlated with the general level of solar activity has stimulated an extensive program of research aimed at the description of the mechanisms by which the sun is capable of influencing the flux of galactic cosmic-ray particles into the inner solar system. Today we still are in the middle of these investigations. Indeed, this type of research ties the field of cosmic radiation to the activities of the International Geophysical Year period (1957–1959) and the International Years of the Quiet Sun (1964–1965).

Both these enterprises include in their aims the exploration of the physical phenomena in interplanetary space, phenomena which are controlled by the outflux of energy from the sun. This energy is essentially emitted in two forms: electromagnetic radiation and particle radiation. It is the latter which interests us in connection with the galactic cosmic radiation. Rapid theoretical as well as experimental developments have taken place in this field during the past years which drastically changed the point of view taken prior to the IGY. I shall not restrict myself to studies during IGY but rather, for a limited part of cosmic-ray research, I shall try to review the work done before, during, and after the IGY and then to look ahead. Webber [25] has published a comprehensive review of much of the cosmic-ray work carried out during the IGY period.

Looking back from today's point of view, it appears surprising that solar influence on cosmic radiation was not discovered much earlier in the course of cosmic-ray research. The reason is this: solar modulation effects are large only in the low-energy portion of the primary cosmic-ray spectrum, and we have only in the past decade learned to study extensively the low-energy primary rays. In this region, however, cosmic-ray particles are a powerful tool to investigate the configuration of magnetic fields and their changes in the solar system. In fact, experiments on the variations of intensity and energy spectrum of the cosmic radiation have greatly contributed to the formulation of the concept of "solar wind," a concept which only afterward could be tested and confirmed through direct experiments.

Figure 1 has been taken from the original paper by Forbush [10], which clearly showed for the first time the anticorrelation between solar activity—here represented by the sunspot number—and the intensity of cosmic radiation. Forbush's paper was published in 1954, two years before

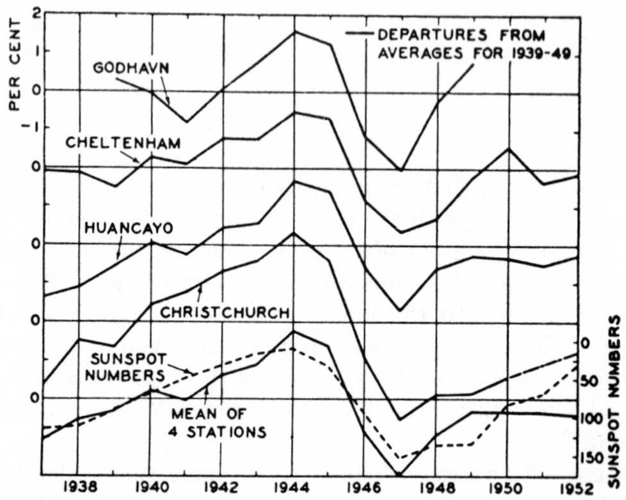

FIG. 1. Cosmic-ray intensity (annual means) from 1937 to 1951 as measured by four ionization chamber stations [10].

the IGY. When the International Geophysical Year got under way, the link between solar activity and cosmic radiation was fully recognized.

Through the balloon experiments by Neher [20] and his coworkers and the airplane experiments of Meyer and Simpson [17], the strong energy dependence of the solar modulation became evident. Figure 2 shows some of the results of Neher with balloonborne ion chambers, displaying the dramatic changes which take place at extremely low primary particle energies between years of high and low solar activity.

Changes in the energy spectrum at higher energies could be demonstrated by flying a neutron monitor at aircraft altitude along identical trajectories of almost constant geomagnetic longitude, in this way using the geomagnetic field as an energy spectrometer [17]. Figure 3 is a reminder of the results obtained in this experiment. One can see how the

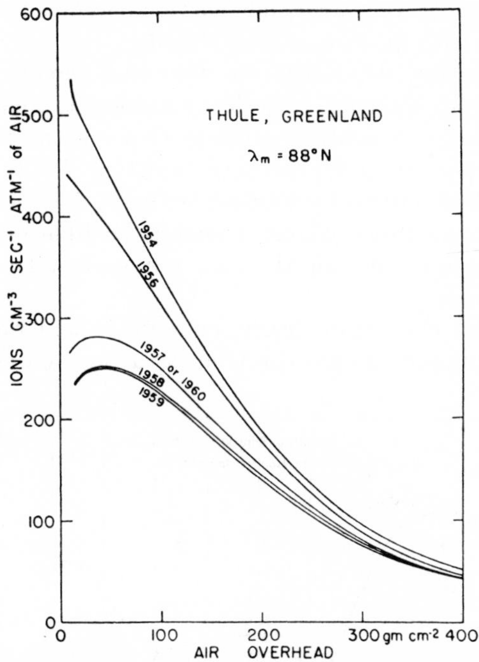

FIG. 2. Altitude dependence of the total ionization produced by cosmic rays measured in Thule from 1954 to 1960 [20].

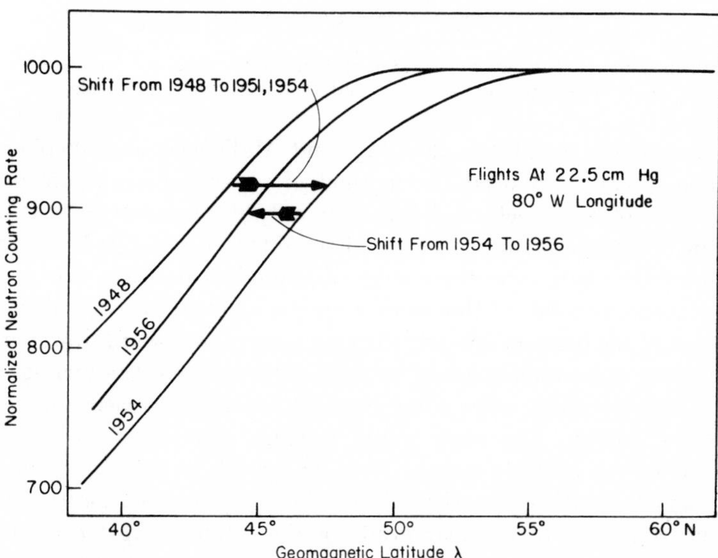

FIG. 3. The nucleonic component latitude curves for 1948, 1954, and 1956 arbitrarily normalized at latitudes >58°N in order to display the magnitude of the shifts in the low-rigidity cutoff of the cosmic-ray spectrum [17].

slope of the intensity versus latitude curve, as well as the position of the "knee," changes with the level of solar activity.

The strong energy dependence of the solar modulation mechanism means that the eleven-year intensity variation is much more readily displayed in cosmic-ray neutron monitors that respond predominantly to the low-energy portion of the primary radiation. Hence, the barely detectable effect, first noticed by Forbush with ion chambers, becomes very large in neutron monitors. Figure 4 shows the time dependence of the neutron monitor intensity for the past ten years taken at the Climax station by Simpson.

The experiment which most clearly shows the behavior of the low-energy portion of the primary proton spectrum as a function of the solar cycle

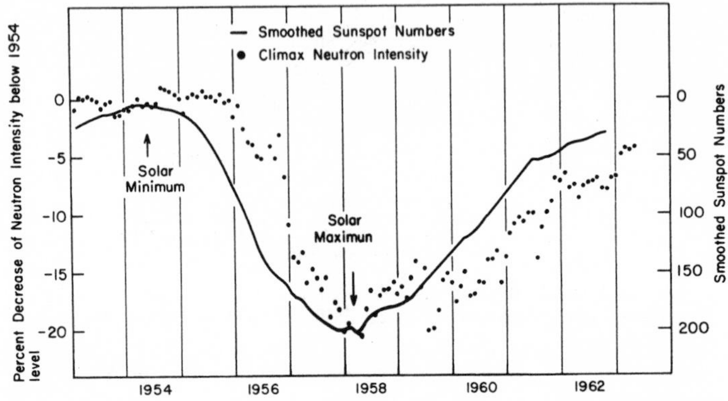

FIG. 4. The monthly average cosmic-ray intensity measured by the Climax neutron monitor between 1953 and 1963 (Simpson, unpublished).

was carried out by McDonald [14], and McDonald and Webber [15]. McDonald had introduced the method of observing simultaneously the energy loss of a particle and the light output produced in a Čerenkov radiator. Through the measurement of these two parameters he was able to determine the charge and the energy of individual particles over a certain energy range. A result of this work is shown in Figure 5, which shows the deviation of the primary spectrum from a power law towards lower energies (interpreted as a suppression of galactic particles from the vicinity of the earth). The intensity, after going through a peak, decreases rapidly with decreasing energy. The peak would roughly correspond to the "knee" observed in the latitude curves. It is important to note the behavior of the primary α-particles, particularly the similarity of the rigidity spectrum and the similarity of the magnitude of the intensity variation of corresponding proton and α-particle rigidities. A number of experiments [8, 12, 13] confirm that, in similar rigidity intervals, α-particles are modulated by the same amount as protons. More recently, experiments [19, 24]

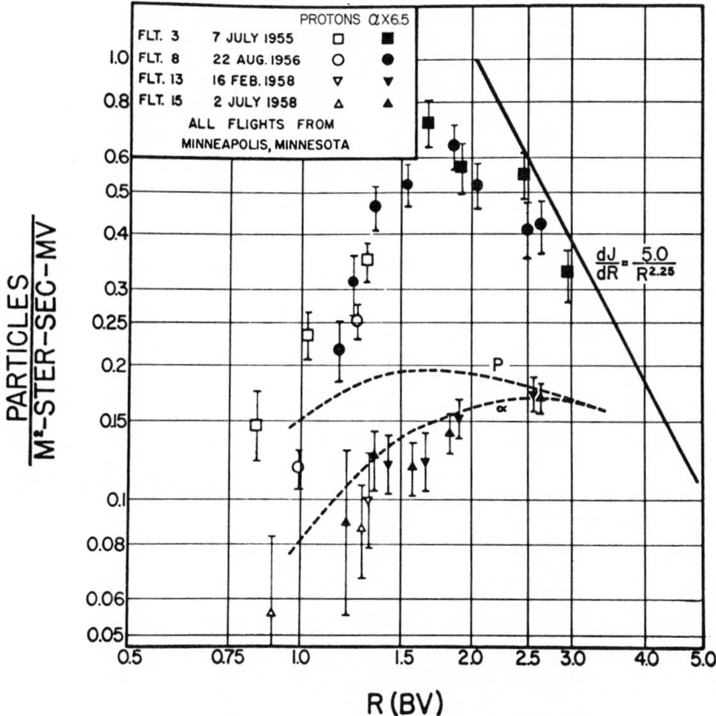

FIG. 5. The primary proton and α-particle rigidity spectrum between 1955 and 1958 [15].

made at higher geomagnetic latitude and with instrumentation suitable for specifically studying the low-energy particles revealed a relatively large flux of protons at low energy near solar maximum, which we now interpret as being of solar origin.

Data on heavier primary particles are much more scarce. They indicate however that the rigidity spectrum is modulated in the same fashion as that of the primary protons and α-particles throughout the eleven-year cycle. The available data on medium and heavy nuclei have been compiled by Webber [25], as shown in Figure 6, where the particle flux is compared with the neutron monitor rate of the Mt. Washington station. The data are consistent with the assumption that the medium and heavy primaries are subjected to the same modulation as the protons and α-particles. This similarity in the behavior of particles with quite different charge and different e/m points strongly toward a rigidity-dependent modulation mechanism.

This discussion has been restricted to the long-term variations of cosmic rays. There exists a number of short-term variations whose amplitude, characteristics, and frequency of occurrence are controlled by solar activity.

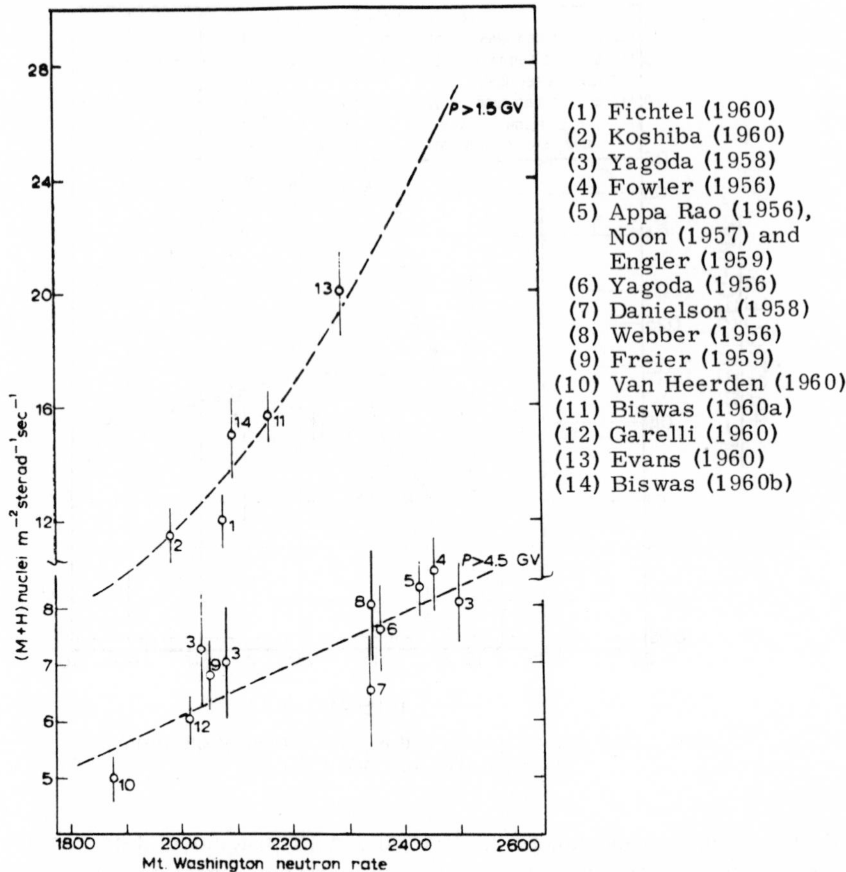

FIG. 6. Integral intensity of medium and heavy primary cosmic-ray nuclei compared with the intensity of the Mt. Washington neutron monitor [25].

In most cases these events can be identified with individual phenomena on the sun. I shall only briefly discuss the short-term fluctuations, most of which are less understood than the eleven-year solar cycle variation. The most outstanding of these phenomena is the Forbush-type decrease, characterized by a sudden drop in cosmic-ray intensity, which slowly recovers in periods of days or weeks. Its occurrence is closely correlated with solar flares. The Forbush decrease follows a flare by one to two days. It is clearly a modulation effect which influences the various components of the primary radiation. Simultaneous observations of protons and α-particles show a complete correlation in corresponding rigidity intervals. Figure 7 shows a comparison between the total cosmic-ray flux as observed by a neutron monitor and the α-particle flux measured at balloon altitude during a number of Forbush decreases [16]. In Figure 8 this correlation is shown by plotting the α-particle flux versus the monitor intensity. On 18 July 1959, the lowest particle intensity ever observed was measured.

The rigidity dependence of the Forbush decrease has been investigated by several authors. The results are not clear-cut: there may or may not be a different dependence than that found for the eleven-year radiation.

The observations of daily variations need no discussion here (but see the recent work by Dessler *et al.* [4] and their interpretation). The 27-day

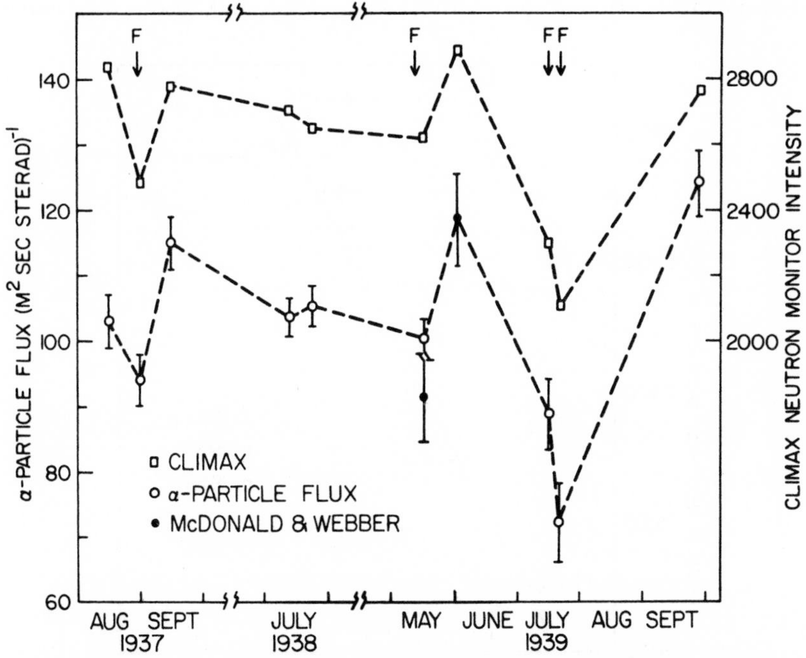

FIG. 7. The cosmic-ray α-particle flux ($E > 530$ Mev/nucleon) under 13.5 gm/cm² of residual atmosphere and the nucleonic component intensity (Climax neutron monitor) during Forbush-type decreases (F) [16].

recurring intensity variations have so far contributed least to our understanding of the solar controlled modulation phenomena.

There is no doubt today—in spite of some alternative details in the models—that solar wind is responsible for the changes in intensity and energy spectrum which we observe in the cosmic radiation. The most important tests of the solar wind model have come about through the availability of space probes carrying cosmic-ray instrumentation to large distances from the earth. Experiments [2, 7] on board Pioneer V were the first to establish the fact that the eleven-year modulation, as well as the Forbush decrease, are phenomena which are not localized near the earth or its immediate environment, but rather affect large volumes of the inner solar system. A triple-coincidence proportional-counter telescope measured protons with energy in excess of 75 Mev. An ion chamber and a Geiger counter observed the total particle flux and ionization separately. This vehicle was launched 11 March 1960 and moved along a trajectory approaching the orbit of Venus. Data were received for about two months. During that period Pioneer V approached the sun by 0.1 A.U. A study of the cosmic-ray flux as a function of distance from the earth revealed that the volume of space affected by the decrease in primary particle intensity in the years of solar activity maximum—and 1960 is only one to

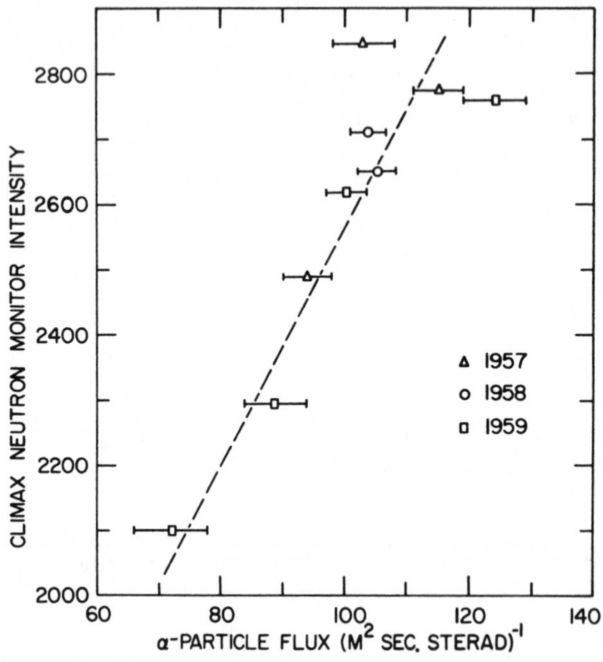

FIG. 8. The cosmic ray α-particle flux ($E > 530$ Mev/nucleon) vs. the Climax neutron monitor intensity from 1957 through 1959 [16].

two years after the maximum—is not restricted to the vicinity of the earth, ruling out any modulation mechanisms which invoke the presence of the earth. It shows in addition that this volume must have linear dimensions at least of the diameter of the orbit of Earth, since we do not observe any seasonal changes of cosmic-ray intensity. The second important result is the evidence that the cosmic-ray intensity stays constant over a radial solar distance from 0.9 A.U. to 1 A.U. This means that the modulating "barrier" is located outside of the orbit of the earth. Figure 9 displays the cosmic-ray intensity as a function of distance from the earth. Similar conclusions can be reached from the results of ion chamber and Geiger counter measurements [2] on Pioneer V. These findings have more recently been confirmed and substantiated by ionization chamber and counter measurements on Mariner II [1]. Although the observations on Mariner II were made in 1962 in the declining phase of solar activity, the low-energy cosmic-ray flux in the vicinity of the earth was still decreased by a factor of about 2 below the value of solar minimum. A change in intensity as a function of solar distance would therefore have to be observable if the modulation "barrier" were located partly within the earth's orbit. Mariner II was able to transmit data until the point of encounter with Venus. No change in the average intensity was noted between 1 and about 0.7 A.U. radial distance from the sun.

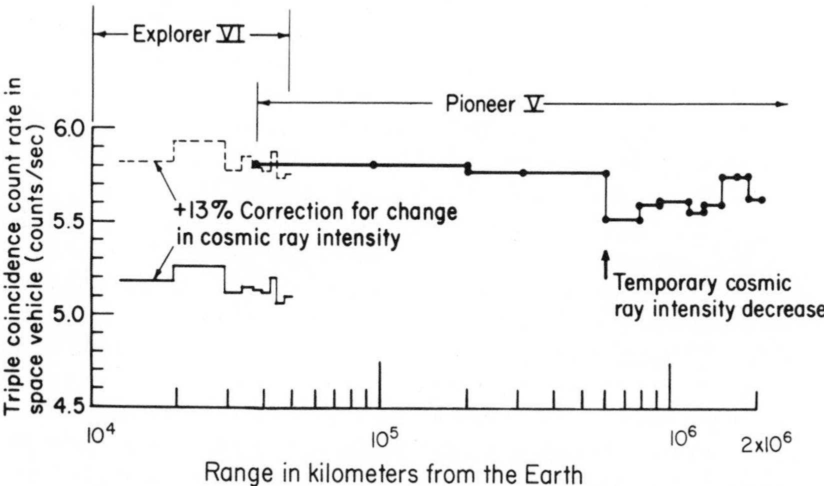

FIG. 9. Counting rate of triple coincidence events on Pioneer V and Explorer VI as a function of the distance from the earth [7].

When Pioneer V was about 5 million miles from the earth, high latitude neutron monitor stations recorded a Forbush decrease of about 20 per cent. An intensity decrease of 30 per cent was simultaneously observed by the cosmic-ray detectors on Pioneer V. Taking into account the difference in the low-energy response of the neutron station and the space probe instruments, one finds that the Forbush decrease occurred with full amplitude in a region far removed drom the earth. This observation, therefore, establishes the fact that the mechanism responsible for the Forbush decrease also operates over a large volume and is not restricted to the vicinity of the earth. The presence of the earth and its magnetosphere is unnecessary for the production of these decreases [6].

The developments which have been discussed took place in the last ten years. Most of the current ideas concerning the solar controlled phenomena in interplanetary space which influence the cosmic radiation were formed in this short period of time. Before discussing some directions of cosmic-ray research which are of particular interest during solar minimum, I summarize some facts from the work of the past years.

The eleven-year modulation of cosmic-ray intensity shows a strong rigidity dependence. Higher amplitudes are observed at progressively lower rigidities. Protons and heavier nuclear species of the same rigidity exhibit the same modulation. This indicates that the mechanism responsible for the modulation is rigidity-dependent. There exists today direct experimental evidence for the presence of interplanetary magnetic fields and there is little doubt that these fields are the agent producing the eleven-year modulation. The configuration of the magnetic fields is controlled by the flux of plasma from the sun. The strength of this "solar wind" has been calculated by Parker [22] on the basis of cosmic-ray observations, geomagnetic evidence, and the known properties of the solar corona. Its existence is now established through direct experiments [21]. Measurements on space probes have shown that the volume affected by the eleven-year modulation has linear dimensions larger than the orbit of earth. Within that volume the intensity appears to be constant and reduced below the galactic cosmic-ray level throughout most of the solar cycle. It is not yet known at what distance from the sun the modulating region is located; its thickness and field configuration are also unknown. There exist, however, theoretical ideas as to the nature and origin of the modulating region. Some interesting evidence was recently obtained by Simpson [23] which bears on this question. Forbush [11] and Neher [20] have pointed out that there exists a time lag between the average sunspot number and the intensity of cosmic rays as a function of time. Using the University of Chicago neutron monitor network, Simpson studied this question in more detail, showing first that the level of solar radio emission and geomagnetic activity are correlated without phase shift with the average sunspot number. One may infer, therefore, that the strength of the solar wind is also in phase with the sunspot number. Simpson then shows that the cosmic-ray intensity is not a simple and unique function of sunspot number, but is quite different for the same level of solar activity at the inclining and the declining portion of the cycle, exhibiting the phase shift discussed by Forbush and by Neher. The nature of this dependence, however, varies with the energy of the primary cosmic-ray particles. In Figure 10 cosmic-ray intensity is plotted against the average sunspot number for various cutoff energies. The large difference in cosmic-ray intensity for similar sunspot numbers in the increasing and declining phase of the solar cycle can be clearly seen. The figure also shows that one is probably not dealing with a simple phase shift but rather a relaxation phenomenon. It is likely that this behavior reflects the change in scale size of the scattering centers involved in the modulation throughout the solar cycle.

In the past few years several new discoveries have been made which lead to experiments of importance at sunspot minimum. Balloon experiments at high geomagnetic latitude [19, 24] give details of the primary proton spectrum in the energy region from 70 to 350 Mev. It was found that even in years of enhanced solar activity there exists a considerable flux of protons in this energy region, which should be absent if our ideas on the modulation mechanism are correct. The presence of these low-

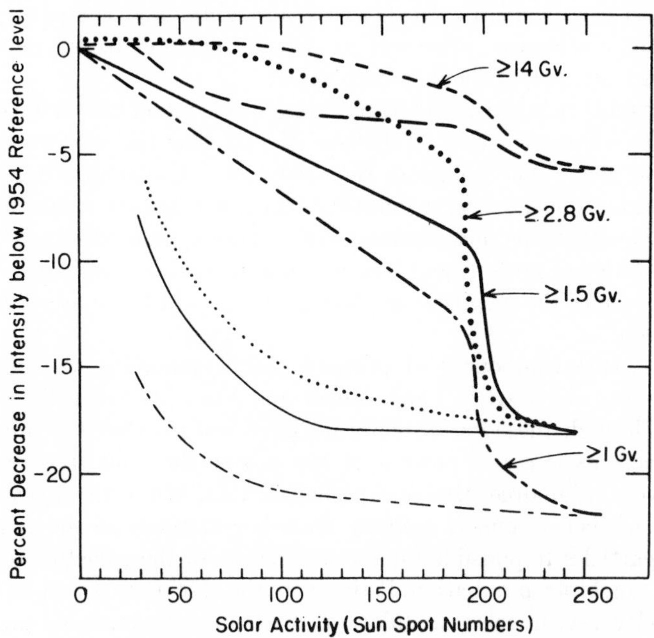

FIG. 10. Neutron monitor cosmic-ray intensity vs. average sunspot number from 1954 to 1962 [23].

energy particles was confirmed by nuclear emulsion studies [9] and through satellite observations [3]. There is still some discrepancy among various experimenters as to the exact flux and shape of the energy spectrum, but the presence of these particles appears to be established. More recent results indicate that these protons are of solar origin during the solar active years. From 1962, on, we begin to see, however, the influx of low-energy galactic protons which show an energy spectrum quite different from the solar protons which were observed earlier. We expect this flux to increase considerably from 1963 to 1965. There is little doubt that the galactic low-energy protons, whose flux now appears to increase as a function of time, are identical with the particles observed by Neher in his measurements with ion chambers. In the coming years these measurements will be further pursued with the hope to gain more complete information of the primary proton spectrum in the period of solar minimum. It would be of considerable interest to find out how much residual modulation persists during minimum solar activity. Experiments are being prepared on various highly eccentric satellites which will yield a knowledge of the primary spectrum to much lower energies than those obtainable by balloon work. These experiments will, in addition, supply the energy spectra of heavier primary particles. It should, then, for the first time be possible to clearly distinguish between a rigidity- and energy-dependent modulation mechanism, since only at very low energies are the momentum and energy not proportional to each other.

It is possible that the modulating region, if it is present at all during solar minimum, will move closer to the sun. If that were the case, experiments carried on deep space probes in the solar and antisolar directions should show a radial dependence in intensity which was absent while the sun is active. Simultaneous measurements at various solar distances of the energy spectra of protons and heavier nuclear species would shed light on the scale size of the magnetic scattering centers which are involved in the modulation.

The electron component of primary cosmic radiation was discovered two years ago by Earl [5] and Meyer and Vogt [18] in balloon experiments. Through these experiments we have learned that the flux of primary electrons is a few percent of the proton flux and that its energy lies between a hundred Mev and perhaps 2 Bev. We have as yet no clear evidence of their origin. It is likely that they originate in the galaxy and are the particles responsible for the production of the galactic radio noise through synchrotron radiation. If this were the case, they would be affected by the eleven-year solar modulation in a similar manner as protons of corresponding rigidity. The forthcoming years of solar minimum, when modulation is least effective, will give an opportunity to measure the energy spectrum and other properties of this component with the least modification by solar modulation. The knowledge of the galactic electron spectrum is of importance since it would yield—if combined with the radio-astronomical data—a measurement of the average strength of galactic magnetic fields.

A further important question is the ratio of electrons and positrons in the primary electron component. A measurement of this ratio will tell us whether proton–proton collisions in the galaxy are the origin of the electrons or whether ambient electrons have been accelerated to cosmic-ray energies. It is one of the few experiments which promises to give direct information on accelerating mechanisms. Both types of experiment, the measurement of the energy spectrum, and the measurement of the electron-positron ratio, are presently under way and will be continued through solar minimum.

References

1. H. R. Anderson, Mariner II: High energy radiation experiment, *Science*, **139,** 42 (1963).
2. R. L. Arnoldy, R. A. Hoffman, and J. R. Winckler, Solar cosmic rays and soft radiation observed at 5,000,000 kilometers from earth, *J. Geophys. Res.*, 65, 3004 (1960).
3. D. A. Bryant, T. L. Cline, U. D. Desai, and F. B. McDonald, Explorer 12 observations of solar cosmic rays and energetic storm particles after the solar flare of September 28, 1961, *J. Geophys. Res.*, **67,** 4983 (1962).
4. A. J. Dessler, H. S. Ahluwalia, and B. Gottlieb, Corotation of the solar magnetic field and the diurnal variation in cosmic-ray intensity, *J. Geophys. Res.*, **67,** 3553 (1962).
5. J. A. Earl, Cloud-chamber observations of primary cosmic-ray electrons, *Phys. Rev. Letters*, **6,** 125 (1961).
6. C. Y. Fan, P. Meyer, and J. A. Simpson, Rapid reduction of cosmic-radiation intensity measured in interplanetary space, *Phys. Rev. Letters*, **5,** 269 (1960).
7. C. Y. Fan, P. Meyer, and J. A. Simpson, Experiments on the eleven-year changes of cosmic ray intensity using a space probe, *Phys. Rev. Letters*, **5,** 272 (1960).
8. C. E. Fichtel, Heavy component of the primary cosmic radiation during solar maximum at a low geomagnetic cutoff energy (*Ph.D. Thesis*, Washington University, St. Louis 1959).
9. C. E. Fichtel, D. E. Guss, G. R. Stevenson, and C. J. Waddington, Cosmic ray hydrogen and helium nuclei during a solar quiet time in July 1961 (to be published).
10. S. E. Forbush, World-wide cosmic-ray variations, 1937–1952, *J. Geophys. Res.*, **59,** 525 (1954).
11. S. E. Forbush, Cosmic-ray intensity variations during two solar cycles, *J. Geophys. Res.*, **63,** 651 (1958).
12. P. S. Freier, E. P. Ney, and P. H. Fowler, Primary α-particle intensity at sunspot maximum, *Nature*, **181,** 1319 (1958).
13. P. S. Freier, E. P. Ney, and C. J. Waddington, Flux and energy spectrum of cosmic ray α-particles during solar maximum, *Phys. Rev.*, **114,** 365 (1959).
14. F. B. McDonald, Direct determination of primary cosmic-ray alpha-particle energy spectrum by new method, *Phys. Rev.*, **104,** 1723 (1956). Study of geomagnetic cutoff energies and temporal variation of the primary cosmic radiation, *Phys. Rev.*, **107,** 1386 (1957). Primary cosmic ray intensity near solar maximum, *Phys. Rev.*, **116,** 462 (1959).
15. F. B. McDonald and W. R. Webber, Proton component of the primary cosmic radiation, *Phys. Rev.*, **115,** 194 (1959).
16. P. Meyer, The cosmic ray alpha-particle flux during sharp Forbush intensity decreases, *J. Geophys. Res.*, **65,** 3881 (1960).
17. P. Meyer and J. A. Simpson, Changes in the low energy particle cutoff and primary spectrum of cosmic radiation, *Phys. Rev.*, **99,** 1517 (1955); **106,** 568 (1957).
18. P. Meyer and R. Vogt, Electrons in the primary cosmic radiation, *Phys. Rev. Letters*, **6,** 193 (1961).
19. P. Meyer and R. Vogt, Primary cosmic ray and solar protons II, *Phys. Rev.*, **129,** 2275 (1963).
20. H. V. Neher, Low-energy primary cosmic-ray particles in 1954, *Phys. Rev.*, **103,** 228 (1956). A summary of secular variations of cosmic rays, *J. Phys. Soc. Japan*, **17,** A-11, 492 (1962).

21. M. Neugebauer and C. W. Snyder, The mission of Mariner II, Preliminary observations: Solar plasma experiment, *Science*, **138**, 1095 (1962).
22. E. N. Parker, *Interplanetary Dynamical Processes*, (Interscience Publishers, 1963).
23. J. A. Simpson, Recent investigations of the low energy cosmic and solar particle radiations (Conference on Cosmic Rays in Interplanetary Space; Pontifical Academy of Sciences, Vatican City, 1962).
24. R. Vogt, Primary cosmic ray and solar protons, *Phys. Rev.*, **125**, 366 (1962).
25. W. R. Webber, Time variations of low rigidity cosmic rays during recent sunspot cycle. *Progress in Elementary Particle and Cosmic Ray Physics, VI* (North-Holland Publishing Co., 1962).

CHAPTER 7

A SURVEY OF MAGNETOSPHERIC BOUNDARY PHENOMENA

L. A. Frank and J. A. Van Allen

1. Introduction

Satellites and space probes have markedly increased our knowledge, both experimental and theoretical, about the interaction of the earth's magnetic field and the solar wind. This interaction is believed to be closely associated with a variety of geophysical phenomena such as the aurora, magnetic storms, and ionospheric disturbances [2, 5, 12, 58]. Experimental results of the past few years give a gross model of an interplanetary plasma streaming, radially and irregularly, outward from the sun [37, 41], compressing the earth's magnetic field on the sunward side and extending it on the night side [6, 12, 32]. There is evidence that a shock [26, 34] is formed at the sunward boundary of the magnetosphere due to the supersonic flow of the plasma past the earth's distorted magnetosphere. Marked spatial asymmetries of charged particle distributions within and near the magnetospheric boundary [23], in the geomagnetic equatorial plane with respect to the earth-sun line, have been observed and may be intimately associated with the flow of solar plasma near the earth. The experimental studies of the geomagnetic field in these distant regions of the magnetosphere have revealed large departures from an unperturbed dipolar field [11, 15, 29]. Although the present discussion emphasizes phenomena at large distances in the geomagnetic equatorial plane, the intimate relationship with low-altitude, high-latitude geophysical phenomena via the geomagnetic lines of force is of crucial importance in the interpretation of experimental results obtained in the vicinity of the magnetospheric boundary.

Our purpose is to summarize present knowledge concerning the immediate region of this interaction near the boundary of the magnetosphere, by reviewing the highlights of experimental and theoretical results as a more or less integrated body of information.

2. Comparison of Trajectories of Several Space Probes and Earth Satellites

The azimuthal asymmetry of charged particle distributions and of the character of the magnetic fields in the geomagnetic equatorial plane with respect to the earth-sun line beyond approximately $7R_E$ is critical to the interpretation of experimental results. Figure 1 shows the projections of trajectories of several satellites and probes onto the geomagnetic equatorial

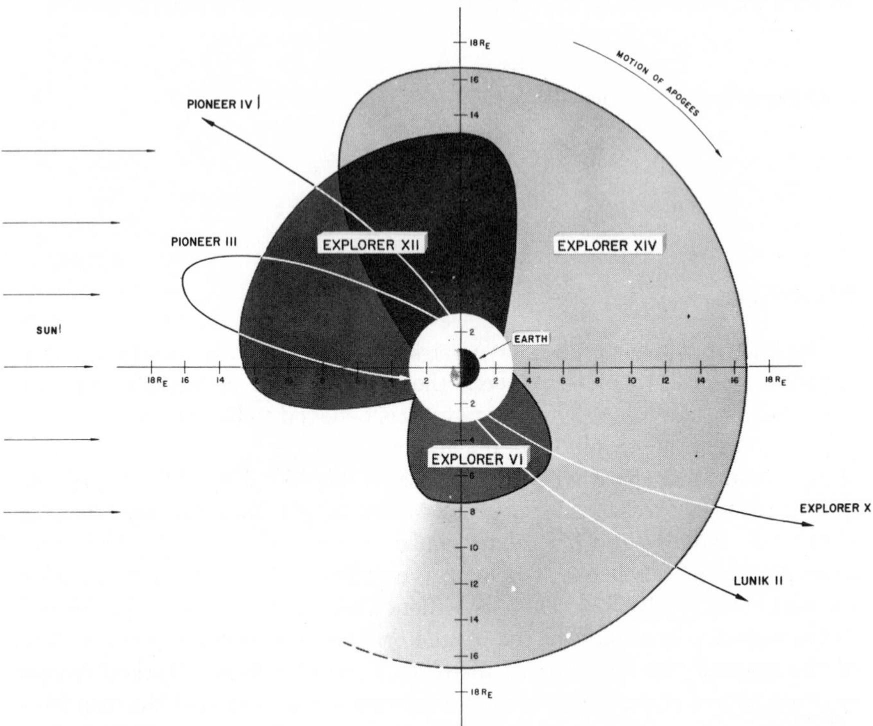

FIG. 1. Graphical summary of the trajectories of several probes and satellites with respect to the earth-sun line and projected onto the geomagnetic equatorial plane: Pioneer III, 6–7 December 1958; Pioneer IV, 3 March 1959; Lunik II, 12 September 1959; Explorer X, 25–28 March 1961; Explorer VI, August–October 1959; Explorer XII, August–December 1961; Explorer XIV, October, 1962 to present (July, 1963).

plane. Pioneers III and IV and Explorers XII and XIV scanned the dawn side of the magnetosphere while Lunik II and Explorers VI, X, and XIV surveyed the night side. Explorer XIV due to its long effective lifetime (October, 1962 to August, 1963) and apogee of a little more than 100,000 km has surveyed such a large portion of the geomagnetic equatorial plane that it may be used as an integrating factor in interpretation of the data of the remaining experiments. The local times at 100,000 km for Lunik I (2 January 1959), Pioneer V (11 March to 26 June, 1960), and Pioneer I (11–12

October, 1958) (not shown in Figure 1) were approximately 0800, 1500, and 1200, respectively [44]. Of the probes and satellites shown in Figure 1, all but Explorer X were within approximately 30° of the equatorial plane for the portions of the trajectories of interest here. The geomagnetic latitude of the Explorer X trajectory was approximately 45°.

3. Low-Energy Particles near the Magnetospheric Boundary

Explorers X and XII and Lunik II obtained some of the more important measurements of low-energy particles near the fringes of the magnetosphere. These results are graphed in Figure 2. The geomagnetic latitude of Explorer X was approximately 45°; the data in Figure 2 [9] have been extrapolated into the geomagnetic equatorial plane by assuming cylindrical symmetry about the earth-sun axis in order to obtain the approximate shape of the magnetosphere on the evening side of the earth-sun line. The intermittent observation of a plasma and of simultaneous changes in the character of the magnetic field beyond 22 R_E on the night side of the earth has been interpreted as the result of the boundary of the magnetospheric tail sweeping intermittently across the trajectory of the probe [8, 29]. Bridge and his collaborators [9] report the measurement of a plasma consisting of protons of approximately 500 ev in energy and fluxes of the order of 10^7–

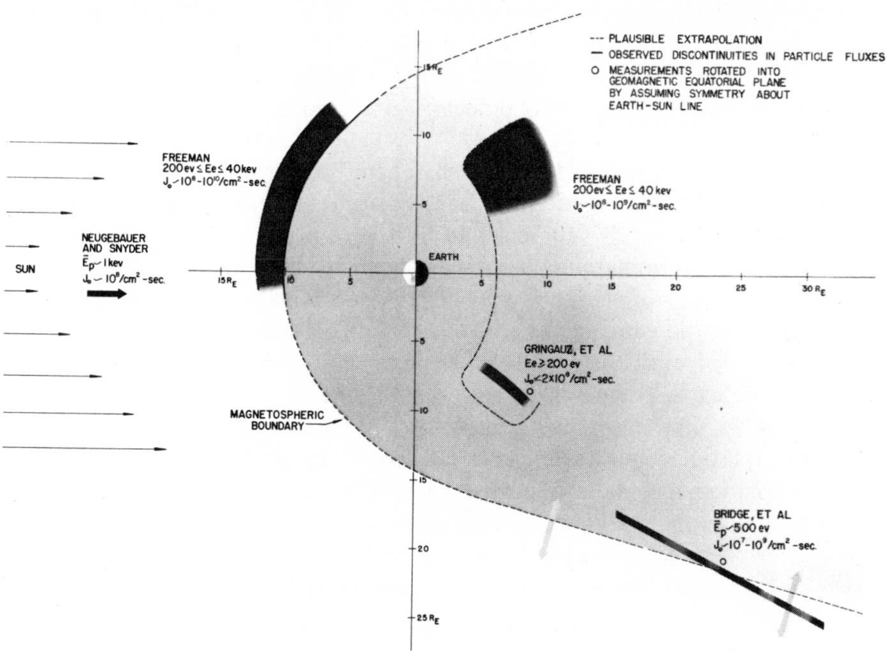

Fig. 2. Graphical summary of principal measurements of low-energy charged particles in the geomagnetic equatorial plane beyond $\sim 7R_E$.

$10^9/cm^2/sec$ just outside the tail of the magnetosphere and an upper limit of $5 \times 10^6/cm^2/sec$ when the instrumentation was within the tail. The measurements of Bridge *et al.* are in quantitative agreement with the interplanetary measurements with the Venus probe Mariner II [37]. Gringauz *et al.* [28] have measured an intense flux of low-energy electrons in the radial distance range of 61,400 to 81,400 km with plasma cups on Lunik II at a sun-earth-probe angle (L_{SEP}, for brevity) of approximately 125° to the east of the earth-sun line [26]. These electrons were characterized by an average energy of 200 ev or greater and a flux of approximately $10^8/cm^2/sec$. This measurement apparently remained unique among the various low-energy charged-particle measurements until Freeman [25] reported a large flux of low-energy electrons at $L_{SEP} \gtrsim 120°$ to the west of the earth-sun line with CdS total energy detectors (one with and one without a deflecting collimator magnet) on Explorer XII. These Explorer XII measurements indicated a flux of $\sim 10^8$ to $10^9/cm^2/sec$ if electrons of an average energy of 10 kev per electron were assumed. With plasma cups on Mars I (launch, 1 November 1962; local time at 15,000 km, ~2100; geomagnetic latitude at 15,000 km, ~50°) Gringauz and his collaborators [27] again measured an electron flux of approximately the same magnitude and energy as with Lunik II but over a radial distance range of 8500 km to 17,000 km, closer to the earth presumably due to the higher geomagnetic latitude of the trajectory. From the summary of the Lunik II and Explorer XII results in Figure 2, it is evident that large fluxes of low-energy electrons exist on the night side of the earth and that further experiments with low-energy electron (and proton) detectors are needed in order to complete this survey.

On the sunward side of the magnetosphere just beyond the boundary as delineated by the limit of durable trapping in the geomagnetic field of energetic electrons ($E \geq 40$ kev) and by the coincident observation of the discontinuity (termination) in the field beyond about 10 R_E, a persistent layer of electrons of energy flux ~30 $ergs/cm^2/sterad/sec$ and of approximately 15,000 km in radial depth has been measured [25]. These fluxes were observed until the apogee of Explorer XII had drifted to the dawn side of the earth where the apogee distance of 84,000 km was no longer sufficient to penetrate the magnetospheric boundary (see Fig. 2). The possible relationship of these electron fluxes to the present theory of shocks and transition regions is discussed later. The characteristics of the solar wind in interplanetary space distant from the influence of the earth's magnetosphere have recently been measured with the Venus probe Mariner II [37]. Typical values recorded were (protons only were measured):

$$v_0 \simeq 500\text{–}800 \text{ km/sec (bulk velocity)}$$

$$n \simeq 2.5/\text{cm}^3$$

$$T \simeq 2\text{–}8 \times 10^{5\,\circ}\text{K}$$

and a fluctuating weak interplanetary magnetic field [13]

$$B \simeq 5\gamma$$

These data are indicative of a supersonic plasma flow past the earth because the Alfvén Mach number

$$M_A = v_0/v_A = \frac{(4\pi m_p n)^{1/2} v_0}{B} \sim 7$$

A rough estimate of $\sim 2/\text{cm}^3$ for the number density of electrons may be obtained by assuming that, the ionized solar plasma is macroscopically neutral; the experimental difficulties of measuring electrons of energy $\sim \frac{1}{2} m_e v_0^2$ ($\sim$1 ev) are overwhelming (the thermal energy of the electrons is $\sim$100 ev if equipartition of energy between protons and electrons is invoked).

4. Energetic Charged Particles near the Magnetospheric Boundary

Electrons of energy greater than 250 kev, which characterize the outer radiation zone, are apparently not found in the vicinity of the magneto-

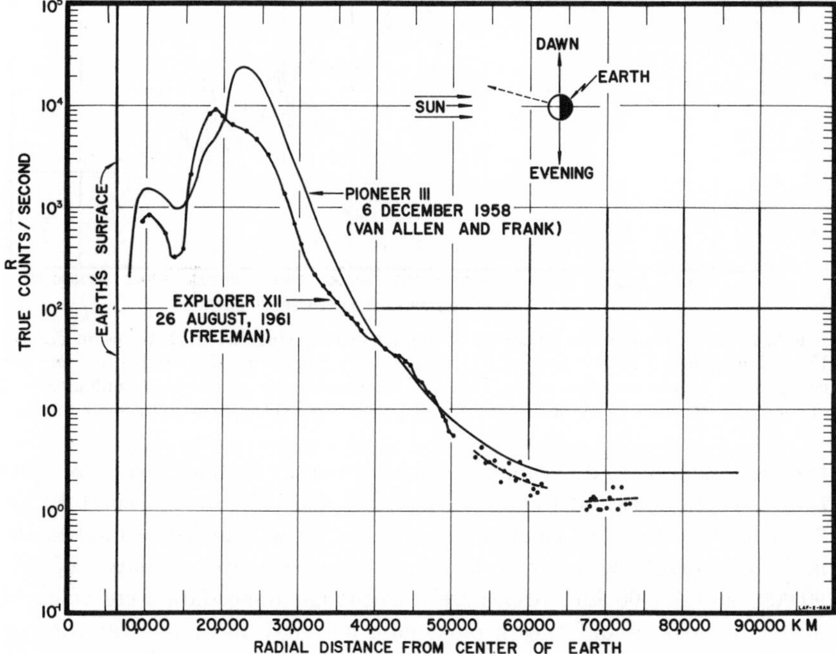

Fig. 3. Comparison of the responses of the similar, heavily shielded G. M. tubes on Pioneer III and Explorer XII for similar trajectories with respect to the earth-sun line.

spheric boundary. Indeed, it has been shown recently that fluxes of electrons of energy less than 250 kev dominate these regions [23]. The fact that some of the high-energy detectors (e.g., the heavily shielded Geiger-Mueller tubes on Pioneers III and IV) have recorded significant responses in this region is now attributed to the inefficient intermediate process of bremsstrahlung production in the walls of the instruments by large fluxes of low-energy electrons [24]. An apparent experimentally anomalous result existed in the determination of the radial extent of the geomagnetically

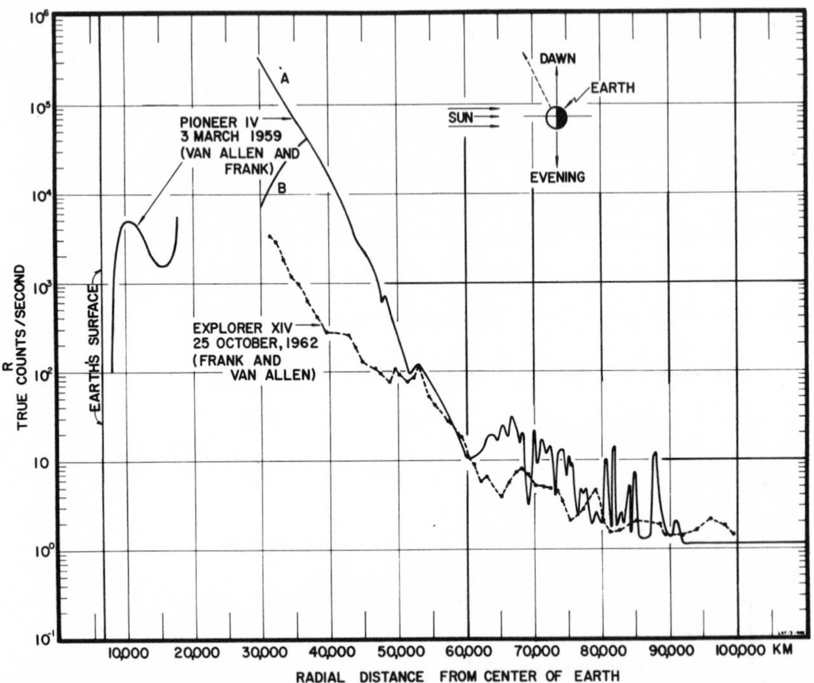

FIG. 4. Comparison of the responses of similar, heavily shielded G.M. tubes on Pioneer IV and Explorer XIV for similar trajectories with respect to the earth-sun line. The consistently higher response of the Pioneer IV detector may be due to an enhancement of energetic electrons ($E \sim 50$ kev) following pronounced geomagnetic and solar activity.

trapped radiation as determined by similar heavily shielded Geiger-Mueller tubes (Anton 302's) on Pioneers III and IV [54, 55] and Explorer VI [3, 30] which returned to galactic background rates (and hence implied the limit of geomagnetic trapping) at radial distances of approximately 65,000, 90,000, and 45,000 km, respectively. Although these data were acquired during periods of differing geomagnetic activity, the large variation in radial extent of significant response over galactic background rates may be attributed in large part to their different trajectory directions with respect to the earth-sun line. Comparison of these data with the recent results of

Explorers XII and XIV in Figures 3, 4, and 5 confirms the importance of this azimuthal asymmetry of low energy electrons in interpreting particle flux measurements beyond 7 R_E. Figure 3 shows the 302 counting rate contours as a function of radial distance for Pioneer III and Explorer XII for similar trajectories with respect to geomagnetic latitude and local time (see also Fig. 1); Figure 4 displays the contours for Pioneer IV and Explorer

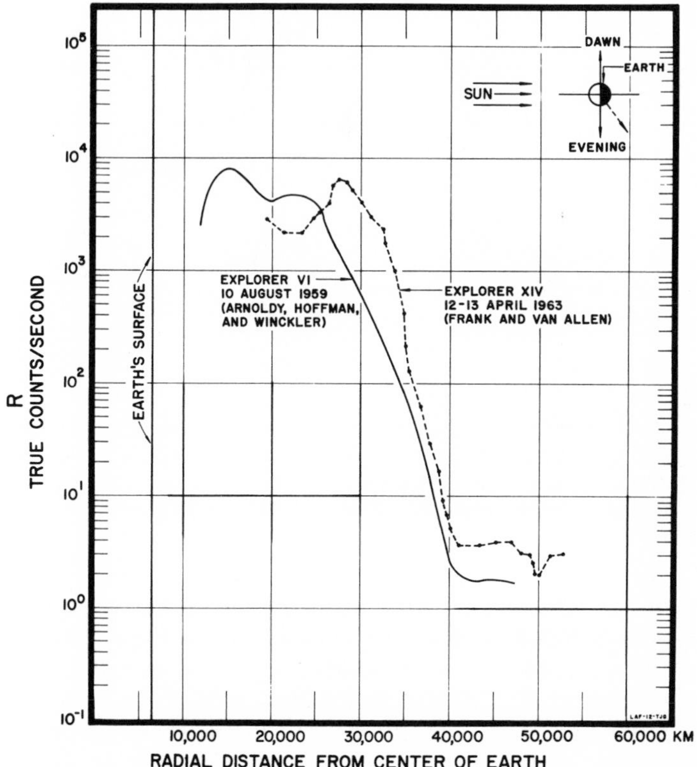

FIG. 5. Comparison of the responses of similar, heavily shielded G.M. tubes on Explorers VI and XIV for similar trajectories with respect to the earth-sun line. Compare the distance of onset of negligible response of ~45,000 km with those of Figures 3 and 4.

XIV, again with similar trajectories; and Figure 5 shows the corresponding data for Explorers VI and XIV. Lunik I (Mechta) charged particle measurements [57] yielded a result similar to that of Figure 4. The agreement among the various experimental results is thus quite remarkable when viewed with reference to a local time coordinate system. The higher count rates of Pioneer IV as compared to those of Explorer XIV in Figure 4 may be attributed to large solar and geomagnetic activity preceding the Pioneer IV flight [55]. By inspection this body of results indicates a relative dearth

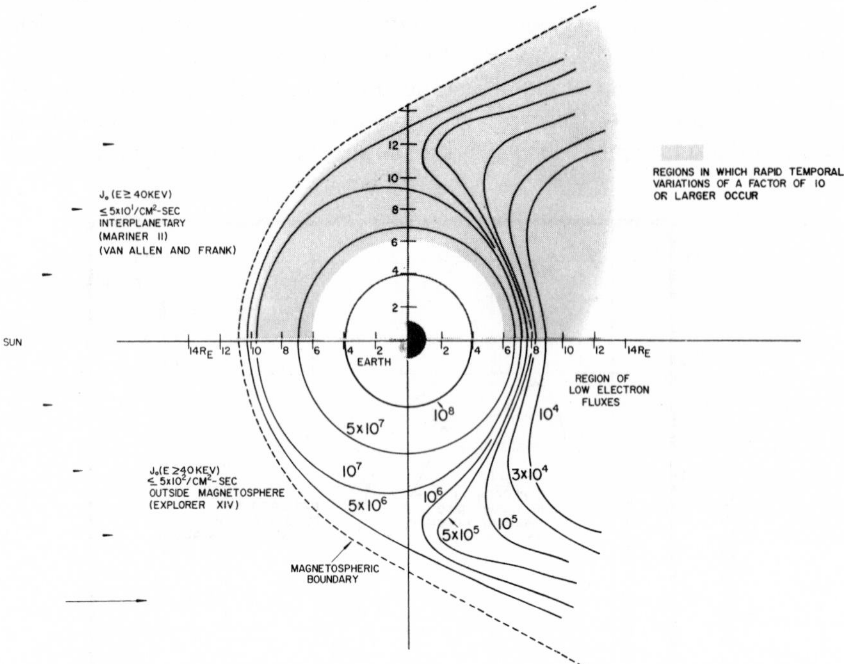

FIG. 6. Graphical summary of measurements of energetic electrons ($E \gtrsim 40$ kev) in the geomagnetic equatorial plane with Explorers XII and XIV on the dawn side of the earth-sun line.

of electrons ($E \gtrsim 50$ kev) on the night side of the earth with respect to similar radial distances toward the sunward side of the magnetosphere.

The results of a comprehensive study [23] of the spatial distribution of electrons of energy $E \gtrsim 40$ kev on the dawn side of the earth-sun line to geocentric radial distances of 105,000 km in the geomagnetic equatorial plane with thin-windowed (1.2 mg/cm^2 mica) G.M. tubes on Explorers XII and XIV are summarized in Figure 6. Salient characteristics of this survey of omnidirectional electron fluxes are:

1. A general lack of electrons beyond $8R_E$ on the night side of the earth.
2. A large "flaring" of the electron fluxes (typically 10^5 to 10^6/cm^2/sec) at dawn and extending beyond the satellite apogee of 105,000 km.
3. A sharp boundary or termination of these electron fluxes on the sunward side of the earth at approximately 10 R_E.

It should be remarked here that during magnetically disturbed periods the "average" contours presented in Figure 6 are apparently greatly distorted and that the evening contours have been extended from the dawn side by the assumption of symmetry about the earth-sun line. This symmetry will be discussed further in more detail in Section 9. Protons of energy greater than 100 kev have been measured with a scintillation detector on Explorer XII [17] and on Explorer XIV [16] in these regions; no azimuthal studies of the proton intensities at large radial distances have been reported. The Mars I data [53] show that the geocentric radial termination of the flux of 70–80 kev electrons as measured on the night side of the earth (~2100 local time) and at a geomagnetic latitude of ~50° was at 15,000 km; it is of interest to compare this high latitude measurement with the termination of electron fluxes on the night side of the earth as shown in Figure 6. Just outside the magnetospheric boundary the Explorer XIV upper limits for the electron ($E_e \gtrsim 40$ kev) and proton ($E_p \gtrsim 500$ kev) fluxes are 5×10^2/cm²/sec [24]. Measurements on Mariner II with a similar G.M. detector yield [56] an upper limit of 5×10^1/cm²/sec for the sum of proton and electron fluxes of the above energy ranges. These measurements imply that the large fluxes of energetic electrons found within the magnetosphere (Fig. 6) are not contributed directly by an efflux from the sun without subsequent acceleration in the vicinity of the magnetosphere.

5. Low-Altitude, High-Latitude Studies

The intimate association of low-altitude, high-latitude phenomena with processes occurring at large radial distances in the geomagnetic equatorial plane via geomagnetic lines of force certainly cannot be neglected. Discussions of related upper-atmospheric physical phenomena and surface magnetic field measurements are not within the scope of this chapter: but interesting surveys are given, for example, in Axford and Hines [5] and Vestine [58]. There has been one notable and interesting preliminary survey [40] of the high-latitude distribution of trapped electrons ($E \gtrsim 40$ kev) with an Explorer XIV-type G.M. tube, flown on Injun I in a nearly circular orbit of 1000 km altitude with an inclination of 67°. This survey revealed the large diurnal effect (Fig. 7) in the limit of the observation of trapped electrons as a function of invariant latitude $\Lambda(\Lambda = \cos^{-1}(\sqrt{L})^{-1})$. (For definition of the B–L coordinate system, see McIlwain [36].) The termination of trapped particle fluxes at local day was at $L \sim 16$ and at local night was at $L \sim 8$ as displayed by the corresponding limits of the loci of points in Figure 7 (solid and broken lines, respectively). The above low-altitude measurements and the equatorial plane surveys of charged particle distributions (Figs. 2 and 6) were used to construct the meridional section of the magnetosphere of Figure 8. Studies of the latitude distributions of trapped and dumped electrons at evening and dawn are also of apparent interest. Important information obviously may be inferred about the dynamics and energy requirements of the outer magnetospheric system by these low-altitude measurements.

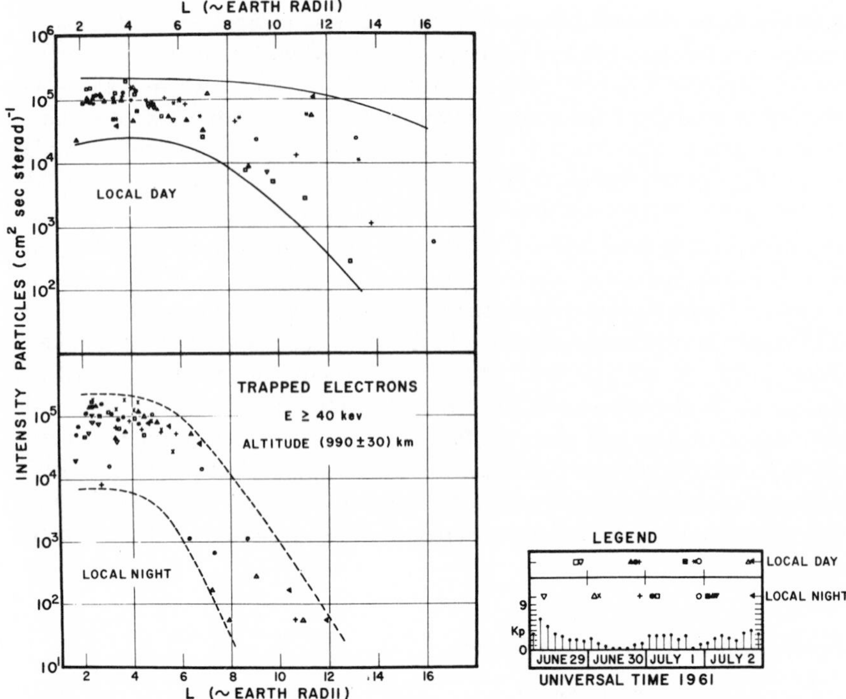

FIG. 7. Latitude profiles of the intensity of trapped electrons obtained in ten passes with local time between 1200 and 1600 hours (local day) and in eleven passes with local time between 1900 and 2300 hours (local night) soon after launch when the satellite was spinning rapidly (after O'Brien [40]). Note the variation of these two graphs with respect to the limit of observed trapped-particle intensity as a function of increasing L indicated by the lines enveloping all data points in each graph.

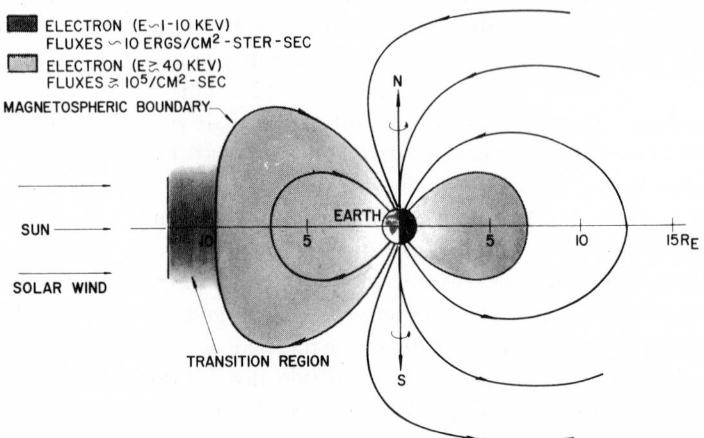

FIG. 8. Illustrative drawing summarizing experimental measurements of charged particles and plausible distortions of the geomagnetic field in the meridional plane containing the earth-sun line. (Mars I energetic electron measurements have also been included. See text.)

6. Gross Character of Fields near the Magnetospheric Boundary

The dynamical behavior of charged particles near the magnetospheric boundary is closely interlocked with the properties of the magnetic fields in these regions. The gross character of these fields [11, 29, 43, 46, 47] has been surveyed in part by Explorers X, XII, and XIV. Figure 9 displays charged particle and magnetic field measurements as Explorer XII passed inward through the magnetospheric boundary at local noon on 13 September 1961 [26]; there were indications of solar activity a few days previous

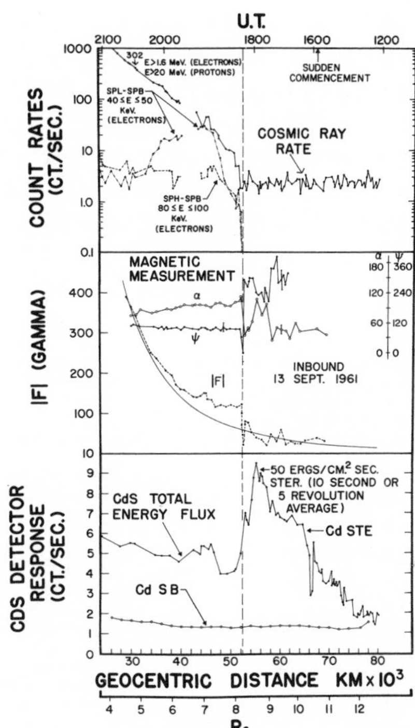

Fig. 9. Particle and magnetic field measurements with Explorer XII for the inbound pass on 13 September 1961. The CdSB (magnet in aperture) detector count-rate has been normalized to the energy scale of the CdSTE (no magnet in aperture) detector. The counting rates of both CdS detectors are nearly linear with energy flux. Both spectrometer channels (SpL and SpH) have been corrected for background counts by the subtraction of the counting rate of the background detector SpB. The CdS optical monitor (not shown) indicated that during this pass the CdS detectors did not have any bright objects within their field of view. F denotes the scalar magnetic field strength; α the angle between the F-vector and the spin-axis of the satellite; and ψ the dihedral angle between the plane containing the F-vector and the spin axis and the plane containing the spin axis and the satellite-sun line (after Freeman *et al.* [26]). The experimenters found the measurements consistent with an electron flux of $3 \times 10^{10}/\text{cm}^2/\text{sec}$ and with an energy of 2.6 kev per electron.

to, and a sudden commencement at 1556 UT on 13 September. The experimenters have interpreted these measurements as follows:

1. The discontinuity in direction, magnitude and general character of the magnetic field at 52,000 km determines the radial extent of the earth's magnetosphere.
2. The observed limit of durable trapping of 40-kev electrons (SpL-SpB of Fig. 9) corresponds closely to the discontinuity in the magnetic field.
3. The magnetic field just inside the boundary has been compressed by a thermalized plasma of electrons—50 ergs/cm²/sterad/sec—approximately 20,000 km thick located just outside of the boundary; the magnetic field just inside the boundary is approximately a factor of 2 larger than the

value computed from Finch and Leaton coefficients and is highly disordered outside the boundary.

4. A betatron acceleration may have produced an enhancement of charged particle energy within the magnetosphere near the magnetospheric boundary.

These general characteristics of the sunward magnetospheric boundary are typical, although often somewhat attenuated since there were noticeably disturbed conditions at the boundary during the Explorer XII measurements in these regions [11]. The results of magnetic field measurements with Pioneers I [48] and V [15] which also crossed the sunward side of the magnetospheric boundary were similar to those of Explorer XII; a graphical survey [8] is given in Figure 10. The disordered magnetic fields of several R_E in radial depth measured by each of these probes and satellites have been interpreted as characteristic of a transition region between a shock wave and the magnetospheric boundary. The generation of hydromagnetic waves in this region and their propagation within the magnetosphere have

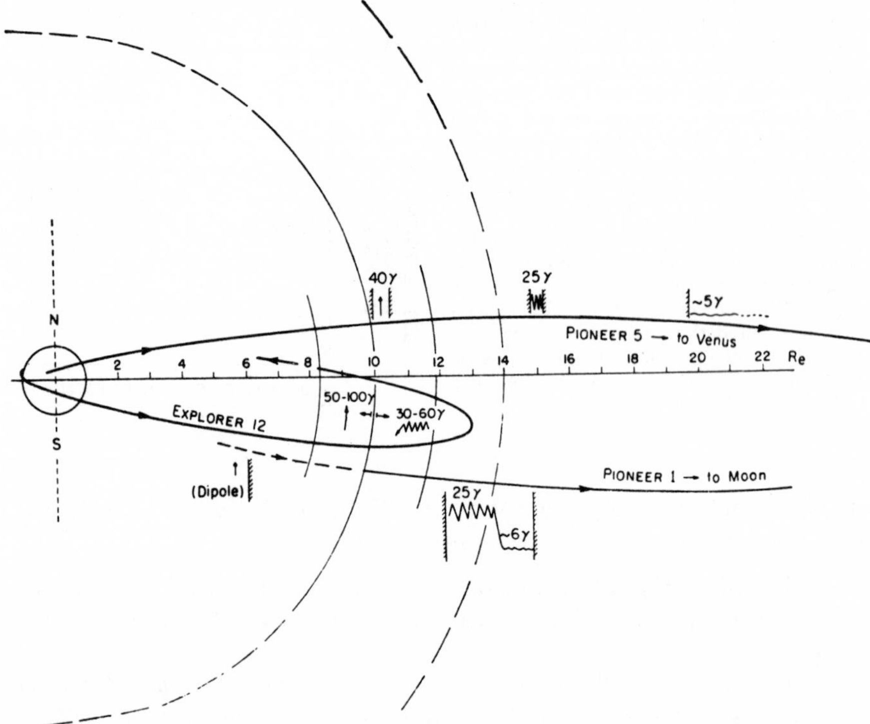

FIG. 10. Pictorial summary of combined results of Pioneer I, Pioneer V, and Explorer XII showing the boundary of the geomagnetic cavity and the location of the bow wave (after Bonetti *et al.* [8]). Local times for these probes are given in the text.

been considered [14, 19, 20, 21, 35, 46, 47]. Recent Explorer XIV magnetic field data [10] to radial distances of approximately 100,000 km on the dawn side of the earth near the geomagnetic equatorial plane (also note Fig. 6 at a similar spatial position) reveal no such discontinuity in the magnetic field as was observed on the sunward side of the earth. Consideration of these magnetic field measurements is mandatory in any interpretation of the asymmetric electron distributions of Fig. 6 (e.g., whether or not these electrons are trapped within the geomagnetic field). Explorer X magnetometer data [29] at distances beyond 22 R_E toward the night side of earth have been interpreted by the experimenters as implying a magnetic field directed radially toward the night side and away from the sun within the magnetospheric tail and a disordered magnetic field external to the tail. This interpretation has been used to construct the rough approximation of the shape of the magnetospheric boundary on the evening side of the earth-sun line in the geomagnetic equatorial plane shown in Figure 2. The relative position of Gringauz' and Freeman's low-energy fluxes with respect to the interpolated magnetospheric boundary of Figure 2 would imply that these electron fluxes are at least temporarily trapped within the geomagnetic field, but a critical judgment rests upon knowledge of the detailed character of the magnetic field in these regions. Hence the results of the large spatial survey of the geomagnetic field by Cahill's apparatus on Explorer XIV are anxiously awaited.

7. Polarization Electric Fields and Charged Particle Dynamics

The possibility that electric fields may play an important role in the dynamics of charged particle motion in the vicinity of the earth's magnetosphere has been stressed by various authors [5, 12]. Indeed such an effect may account for the marked departure from rotational symmetry of the flux contours of electrons ($E \gtrsim 40$ kev) at local dawn as shown in Figure 6. The motion of charged particles in an inhomogeneous magnetic field and under the influence of external forces has been studied previously [1, 49]. For motion in which the first adiabatic invariant $\mu = W_\perp / B$ is conserved, Figure 11 schematically depicts the corresponding drift motion for positive ions and electrons in an inhomogeneous magnetic field and an external electric field. These drifts or combinations of these drifts have provided several authors [33, 41] with a basic mechanism for populating the magnetosphere with charged particles by radial diffusion from a source; an example of such a source might be found in the vicinity of the magnetospheric boundary. Our specific realm of interest lies with the Chapman-Ferraro [12] and Axford-Hines [5] models of the magnetosphere. With regard to the Chapman-Ferraro model, Vestine [58] has called attention to the fact that the polarization charge on the dawn and evening sides of the magnetospheric boundary induced by the flow of solar plasma through the

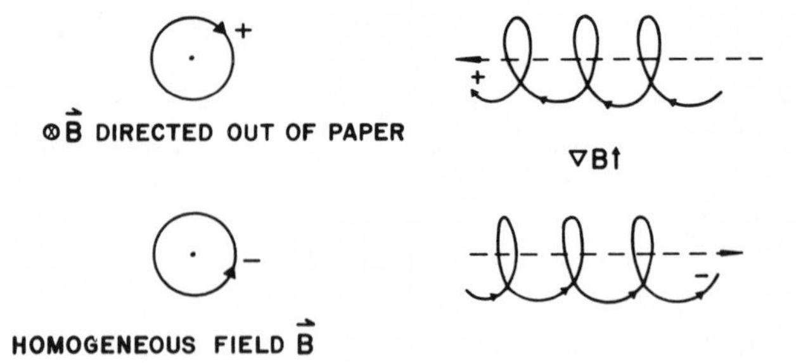

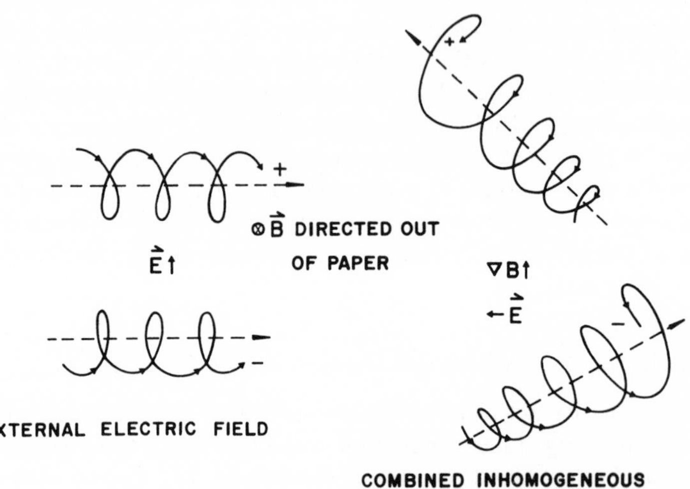

FIG. 11. Illustrative diagram of gradient drift and electric field drift motions of positive ions and electrons.

magnetic field in the vicinity of the boundary results in an electric field (see Fig. 12) across the cavity which is in a direction which will tend to drive positive ions and electrons along the boundary toward the earth. Axford and Hines [5] have developed a model of the magnetosphere in which there is a convective interchange of geomagnetic tubes of force driven by corotation of the earth's magnetic field and/or a viscous interaction with the solar wind. The lines of constant potential of electric polarization for these two physical situations are displayed in Figure 13; the geophysical situation may actually be a linear combination of the two effects. An electron of say 50 kev would then experience a force associated with its gradient drift, which is $\mu \nabla B$, and that due to the polarization electric fields, $e\bar{E}$. In the Axford-Hines model of the magnetosphere if polarization fields predomi-

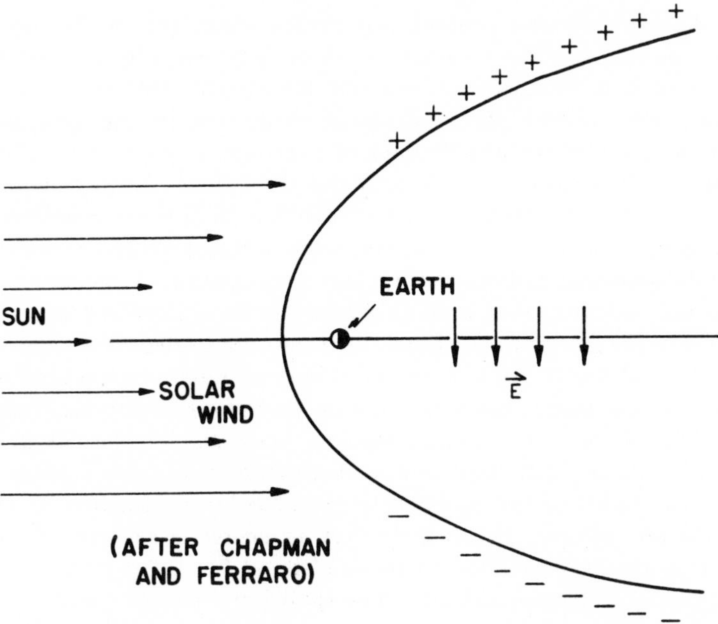

FIG. 12. (After Chapman and Ferraro [12].) The hollow and the polarization charge distribution formed by the interaction of the geomagnetic field with the solar wind.

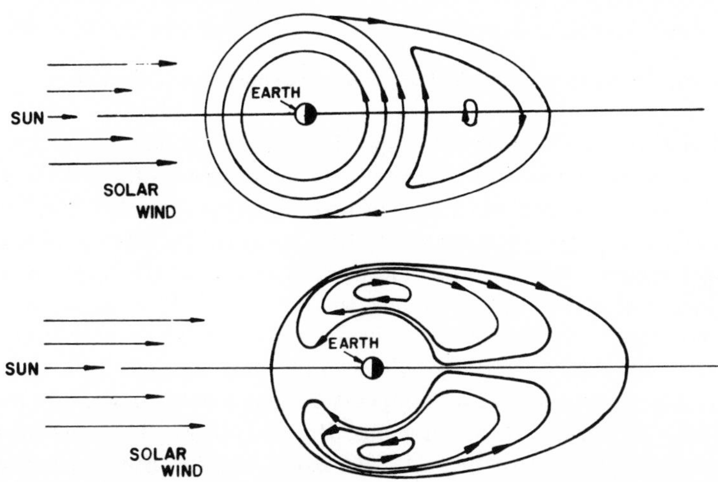

FIG. 13. An equatorial section of the magnetosphere viewed from above the North Pole, showing streamlines for the case in which the magnetosphere is corotating with the earth. The streamlines are also equipotentials of electric polarization that is induced by the rotation (top figure) (after Axford and Hines [5]).

The proposed pattern of streamlines in the equatorial plane (or alternately of the equipotentials of the electric field) resulting from the motion impressed on the magnetosphere by a viscous-like interaction with the solar wind (bottom figure) (after Axford and Hines [5]).

nate, the electrons and protons will stream essentially in the direction of the convection of the magnetic tubes of force (see Fig. 13). Since the gradient drift is energy-dependent and the electric drift is energy-independent, the approximately azimuthal symmetry in the geomagnetic equatorial plane of the distributions of electrons of energy $E \gtrsim 230$ kev [Frank and Van Allen, unpublished] and the diverse distribution of electrons of energy $E \lesssim 100$ kev may be important parameters in determining the magnitude of polarization electric fields if B and ∇B have been simultaneously measured and other drifts may be neglected. A similar study of the spatial distribution of protons would also be of significance since the direction of the gradient and electric drifts are charge-dependent and -independent, respectively. An interesting set of quantitative calculations of the drift paths and energy changes along these paths for energetic electrons and protons moving in a model magnetosphere under the influence of gradient drift in an image dipole field and polarization electric fields induced by a diurnal corotation of the geomagnetic field has been calculated by Hones [31]. As an example, Hones finds that an energetic electron of 50 kev drifting in the geomagnetic equatorial plane at 7.2 R_E at local noon will drift to 6.2 R_E at local midnight. The spatial and energy distributions of charged particles within and near the magnetospheric boundary may become important instruments in understanding the dynamics of the earth's magnetosphere.

8. Shocks, Deformation, and Motion of the Magnetospheric Boundary

Various computations of the shape of the hollow carved out of the solar plasma flow by the earth's magnetic field have been performed [6, 7, 50–52]. Figure 14 displays the results of three of these computations. Beard's result [6] was based upon an interaction between the solar wind and the earth's magnetic field within a thin current sheath at the magnetospheric boundary; the shape of the boundary was determined by equating the pressure due to the solar wind on the sunward side of the hollow with the energy density of the diamagnetically enhanced geomagnetic field just inside the cavity. The results for a zero temperature and finite temperature plasma are shown in Figure 14. Spreiter and Briggs [50, 51] have performed a similar computation (see Fig. 14) and more recently, Spreiter and Jones [52] have recalculated the form of the cavity utilizing the experimental measurements of the solar wind with Mariner II [37]. The general shape of these cavities in the geomagnetic equatorial plane are consistent with the known experimental results (see Figs. 2 and 6) but Heppner and his colleagues [29] and Bonetti *et al.* [8] have questioned some of the detailed structure of the interface on experimental grounds. Except for the single traversal of the magnetosphere at a geomagnetic latitude of ~50° by Mars

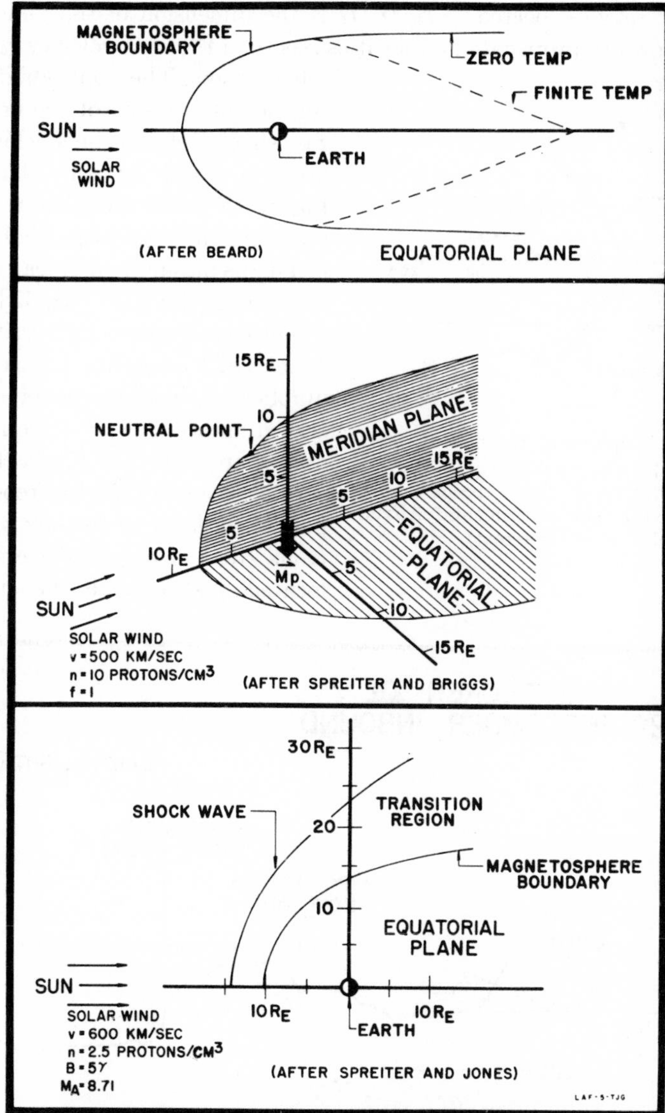

FIG. 14. Several results of computations concerning the form of the hollow produced by the interaction of the solar wind with the geomagnetic field.

I, no direct experimental evidence concerning the form of the hollow in the meridional planes at high latitudes is available at present.

Kellogg [34] (see also Axford [4] and Davis *et al.* [18]) has considered the supersonic flow of a collisionless solar plasma past the magnetosphere which acts as an obstacle to the flow and results in a shock wave on the sunward side of the geomagnetic hollow since any pressure wave of the frequency range expected, $\sim v_0/D$ (D is the dimension of the "bubble"), can be shown to propagate at velocities less than the bulk velocity v_0 of the solar plasma. The applicability to a collisionless plasma of the ordinary gas shock relationships which are used to construct the shocks of Figure 15 is not completely known but apparently can be partially justified if the plasma is permeated by a weak magnetic field [38, 52]. More recent computations by Spreiter and Jones [52] using an Alfvén Mach number M_A in the range of the observed interplanetary experimental values are shown in Figure 14. Recently Freeman [25] has reported a persistent layer of low-energy electrons (tens of ergs/cm²/sterad/sec) located just outside the sunward

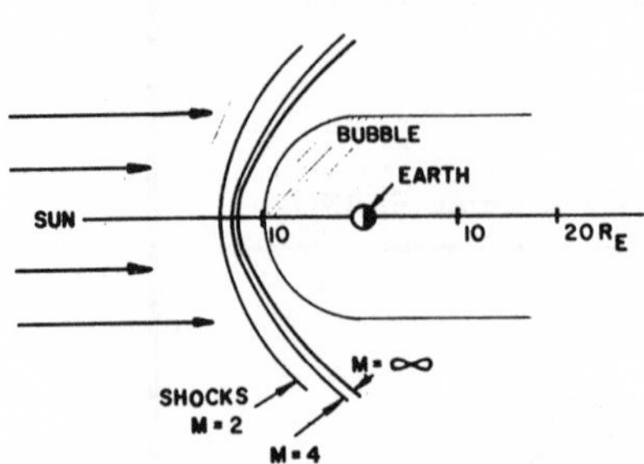

FIG. 15. Structure of the flow of interplanetary plasma around the earth for various supersonic flow speeds (after Kellogg [34]). The experimental Alfvén Mach number is ~7 (see text).

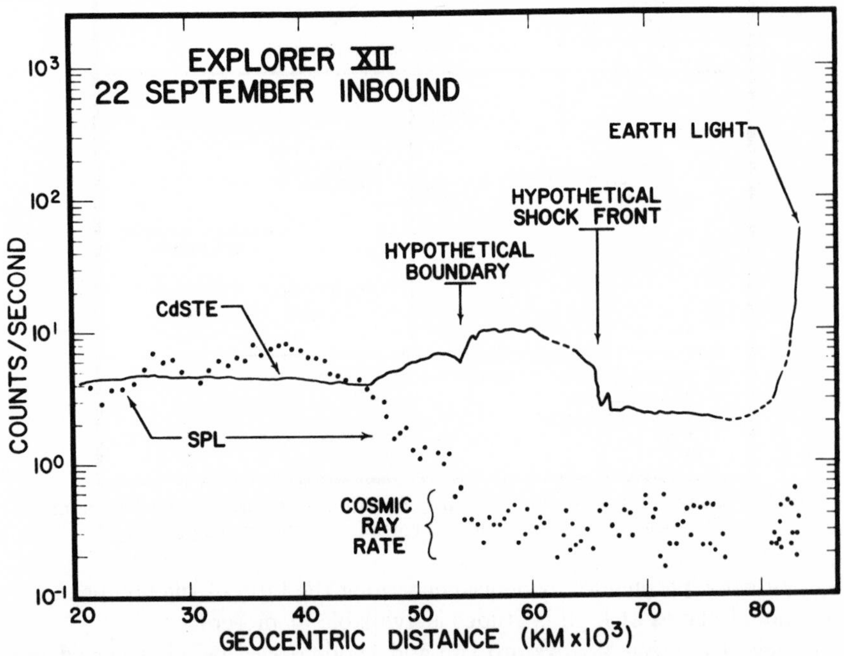

FIG. 16. Explorer XII observations (22 September 1961) of a region of large electron flux (50 ergs/cm²/sterad/sec at maximum) observed over a geocentric radial range of 55,000 to 67,500 km lying just beyond the magnetospheric boundary identified by the termination of ~50 kev electron fluxes (SpL) (after Freeman [25]).

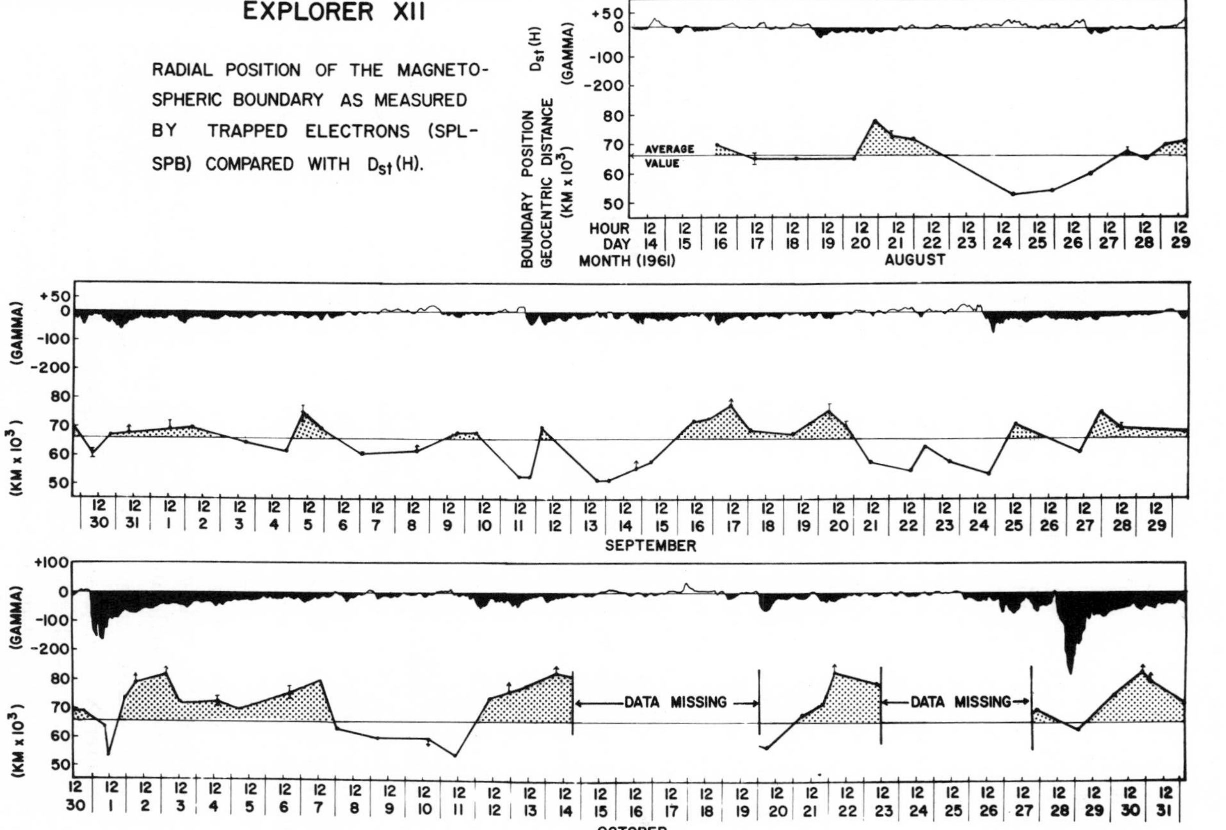

FIG. 17. The time history of the radial position of the magnetospheric boundary as determined by the radial termination of counts above background in the SpL detector (Explorer XII). Also shown is the $D_{ST}(H)$ value from the San Juan and Honolulu magnetograms (after Freeman [25]).

magnetospheric boundary near the geomagnetic plane, found with CdS total energy detectors on Explorer XII (Figs. 2 and 16). This layer has a radial dimension of approximately 2 or 3 R_E in agreement with the aforementioned theoretical results and may represent more direct experimental evidence of a shock on the sunward side of the magnetosphere. If the solar wind and the sunward side of the earth's magnetosphere are in a state of dynamic quasi-stationary equilibrium, it is reasonable to expect that a radial motion of the sunward boundary would be impressed by the action of the fluctuating solar wind. Along these lines of thought, Freeman [25] has studied the position of the magnetospheric boundary, delineated by the radial termination of fluxes of electrons of energy ~40 kev, as a function of time with instrumentation on Explorer XII (Fig. 17). Along with a definite correlation with D_{ST} as shown in Figure 17 the experimenter interprets these data as signifying a compression of the magnetosphere during the initial phase of a magnetic storm, a closer-than-average position maintained during the main phase and an outward motion of the boundary during the recovery phase. The fluctuation in the radial position of the boundary is approximately 2 or 3 R_E about an average position of 10 R_E. It is of interest to also note that the standard surface parameter for solar plasma activity, K_p, has been shown experimentally to have a positive correlation with the velocity of the solar wind [45] and the variability of the energy fluxes observed by Explorer XII just outside the sunward side of the magnetospheric boundary [25].

9. Dawn-Evening Distribution of Energetic Electrons

A preliminary survey [23] of energetic electrons (40 kev $\leq E \leq$ 230 kev) with Explorer XIV on the dawn side of the earth at large radial distances ($\gtrsim 7\ R_E$) in the geomagnetic equatorial plane revealed a large asymmetry in the spatial distributions of electrons within the magnetosphere. These distributions are closely related to the shape of the magnetospheric boundary, the nature of the magnetic fields in the vicinity of these charged particles, and the dynamical processes occurring within the magnetosphere. A study of the spatial and temporal behavior of these particle fluxes on the evening side of the earth-sun line is thus of significant importance. Investigations of this nature are now possible by means of data recently acquired with Explorer XIV in these regions. This study has not advanced to the stage where it is possible to construct the contours of constant omnidirectional intensity of electrons on the evening side of the earth-sun line as has been done previously on the dawn side in Figure 6; but several interesting unpublished samples of Explorer XIV data are presented in Figures 20 through 22. (The graphs are presented in chronological order; apogee progresses from the dawn, through the night, and into the evening side of the magnetosphere.)

Figure 18 shows the crossing of the magnetospheric boundary at 70,000 km at ~800 local time on 6–7 October 1962; Figure 19 displays measurements in the dawn flange where significant electron fluxes extend beyond

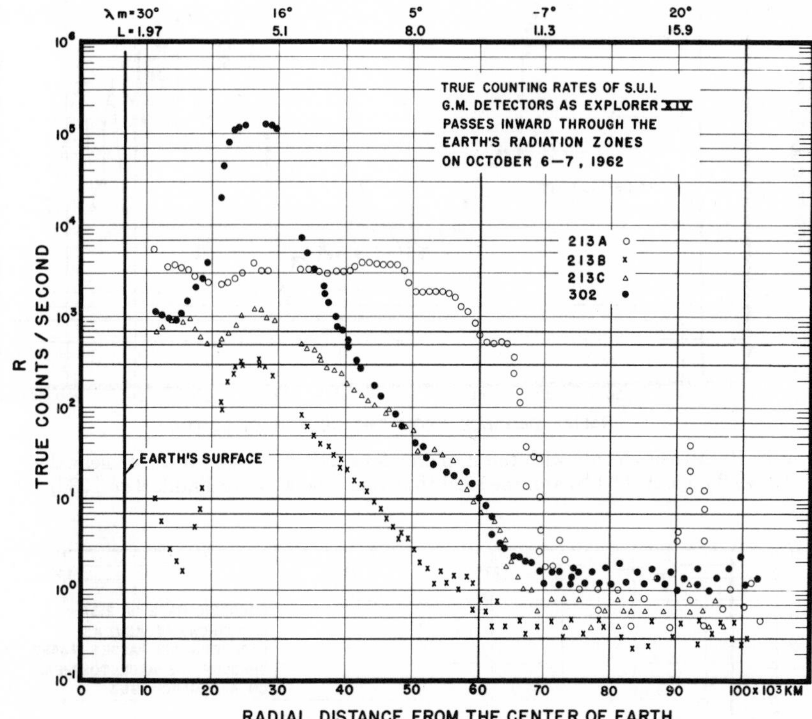

FIG. 18. The first of a series of radial plots of the response of the 213 Å detector (E, electrons $\gtrsim$ 40 kev) on Explorer XIV. The graphs are given in chronological order (and hence from local dawn to local evening). Conversion factor: $J_0(E \gtrsim 40 \text{ kev}) \simeq 5 \times 10^3$ R/cm²/sec. In this figure Explorer XIV crossed the magnetospheric boundary at 72,000 km on the dawn side of the earth-sun line. At 60,000 km, the local time was ~0830 (after Frank *et al.* [23]).

the satellite's apogee radial range of 105,000 km; Figure 20 is exemplary of measurements in the night side of the magnetosphere where a dearth of energetic electrons exists beyond approximately 45,000 km; Figure 21 displays the counting rates of the same detector at local evening and demonstrates that significant fluxes of electrons extended beyond apogee in a similar fashion as at local dawn for this particular pass; Figure 22 presents a late pass when the satellite's apogee has progressed sufficiently toward the earth-sun direction to allow the instrumentation to pass through an ap-

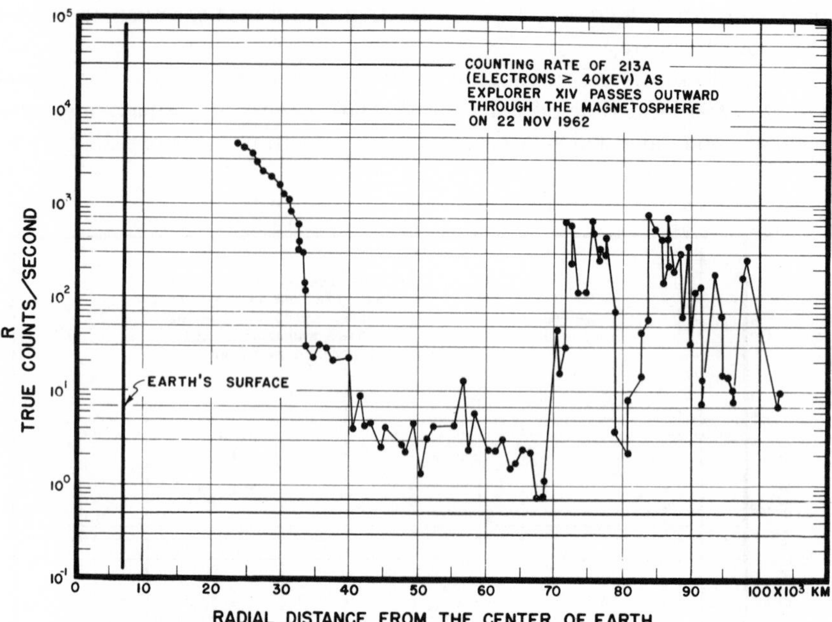

FIG. 19. Measurements with the Explorer XIV 213 Å electron detector near the dawn flange. At 60,000 km, the local time was ~0400 (after Frank *et al.* [23]).

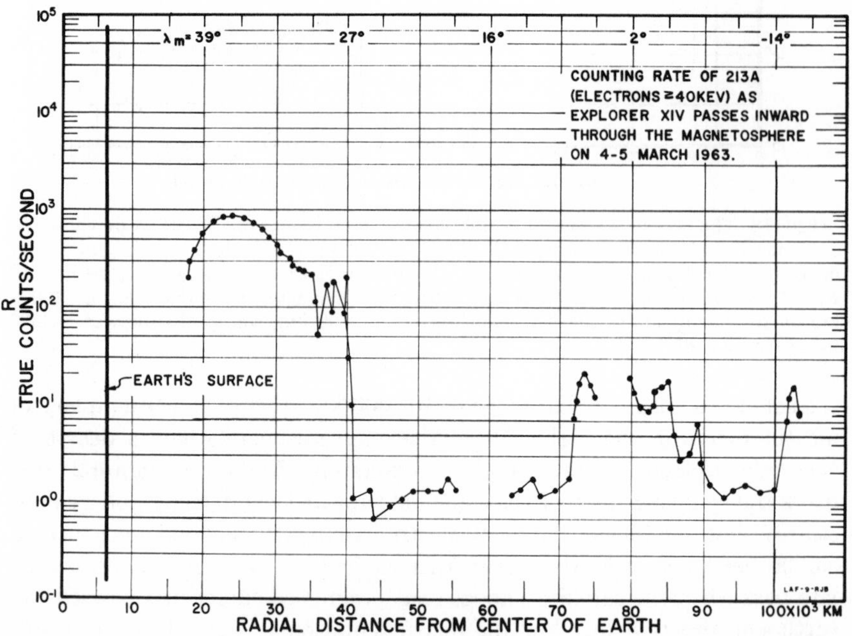

FIG. 20. Measurements on the night side of earth where there is a dearth of electrons. Note the sudden decrease of electron intensities at ~40,000 km. Local time at 60,000 km was ~2200 [Frank and Van Allen, unpublished].

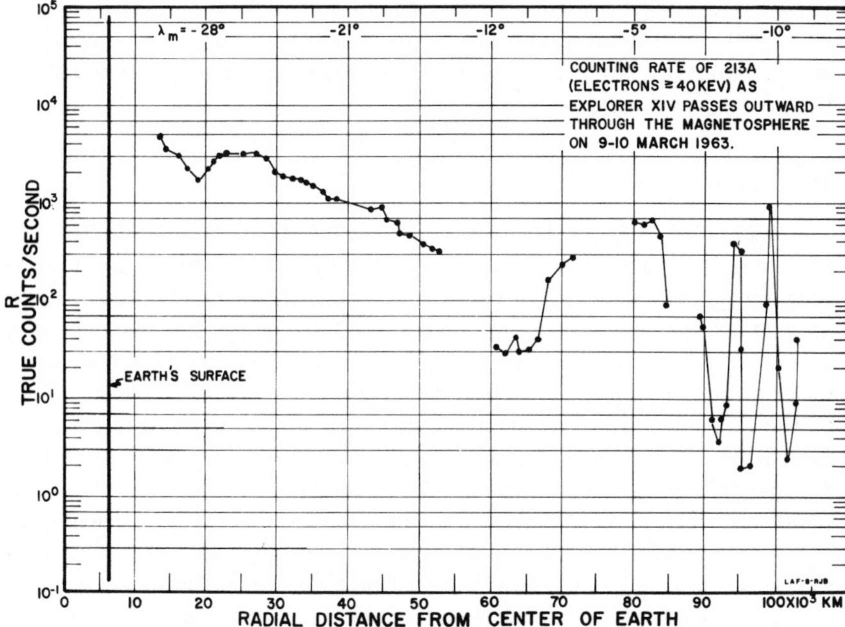

FIG. 21. An interesting pass through the magnetosphere near local evening. Note that large, sporadic electron intensities persist at least to 100,000 km. Local time at 60,000 km was ~1900 [Frank and Van Allen, unpublished].

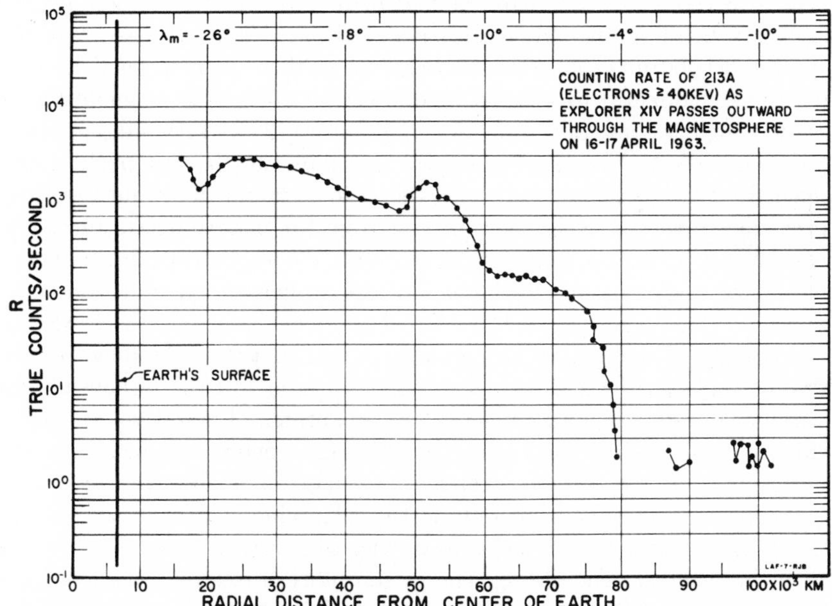

FIG. 22. Another 213 Å contour, but now with Explorer XIV nearer to the earth-sun line, in which an apparent traversal of the evening magnetospheric boundary has occurred. Local time at 60,000 km was ~1700 [Frank and Van Allen, unpublished].

parent magnetospheric boundary on the evening side of the earth-sun line at 80,000 km. A detailed analysis of the composite Explorer XIV data will be of significant importance toward the understanding of magnetospheric boundary phenomena.

10. Summary

A significant lack of experimental knowledge concerning the distribution of charged particles and the nature of the magnetic fields in the distant magnetosphere exists, particularly concerning those regions at high geomagnetic latitudes and in the night side "tail" of the magnetosphere at geocentric radial distances exceeding 17 R_E (Fig. 2). Progress has been made in many areas of study of the magnetospheric boundary. The general shape of the magnetosphere traced in the geomagnetic equatorial plane as predicted by the models of Beard [6] and Spreiter *et al.* [50–52] are in substantial, although not complete, agreement with the observations of Explorers X, XII, and XIV. Also a true symmetry about the earth-sun line of the dawn and evening boundaries in the geomagnetic equatorial plane is yet to be shown. There now is both theoretical and experimental support for the existence of a shock wave in front of the sunward side of the earth's magnetosphere. Recent observations of the marked azimuthal asymmetries of the distributions of charged particles of a few tens of kilovolts of energy in the geomagnetic equatorial plane of the distant magnetosphere suggest that drift motions other than gradient drifts are effective in these regions and may be attributed to polarization electric fields. Such a study of the spatial distributions and temporal behavior of these charged particles may thus lead indirectly to a critical examination of various magnetospheric models such as those of Chapman and Ferraro [12] and Axford and Hines [5]. The interlocking dependence of simultaneous charged particle and magnetic field measurements is easily seen to be vital throughout the interpretations reviewed in this survey. The subject of neutral points and possible charged particle injection mechanisms via the magnetospheric boundary have been neglected due to the lack of discriminating experimental information. It has been suggested that acceleration of charged particles exists in the vicinity of the distant magnetosphere and that the subsequent downflux of these particles along geomagnetic lines of force is responsible for various ionospheric phenomena such as auroras. Utilization of recent experimental results concerning the average energy dumped into the atmosphere in the form of corpuscular energy and the average energy available to the magnetosphere from the solar wind enables us to estimate the gross efficiency of a magnetospheric acceleration mechanism in the following manner. The average energy downflux of electrons of energy $\gtrsim 1$ kev into the auroral regions has been inferred from measurements with the low-altitude satellite Injun I as approximately 1 erg/cm^2/sec [39]; via integration over the surface area of the earth where this dumping is significant ($\sim$55° to $\sim$75° geomagnetic latitude), the average total power output to the earth's atmosphere becomes approximately 10^{18} ergs/sec. The average power input available to the magnetosphere can be obtained from the Mariner II measurements [37] of the average solar wind energy flux, $\sim 3 \times 10^{-1}$ ergs/cm²/sec, and by assuming the gross dimensions of the magnetosphere are that of a disk 15 R_E in diameter; the total power input becomes $\sim\pi(15\ R_E)^2\ (0.3) \sim 5 \times 10^{19}$ ergs/sec. The efficiency of this "black box" magnetosphere for producing the dumped corpuscular radiation from the energy available from the solar wind is hence of the order of $10^{18}/5 \times 10^{19} = 2$ per cent, a high, but apparently acceptable efficiency. Thus an acceleration mechanism for producing the corpuscular radiation dumped into the earth's atmosphere and located in the distant magnetosphere cannot be excluded on an energetic basis.

The close passage (41,000 km) of Mariner II past the planet Venus has been the only opportunity to observe the magnetosphere of another planet *in situ*; none of the Mariner II detectors (electrostatic analyzer, magnetometers, G.M. tubes) indicated the presence of a Venusian magnetosphere [22, 44].

Definite progress has been accomplished since the advent of space probes and earth satellites toward the understanding of the processes occurring in the vicinity of the magnetospheric boundary, a region which is intimately associated with the sun via the solar wind and which in turn has a profound influence upon the physics of the upper atmosphere; the next few years of experimental and theoretical study of these phenomena show great promise in being fruitful ones.

References

1. H. Alfvén, *Cosmical Electrodynamics* (Clarendon Press, 1950).
2. S.-I. Akasofu and S. Chapman, A neutral line discharge theory of the aurora polaris, *Phil. Trans. Roy. Soc.*, **A253**, 359–406 (1961).
3. R. L. Arnoldy, R. A. Hoffman, and J. R. Winckler, Observations of the Van Allen radiation regions during August and September 1959, Part I, *J. Geophys. Res.*, **65**, 1361–1376 (1960).
4. W. I. Axford, The interaction between the solar wind and the earth's magnetosphere, *J. Geophys. Res.*, **67**, 3791–3796 (1962).
5. W. I. Axford and C. O. Hines, A unifying theory of high-latitude geophysical phenomena and geomagnetic storms, *Can. J. Phys.*, **39**, 1322 (1961).
6. D. B. Beard, The interaction of the terrestrial magnetic field with the solar corpuscular radiation, *J. Geophys. Res.*, **65**, 3559–3568 (1960).
7. D. B. Beard, The interaction of the terrestrial magnetic field with the solar corpuscular radiation. 2. Second order approximation, *J. Geophys. Res.*, **67**, 477–483 (1962).
8. A. Bonetti, H. S. Bridge, A. J. Lazarus, B. Rossi, and F. Scherb, Explorer 10 plasma measurements, *J. Geophys. Res.*, **68**, 4017–4064 (1963).
9. H. S. Bridge, C. Dilworth, A. Lazarus, E. F. Lyon, B. Rossi, and F. Scherb, Direct observations of the interplanetary plasma, *J. Phys. Soc. Japan*, **17**, Suppl. A II, 553 (1963).

10. L. J. Cahill (Paper presented at the Explorer XIV Symposium, Washington, D.C., February 1963).
11. L. J. Cahill and P. G. Amazeen, The boundary of the geomagnetic field, *J. Geophys. Res.*, **68,** 1835 (1963).
12. S. Chapman and V. C. A. Ferraro, A new theory of magnetic storms, *Terr. Mag. Atmos. Elec.*, **36,** 77, 171 (1931); **37,** 147, 269, 421 (1932); **38,** 79 (1933).
13. P. J. Coleman, Jr., L. Davis, Jr., E. J. Smith, and C. P. Sonett, The mission of Mariner II: Preliminary observations: Interplanetary magnetic fields, *Science*, **138,** 1099–1100 (1962).
14. P. J. Coleman, Jr., and C. P. Sonett, Note on hydromagnetic propagation and geomagnetic field stability, *J. Geophys. Res.*, **66,** 3591–3592 (1961).
15. P. J. Coleman, Jr., C. P. Sonett, D. L. Judge, and E. J. Smith, Some preliminary results of the Pioneer V magnetometer experiment, *J. Geophys. Res.*, **65,** 1856–1857 (1960).
16. L. R. Davis (Paper presented at the Explorer XIV Symposium, Washington, D.C., February 1963).
17. L. R. Davis and J. M. Williamson, Low-energy trapped protons, *Space Research III*, 365 (North-Holland Publishing Co., 1963).
18. L. Davis, Jr., R. Lüst, and A. Schlüter, The structure of hydromagnetic shock waves, *Z. Naturforsch.*, **13a**, 916 (1958).
19. A. J. Dessler, Large amplitude hydromagnetic waves above the ionosphere, *J. Geophys. Res.*, **63,** 507–511 (1958).
20. A. J. Dessler, The stability of the interface between the solar wind and the geomagnetic field, *J. Geophys. Res.*, **66,** 3587–3590 (1961).
21. A. J. Dessler and E. N. Parker, Hydromagnetic theory of geomagnetic storms, *J. Geophys. Res.*, **64,** 2239–2252 (1959).
22. L. A. Frank, J. A. Van Allen, and H. K. Hills, Mariner II: Preliminary reports on measurements of Venus: Charged particles, *Science*, **139,** 905–907 (1963).
23. L. A. Frank, J. A. Van Allen, and E. Macagno, Charged particle observations in the earth's outer magnetosphere, *J. Geophys. Res.*, **68,** 3543–3554 (1963).
24. L. A. Frank, J. A. Van Allen, W. A. Whelpley, and J. D. Craven, Absolute intensities of geomagnetically trapped particles with Explorer XIV, *J. Geophys. Res.*, **68,** 1573–1579 (1963).
25. J. W. Freeman, The morphology of the electron distribution in the outer radiation zone and near the magnetospheric boundary as observed by Explorer XII, *State Univ. Iowa Rept.* **63-20** (1963).
26. J. W. Freeman, J. A. Van Allen, and L. J. Cahill, Jr., Explorer 12 observations of the magnetospheric boundary and the associated solar plasma on September 13, 1961, *J. Geophys. Res.*, **68,** 2121–2130 (1963).
27. K. I. Gringauz, V. V. Bezrukikh, L. S. Musatov, R. E. Rybchinsky, and S. M. Sheronova, Measurements made in the earth's magnetosphere by means of charged particle traps aboard the Mars I Probe, *Space Research IV* (North-Holland Publishing Co., in press).
28. K. I. Gringauz, V. G. Kurt, V. I. Moroz, and I. S. Shklovskii, Results of observations of charged particles observed out to $R = 100{,}000$ km, with the aid of charged-particle traps on Soviet space rockets, *Astron. Zh.*, **37,** 716 (1960; translation in: *Soviet Astronomy-AJ*, **4,** 680 1961).
29. J. P. Heppner, N. F. Ness, C. S. Scearce, and T. L. Skillman, Explorer 10, magnetic field measurements, *J. Geophys. Res.*, **68,** 1–46 (1963).
30. R. A. Hoffman, R. L. Arnoldy, and J. R. Winckler, Observations of the Van Allen radiation regions during August and September 1959, Part 6: properties of the outer region, *J. Geophys. Res.*, **67,** 4543–4573 (1962).
31. E. W. Hones, Motions of charged particles trapped in the earth's magnetosphere, *J. Geophys. Res.*, **68,** 1209–1220 (1963).
32. F. S. Johnson, The gross character of the geomagnetic field in the solar wind, *J. Geophys. Res.*, **65,** 3049–3051 (1960).
33. P. J. Kellogg, Van Allen radiation of solar origin, *Nature*, **183,** 1295 (1959).
34. P. J. Kellogg, Flow of plasma around the earth, *J. Geophys. Res.*, **67,** 3805–3811 (1962).

35. G. J. F. MacDonald, Spectrum of hydromagnetic waves in the exosphere, *J. Geophys. Res.*, **66,** 3639–3670 (1961).
36. C. E. McIlwain, Coordinates for mapping the distribution of magnetically trapped particles, *J. Geophys. Res.*, **66,** 3681–3692 (1961).
37. M. Neugebauer and C. W. Snyder, The mission of Mariner II: Preliminary observations: Solar plasma experiment, *Science,* **138,** 1095–1097 1(962).
38. T. Obayashi, Interaction of solar plasma streams with the outer geomagnetic field (Paper presented at the Symposium on Cosmic Plasma Physics, Institute of Plasma Physics, Nagoya University, November 1962).
39. B. J. O'Brien, Lifetimes of outer-zone electrons and their precipitation into the atmosphere, *J. Geophys. Res.*, **67,** 3687–3706 (1962).
40. B. J. O'Brien, A large diurnal variation of the geomagnetically trapped radiation, *J. Geophys. Res.*, **68,** 989–996 (1963).
41. E. N. Parker, Interaction of the solar wind with the geomagnetic field, *Phys. Fluids*, **1,** 171 (1958).
42. E. N. Parker, Geomagnetic fluctuations and the form of the outer zone of the Van Allen radiation belt, *J. Geophys. Res.*, **65,** 3117–3130 (1960).
43. E. J. Smith, Theoretical and experimental aspects of ring currents, *Space Science,* D. P. LeGalley (ed.), 316–371 (Wiley and Sons, 1963).
44. E. J. Smith, L. Davis, Jr., P. J. Coleman, Jr., and C. P. Sonett, Magnetic field (near Venus with Mariner II), *Science,* **139,** 909 (1963).
45. C. W. Snyder and M. Neugebauer, Interplanetary solar wind measurements by Mariner II, *Space Research IV* (North-Holland Publishing Co., in press).
46. C. P. Sonett, Rocket experiments in cosmic magnetism and their significance, *Space Science,* D. P. LeGalley (ed.) 374–421 (Wiley and Sons, 1963).
47. C. P. Sonett, The distant geomagnetic field. Part 4. Microstructure of a disordered hydromagnetic medium in the collisionless limit, *J. Geophys. Res.*, **68,** 1265–1294 (1963).
48. C. P. Sonett, E. J. Smith, and A. R. Sims, Surveys of the distant magnetic field: Pioneer I and Explorer VI, *Space Research,* 921 (North-Holland Publishing Co., 1960).
49. L. Spitzer, *Physics of Fully Ionized Gases* (Interscience Publishers, 1962).
50. J. R. Spreiter and B. R. Briggs, Theoretical determination of the form of the hollow produced in the solar corpuscular stream by interaction with the magnetic dipole field of the earth, *J. Geophys. Res.*, **67,** 2985 (1962).
51. J. R. Spreiter and B. R. Briggs, On the choice of condition to apply at the boundary of the geomagnetic field in the steady-state Chapman-Ferraro problem, *J. Geophys. Res.*, **67,** 2983 (1962).
52. J. R. Spreiter and W. P. Jones, On the effect of a weak interplanetary magnetic field on the interaction between the solar wind and the geomagnetic field. *J. Geophys. Res.*, **68,** 3555–3564 (1963).
53. P. V. Vakulov, S. N. Vernov, E. B. Gorchakov, Yu. I. Logachev, A. N. Charakhchyan, T. N. Charakhychyan, and A. E. Chudakov, Investigation of cosmic rays, *Space Research IV* (North-Holland Publishing Co., in press).
54. J. A. Van Allen and L. A. Frank, Radiation around the earth to a radial distance of 107,400 kilometers, *Nature,* **183,** 430–434 (1959).
55. J. A. Van Allen and L. A. Frank, Radiation measurements to 658,000 km with Pioneer IV, *Nature,* **184,** 219–224 (1959).
56. J. A. Van Allen and L. A. Frank, The mission of Mariner II: Preliminary observations: The Iowa radiation experiment, *Science,* **138,** 1098–1099 (1962).
57. S. N. Vernov, A. E. Chudakov, P. V. Valukov, Yu. I. Logachev, and A. G. Nikolaev, Radiation measurements during the flight of the second lunar rocket, *Artificial Earth Satellites No. 5,* 24 (Moscow, 1960; translation in: *ARS J.*, **31,** 967, 1961).
58. E. H. Vestine, Some comments on the ionosphere and geomagnetism (Paper presented at the XIV General Assembly, International Scientific Radio Union, Tokyo, September 1963).

CHAPTER 8

THE GEOCORONA

Joseph W. Chamberlain

When the hydrogen geocorona is understood, it will probably seem very simple and we may even look back wondering what all the confusion was about. The confusion persists partly because the subject has had a rather slow start by space-age standards. And yet a planetary corona offers great potential for studying aspects of an atmosphere that have heretofore been untouchable.

1. The Observations Prior to IGY

At a symposium in June 1956, Byram, Chubb, Friedman, and Kupperian [7] announced the discovery, made six months earlier from an Aerobee rocket, of ultraviolet radiation in the night sky. The investigators suspected that the radiation arose from the Lyman α transition of atomic hydrogen, which later turned out to be the case. The motivation for the experiment seems to have been the possibility of observing neutral hydrogen in the interplanetary gas [14]. Further observations were made in March, 1957 [28, 29]. The Ly α flux was found to be about 10^{-2} erg/cm^2/sec, but not quite uniform over the nighttime hemisphere, being rather weaker in the antisolar direction. The Ly α radiation was also found to be reflected back into space from the earth's upper atmosphere (i.e., from the 100-km region) with an albedo of about 42 per cent. The albedo for direct solar radiation was less than 2 per cent.

It was first pointed out by Shklovsky [40] that the Ly α glow, as well as a much weaker (Balmer transition) Hα found by Prokudina and Kvifte [39, 30] on airglow spectra, did not necessarily arise from interplanetary hydrogen, but that it might instead be scattered by a geocorona. Shklovsky himself seemed to favor the interplanetary origin, however [40].

No Ly α observations were obtained during the years of IGY and IGC, and there are several good reasons for the omission: a geocorona observable on the night side had not been predicted, so that planners of IGY programs were not aware of all the geophysical possibilities in a Ly α experiment. Further, serious debate on whether the observed Ly α might be of terrestrial origin did not begin until 1959, too late to affect IGY or IGC programs.

2. Early Interpretations: Interplanetary or Terrestrial?

By late 1959 the debate on the location of the H-atoms scattering solar Ly α to the night hemisphere was well developed. Brandt and Chamberlain [6] gave a detailed treatment of the interplanetary hypothesis, including an analysis of the albedo of night-sky and direct solar radiation. They interpreted the data available in terms of the H density, its location in the solar system, and its optical thickness and temperature.

Lyman α incident from the interplanetary gas would have large Doppler shifts (depending on the particular direction) due to the earth's motion; and the albedo, arising from scattering by cool, atmospheric hydrogen should then be small, as it is for the broad solar radiation. Consequently, with the interplanetary origin, Brandt and Chamberlain faced an inconsistency that could be dismissed only with an ad hoc assumption of either a strong self-reversal in the solar-emission profile or local airglow excitation of Ly α. The latter seems especially unrealistic and the profile [37] was found not to show the required absorption core.

The geocoronal hypothesis was advocated most forcibly by F. S. Johnson. Somewhat earlier Chapman [11] had called attention to the likelihood that H would be the main atmospheric constituent at high altitudes. If the geocorona were the source of Ly α scattering, the night emission would have to arise from H-atoms at very great altitudes (where they would be illuminated by direct sunlight) or else multiple scatterings would have to occur frequently enough to transfer radiation from the day hemisphere. Accordingly Johnson and Fish ([25]; also see corrections and further discussion by Johnson [23]) developed the statistical orbit theory for atoms in the geocorona in order to derive the density distribution with height. (The isothermal barometric law becomes increasingly inaccurate at great distances from the planet.) The orbit theory was developed independently by Öpik and Singer ([33]; also see correction [34]; [35]) for the geocorona and by Chamberlain [8] for application to the solar corona. (The latter paper, dealing with a plasma, considered low-energy particles in the gas to be kept isotropic through frequent deflecting collisions, and all captive particles were therefore treated as a single group. Otherwise, these three independent approaches to the orbit theory were equivalent.)

Johnson found that direct illumination of a spherical corona would not account for the nighttime Ly α and argued qualitatively for an important radiative-transfer contribution. The day and night albedos seemed to him to rule out the interplanetary origin, whereas Brandt and Chamberlain had felt that the role necessarily imposed on multiple scatterings would eliminate the terrestrial origin.

3. Observations Since the IGY

At this point new data began to appear. In early 1960 a group at the Naval Research Laboratory [13] fired a Javelin rocket, which measured the variation of Ly α intensity from above and below, between 350 and 1120 km. These data allowed estimates of the amount of secondary scattering in the lower corona and of the density of H-atoms [4, 27].

Rocket measurements of the absorption core in solar Ly α [37, 38] were utilized by Bates and Patterson [1] to derive integrated H-densities.

Whereas previous experiments had used photometers designed to see a particular wavelength range that included Ly α, an actual spectrum was first obtained by Morton [31]. Also Morton and Purcell [32] used an atomic-hydrogen cell to obtain a crude measurement of the line width. The radiation reflected by atmospheric hydrogen from below the rocket was almost completely absorbed by the cell (as expected), but 15 per cent of the radiation from above was transmitted, indicating the fraction of atoms with radial velocities exceeding 10 km/sec.

Day as well as night observations were obtained in June, 1962 by Heath and Fastie [17, 21]. The nighttime flight gave a steadily increasing intensity from 120–200 km, suggesting considerably greater nighttime H-densities in this region than did the earlier observations. Donahue [16, 17] has also proposed that there is a substantial increase in the density of H in the 120–200 km region at night compared with daytime, a result also in conflict with conclusions based on earlier data [27], perhaps indicating 11-year variations. (Post-IGC observations by the group at the Naval Research Laboratory have been summarized by Chubb and Byram [12].)

4. Models of the Hydrogen Distribution in Space

Most of the work of developing a satisfactory model has concentrated lately on the geocorona as the source of the night, as well as day, diffuse Ly α glow. However, a substantial interplanetary component is not completely ruled out. The principal argument for an interplanetary contribution is the high-velocity component of the profile. Patterson *et al.* [36] have argued that fast neutral H may be created by charge exchange between solar-wind protons and neutral interstellar gas, several astronomical units from the sun. Some of these fast atoms would then diffuse back into the solar neighborhood before being photoionized or swept back out by collisions. The principal uncertainty at the moment seems to be whether the interstellar gas can be mainly neutral, because of ionizing radiation from both the sun and the very hot O-type stars in the sun's region of the galaxy.

An alternative proposal for the wide profile is due to Brandt [2, 3, 5], who had earlier speculated that the solar wind would interact with the escaping component of terrestrial H and sweep it into a *geocoma*, extending down wind from the earth. This idea that a substantial part of the hydrogen lay in an intermediate location—in the form of a gaseous tail—was first presented in an effort to overcome objections to both the models previously proposed. For the interplanetary origin, the nighttime albedo was too high and the interplanetary H-density expected theoretically was too low. And for the conventional terrestrial origin, there seemed to be difficulties in having sufficient secondary scatterings to fill in the shadow, with the amount of H thought to be present. In the geocoma model, single scattering by distant, escaping H-atoms is an important contributor.

The distribution of intensity over the night hemisphere has caused serious difficulties of explanation. The main problem concerns the emission from the antisolar direction. With a spherical geocorona at temperatures the order of 10^{3}°K, virtually all of the hydrogen is within three earth radii and lies within the earth's shadow at night. Thus the partial filling in of this shadow seems to require a more distant source, such as Brandt's geocoma or an interplanetary component, or else the nighttime corona must be optically thick in the center of Ly α to provide enough secondary scatterings to diffuse the shadow. The latter explanation has been advocated by Donahue [15–19]. As noted above, his proposal also includes a substantial daily variation in the H-abundance at high altitudes, raising a matter for both observational and theoretical investigation.

To select the most appropriate model, more definitive observations are required. Not only have the absolute intensities been uncertain, but there is a distinct possibility of a variation over the solar cycle. Absolute measurements from well outside the geocorona would be of enormous value.

Some of the problems involved in fitting the various data together into a consistent picture have been described more fully in other recent reviews [10 Sec. 9a, 15, 18].

5. Areas of Theoretical Work

In addition to the development of special models for the H-distribution in space, there are several diversified areas of theoretical work that have a bearing on one or another aspect of planetary coronas. It is the intent here to list these areas and reference the principal papers now available in these subjects.

Radiation Theory

For an optically thin cloud of H-atoms, Brandt and Chamberlain [6] have dealt with the Ly α/Hα ratio and the polarization (the latter still unobserved). This paper also treats the albedo theory. For an optically thick case the radiative transfer problem is quite complicated compared with similar problems in plane-parallel atmospheres. The only quantitative treatment is due to Thomas [41]; it has been discussed and applied in the recent papers by Donahue.

Simple-Corona Theory

A simple planetary corona is one that is spherically symmetric and controlled only by gravitation and heat conduction from below. While the H-geocorona may differ significantly from this first approximation, the simplified theory provides a convenient standard for comparison. The early statistical orbit theory was referenced in Section 2. Recently an examination of the entire subject has been published [10]. This paper provides an approximate means of allowing for the contribution to the density of atoms in satellite orbits and gives numerical tables that readily yield the density at any altitude and the integrated densities along a line of sight for a corona of specified parameters (the temperature, density, and height of the base of the corona). The paper also gives expressions for the Doppler profiles of spectral lines in terms of the coronal parameters, and it treats several problems of fundamental, but fairly abstract, interest to the theory.

Departures from a Simple Corona

Even without interaction of the outer corona with interplanetary particles (mentioned in Section 4), the geocorona may be decidedly unsymmetric, owing to latitude and daily variations, and its characteristics may vary with the level of solar radiation. Such variations with time could arise from temperature variations in the thermosphere. The rate of escape of H is fixed by the temperature at the base of the corona, and this loss rate, being replaced through upward diffusion, determines the abundance of H in the corona. A lower temperature leads to a higher equilibrium abundance of coronal H [24, 1, 26]. When the lateral flow of H-atoms near the critical level is considered, the daily variation of coronal H-abundance imposed by the daily variation of temperature becomes partly smoothed out [20].

6. Planetary Coronae and Atmospheric Physics

The study of planetary coronae may provide much information not easily obtainable from the lower, denser regions of an upper atmosphere.

Perhaps the most important parameter that can be so obtained is the *escape temperature*—the kinetic temperature at the top of the thermosphere or the base of the corona. This temperature governs the rate of thermal evaporation and as such is important to any evolutionary understanding of an atmosphere. If the corona is close to the "simple" model described in Section 5, the radial variation of density or, what is more readily observable, the integrated density, provides a direct measure of the temperature.

The classical approach to the terrestrial escape temperature has been to derive it from an equilibrium calculation of the abundance and rate of production of helium. However, numerous complications have become apparent in recent years (see Sec. 9b of [10]), making it highly desirable to measure the temperature, and its temporal and spatial variations, directly. Similarly the helium (at least the more abundant He^4) abundance might be derived directly from photometric coronal observations in $\lambda584$, the He resonance line.

As Johnson [22] has noted, the hydrogen geocorona must interact with ions through charge exchange, thereby having important influences on the ionized corona (the radio-whistler medium) and on trapped particles of moderate energies. An understanding of these phenomena will require definitive information on the coronal properties. Further, if the solar wind distorts the corona appreciably, direct observations of Ly α from satellites or a deep-space probe looking back at the planet would seem to be the surest way of establishing this fact.

Coronal observations of other planets also seem to hold much potential information. In the case of Venus, knowledge of the chemical composition of the lower atmosphere is in such an unsatisfactory state that little in the way of intelligent guesses can be made on the escape temperatures. For Mars, some preliminary estimates [9] suggest an atomic oxygen corona, well distended and fairly easily detectable in the light of $\lambda1302$. The H and He coronas there are likely far too tenuous to be seen.

For the heavier planets the upper atmospheres must be so compact and cold that a neutral-particle corona, of the type on Venus, Mars, and the earth, can scarcely be of any importance. On the other hand, any trace of atmosphere on the moon or Mercury will be, essentially, a corona characteristic of temperatures at the surface, which then serves as the base of the planetary corona.

References

1. D. R. Bates and T. N. L. Patterson, Hydrogen atoms and ions in the thermosphere and exosphere, *Planet. Space Sci.*, **5**, 257–273 (1961).
2. J. C. Brandt, Interplanetary gas. V. A hydrogen cloud of terrestrial origin, *Astrophys. J.*, **134**, 394–399 (1961).
3. J. C. Brandt, On the interpretation of the night sky Lyman-α radiation and related phenomena, *Space Research II*, H. C. van de Hulst, C. de Jager, and A. F. Moore, (eds.), 624–638 (North-Holland Publishing Co., 1961).

4. J. C. Brandt, On the role of secondary scattering in the Lyman-α problem, *Planet. Space Sci.*, **9**, 67–78 (1962).
5. J. C. Brandt, The Lyman-α problem and the geocoma hypotheses, *Nature*, **195**, 894–895 (1962).
6. J. C. Brandt and J. W. Chamberlain, Interplanetary gas I. Hydrogen radiation in the night sky, *Astrophys. J.*, **130**, 670–682 (1959).
7. E. T. Byram, T. A. Chubb, H. Friedman, and J. Kupperian, Far ultraviolet radiation in the night sky, *The Threshold of Space*, M. Zelikoff, (ed.), 203-210 (Pergamon Press, 1957).
8. J. W. Chamberlain, Interplanetary gas, II. Expansion of a model solar corona, *Astrophys. J.*, **131**, 47–56 (1960).
9. J. W. Chamberlain, Upper atmospheres of the planets, *Astrophys. J.*, **136**, 582–593 (1962).
10. J. W. Chamberlain, Planetary coronae and atmospheric evaporation, *Planet. Space Sci.*, **11**, 901 (1963).
11. S. Chapman, Speculations on the atomic hydrogen and the thermal economy of the upper atmosphere, *The Threshold of Space*, M. Zelikoff, (ed.), 65–72 (Pergamon Press, 1957).
12. T. A. Chubb and E. T. Byram, Rocket observations of the far ultraviolet sky, *Space Research III*, W. Priester, (ed.), 1046–1060 (North-Holland Publishing Co., 1963).
13. T. A. Chubb, H. Friedman, R. W. Kreplin, and P. Mange, Lyman-alpha radiation in the night sky, *Mém. Soc. Roy. Sci. Liège*, [5] **4**, Pt. 1, 437–446 (1961).
14. T. A. Chubb, H. Friedman, and J. E. Kupperian, A satellite experiment to determine the distribution of hydrogen in space, *Scientific Uses of Earth Satellites*, J. A. Van Allen, (ed.), 152–156 (Univ. of Mich. Press, 1956).
15. T. M. Donahue, Excitation of the Lyman-α in the night sky, *Space Sci. Rev.*, **1**, 135–153 (1962).
16. T. M. Donahue, On a large diurnal variation in hydrogen abundance, *J. Geophys. Res.*, (in press, 1964).
17. T. M. Donahue and W. G. Fastie, Observation and interpretation of resonance scattering of Lyman α and OI (1300) in the upper atmosphere, *Space Research IV* (North-Holland Publishing Co., in press).
18. T. M. Donahue and G. Thomas, Distribution of hydrogen in the outer atmosphere, *Planet. Space Sci.*, **10**, 65–72 (1963).
19. T. M. Donahue and G. E. Thomas, Lyman-α scattering in the earth's hydrogen geocorona, II, *J. Geophys. Res.*, **68**, 2661–2667 (1963).
20. W. B. Hanson and T. N. L. Patterson, Diurnal variation of the hydrogen concentration in the exosphere, *Planet. Space Sci.*, **11**, 1035 (1963).
21. D. F. Heath and W. G. Fastie, Spectra of the day airglow and the night airglow in the 1100–2000 A region, *Trans. Amer. Geophys. Un.*, **43**, 435–436 (1962).
22. F. S. Johnson, The telluric hydrogen corona and some of its consequences, *Space Research I*, H. Kallmann Bijl, (ed.), 736–745 (North-Holland Publishing Co., 1960).
23. F. S. Johnson, The distribution of hydrogen in the telluric hydrogen corona, *Astrophys. J.*, **133**, 701–703 (1961).
24. F. S. Johnson, Structure of the upper atmosphere, *Satellite Environment Handbook*, Francis S. Johnson, (ed.), 17 (Stanford Univ. Press, 1961).
25. F. S. Johnson and R. A. Fish, The telluric hydrogen corona, *Astrophys. J.*, **131**, 502–515 (1960).
26. G. Kockarts and M. Nicolet, Le problème aéronomique de l'hélium et de l'hydrogène neutres, *Ann. Géophys.*, **18**, 269–290 (1962).
27. R. W. Kreplin, H. Friedman, T. A. Chubb, and P. Mange, Further comments on the role of secondary scattering in the Lyman-α problem, *Planet. Space Sci.*, **9**, 68–69 (1962).
28. J. E. Kupperian, E. Byram, T. A. Chubb, and H. Friedman, Extreme ultraviolet radiation in the night sky, *Ann. Geophys.*, **14**, 329 (1958).
29. J. E. Kupperian, Jr., E. T. Byram, T. A. Chubb, and H. Friedman, Far ultraviolet radiation in the night sky, *Planet. Space Sci.*, **1**, 3–6 (1959).

30. G. Kvifte, Auroral and nightglow observations at Ås, Norway, *J. Atmos. Terr. Phys.*, **16,** 252–258 (1959).
31. D. C. Morton, Spectroscopic observations of the night sky in the extreme ultraviolet, *Planet. Space Sci.*, **9,** 459–460 (1962).
32. D. C. Morton and J. D. Purcell, Observations of the extreme ultraviolet radiation in the night sky using an atomic hydrogen filter, *Planet. Space Sci.*, **9,** 455–458 (1962).
33. E. J. Öpik and S. F. Singer, Distribution of density in a planetary exosphere, *Phys. Fluids*, **2,** 653–655 (1959).
34. E. J. Öpik and S. F. Singer, Distribution of density in a planetary exosphere, *Phys. Fluids*, **3,** 486–488 (1960).
35. E. J. Öpik and S. F. Singer, Distribution of density in a planetary exosphere, II, *Phys. Fluids*, **4,** 221-233 (1961).
36. T. N. L. Patterson, F. S. Johnson, and W. B. Hanson, The distribution of interplanetary hydrogen, *Planet. Space Sci.*, **11,** 767–778 (1963).
37. J. D. Purcell and R. Tousey, The profile of solar hydrogen Lyman-α *J. Geophys. Res.*, **65,** 370–372 (1960).
38. J. D. Purcell and R. Tousey, Photography of the sun in Lyman-α and other wavelengths, *Mém. Soc. Roy. Sci. Liège* [5] **4,** Pt. 1, 274–282 (1961).
39. V. S. Prokudina, Observations of the line λ 6562 A in night airglow spectrum, *Spectral, Electrophotometrical, and Radar Researches of Aurorae and Airglow No. 1*, 43–44 (Section IV of IGY Program, Acad. Sci. USSR, Moscow, 1959; English translation, Royer and Roger, Inc., International Division, New York and Washington, D.C., p. 31, 1959).
40. I. S. Shklovsky, On hydrogen emission in the nightglow, *Planet. Space Sci.*, **1,** 63–65 (1959).
41. G. E. Thomas, Lyman-α scattering in the earth's hydrogen geocorona. I. *J. Geophys. Res.*, **68,** 2639 (1963).

CHAPTER 9

IONOSPHERIC CONSTITUTION AND SOLAR CONTROL

Herbert Friedman

The IGY and subsequent years have witnessed the acquisition of a great volume of new information leading to important refinements in theories of ionospheric behavior under the influence of solar radiation, but also emphasizing many fundamental areas of uncertainty. To construct a theory of the ionosphere, it is necessary to know (1) the spectral distribution of ionizing radiation, (2) the structure of the atmosphere, (3) the photoabsorption cross sections of the constituent atoms and molecules, and (4) the nature of ionic interactions and electron loss processes. Although solar spectrum data are more complete now than during IGY, large uncertainties about intensities below the Lyman limit (910 Å) still exist and arguments persist concerning the role of corpuscular radiation relative to ultraviolet and X-rays. The structure of the atmosphere cannot yet be specified with confidence between 100 and 200 km. Ionic reactions which control the electron loss processes are generally uncertain by an order of magnitude. Especially important is the recognition that, under the impact of solar wind and ionizing radiation, the atmospheric structure varies greatly over diurnal, seasonal, and solar cycle time scales. Large perturbations of a transient nature appear in dramatic response to sporadic solar activity. At heights well above 200 km, information now developing about the topside ionosphere indicates that its structure is not a simple extension of the bottomside ionosphere, for the magnetic field assumes a major control over the movements of charged particles.

1. Solar Ionizing Radiation

Although the solar emission line spectrum can now be identified in almost complete detail to the shortest X-ray wavelengths, our knowledge of the intensity distribution is still subject to large uncertainties. Individual rocket measurements have been relatively infrequent. The temporal differences observed are certainly partly real but also partly the result of imprecise calibration techniques. Attempts to monitor solar X-rays and ultraviolet radiation from satellites have thus far been rather primitive, limited in spectral range, and not sufficiently continuous. The orbiting solar observatory, OSO-1, launched by NASA in 1962, was a major advance and future observatories in this series will offer appropriate platforms for continuous solar monitoring in great spectral detail.

The photoionization threshold of nitric oxide is 1340 Å, so that ionization by the strong Lyman α line of hydrogen at 1216 Å is possible. This interaction is the longest wavelength source of atmospheric ionization of primary importance, even though nitric oxide exists only as a trace constituent. All of the major atmospheric constituents are ionized by much shorter wavelengths. The thresholds for molecular oxygen and atomic oxygen are 1026 Å and 910 Å. Molecular nitrogen has its ionization threshold at 796 Å, and an important secondary maximum at 510 Å, below which N_2 is dissociated into a neutral atom and an atomic ion. Atomic nitrogen is ionized below 852 Å.

The flux of Lyman α (1216 Å) [29] has been observed to vary between 3 and 6 ergs/cm²/sec (1.8×10^{11} and 3.6×10^{11} photons/cm²/sec). Increased emission is associated with plages and the variability may be attributed largely to the variation in plage area over the solar disc. Lyman β (1025.7 Å) and C II (977 Å) have been observed [22] with intensities of

TABLE 1

SOLAR PHOTON FLUXES

Wavelength Interval	Photons/cm²/sec
910–850	9.5×10^9
850–800	2.5×10^9
800–700	5.0×10^9
700–600	4.7×10^9
600–500	5.9×10^9
500–400	2.4×10^9
400–300	7.2×10^9
300–230	3.1×10^9
230–170	3.3×10^9
170–110	3.5×10^8
110–80	2.4×10^8
80–60	1.8×10^8
60–30	1.6×10^8

about 2.5 × 10^9 photons/cm²/sec and 3.7 × 10^9 photons cm²/sec under average conditions of solar activity. Both these wavelengths ionize O_2.

Table 1 is based on data reported by Hinteregger [39] from rocket flights in 1960 under conditions corresponding to sunspot index $R = 87$ and $S = 168 \times 10^{-22}$ watt/m²/cm/sec of solar microwave flux. The listed intensities are almost an order of magnitude less than those derived by Ivanov-Kholodny [43] largely on the basis of theoretical considerations.

From 1–100 Å, Kreplin [50] has observed a solar flux of about 0.13 erg/cm²/sec at sunspot minimum (1954) and increasing to 0.9 erg/cm²/sec at maximum (1958). At wavelengths shorter than 10 Å, which penetrate to *D*-region, the solar cycle variation exceeds a factor of 50 even in the absence of flares.

Even under quiet-sun conditions, i.e., in the absence of flares, the non-uniform distribution of emission brightness over the disc in various ultraviolet and X-ray lines causes marked variations to occur in photoionization rates as the sun rotates. Improved observations with monochromatic ultraviolet cameras, X-ray pinhole cameras, and slit telescopes have begun to provide a quantitative picture of the relative concentrations of sources in active regions as compared to the background disc. These observations will be discussed later.

2. Atmospheric Models

The interaction of radiation with the atmosphere affects the pressure, temperature, density, composition, and degree of ionization. With resolved spectra, we can proceed to detailed computations of the interactions with a model atmosphere, provided that accurate cross sections are known. Many of the cross sections required for ionospheric computations are known only theoretically or from laboratory experiments often using inadequate resolution. An error of only a factor of 2 in cross section produces an order of magnitude error in the computation of the interaction at the level of maximum rate of absorption. Current research in laboratory spectroscopy promises to improve the absorption cross-section values through the development of continuum radiation sources and very high resolution spectrographs. The absorption of Lyman γ (972.537 Å) by molecular nitrogen is a good example of the problems involved. The absorption cross section is of the order of 1×10^{-16} cm² averaged over the N_2 bandhead, spreading from 972.2 Å to slightly longer wavelengths, but may be three times as great if it coincides with one of the many rotational lines.

Although satellite drag measurements have provided rather accurate measures of atmospheric density above 200 km, rocket exploration of the atmosphere below this level has been both inadequate in regard to the amount of sampling and also in reliability. Since the major portion of solar ionizing radiation is absorbed below 200 km the uncertainty about atmospheric structure precludes any accurate calculations of ionospheric structure.

At the start of the IGY, it was not appreciated that the atmosphere was highly variable. The early Rocket Panel model atmosphere [84] made no allowance for solar cycle as well as diurnal variability, and gross discrepancies between sets of measurements made years apart were attributed to experimental inaccuracies rather than real effects. On the other hand, experimental progress has been so slow that, even today, it is not certain what values to assign to fundamental parameters such as the ratios O/O_2, N/N_2, and O_2/N_2. Since the IGY many model atmospheres have been proposed varying in mean molecular weight from 29 to 16 in the 100–200 km height range. More recent measurements [65, 74] show that the $N(O)/N(O_2)$ ratio reaches unity near 120 km. The ratio appears to be less than 3 at 130 km and sufficient O_2 persists at higher levels so that the mean molecular weight is probably not less than 24 at 200 km. With respect to ion composition, direct measurements have been similarly lacking. 1963 has produced the first ion composition measurements during midday and midnight at the same location [40].

3. Ionic Reactions and Electron Loss Processes

As in atmospheric models, absorption cross sections, and solar spectral energy distributions, a considerable spread is found in theoretical and calculated rates of ionic reactions and electron loss processes.

Consider first the charge transfer and ion-atom interchange reactions. Measurements of ion composition, described later in this paper, show ambient distributions remarkably different from the primary ions created by the absorption of solar radiation. In the course of ionic reactions, some ions disappear so quickly after being created that they are barely observable with the most sensitive mass spectrometers flown in rockets. The more important reactions are:

$$O^+ + N_2 \rightarrow N + NO^+ + 1.12 \text{ ev} \tag{1}$$

$$O^+ + O_2 \rightarrow O + O_2^+ + 1.54 \text{ ev} \tag{2}$$

$$O_2^+ + N_2 \rightarrow NO + NO^+ + 0.87 \text{ ev} \tag{3}$$

$$N_2^+ + O_2 \rightarrow N_2 + O_2^+ + 3.50 \text{ ev} \tag{4}$$

$$N_2^+ + O \rightarrow N_2 + O^+ + 1.96 \text{ ev} \tag{5}$$

Recent laboratory measurements show a spread of values for the rate constants. Langstroth and Hasted [54] found $k_1 = (4.7 \pm 0.5) \times 10^{-12}$ cm^3/sec at 300°K. Sayers [73] obtained $k_1 = 2.5 \times 10^{-11}$ cm^3/sec. Talrose *et al.* [80] give $k_1 \leq 6.7 \times 10^{-12}$ cm^3/sec.

Laboratory results for k_2 have a similar spread. Dickinson and Sayers

[23] give $k_2 = 2.5 \times 10^{-11}$ cm³/sec at 200–300°K. Sayers [73] reports $k_2 = 1.6 \times 10^{-11}$ cm³/sec. Langstroth and Hasted [54] find $k_2 = 1.8 \times 10^{-12}$ cm³/sec and Fite *et al.* [28] give $k_2 = (1\text{–}15) \times 10^{-11}$ cm³/sec.

Reaction 3, which converts O_2^+ to NO^+, may be expected to go very slowly because two molecular bonds are broken and k_3 may be smaller than 10^{-13} cm³/sec. Reactions 4 and 5, the charge exchange with O_2 and O, may be important processes for the depletion of molecular nitrogen ions. According to Fite *et al.* [28], an experimental value for k_4 is 2×10^{-10} cm³/sec.

The following two processes, which convert N_2^+ to ON^+, have been proposed as important contributors to the equilibrium ionization:

$$N_2^+ + O \rightarrow ON^+ + N + [3.08 - E(^3\pi)] \text{ ev} \tag{6}$$

$$N_2^+ + O_2 \rightarrow ON^+ + NO + [4.47 - E(^3\pi)] \text{ ev} \tag{7}$$

Nicolet and Swider [64] have pointed out, however, that both the ion-atom interchange 6 and the double ion-atom interchange 7 are endothermic. They cite Stupochenko *et al.* [76] as giving a value of 4.6 ev for the $(^3\pi)$ state of NO^+.

Although nitric oxide is a minor constituent and, therefore, contributes little ionization as a result of direct photoionization, it is found to be a major constituent of *E*-region and lower *F*-region. This is readily understandable because the NO-ion is an end product of the important reaction 1. Once formed, NO^+ persists because it cannot charge exchange with the constituents N_2, N, O_2, or O, all of which have higher ionization potentials. Neither can it enter into ion-atom interchange processes because of its high dissociation energy. In contrast, the molecular nitrogen ion, because of its higher ionization potential, is lost on collision with any of the ambient constituents N, O, O_2, and NO.

Two processes are important for neutralization of ionospheric ions. Atomic ions disappear by radiative recombination with electrons according to

$$X^+ + e \rightarrow X' + h\nu \tag{8}$$

Molecular ions undergo dissociative recombination according to

$$XY^+ + e \rightarrow X' + Y' \tag{9}$$

where the primes indicate the various possible final states. Theoretical values of the radiative coefficients, according to Bates and Dalgarno [3], are 4.8×10^{-12} cm³/sec for H^+ and He^+ and 3.7×10^{-12} cm³/sec for O^+. For the dissociative recombination coefficients of N_2^+, O_2^+, and NO^+, a variety of experimental data are available. These are listed in Table 2. It appears that the most probable value is about 10^{-7} cm³/sec for all three ions at 300°K.

TABLE 2

LABORATORY DETERMINATIONS OF DISSOCIATIVE RECOMBINATION COEFFICIENTS α_D (cm^3/sec)

Experimenters	$\alpha_D(N_2^+)$	$\alpha_D(O_2^+)$	$\alpha_D(NO^+)$
Kasner, Rogers, and Biondi [47]	$(5.9 \pm 1) \times 10^{-7}$	$(3.8 \pm 1) \times 10^{-7}$	
	$T \sim 300°K$, pressure $\lesssim 0.01$ mm Hg		
Biondi [7]	$(2.8 \pm 0.5) \times 10^{-7}$	$(1.7 \pm 1) \times 10^{-7}$	
Holt [41]		3×10^{-7}	
Faire and Champion [26]	4.0×10^{-7}		
Bialecke and Dougal [6]	6.7×10^{-6} $T \sim 92°K$ 8.7×10^{-7} $T \sim 300°K$		
Sayers [72]	1.1×10^{-7} $T \sim 3200°K$	4×10^{-8} $T \sim 2500°K$	
Gunton and Inn [36]			1.3×10^{-6} $T \sim 300°K$, pressure > 0.1 mm Hg
Lin [56]			10^{-9} $T \sim 5000°K$
Doering and Mahan [24]			2×10^{-6} (probe) 3×10^{-7} (decay)
Syverson, Stein, Shaw [79]			1.3×10^{-7}
Scheibe and Gunton			$T \sim 3000°K$

4. Production of the Ionosphere

Although the uncertainties in our knowledge of radiation intensity, atmosphere structure, radiation cross sections, ionic reaction rates, and electron loss processes prevent us from formulating an accurate theory of ionospheric behavior, a qualitative picture of the major features can be drawn from available information. In the following, use is made of various published models without any intent to pose these as accurate models. They are offered only as illustrations of the general character of the problems being considered.

Figures 1 and 2 illustrate the theoretical transmission of assumed model atmospheres for various wavelengths from 1 Å to Lyman α (1216 Å). With

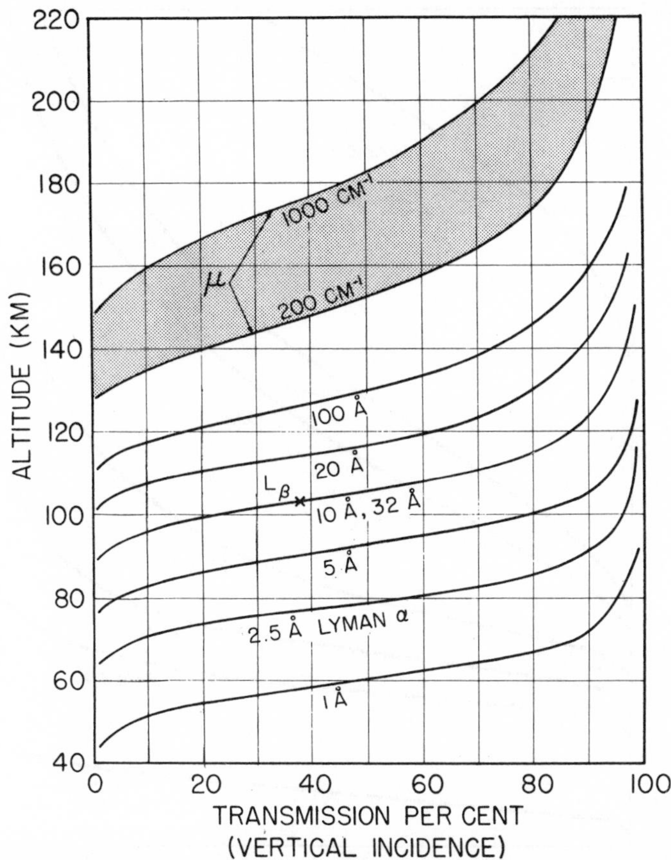

FIG. 1. Penetration of the atmosphere by solar X-rays and ultraviolet radiation. The shaded portion includes the broad range of wavelengths from 100–850 Å for which the linear absorption coefficients lie between 200 and 1000/cm⁻¹.

such data, it is possible to deduce the rate of production of ionization versus height.

4.1. D-Region

Under normal conditions, the *D*-region is taken to be the 60–90 km altitude range. From Figure 1 it can be seen that Lyman α and X-rays from 1 to 8 Å would contribute ionization at these altitudes. An important contribution is also made by galactic cosmic rays in the lower portion of *D*-region.

At sunspot minimum, the spectrum of the quiet sun rarely extends below 10 Å and X-rays play no role in *D*-region. With increasing activity, X-ray emission appears below 10 Å and penetrates the 100-km level. Solar flares

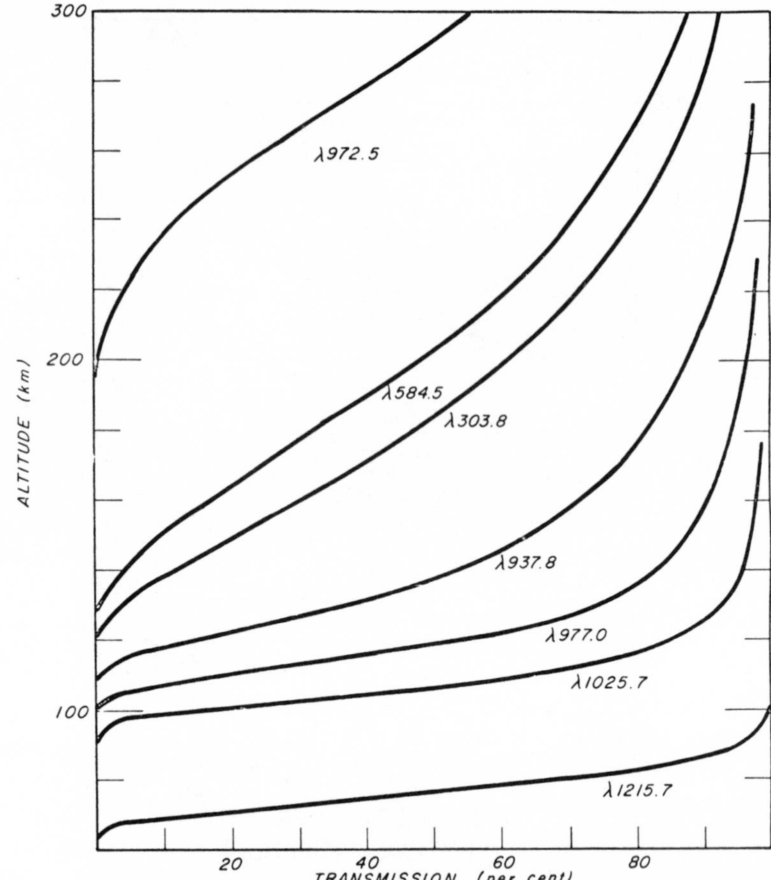

FIG. 2. Penetration of the atmosphere by solar ultraviolet radiation (Watanabe and Hinteregger [87]).

shower relatively large fluxes of X-rays into the deepest portions of *D*-region and produce sudden ionospheric disturbances. These will be discussed later.

For all electromagnetic radiation capable of ionizing molecular nitrogen or oxygen, the absorption cross section is greater than 10^{-18} cm^2 which places the level of unit optical depth above the *D*-region (number of molecules per square centimeter column above 85 km $= 10^{20}$). To reach the *D*-region, the wavelength must, therefore, be longer than 1026.5 Å, the ionization potential of O_2, and must fit one of the windows in the O_2 absorption spectrum near 1108 Å, 1143 Å, 1157 Å, 1167 Å, 1187 Å, and 1216 Å. The window at 1216 Å matches Lyman α perfectly, which makes it possible for the very strong solar flux in this line to ionize the trace of nitric oxide that exists in the *D*-region [E_i (NO) $= 9.4$ ev]. Lyman α is observed by means of rockets to penetrate to 75 km when the sun is overhead.

Nicolet's [62] estimate of the concentration of nitric oxide at 85 km is about 10^{-10} of the total concentration, or only $10^4/cm^3$. This estimate is based on the production of nitric oxide by the reaction

$$N + O_2 \rightarrow NO + O \quad (10)$$

with atomic nitrogen being supplied through the ionization of molecular nitrogen by solar X-rays, followed by dissociative recombination and a subsequent downward diffusion of atomic nitrogen. Cosmic-ray primaries produce between 100 and 300 ion pairs per cm^3/sec between geomagnetic latitude 40° and 60° at sea-level pressure. At any altitude where the particle density is n, the ionization rate q, at latitude ϕ, is given by

$$q(\phi) = q_0(\phi)n/n_0 \quad (11)$$

We use $n_0 = 2.5 \times 10^{19}/cm^3$ and obtain

$$q(\phi = 50°) = 10^{-17}\ n/cm^3/sec$$

Nicolet and Aikin [63] adopted the following values for dissociative recombination coefficients

$$\alpha_D(N_2) = 5 \times 10^{-7}\ cm^3/sec$$

$$\alpha_D(O_2) = 3 \times 10^{-8}\ cm^3/sec$$

$$\alpha_D(NO) = 3 \times 10^{-9}\ cm^3/sec$$

and, including the effects of negative ion formation (negligible above 80 km but important below 70 km), arrived at the *D*-region electron density profiles shown in Figure 3. The effect of cosmic rays is apparent in the region below 70 km. Lyman α produces the maximum in the distribution for an overhead sun near 85 km. At the mesopause, ionization is contributed by the tail of the X-ray spectrum.

Experimental information concerning *D*-region electron density profiles is still derived almost entirely from ground-based RF experiments. These include: (*a*) VLF propagation at frequencies below 300 kc/sec; (*b*) Partial reflection sounders operating at a frequency such as 2 Mc/sec, which exceeds the plasma frequency; (*c*) Wave interaction (cross modulation); (*d*) Cosmic noise absorption (riometer). Typical n_e derived from these methods are: for a quiet day, $10^3/cm^3$ at 80 km, decreasing to $10/cm^3$ at 60 km; for a quiet night, $10^3/cm^3$ at 90 km, falling to $10/cm^3$ at 80 km; and for a disturbed day (i.e., polar blackout), 10^4 at 80 km and 10^3 at 60 km. Only on the quietest days in temperate latitudes is there a simple dependence of n_e on solar zenith angle as predicted by a Chapman-type layer.

No experimental data exist for negative ion concentrations. Nicolet and Aikin [63] predict $100/cm^3$ at 75 km for a quiet sun, increasing to about $10^3/cm^3$ at 55 km. Balloon measurements below *D*-region indicate about $4 \times 10^3/cm^3$ at 30 km.

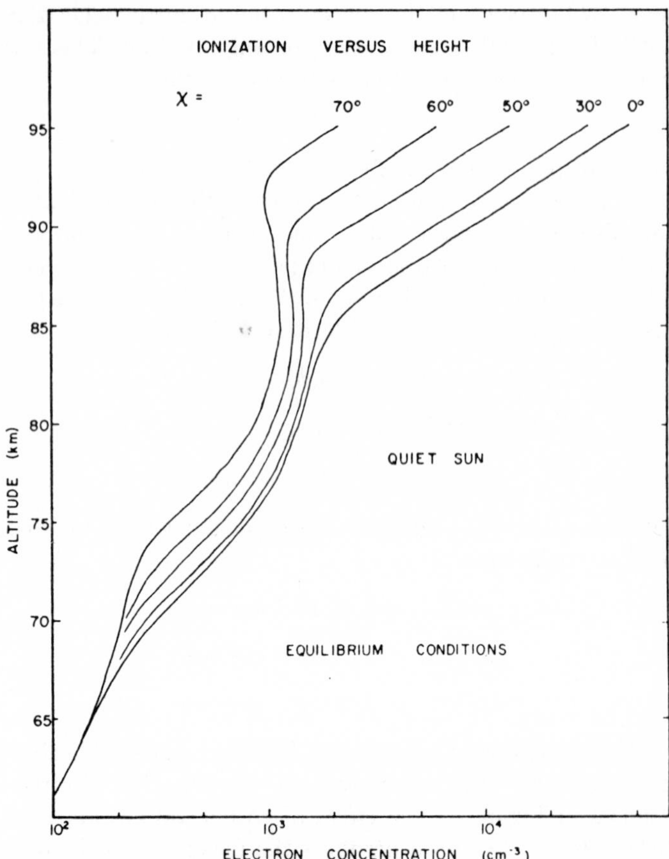

FIG. 3. Electron density distribution in the D-region as a function of solar zenith angle (Nicolet and Aikin [63]).

Direct measurements from rockets have been made using RF propagation techniques, RF resonance probes, and the Faraday rotation technique, but these seem limited to $n_e \geq 100/\text{cm}^3$ and give little information below 75 km. Ion traps have been used to measure positive ion densities of the entire D-region, but it is not clear how to interpret instrumental behavior below 80 km.

An experimental value for α_D in D-region has been derived by R. E. LeLevier [55] from measurements of the magnitude and time dependence of X-ray induced absorption associated with the high-altitude nuclear explosion of 9 July 1962. The observations were made over Midway Island about 1500 km northwest of the Johnston Island site of the explosion. The X-rays from the explosion were in the range one to a few kev and produced electron densities of 10^6–$10^8/\text{cm}^3$ above Midway. By utilizing riometers to study cosmic noise absorption, it was determined that α_D lay between

3×10^{-7} and 7×10^{-7} cm^3/sec with a probable best value of 4×10^{-7} cm^3/sec if taken with a negative ion-positive ion recombination coefficient of 3×10^{-8} cm^3/sec. The bulk of the absorption occurred in the region 70–80 km.

5. *E*-Region

Rocket measurements of the variation of electron density with height give reliable profiles of the *E*- and *F*-regions. Representative illustrations are offered in Figures 4, 5, and 6. Figure 4 shows the excellent agreement

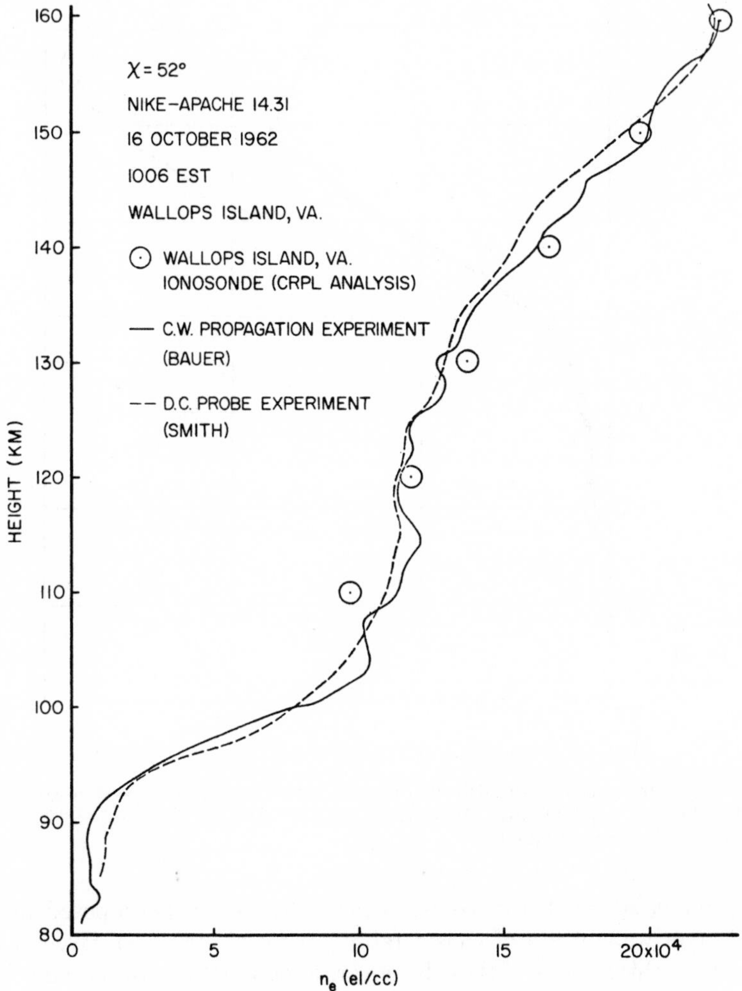

FIG. 4. A "true height" profile compared with rocket results (Bauer and Jackson [4]).

between rocket measurements using cw propagation and dc probe techniques, and ionosonde data reduced to a true height profile.

Nighttime rocket observations are still seriously lacking. Rocket data obtained by Smith [75] with a Langmuir probe technique showed a main

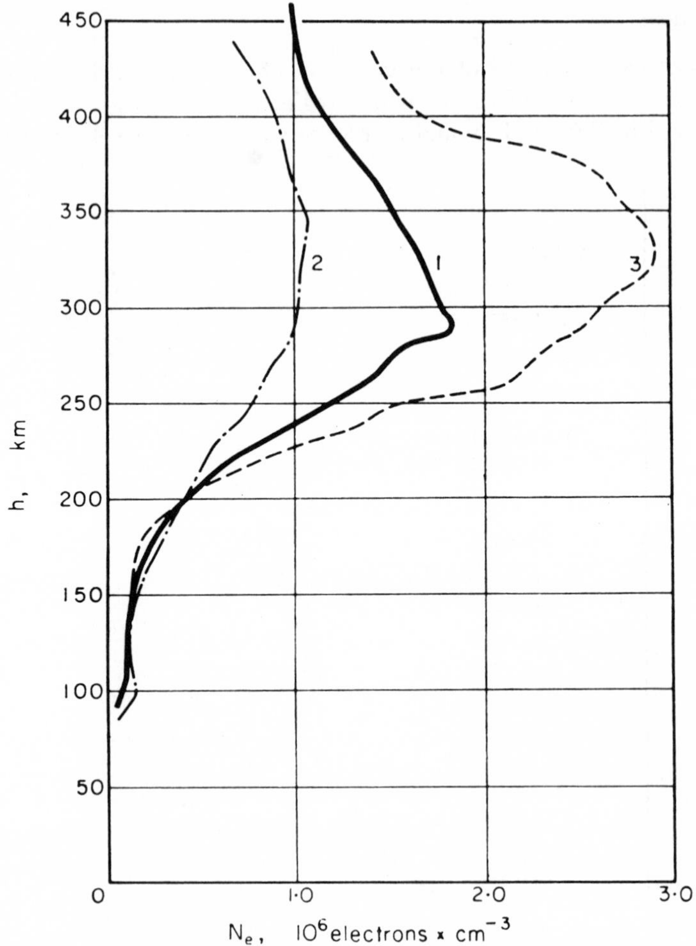

Fig. 5. Electron density vs. altitude obtained by rocketborne dispersion experiment. (1) 21 February 1958, 11:40; (2) 27 August 1958, 8:06; (3) 31 October 1958, 15:54 (Gringauz and Rudakov [35]).

layer, about 20 km thick, centered near 102 km. Superimposed on this broad layer were strata of considerably greater electron density, but only about 1 km thick. Some of these layers are apparently due to sporadic E and have large horizontal extent, whereas others are highly localized and presumably are diffused meteor trails. The thickness of the main E-layer was roughly equal to the noon dimension but the level was lower at night by about 8 km. For two flights, the first of which occurred three hours after sunset and the second eleven hours after sunset, the measured maximum electron densities were 3×10^3 and $1 \times 10^3/\text{cm}^3$. The results suggested a decay of ionization with a recombination coefficient of 2.3×10^{-8} cm³/sec and an extrapolated maximum density at sunset of $1.3 \times 10^4/\text{cm}^3$. It was concluded that there was no evidence for any significant source of ionization in the nighttime E-region. In the trough above the maximum of E-region,

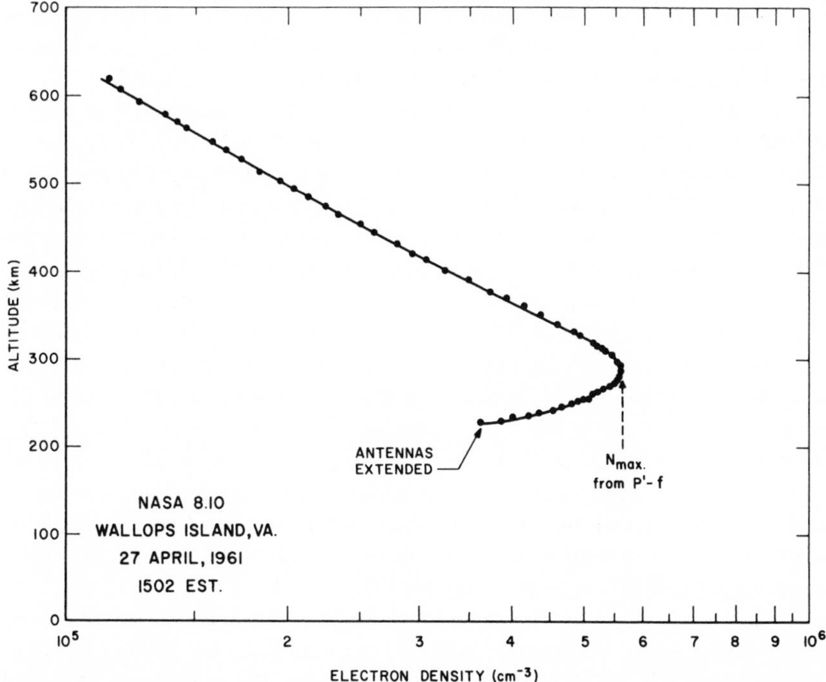

FIG. 6. Ionospheric electron density distribution measured by means of Seddon's cw propagation technique from rocket that reached 620 km above Wallops Island, Va. (Jackson and Bauer [45]).

the flight shortly after sunset showed a reduction of electron density to about 200/cm³ in contrast to the relatively shallow trough observed in the daytime. It is clearly important to repeat a series of such experiments during the course of a single night.

5.1. E-Region Production

Daytime E-region normally refers to the altitude range from 90 to 140 km. At sunspot minimum, the peak electron density is about $10^5/\text{cm}^3$; it increases about 50 per cent at sunspot maximum. For the production of the

E-region, the effective solar radiations are X-rays (10–100 Å), Lyman β (1025.7 Å), C III (977 Å), and the Lyman continuum (910–800 Å).

The X-ray range may be divided into two parts, 10–31 Å and 31–100Å, which have comparable absorption cross sections. The division is produced by the *K* absorption edge of nitrogen. Although the shorter wavelength range, 10–31 Å, has been found to be highly variable over the solar cycle, it contains far less energy than the 31–100 Å range which is more stable and accounts for most of the *E*-region ionization. For most of the past solar cycle, the sun has been observed repeatedly [30] in at least two bands, 8–18 Å and 44–60 Å. Under quiet conditions the maximum solar variations have been factors of 45 and 7, respectively, with the flux at sunspot maximum being about 0.9 erg/cm^2/sec for the entire 10–100 Å band.

From the penetration curves of Figure 1, it is apparent that X-ray ionization will spread over the entire range of the *E*-region with a maximum effect near 120 km. Lyman β (Fig. 2) reaches unit optical depth at about 105 km; C III (977 Å) at about 115 km; and the Lyman continuum at 140 km. Since the nitrogen molecule exhibits band structure in its absorption of the Lyman continuum, there may be appreciable penetration within the bands to 120 km. Near solar maximum the observed flux at Lyman β was about 0.05 erg/cm^2/sec and at C III (977 Å), about 0.08 erg/cm^2/sec. Both of these lines ionize molecular oxygen exclusively. Between 796 Å, the threshold for ionization of N_2, and 911 Å, the onset of ionization of atomic oxygen, the Lyman continuum contains about 0.36 erg/cm^2/sec [22]. Over this range, absorption by atomic oxygen sets in at relatively high altitudes and is the major source of attenuation, except for those wavelengths in the continuum which are absorbed by the band structure of N_2, in which the cross section reaches values as high as 10^{-16} cm^2 at certain wavelengths and as low as 10^{-18} cm^2 for others.

If one simply adds up the ultraviolet fluxes mentioned above, the total is 0.5 erg/cm^2/sec compared with 0.9 erg/cm^2/sec for X-rays at solar maximum. At the 1953–1954 solar minimum, the X-ray flux was observed to decline to about 0.13 erg/cm^2/sec; but no comparable data are yet available for the ultraviolet, although it appears that it does not change by more than a factor of 2. It does not follow necessarily from the fact that X-ray intensity may exceed ultraviolet intensity that the behavior of *E*-region ambient electron density is controlled by X-rays. Pre-IGY theories of ionospheric formation had begun to realize the importance of ionic reactions in transforming the primary ionization to secondary species, but the acquisition of positive ion profile data directly with rocketborne mass spectrometers during and since the IGY has made profound changes in theories of ionospheric processes. To appreciate the surprise generated by the first ion composition measurements, it is only necessary to compare the ion profiles with the production profiles.

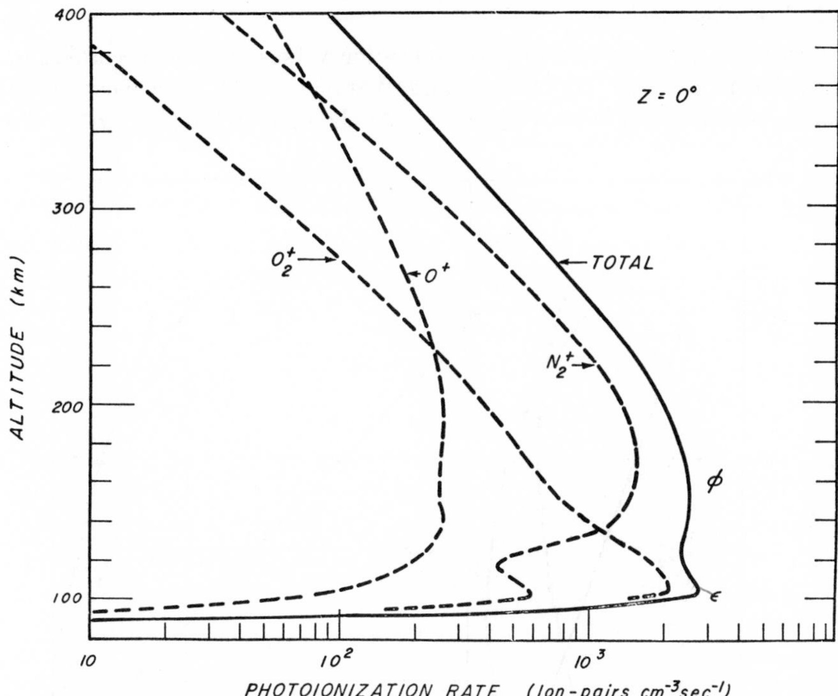

FIG. 7. Photoionization rates for production of O_2^+, O^+, and N_2^+ (Watanabe and Hinteregger [87]).

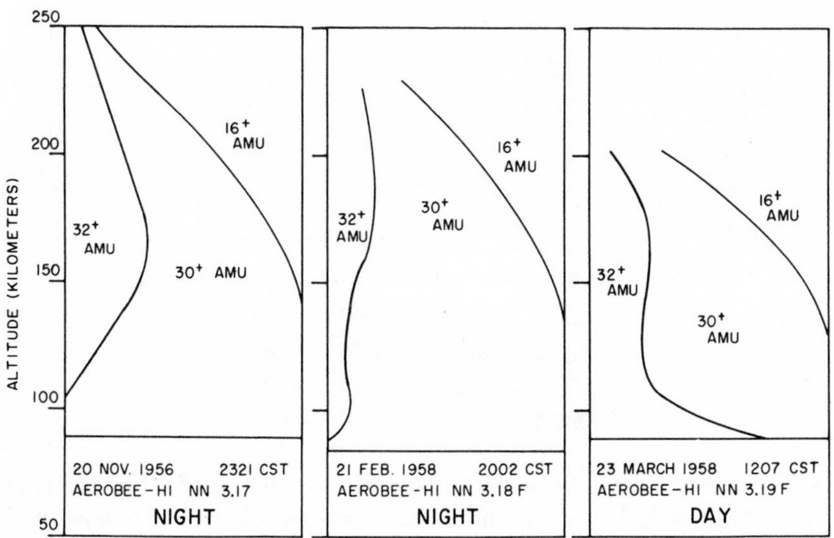

FIG. 8. Ion distribution measured by rocketborne mass spectrometer above Fort Churchill (Johnson *et al.* [46]).

5.2. E-Region Reactions

Figure 7 shows the rate of photoionization versus altitude, according to a model adopted by Hinteregger and Watanabe [87]. The most abundantly produced ion below F_{max} is N_2^+. At the nose of E-region, O_2^+ is the

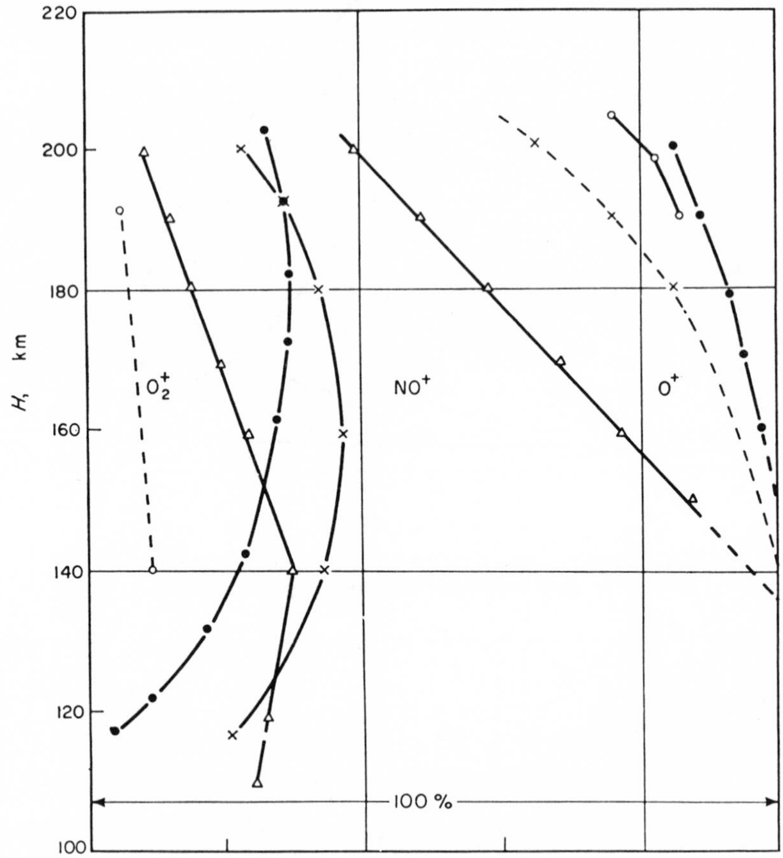

FIG. 9. Ion composition vs. altitude (Istomin and Pokhunkov [42]).

○○○ 9 September	1957	$\chi = 96°$
△△△ 2 August	1958	$\chi = 54°$
××× 13 August	1958	$\chi = 90°$
●●● 22 July	1959	$\chi = 90°$

major source and only above 350 km does the production of O^+ exceed that of N_2^+. Figures 8, 9, 10, 11, and 12 illustrate ion distributions measured directly by rockets launched from different latitude sites and at different times of day and night. The abundance of N_2^+ below F_{max} is essentially negligible and the most important ion through most of E-region is NO^+.

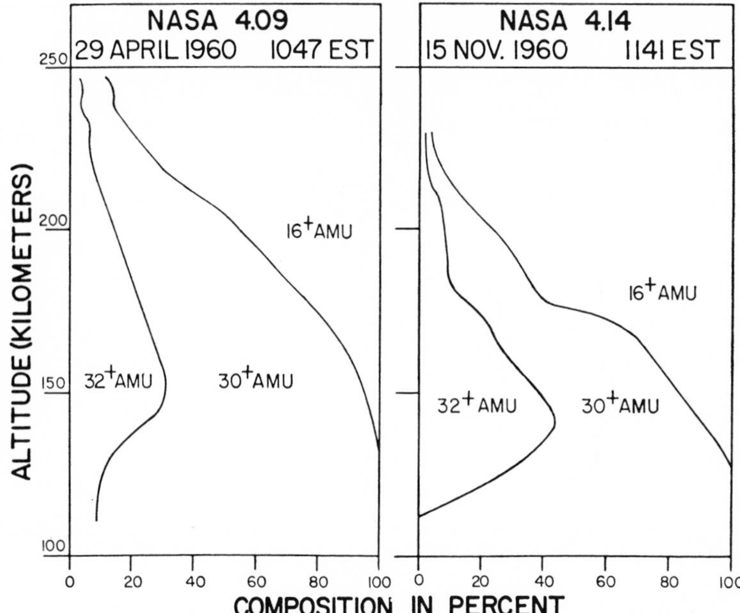

Fig. 10. Ion composition vs. altitude (Taylor and Brinton [82]).

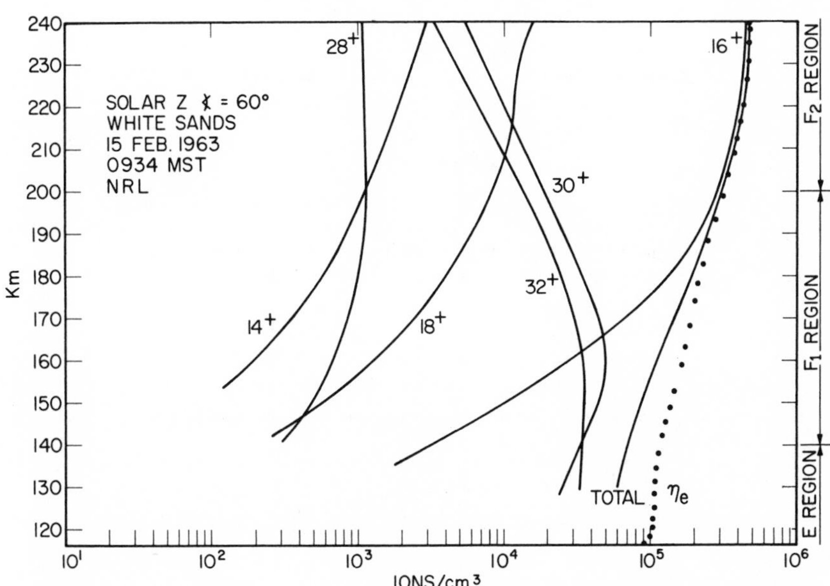

Fig. 11. Ion composition vs. altitude. N_e is "true height" profile obtained from ionosonde. Water vapor, 18^+, is rocket contaminant (Holmes and Young [40]).

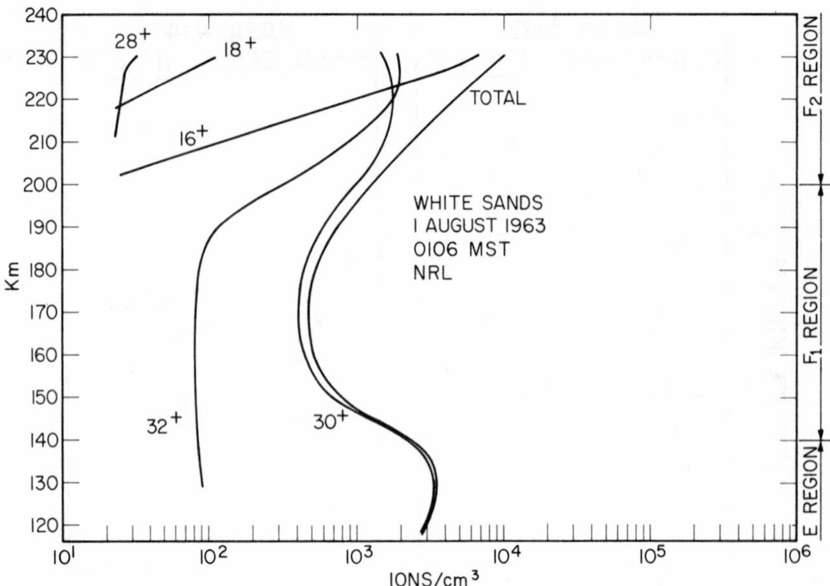

FIG. 12. Ion composition vs. altitude (Holmes and Young [40]).

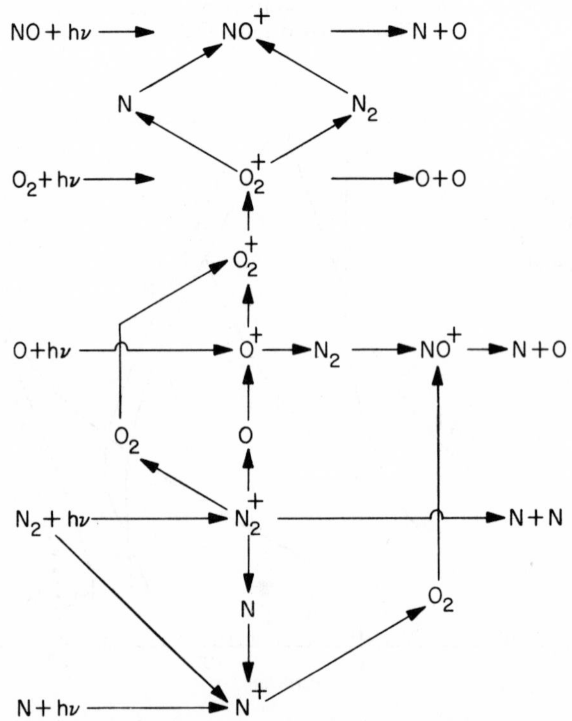

FIG. 13. Ion reaction diagram (after Nicolet and Swider [64]).

The transformation from primary ions to secondary ions is a consequence of the atmospheric chemistry described by reactions 1 to 5 and illustrated by the reaction chart, Figure 13, according to Nicolet and Swider [64].

The most recent data, by Holmes and Young, [40] provide the first ion profiles at midnight at middle latitudes and provide interesting comparisons with IGY Fort Churchill data. During the day, N_2^+ (28^+) did not exceed 1 per cent of the total ion density at any height. With increasing altitude, the primary rate of ionization must decrease and the increasing electron density should accelerate the loss through dissociative recombination. Instead, the concentration of N_2^+ remained nearly constant. Holmes and Young concluded that the loss of N_2^+ at lower altitudes through ionic reactions 6 and 7 must exceed the loss through dissociative recombination. With increasing altitude, the decreasing concentrations of O and O_2 cause the loss rate to decrease sufficiently to balance the decreasing production rate.

The molecular oxygen ion (32^+) and the nitric oxide ion (30^+) followed similar distributions with a crossover near 140 km, O_2^+ being greater below and NO^+ above. The height distribution of NO^+ presumably follows the ion-atom interchange process 1 between N_2 and O^+. In fact, at altitudes above 160 km where $N(O^+)/n_e$ is approximately 1, the concentration of NO^+ followed the neutral N_2 distribution. Similarly, the behavior of O_2^+ was tied to the neutral O_2 distribution by reaction 2 in which O_2^+ is formed by charge exchange with O^+.

The atomic nitrogen ion is always a minor constituent. It is produced directly by photoionization and at lower altitudes is probably lost by an ion-atom interchange reaction 8 with O_2,

$$N^+ + O_2 \rightarrow NO^+ + O + [6.69 - E(^3\pi)] \text{ ev} \tag{12}$$

The increasing concentration of N^+ with altitude is the result of the decreasing rate of this reaction and the height at which radiative recombination becomes dominant must exceed 240 km. Above 160 km, O^+ becomes the most abundant ion.

Consider next the nighttime distribution (Fig. 12). Here O^+ disappeared completely below 200 km through the mechanisms of the ion-atom interchange reactions 1 and 2, thereby supporting the concentrations of NO^+ and O_2^+ during the night. The minimum in the profile centers near 170 km. Holmes and Young [40] suggest that the dissociative recombination coefficient increases with increasing temperature as the altitude increases, leading to the minimum at 170 km. As the altitude increases further, the increasing O^+ abundance overcomes the loss process by conversion to NO^+ and O_2^+ via reactions 1 and 2.

With a dissociative recombination coefficient of 10^{-7} cm^3/sec, N_2^+ should disappear almost instantly after sunset, yet a small trace is observed above 200 km. This may indicate a production mechanism effective at night, either corpuscular or ultraviolet. If a resonantly scattered helium glow at 304 Å and 584 Å exists at night analogous to the glow of the hydrogen geocorona [12], only 10^6 quanta per square centimeter per second would be needed to support the observed N_2^+.

The nighttime maximum in total ion concentration observed by Holmes and Young near 130 km resembles the maximum observed by Smith's Langmuir probe near 110 km. The minimum found in the ion composition measurement is not as low in concentration as Smith's electron density and appears to occur at higher altitude.

Returning now to the question of the relative importance of X-rays and ultraviolet radiation in *E*-region, it is clear that ionic reactions play a very important role. If N_2^+ formed by X-rays were lost entirely by dissociative recombination at a rate much faster than the ionic reactions 4 and 5, 80 per cent of the X-ray flux would not contribute appreciably to the ambient electron density. According to the Holmes and Young data, however, it appears that N_2^+ is lost primarily by charge exchange with O_2 and O in *E*-region, followed by the production of NO^+ from O^+ via reaction 1.

Much of the NO^+ in *E*-region may appear through reaction 1, following the direct photoionization of atomic oxygen. At 110 km, the only effective source of O^+ is the X-ray spectrum. Assuming that four-fifths of the X-ray flux is absorbed by N_2 and that oxygen is 65 per cent dissociated in *E*-region, about 13 per cent of the total X-ray energy must be absorbed by atomic oxygen. At solar maximum, then, we may expect about 0.1 erg/cm²/sec of X-rays to produce O^+ and therefrom NO^+, according to reaction 1. About 0.05 erg/cm²/sec of X-rays and 0.13 erg/cm²/sec of Lyman β and C III could produce O_2^+ directly. Only a relatively small portion of the Lyman continuum flux would be effective below 120 km.

In summary, the ion profiles, Figure 11, show almost equal amounts of NO^+ and O_2^+ in *E*-region. Essentially all of the NO^+ is derived from the primary ionization of O and N_2 by X-rays. The direct production of O_2^+ seems to depend more heavily on ultraviolet radiation than X-rays, but O_2^+ can also be produced by charge exchange with N_2^+ derived from X-rays. It is difficult to reach a quantitative conclusion that there is a predominant control of *E*-region by either X-rays or ultraviolet. When the solar cycle variation of *E*-region critical frequency is translated into solar flux variation, however, it appears to require the larger variation characteristic of the solar X-ray spectrum [31].

5.3. E-Region Eclipses

Observations of the variation of solar X-ray and ultraviolet emissions which were made during the IGY eclipse expedition of 12 October 1958 in the South Pacific [15] tend to support the theory of X-ray control of *E*-region density. Several rockets were launched during the course of the eclipse, including the totality phase at which time 10 to 13 per cent of the

X-ray flux still remained, whereas the Lyman α intensity had dropped by a factor of 2000. The X-ray eclipse curve also showed strong correlation with the distribution of active regions on the disc. It has long been known from ionosonde observations during eclipses that the E-region electron density does not follow the visible light eclipse curve. Often the minimum of the electron concentration is not delayed relative to totality as would be expected if the source of ionization were completely cut off, but may even precede it. Such observations have, therefore, led to the conclusion that the sun's disc is not uniformly bright in ionizing radiation and that an important fraction of the flux is emitted by discrete sources irregularly distributed.

Ratcliffe [69] observed that many eclipse data could be explained by a residual ionizing flux of from 10 to 15 per cent at totality. The X-ray observations of the 1958 eclipse are, therefore, in good agreement with this requirement. Since Lyman β and the Lyman continuum should originate at lower levels in the chromosphere than Lyman α, the essentially complete disappearance of Lyman α at totality in the 1958 experiment also requires the absence of any E-region contribution by Lyman β and Lyman continuum at totality.

5.4. X-rays, Decimeter Waves, and the E-Region

Radio interferometric measurements of the slowly varying component of microwave emission between wavelengths of 3 and 21 cm show bright regions of electron density 10 to 20 times the density of the surrounding inner corona at temperatures of (2–5) $\times$ 10^6°K. The radio bright regions are centered over calcium plages of the solar chromosphere. A similar picture of concentrated emission was observed in an X-ray pinhole photograph of the sun [8] in the wavelength range 10 to 60 Å. The resolution of the camera was about one-tenth of the solar diameter. It revealed discrete sources no larger than the camera resolution which coincided in position with bright calcium plages. About 80 per cent of the X-ray emission originated in such local sources occupying no more than 5 per cent of the area of the disc and the brightest X-ray source was 70 times as bright as the general X-ray background. Comparison of the X-ray photograph with the 10-cm radioheliograph showed almost identical source distributions.

Kundu and Denisse [53] have shown that a strong correlation exists between E-layer critical frequency and solar decimeter wave emission. At 10.7 cm, records covering more than a solar cycle correlate as well as sunspot numbers or coronal green line intensities with ionospheric electron content on a time scale of a month or longer, and the correlations are even better on a shorter time scale. Using subsequent measurements on wavelengths up to 70 cm, Kundu [52] found the range 3–30 cm to correlate especially well with E-layer, whereas the correspondence disappeared rapidly at wavelengths as long as 50–70 cm. Since the X-ray sources match the slowly varying component at wavelengths between 3 and 30 cm, it appears that the X-rays responsible for *E* layer ionization originate primarily in the 10,000–20,000 km height range of the corona as does the microwave radiation. In fact, measurement of the solar diameter on the X-ray pinhole photograph indicates an upper limit of detectable emission at a height of about 40,000 km above the photosphere.

5.5. Slowly Varying Components of Ionizing Radiations

Recent observations of the distribution of sources of ultraviolet and X-ray emission over the solar disc give further insight into the variability of ionospheric production as a function of solar rotation. To define the dimensions of the enhanced regions and their brightnesses relative to the general disc background, fan beam scans have been made with slit telescopes [9] in wavelength bands 44–60 Å, 8–20 Å, and 8–15 Å. Figure 14 is an example of the kind of information derived from such measurements. At the longer wavelengths the background sun contributed substantially to the total flux, even though the active region was markedly brighter. At 8–15 Å, however, the background disc intensity was almost negligible and the active region provided nearly all the flux. The fan beam width was 1 minute of arc at 8–15 Å and 0.5 minute at 44–60 Å. It is clear that the finest structure at 8–15 Å is smaller than the instrumental resolution.

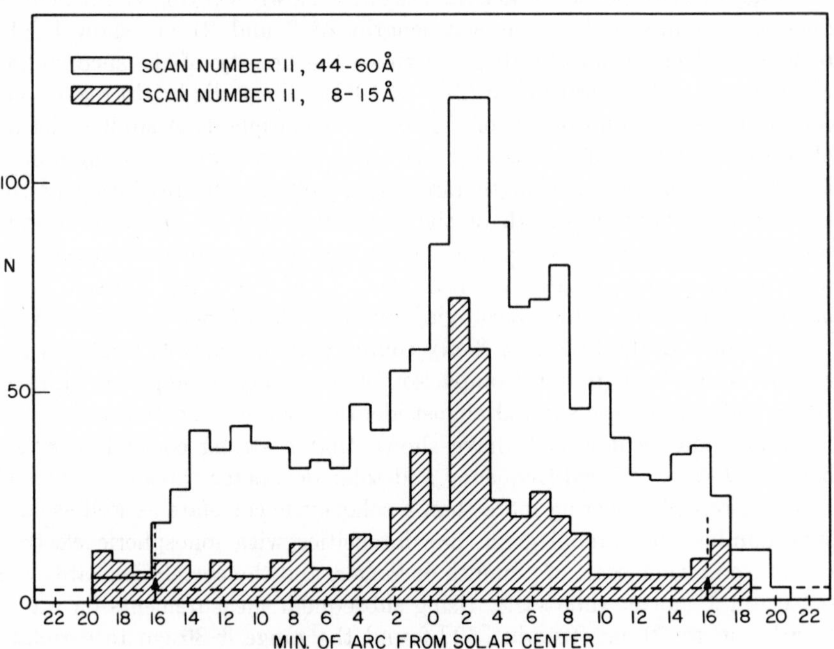

Fig. 14. Fan beam scans of X-ray intensity across solar disc, obtained with slit telescopes carried in Aerobee rocket (Blake *et al.* [9]).

Spectroscopic measurements [9] have shown that the principal emission lines in the 8–15 Å region are those of Fe XVII. In association with plages of average brightness, it has been found typically that the X-ray brightness ratios of active regions to quiet disc are as follows:

44–60 Å,	4:1
8–20 Å,	10:1
8–15 Å,	25:1

This picture of concentrated emission regions at wavelengths below 50 Å is

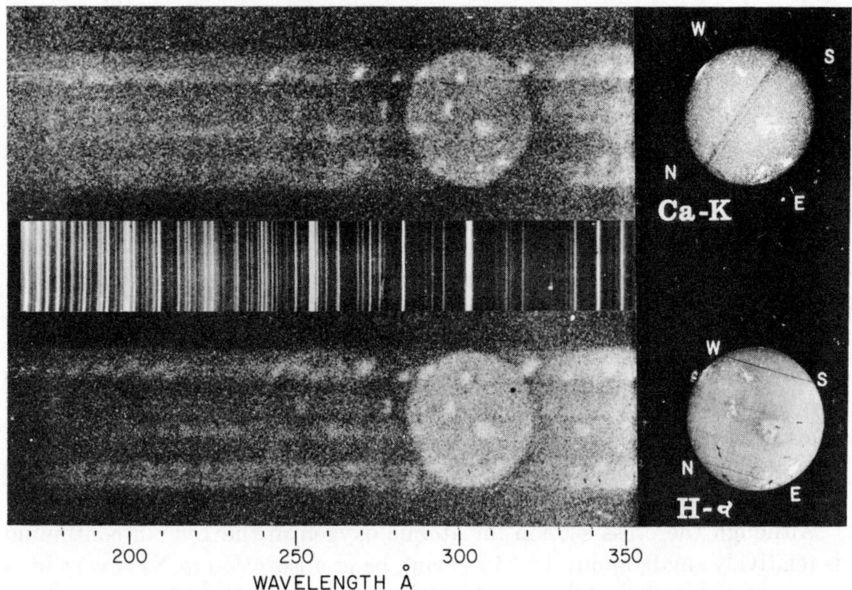

Fig. 15. Spectroheliograms in ultraviolet wavelengths (Purcell and Tousey [68]).

duplicated in recent ultraviolet spectroheliograms [68] at wavelengths near 300 Å. Figure 15 shows a series of overlapping spectroheliograms in two exposures, with a grazing incidence spectrum of the sun sandwiched between and printed to the same scale of dispersion. The bright He II (304 Å) line can be seen to produce an image of the full disc with enhancement in the plages, which are identified with the CaK and Hα images at the right. Six major plage regions are present, aligned approximately in two diagonal rows.

In contrast to the He II (304 Å) image are the images corresponding to Fe XV (284.1 Å) and Fe XVI (335.4 Å) which are restricted almost exclusively to the plages as was observed for Fe XVII in the X-ray region. It appears, therefore, that with increasing degree of ionization the emission becomes more and more confined to active centers of presumably higher temperature.

6. F-Region

There is no sharp demarkation between the various ionospheric regions E, F_1, and F_2. We may refer to the range from 140–200 km as F_1 and the higher ionosphere as F_2. Maximum electron density of F_1 is about 2.5×10^5/cm^3 near sunspot minimum and about 4×10^5/cm^3 at sunspot maximum. The primary source of the F_1-region is the Lyman continuum of hydrogen and the region 350–200 Å, which contains about 1 erg/cm^2/sec, including the very intense He II (304 Å) resonance line. The predominant ions are NO^+ and O_2^+ in the lower portion of F_1. As the altitude increases, O^+ becomes progressively more important until it is the major ion at 200 km. The electron loss process is controlled indirectly by ion-atom interchange which converts the atomic ions to molecular species more rapidly than they are lost by photorecombination.

The principal radiation source in the F_2-region is the same as for F_1, with the additional contribution of the 650–450 Å range. An F_2-ionization peak is formed because of the decreasing rate of electron loss process with increasing altitude. Mass spectrometer measurements [42] have shown that the ions are principally O^+ with a small amount (about 10 per cent) of N^+. Ion-atom interchange with the neutral molecular constituents accelerates the loss process in proportion to the molecular concentration. As the concentration of molecular constituents falls off with altitude, the effective recombination coefficient decreases rapidly until it is of the order of 10^{-10} cm^3/sec at F_2 maximum.

Although the cross section for atomic oxygen in the Lyman continuum is relatively small, about 3×10^{-18} cm^2, band absorption in N_2 is very high over a large fraction of the wavelength interval 910–800 Å. A major portion of the absorption by N_2, therefore, goes into excitation rather than ionization. At shorter wavelengths, between 650–450 Å, absorption cross sections for photoionization of atomic oxygen reach their highest values; maximum rate of absorption take place in the 160–180 km region and less than 10 per cent penetrates below 145 km. Included in the 650–350 Å range are the emission lines of He I (584 Å), Mg X (625, 610 Å) and Si XII (520, 500 Å), the total flux adding up to approximately 0.4 erg/cm^2/sec according to Table 1.

The phenomenology of the F_2-region is very complex. In addition to the production of ionization by electromagnetic radiation and the ionic reactions involved in the electron loss mechanism, F_2 is strongly affected by transport of ionization under electromagnetic forces, diffusion, and temperature variations. The complex variation of N_mF_2 has been described in detail by Martyn [59]. A strong seasonal anomaly and annual effect give rise to a pronounced maximum of N_e in winter in the Northern Hemisphere. According to Rishbeth [70] the peak electron density observed at Slough is three times as great in winter as in summer, and immediately after sunrise the rate of growth of electron density near the F_2-peak is four times as great in winter as in summer. Thomas [83] has discussed the changes in h_mF_2 as a function of local time, season, and sunspot cycle. The height of maximum density varies from 200 km to 400 km at medium latitude stations with h_mF_2 higher at night than during the day in high latitudes, and the reverse situation being true near the equator. At the highest levels of the ionosphere, the composition must be dominated by protons formed as the result of charge exchange with O^+ at lower levels. The so-called magnetosphere is the medium in which radio whistlers proprogate from one hemisphere to the other along magnetic lines of force.

The behavior of the very high ionosphere is beyond the scope of the present paper, which is concerned primarily with the region of solar control through the photoionization medium of X-rays and ultraviolet radiation. At levels above the F_2 maximum, the ionized particle concentrations become comparable with the neutral and no important influence of direct photoionization is possible.

7. Ionization by Energetic Particles

The question of the relative importance of energetic particles and electromagnetic radiation in the ionization and heating of the upper atmosphere has been debated since the first reports of Sputnik III measurements by Krassovsky [49] in 1959. Measured fluxes of about 10-kev electrons exceeded 100 ergs/cm²/sec at 1900 km and Krassovsky estimated that about 1 erg/cm²/sec would reach the F-region at midlatitudes. Antonova and Ivanov-Kholodny [2] in 1961 reported measurements at 70 to 100 km at moderate latitudes and in polar regions of electron fluxes in the 20 to 40 kev range amounting to 10^{-2} to 5×10^{-2} erg/cm²/sec/sterad, and proposed that fluxes of $\backsim$100-ev electrons at 300 km could amount to 1 to 10 ergs/cm²/sec/sterad.

Data obtained by O'Brien [66] from Injun I revealed median fluxes of about 10^6 trapped electrons cm²/sec with $E \geq 40$ kev at heights of about 1000 km in high latitudes. Assuming an exponential differential spectrum with index 4 above 1 kev, the mean energy would be 1.5 kev and the flux 5×10^9/cm²/sec, with lifetimes of 10^3–10^4 seconds before dumping. The dumped flux would accordingly be 10^5–10^6 particles/cm²/sec/sterad, or about 10^{-4}–10^{-3} erg/cm²/sec. O'Brien's measurements were obtained when the sunspot number was 50.

Nicolet [61] has argued that the normal steady contribution to heating and ionization by corpuscular sources must be low compared to ultraviolet and X-rays because of the relatively small effects observed in conjunction with very large magnetic storms. From observations of Sputnik II and III, it was found that the nighttime density at 220 km at the times of the great storms of 8–10 July and 3–4 September 1958, increased only 30–40 per cent. The normal contribution very likely does not exceed a few per cent of the storm effect and should, therefore, amount to less than 1 per cent of the electromagnetic contribution.

The ultraviolet fluorescence of N_2^+ under particle bombardment is a quantitative gauge of the particle flux. The computed cross sections for the three bands, 0–0 (3914 Å), 0–1 (4278 Å), 0–2 (4709 Å) of the first negative system of N_2^+ are 2 per cent, 0.7 per cent, and 0.2 per cent, respectively. If the mean energy expended per ion of N_2^+ is 35 ev, the energy conversion efficiencies from electron kinetic energy to radiation are 2×10^{-3} for the 0–0, 7×10^{-4} for the 0–1, and 2×10^{-4} for 0–2. Hartman and Hoerlin [38], by direct measurements in air, have determined that the efficiency of excitation of 3914 Å radiation is 4×10^{-3}, about double the value deduced from cross-section data. According to Dalgarno and Griffing [17], when the primary electron energies are less than 100 ev, the efficiency of excitation and ionization falls rapidly.

Assuming a value of 1×10^{-3} for the efficiency, each erg of electron energy should give rise to 200 rayleighs of 3914 Å. According to Roach [71] an upper limit to the low-latitude flux is about 60 rayleighs, which would correspond to 0.3 erg/cm²/sec. Galperin [33] has reported that very careful measurements at Zvenigorod (geomagnetic latitude 51.1°N) did not detect a flux as high as 1.5 R in the 4278 Å band. Using a conversion efficiency of 3×10^{-4} for the combined effects of excitation efficiency and photoelectric response in the photocell, he concluded that the electron energy input was less than 3×10^{-2} erg/cm²/sec.

Recent measurements above 100 km by Bowyer *et al.* [10] indicate an isotropic soft X-ray flux of about 10^{-8} erg/cm²/sterad in a band covering 1–8 Å. The source may be galactic or atmospheric. If it is bremsstrahlung in the atmosphere produced by dumped electrons, the efficiency of X-ray production would be about 10^{-5}. The observations, therefore, set an upper limit of about 10^{-3} erg/cm²/sec/sterad to the electron energy input.

Antonova and Ivanov-Kholodny [2], Danilov [18, 19], and Ivanov-Kholodny and Nikolsky [44] have proposed that the ionosphere at night is supported by a flux of energetic electrons greater than 1 erg/cm²/sec. During the day the electron energy input is supplemented by the influx of X-rays and ultraviolet which they estimate to be as great as 10 to 100 ergs/cm²/sec. To match this very large solar flux, they adopt a very rapid electron loss process. According to their theories, recombination takes place so rapidly that the F-region maximum electron density decreases by an order of magnitude within 3 to 30 minutes after sunset and by a factor of 100 in 1 to 10 hours. Since a reduction by only a factor of 3 to 10 is observed during the course of the night, they proposed that the residual ionization comes entirely from the electron flux at night. However, the consensus of direct measurements of the solar flux to date indicates that the total daytime energy input below 1000 Å is less than 3 ergs/cm²/sec and the evidence cited above based on N_2^+ emission and X-ray flux from the midlatitude night sky sets the nighttime input of electron energy below 0.01 erg/cm²/sec.

At high magnetic latitudes there is considerable evidence for a large energy input to the atmosphere from particle radiation. Lytle and Hunten [57] observed a steady intensity of about 30 rayleighs of N_2^+ emission during 1960, falling to somewhat less than 20 rayleighs in 1961 at magnetic latitude 60.5°N. Galperin [33] and Mulyarchik and Shcheglow [60], observing from Loparskaya at somewhat higher geomagnetic latitude, 63.7°N, found a steady flux of N_2^+ emission corresponding to about 1 erg/cm²/sec of electrons at solar maximum and falling to about 0.3 erg/cm²/sec at solar minimum. These airglow intensities indicate an important contribution of electron energy to F-region ionization at geomagnetic latitudes near 60 degrees and higher.

Referring again to the ion profiles of Figures 8, 11, and 12, little difference was observed between day and night at Fort Churchill. The recent day-night measurements at White Sands, however, show a collapse of the ionosphere at night indicative of a substantially complete cessation of ion production. The conclusion to be drawn is that the Fort Churchill ion spectra at night reflect a continuous source of primary ionization of a corpuscular nature.

8. Solar Flares and Sudden Ionospheric Disturbances

Until shortly after World War II, solar flares were photographed and photometered almost exclusively in the hydrogen Hα line. The Hα flash was considered to be the most fundamental feature of the entire flare event. Today it is recognized that the visible flare is part of a vastly more complex phenomenon involving strong and varied forms of radio emission, energetic X-rays, particles of cosmic-ray energies, and shock waves. The visible flare may be only a secondary manifestation of more fundamental processes.

Although a flare is born in a nucleus that measures only a few tenths of a per cent of the area of the solar disc, once the rapid brightening begins it may spread within minutes over hundreds of millions of square miles. Simultaneously, there are dramatic terrestrial disturbances such as radio fadeout, which results from enhanced ionization in the deepest portions of the ionosphere. On rare occasions flares reach intensities detectable in white light and may be accompanied by the acceleration of solar protons to Bev energies. Small flares are common phenomena; as many as 100 microflares a day, each lasting only a few minutes, may occur near large, complex sunspots. At solar maximum, one large flare per day may be expected near large spots. Regardless of size, nearly all flares follow the same variation—a rapid rise to peak Hα intensity, a brief persistence of the peak intensity, and a slower return to the preflare brightness. The mean duration of a large sample of great flares (Class 3^+) during the International Geophysical Year was 3 hours and the smallest and greatest lasted 1 hour and 7 hours, respectively.

The most important contribution of the IGY to our understanding of the relationship of the flare phenomenon and the SID was the discovery of X-ray emission associated with flares. A search for X-rays from flares was motivated in 1956 by a desire to explain radio fadeouts. Dellinger [21] in 1937 had discovered that a solar flare produced abrupt fadeout of short-wave radio communications and he attributed this effect to ionization produced deep in the ionosphere by a burst of solar ultraviolet radiation. Whereas ionization at *E*- and *F*-region levels improves ionospheric reflectivity, ionization in the *D*-region leads to absorption and fadeout. At the time Dellinger made his discovery, solar X-ray emission was unknown and all ionospheric ionization was assumed to be produced by ultraviolet emission.

When rocket measurements revealed that the Lyman α line produced the normal *D*-region, it seemed logical to assume that since the flare showed intense brightness at Hα, the resonance line, Lyman α would be enhanced sufficiently to account for the increased *D*-region ionization. A review [32] of all of the SID phenomena associated with flares proved that a monochromatic emission such as Lyman α was inadequate to explain such effects as, for example, the great decrease in height of the base of the *D*-region (SPA). This deep-seated ionization would require an increase in Lyman α equal to 100,000 times the normal emission from the entire sun. Since the flare occupies roughly one-thousandth of the area of the disc, the flare region itself would have to increase its Lyman α output by a factor of 10^8. It seems impossible to explain such an outburst by any astrophysical mechanism. On the other hand, the emission of X-rays in the 1–2 Å range would produce the observed lowering of the base of the *D*-region with a flux of only 10^{-5} erg/cm^2/sec.

8.1. *Flare X-Rays*

The study of X-ray emission during the course of solar flares began with a pre-IGY series of Rockoon experiments in 1956 [16]. A pronounced increase in X-ray emission accompanying a Class 1 flare was observed by means of a G.M. counter sensitive to a wavelength band from 1–10 Å. No increase in Lyman α was detected. The Rockoon technique was superseded during the IGY by the two-stage Nike-Deacon combination of solid-propellant motors, which could be launched to ionospheric heights from the ground. Photon counters with windows of different filtration characteristics provided some measure of spectral definition. By 1959, during the IGC, scintillation and proportional counter techniques had been developed to give more detailed spectral information based on pulse amplitude distributions, covering the range from 2–20 kev with proportional counters, and 20–150 kev with scintillation counters. These rocket measurements and subsequent satellite observations have thoroughly confirmed the relation-

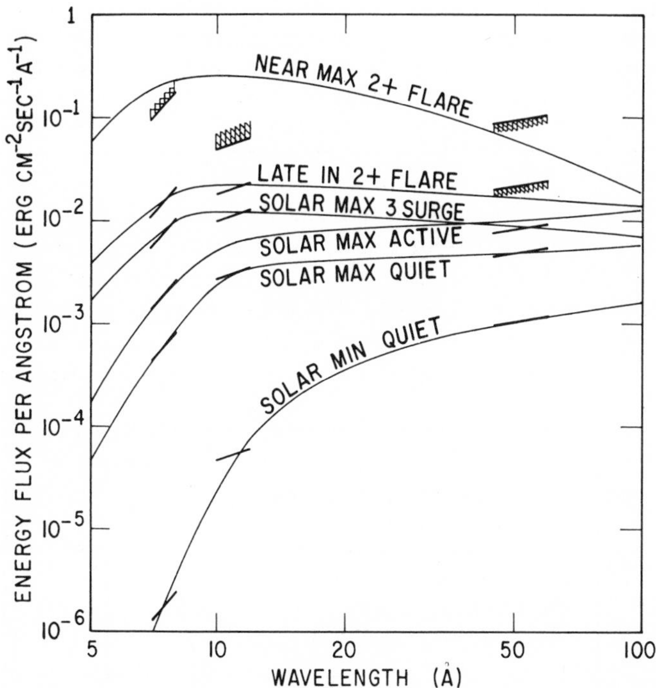

FIG. 16. Solar X-ray emission for various solar conditions. The curves indicate the approximate energy distributions for sunspot minimum, sunspot maximum, and solar flare conditions. The curves are drawn on the basis of measurements made in three wavelength bands, as indicated by heavy bar segments. The slopes of the bar segments are the slopes of the assumed X-ray emission functions used to reduce the photometer responses to the energy fluxes plotted on the chart. Energy fluxes refer to values observed just outside the earth's absorbing atmosphere.

ship between sudden ionospheric disturbances and X-ray flare emission. Figure 16 illustrates qualitatively the changes in X-ray spectrum with sunspot cycle and with major forms of activity, such as surge prominences and flares.

At the peak of a moderately large flare, the entire X-ray spectrum increases in brightness up to several times the normal intensity. The increases may be orders of magnitude at the shortest wavelengths, although the energy content is usually only a very small portion of the total X-ray out-

TABLE 3

X-RAY INTENSITIES (erg/cm²/sec) FOR VARIOUS STATES OF SOLAR ACTIVITY FOR WAVELENGTH INTERVALS OF ±1 Å CENTERED AT THE INDICATED WAVELENGTHS

	2 Å	4 Å	6 Å
Completely Quiet	10^{-8}	10^{-7}	10^{-6}
Quiet	10^{-7}	10^{-6}	10^{-5}
Slightly Disturbed	10^{-6}	10^{-5}	10^{-4}
Disturbed	10^{-5}	10^{-4}	10^{-3}
Flares, Class 2	10^{-4}	10^{-3}	10^{-2}
Flares, Class 3	10^{-3}	10^{-2}	10^{-1}

put. The most effective range in terms of its ionospheric effect appears to be the wavelength band from 1–8 Å, in which the dependence of X-ray emission on the quality of solar activity is summarized by Table 3, according to Nicolet and Aikin [63]. The fluxes shown in the table and the various electron density distributions of Figure 17 illustrate the contribution of X-rays to the *D*-region for a variety of conditions from quiet to

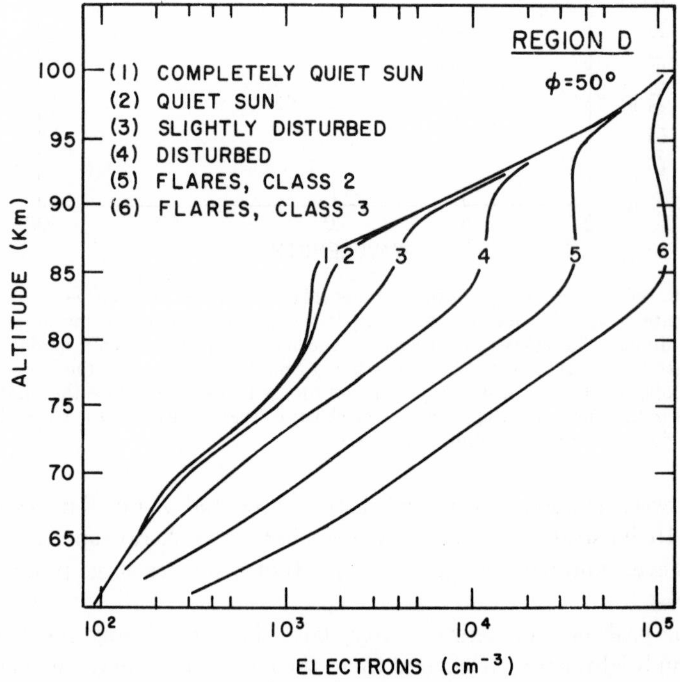

FIG. 17. Variation of *D*-region electron density with solar activity (Nicolet and Aikin [63]).

strong flare activity. Under quiet conditions, the X-rays make a negligible contribution to the region below 85 km. With increasing X-ray activity, the absorbing region is lowered about 2 km for condition 3, 5 km for condition 5, and 10 km for condition 6. In the absence of flares, the solar cycle variation is of the order of a factor of 7 for the entire range below 100 Å, a factor of 70 at 12 Å, and 300 at 8 Å.

8.2. Satellite Monitors

Satellites offer the opportunity to monitor solar X-ray and ultraviolet emission on a continuous basis. Successful observations were made in 1960 by the NRL Solar Radiation 1 Satellite (1960 Eta II), which was followed in 1962 by NASA's S-16 Solar Observatory and the British satellite UK-I. In recent years, Russian observers [58] have also made substantial contributions to the body of information on solar X-ray emission. The NRL monitoring program continued with 1961 Omicron II, 1963-21-C, and 1964-1-D. SR-I (1960 Eta II) carried two ionization chambers to monitor X-rays (1–8 Å) and Lyman α (1216 Å). Because 1960 Eta II was not equipped with a memory system, all data were transmitted in real time and recorded at a few ground stations. Only a very small fraction of the potential information was therefore received, but over its six months' life-span more than 100 X-ray events were measured [51]. Figure 18 illustrates graphically the relatively poor correlation between optical flare classifications and the X-ray intensities. The most intense X-ray events were associated with visible phenomena identified as Class 1 and the largest optical phenomena produced relatively modest X-ray emissions. The great sensitivity of solar X-ray output to relatively minor forms of optical activity is indicated by the large number of X-ray events not identified with any optical events. The results of the 1960 Eta II measurements can be summarized as follows.

(*a*) For a period from 13 July to 3 August 1960, Lyman α day-to-day changes did not exceed 18 per cent. During a Class 2 flare, Lyman α did not rise above the quiet sun level by more than 11 per cent. Although insufficient to be of geophysical significance, an 11 per cent increase in total flux from the solar disc could mean a factor of 100 increase in local brightness within the limited area of the flare region. It should be recognized, however, that the accuracy of the Lyman α measurement was poor and that the figure quoted for the upper limit does not imply that any real increase of Lyman α was positively detected.

(*b*) The quiet sun did not emit an X-ray flux below 8 Å in excess of the limit of measurement which was 0.6×10^{-3} erg/cm²/sec. When X-rays in the 1–8 Å band were observed above this level, some optical indication of activity was usually detected.

(*c*) If the X-ray flux exceeded 2×10^{-3} erg/cm²/sec, radio fadeout and other SID phenomena occurred simultaneously.

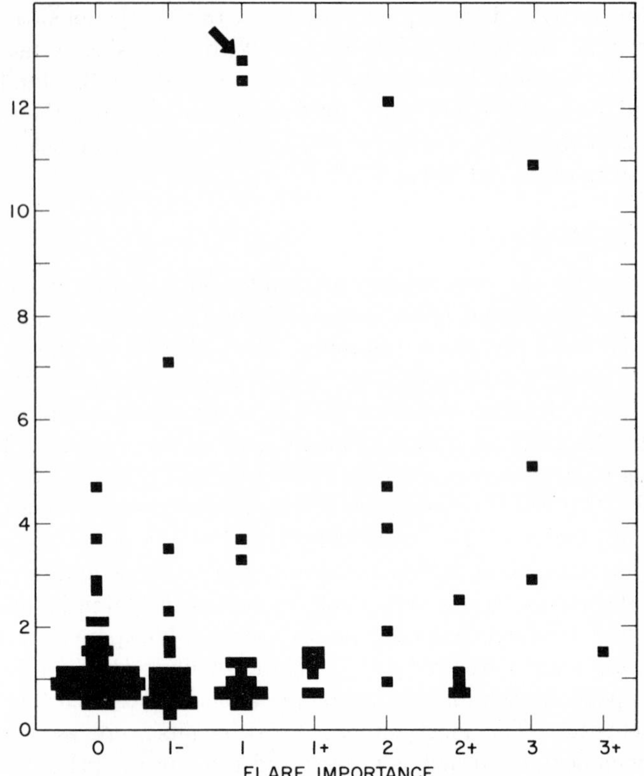

Fig. 18. Distribution of X-ray events observed by SR-1 (1960 Eta II) relative to optical flare importance (Svestka [77]).

(*d*) Important variations in X-ray emission in this wavelength band take place on a time scale of the order of one minute.

(*e*) Active prominence regions, bright limb surges and small limb flares produced X-ray events that resembled those accompanying disc flares.

(*f*) Long duration X-ray events of sufficient intensity to produce ionospheric disturbances can accompany rising limb prominences. On 24 July 1960 a disappearing prominence seen above the limb between 0900 UT and 1200 UT was well recorded photographically and observed in its X-ray emission. As this event progressed, enhanced X-ray emission was detected on six successive telemetered records, Figure 19, the mean flux reaching 5×10^{-3} erg/cm^2/sec at 1020 UT. There were no flares visible on the disc at that time. A search of ionospheric records revealed that radio fadeout occurred simultaneously with the increase of X-ray emission and persisted until the X-ray intensity dropped below the critical level.

SR-3 (1961 Omicron II) went into orbit without separating from its launch partner, Injun I, and as a result did not acquire the desired spin stabilization. Although far less productive of data than SR-1, it nevertheless produced some interesting results [1]. SR-3 was instrumented with an ionization chamber sensitive to an 8–15 Å band as well as one for the 2–8 Å band. Again it was found that solar flares produced enhanced X-ray emission; but whereas emission in the 2–8 Å band had a temporal characteristic much like the Hα flare, the 8–15 Å emission had much greater persistence. Following a flare, the longer wavelength radiation tended to remain at above normal levels well after the Hα event was ended. Relatively large 8–15 Å increases were noted without accompanying ionospheric disturbances. These observations demonstrate that X-rays

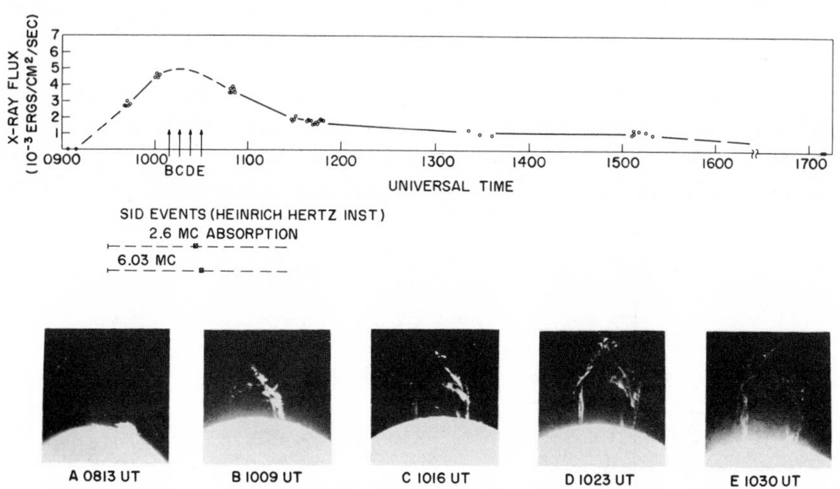

FIG. 19. Solar X-ray emission accompanying vanishing prominence as recorded by SR-1 (1960 Eta II).

of wavelength greater than 8 Å, which are absorbed above the *D*-region, do not contribute to SID phenomena; whereas 2–8 Å X-rays absorbed within the *D*-region are the important influence.

1963-21-C and 1964-1-D in the NRL monitor series included still longer wavelength monitoring in the neighborhood of 50 Å. In January, 1964, solar X-ray emission in the 50 Å band had fallen to a level as low as the weakest flux measured in 1953 and 1954. With flare activity, pronounced increases are observed in the 50 Å range of the spectrum as well as at the shorter wavelengths. These softer rays are effective in *E*-region and the increases observed are capable of doubling the ionization density. The influence of the softer radiation may, therefore, be important in understanding the magnetic crotchet phenomenon.

The UK-I satellite, launched on 26 April 1962, carried an X-ray proportional counter spectrometer to study solar emission below 15 Å and pulses were amplitude sorted in five energy channels [67]. Analysis of the early results showed:

(*a*) The spectrum declined very rapidly with wavelength to less than the threshold sensitivity, 3×10^{-5} erg/cm²/sec, below 6 Å;

(*b*) the nonflare spectrum was variable to the extent that intensity changes of 75 per cent occurred in a period of one-half hour;

(*c*) the average level of intensity had a long period drift that correlated with Fe XIV green line intensity;

(*d*) flares produced an X-ray flux increase and hardening; fluctuations lasting less than 1 minute were present in the main growth phase.

Data from the NASA OSO 1 have been reported only in preliminary fashion, but it is clear that they contain many interesting details of the variation of solar ultraviolet and X-ray emission. Behring *et al.* [5] reported an increase in the He 304 A line of 33 per cent during an increase of the

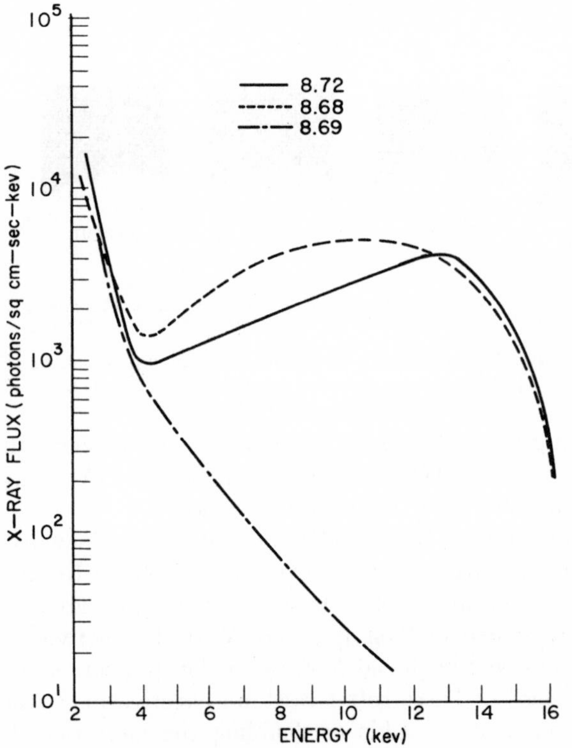

FIG. 20. Spectra of solar X-rays averaged over durations of three Nike-Asp rocket flights (Chubb *et al.* [14]).

sunspot number index from zero to 94. The change in intensity with a solar flare of Class 2, however, was less than a factor of 2.

8.3. X-Ray Spectra

The complexity of the variations in X-ray spectral distribution during relatively small flares is illustrated by a few observations carried out with Nike-Asp rockets as part of the IGC program, during the summer of 1959

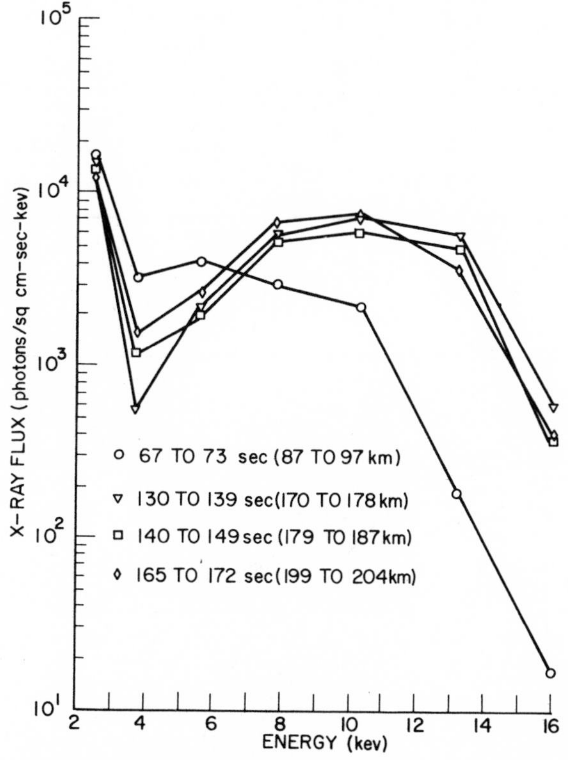

FIG. 21. Spectral variations during the course of a single rocket flight coincident with weak flare activity (Chubb *et al.* [14]).

[14]. Measurements were made in the 2–20 kev energy range by means of proportional counters with crude spectral resolution derived from pulse-height analysis. Figure 20 illustrates spectra obtained from three rockets, one launched during very quiet conditions, the other two during micro-flare or Class 1 activity. Under quiet conditions, Flight 8.72 revealed an intensity decreasing monotonically with increasing energy. The spectrum from 2 to 4 kev roughly fitted a 4×10^{6}°K Planckian distribution. In contrast, Flights 8.68 and 8.69 showed a marked increase in flux above 4 kev, maximizing in the 10 to 13 kev range and then fading out rapidly

TABLE 4

RELATIVE INTENSITIES OF X-RAY LINES

	λ(Å)	10^7 deg	2×10^7	5×10^7	10^8
Fe XXIII	12.0	5.2	1.5		
Fe XXIV	11.0	2.1	3.6	0.1	
Mg XI	9.3	0.6			
Mg XII	8.4	1.3	0.9	0.2	
Si XIII	6.7	2.2	0.6		
Si XIV	6.3	0.6	1.9	0.7	
S XV	5.2	0.5	1.0		
S XVI	4.3		0.6	0.5	0.007
Fe XXV	1.9		0.39	8.3	10.0
Fe XXVI	1.7		0.10	0.64	5.0

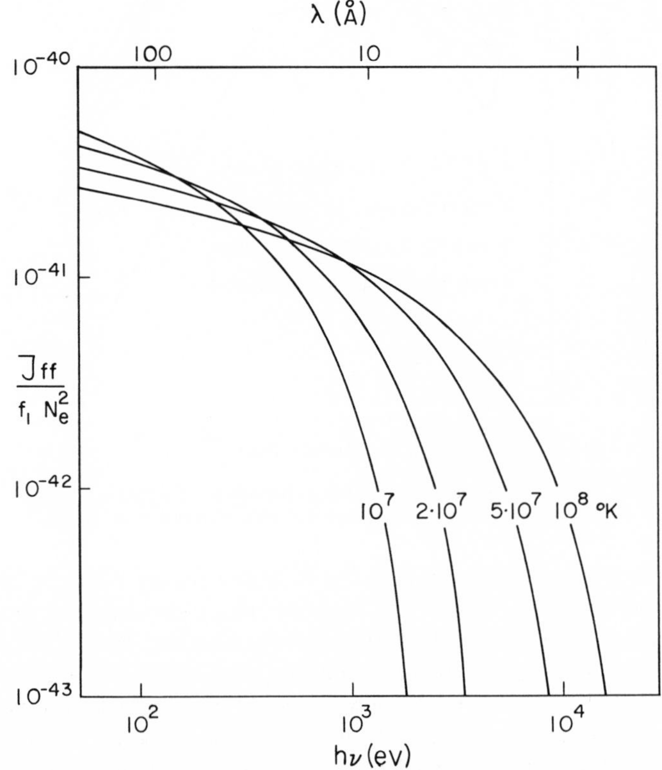

FIG. 22. Free–free X-ray emission spectra computed by Kawabata [48]. Intensities are in erg/cm^3/sec at the sun.

toward higher energies. Figure 21 shows that the spectrum underwent marked variations even during the few minutes of a rocket flight.

In interpreting these results, only qualitative significance should be attached to the position of the spectral peak. The experiments were performed under relatively primitive conditions by today's standards. We may therefore conclude only that the data indicate a pronounced peak in the 5–15 kev region, but cannot specify the maximum energy with any better definition. Table 4 lists the wavelengths and relative intensities of X-ray emission lines to be expected at various solar plasma temperatures, according to Elwert's theory [25]. The Fe XXV and XXVI emission lines near 7 kev become relatively intense at the higher temperatures. The series limit of Fe XXVI is 1.37 Å and its recombination radiation should therefore

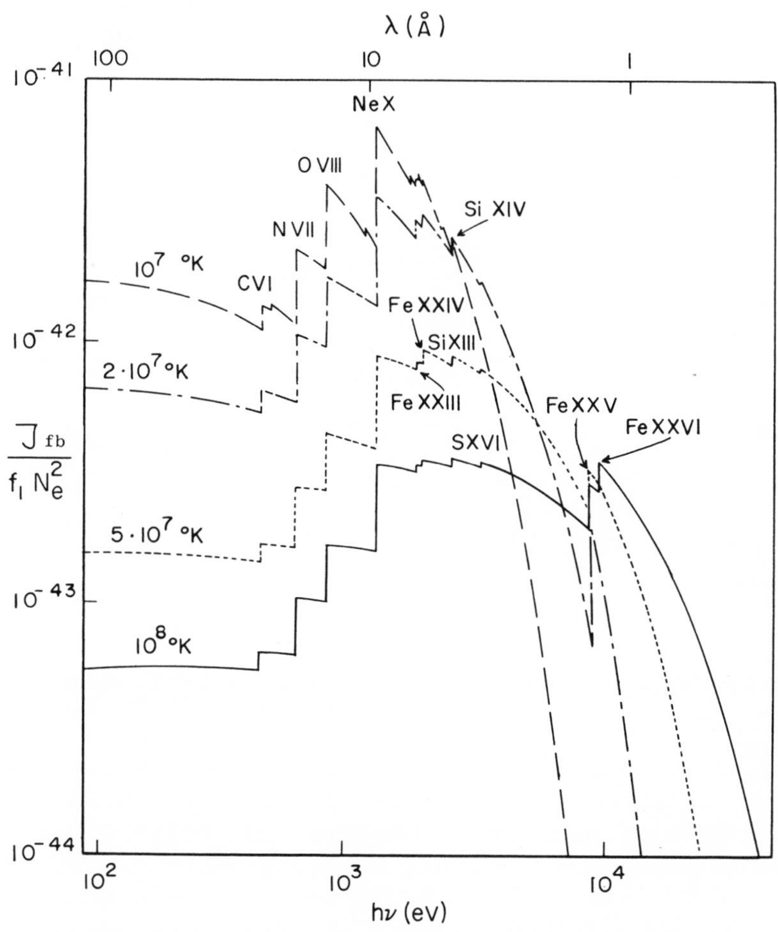

FIG. 23. Free-bound X-ray emission spectra computed by Kawabata [48].

exhibit a pronounced edge at about 9 kev. Since the resolution of the proportional counter was only about 25 per cent, an emission line or recombination limit would appear as a broad peak in the pulse amplitude spectrum.

According to Kawabata [48] the spectral distribution of X-ray emission should vary with temperature as shown in Figures 22, 23, and 24 for free-free, free-bound, and line emission. From 2–8 Å, X-ray emission is pre-

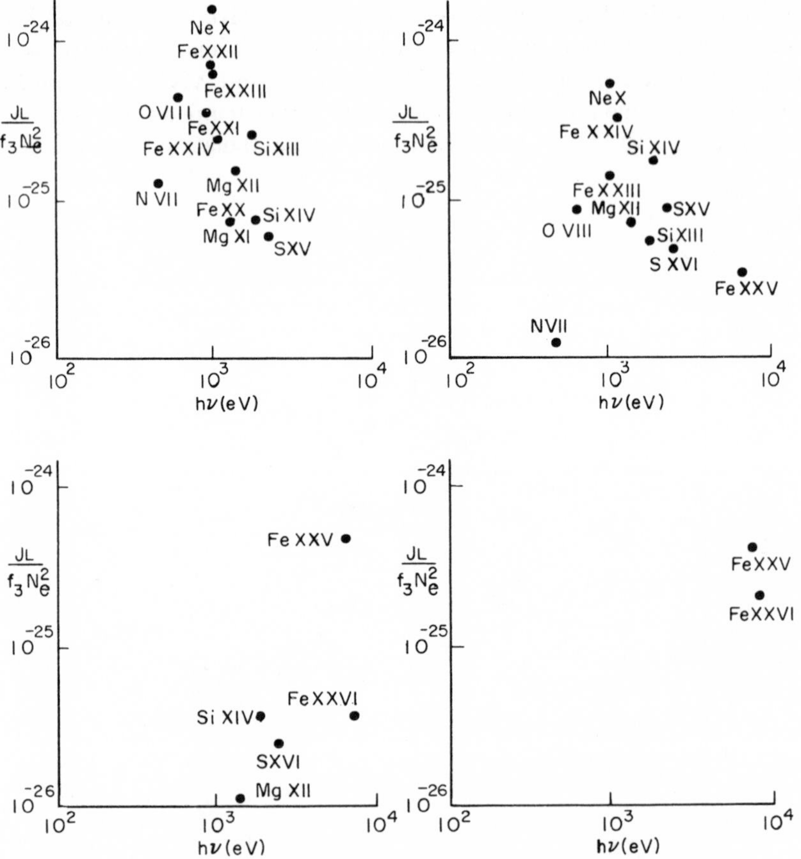

Fig. 24. X-ray line emission computed by Kawabata [48]. Intensities are in erg/cm³/sec at the sun.

dominantly the result of free-bound transitions to the K-shells of carbon, nitrogen, oxygen, and neon, if the temperature is less than about 3×10^7°K. Above this temperature, free-free transitions rapidly become more important. The integral of line emission is always less than the continuum flux above 10^7°K. These calculations suggest that the recombination limit at Fe XXV may show up prominently at temperatures of a few tens of millions of degrees. When scanned with the relatively broad resolution of a proportional counter, the increased radiation to the high-energy side of the limit may account for a hump in the spectral distribution with an apparent peak at 10–12 kev. Although line emission from Fe XXV and Fe XXVI would come up sharply at temperatures greater than 5×10^7 degrees, it would be swamped by continuum radiation when scanned with the resolution of the proportional counter. In summary, the measurements and theory are suggestive of local temperatures of 20–30 million degrees in active regions characterized by subflare activity. High-resolution line spectroscopy could resolve the question of the existence of such thermal regions, because of the strong temperature dependence of ion abundances and their resulting line intensities. Such spectroscopy is being planned for future OSO satellites.

8.4. X-Ray Spectra and SID Characteristics

It is interesting to consider the evidence for spectral variations in solar X-ray flux in relationship to ionospheric behavior. Taubenheim [81] has used analyses of oblique incidence field strength records and simultaneous observations of solar microwave radio noise to derive a model of the absorbing region responsible for sudden ionospheric disturbances. From a study of the rate of change of the excess total absorption with time during a short-wave fadeout, Taubenheim concluded that the absorbing layer had a thickness of about 10 km. Although absorption data do not by themselves indicate the height level at which absorption takes place, the coincidence of short wave fadeout with long wave and very low frequency (VLF) effects supports the hypothesis that the flare radiation ionizes a layer centered between 70 and 75 km. According to Volland [85], comparison of SWF and VLF effects shows that at least 50 per cent of the excess absorption produced by flare radiation takes place below 80 km. To produce a thin layer for the short-wave fadeout, the ionizing radiation must be largely monochromatic. Since the scale height in *D*-region is 6 km, a simple Chapman layer would be consistent with Taubenheim's model. He estimates that X-rays of wavelength 2.5–3 Å are required to produce a layer at 70–75 km.

Radio observations may also contain information about the temporal behavior of the ionizing flux. Statistical studies by Hachenberg and Kruger [37] have shown a strong coincidence between 3.2-cm bursts and SWF. Of 18 SWF effects, Taubenheim found that the radio burst at 3.2 cm had ended before the exponential decrease in radio absorption had begun. In the remaining cases, the exponential decay began when the radio burst had decreased in intensity to a few per cent of its maximum value and continued beyond the end of the microwave burst. Maximum absorption was delayed by an average of 5 minutes after the burst maximum. Assuming a simple attachment law, Taubenheim calculated the radiation intensity vs. time from the absorption. Some of the computed intensity curves exhibited a complex form, corresponding to similar complexity in the radio bursts. At other times, the computed intensity distribution with time showed a simple maximum similar to the 3.2-cm burst wave. A common feature in all cases was a sharp maximum of the ionizing radiation generally coinciding with the peak of the radio burst. This coincidence was not always precise—the X-ray peak sometimes being delayed up to 3 minutes beyond the 3-cm peak.

Various investigators have proposed models of a sudden ionospheric disturbance based on flashes of radiation ionizing the lower portion of the *D*-region. Warwick and Zirin [86], by fitting ionization and recombination rates to the observed time variation of electron density during a short-wave fadeout, concluded that the excess ionizing radiation appears as an instan-

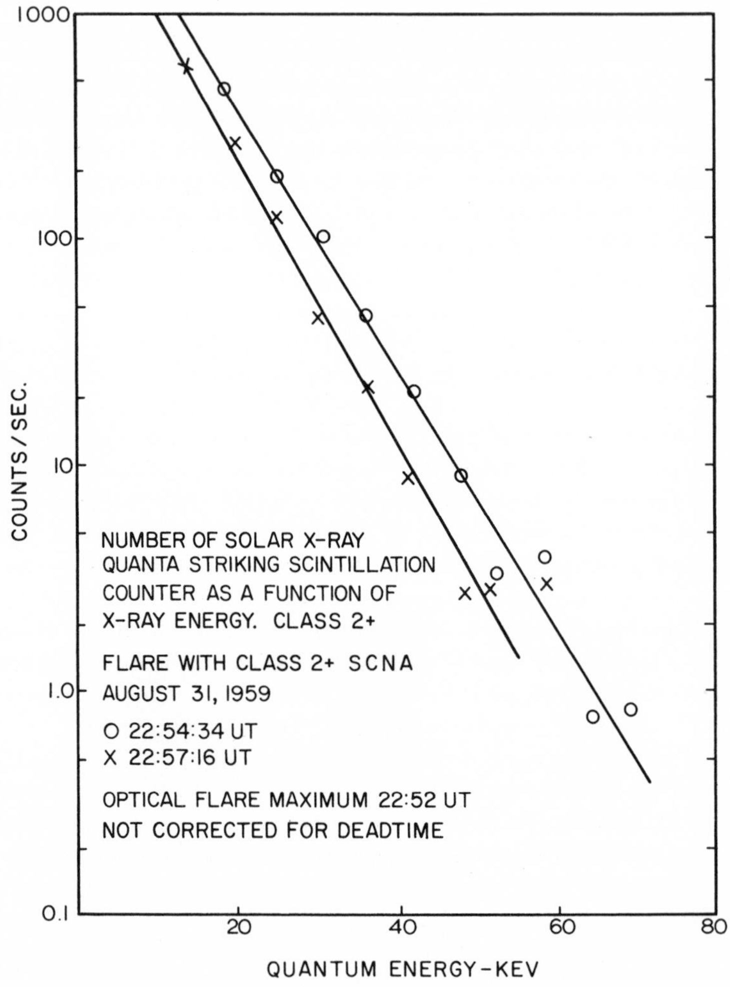

FIG. 25. Spectra of flare X-ray emission 20–80 kev (Chubb *et al.* [13].)

taneous flash. Swift's model [78] proposes a short burst of hard radiation at about 13 kev, lasting for only 6 minutes in a typical SID.

Analysis of events corresponding to ionization at different levels of *D*-region indicate complex time variations in the ionization at different levels. Bureau [11] has pointed out that the different types of SID have quite different temporal distributions. The sudden enhancement of atmospherics (SEA) on 8–16 km wavelengths is associated with reflection at a height of about 85 km. The SEA phenomenon starts to recover later and persists beyond the effects of the sudden phase anomaly (SPA) at longer wavelengths and the short-wave fadeout at shorter wavelengths. The SPA presumably occurs at lower and the SWF at higher altitudes than the SEA. Gregory's observations [34] of fixed frequency soundings at 1.75 Mc/sec during two SID's showed that: in one case echoes from the lowest level disappeared first and were replaced at maximum of the fadeout by echoes which were displaced downward by a few kilometers; in the second case, high *E*-region echoes disappeared first. The echoes moved progressively to lower levels as they faded away, leaving lowest level echoes at the maximum of the SID. During the recovery phase, the echoes returned from the bottom up with the lowest levels recovering first and the *E*-region echoes last. These observations suggest that temporal variations in the spectrum and, therefore, the penetrating power of the flare X-ray emission may be an important factor in the shifting levels of ionization.

The evidence presented here from rocket experiments is very fragmentary but it appears that complex spectral variations in the radiation affecting *D*-region do occur during the course of even a small flare. Emission has been detected at energies above 20 kev during Class 2^+ flares [13] and is undoubtedly bremsstrahlung produced by thermalized electrons, although it is not clear whether the original production of high energy electrons is by a thermal or nonthermal process. If the observed spectrum (Fig. 25) is extrapolated back to lower energies, the flux falls one to two orders of magnitude short of that required to produce the ionization deduced by Taubenheim at 70–75 km. On the other hand, an emission peak such as observed in the proportional counter measurements would produce adequate ionization at the required level.

8.5. *Solar Flare Effects in E- and F-Regions*

Davies [20] observations of the effects of changes in height and shape of the ionosphere on the frequencies received from stable transmitters provide a sensitive means of studying flare effects at levels above the absorption region. For a large flare, increased ionization occurs at all levels up to F_2, whereas small flares appear to affect only the lower levels of the ionosphere. Davies remarks that no two flares are alike and that there is little relationship between Hα intensity and ionospheric effect. Such statements are consistent with the observations of solar flare X-ray emission from the satellites described above. Longer wavelength X-rays affect higher levels of the ionosphere, so that the ionospheric behavior varies with altitude in response to the spectral mixture of flare radiations. The various wavelength regions may be associated with different mechanisms of emission, thermal and nonthermal, occurring in different regions of the solar atmosphere and having different rise and decay characteristics.

Ferraro *et al.* [27] have developed a theory of flare effects in the F_2-region that predicts considerable complexity in the response of the ionosphere to the input of ultraviolet radiations. Marked effects are to be expected where h_mF_2 is low and minor effects where h_mF_2 is high. It should be possible to check the ratios between maximum electron density and ionization rate as predicted by theory with direct measures of the ionizing ultraviolet radiation monitored by the OSO series of satellites of NASA.

Conclusion

This review has been confined to the major features of ionospheric behavior under the influence of solar electromagnetic radiation. Since essentially all of the radiation input is effective below $F_{\max}$, no attempt has been made to describe the topside ionosphere. Furthermore, the treatment has been confined largely to the normal midlatitude ionosphere. In this simple framework, the discussion has emphasized the broad qualitative features and shown the difficulties of developing precise models from experimental parameters containing order of magnitude uncertainties. Considerable progress has been made since the IGY to the extent that we now understand how complex the problems are. As the IQSY programs begin, we may be confident that the time is near when experimental techniques will be capable of providing accurate aeronomic parameters for ionospheric models.

References

1. L. W. Acton, R. W. Kreplin, T. A. Chubb, and J. F. Meekins, Observations of solar X-ray emission in the 8–20 A band, *J. Geophys. Res.*, **68**, 3335 (1963).
2. L. A. Antonova and G. S. Ivanov-Kholodny, Corpuscular hypothesis for the ionization of the night-time ionosphere, *Geomag. & Aeron.*, **1**, 164 (1961).
3. D. R. Bates and A. Dalgarno, Electronic recombination, *Atomic and Molecular Processes*, D. R. Bates (ed.) (Academic Press, 1962).
4. S. J. Bauer and J. E. Jackson, A small multi-purpose rocket payload for ionospheric studies, *Space Research IV* (North-Holland Publishing Co., 1964, in press).
5. W. E. Behring, J. C. Lindsay, and W. M. Neupert, Preliminary observations on variations of extreme ultra-violet solar fluxes with variations in solar activity, *Trans. Amer. Geophys. Un.*, **43**, 462 (1962).
6. E. P. Bialecke and A. A. Dougal, Pressure and temperature variation of the electron-ion recombination in nitrogen, *J. Geophys. Res.*, **63**, 539 (1958).
7 M. A. Biondi, Atomic collisions involving low energy electrons and ions, *Advances in Electronics and Electron Physics*, 18, L. Marton (ed.) (Academic Press, 1963).
8. R. L. Blake, T. A. Chubb, H. Friedman, and A. E. Unzicker, Interpretation of X-ray photograph of the sun, *Astrophys. J.*, **137**, 3 (1963).
9. R. L. Blake, T. A. Chubb, H. Friedman, and A. E. Unzicker, unpublished.

10. S. Bowyer, E. T. Byram, T. A. Chubb, and H. Friedman, X-ray sources in the galaxy, *Nature* (in press).
11. R. Bureau, Les éruptions de la chromosphère solaire et leurs répercussions sur l'ionosphère et sur la propagation des ondes, leurs effets dans les diverses régions du spectre radio électrique, *L'Onde Electrique*, **27,** 45 (1947).
12. E. T. Byram, T. A. Chubb, and H. Friedman, Attempt to measure night helium glow—evidence for metastable molecules in the night ionosphere, *J. Geophys. Res.*, **66,** 2095 (1961).
13 T. A. Chubb, H. Friedman, and R. W. Kreplin, Measurements made of high energy X-rays accompanying three class 2^+ solar flares, *J. Geophys. Res.*, **65,** 1831 (1960).
14. T. A. Chubb, H. Friedman, and R. W. Kreplin, Solar flare X-ray emission in the 2–20 kev range, *Space Research IV* (North-Holland Publishing Co., 1964, in press).
15. T. A. Chubb, H. Friedman, R. W. Kreplin, R. L. Blake, and A. E. Unzicker, X-ray and ultraviolet measurements during the eclipse of October 12, 1958, *Mém. Roy. Soc. Liège*, **4,** 228 (1961).
16. T. A. Chubb, H. Friedman, R. W. Kreplin, and J. E. Kupperian, Jr., Rocket observation of X-ray emission in a solar flare, *Nature*, **179,** 861 (1957).
17. A. Dalgarno and G. W. Griffing, Energy per ion pair for electron and proton beams in atomic hydrogen, *Proc. Roy. Soc.*, **A248,** 415 (1958).
18. A. D. Danilov, Molecular ions in the upper atmosphere, *Izv. Akad. Nauk SSSR*, **137,** 1098 (1961).
19. A. D. Danilov, On the problem of O_{2^+} formation in the high atmosphere, *Artificial Earth Satellites No.* **7,** 56 (Moscow, 1961).
20. K. Davies, Doppler studies of the ionospheric effects of solar flares, *Proc. Intn'l Conf. The Ionosphere*, 76 (Inst. Phys. and Phys. Soc., London, 1963).
21. J. H. Dellinger, Sudden ionospheric disturbances, *Terr. Mag. Atmos. Elect.*, **42,** 49 (1937).
22. C. R. Detwiler, D. L. Garrett, J. D. Purcell, and R. Tousey, The intensity distribution in the ultraviolet solar spectrum, *Ann. Géophys.*, **17,** 263 (1961).
23. P. H. G. Dickinson and J. Sayers, Ion charge exchange reaction in oxygen afterglows, *Proc. Phys. Soc.*, **76,** 137 (1960).
24. J. P. Doering and B. H. Mahan, Photoionization of nitric oxide, *J. Chem. Phys.*, **36,** 669 (1962).
25. G. Elwert, Theory of X-ray emission of the sun, *J. Geophys. Res.*, **66,** 391 (1961).
26. A. C. Faire and K. S. W. Champion, Measurement of dissociative recombination and diffusion in nitrogen at low pressures, *Phys. Rev.*, **113,** 1 (1959).
27. V. C. A. Ferraro, J. E. C. Gliddon, and P. C. Kendall, Solar eclipse and flare effects in the F_2 region, *Proc. Intn'l Conf. The Ionosphere*, 71 (Inst. Phys. and Phys. Soc., London, 1963).
28. W. L. Fite, J. A. Rutherford, W. R. Snow, and V. A. J. Van Lint, Ion-neutral collisions in afterglow, *Discussions Faraday Soc.*, **33,** 264 (1962).
29. H. Friedman, Lyman-α radiation, *Ann. Géophys.*, **17,** 245 (1961).
30. H. Friedman, Solar observations obtained from vertical soundings, *Repts. on Progress in Physics*, **25,** 163 (1962).
31. H. Friedman, Ionospheric constitution and ionizing radiation, *Proc. Intn'l Conf. The Ionosphere*, 3 (Inst. Phys. & Phys. Soc., London, 1963).
32. H. Friedman and T. A. Chubb, Solar X-ray emission and the height of *D*-layer during radio fadeout, *Rept. Phys. Soc. Conf. on the Physics of the Ionosphere, Cambridge 1964* (London, 1955).
33. Yu. I. Galperin, On the question of energy sources in the upper atomsphere, *Izv. Akad. Nauk SSSR, Geophys. Ser.*, **2,** 252 (1962).
34. J. B. Gregory, Medium-frequency observations of the lower ionosphere during sudden disturbances, *J. Geophys. Res.*, **63,** 273 (1958).
35. K. I. Gringauz and V. A. Rudakov, *Artificial Earth Satellites No.* **6,** 48 (Moscow, 1961).
36. R. C. Gunton and E. C. Y. Inn, Rates of electron removal by recombination, attachment and ambipolar diffusion in nitric oxide plasmas, *J. Chem. Phys.*, **35,** 1896 (1961).

37. O. Hackenberg AND A. KRUGER, The correlation of bursts of solar radio emission in the centimeter range with flares and sudden ionospheric disturbances, *J. Atmos. Terr. Phys.*, **17,** 20 (1959).
38. P. L. HARTMAN AND H. HOERLIN, Measurements of the fluorescent efficiency of air under electron bombardment, *Bull. Am. Phys. Soc., Ser. II*, **7,** 69 (1962).
39. H. E. HINTEREGGER, Preliminary data on solar extreme ultraviolet radiation in the upper atmosphere, *J. Geophys. Res.*, **66,** 2367 (1961).
40. J. C. HOLMES AND J. M. YOUNG, Positive ion composition above White Sands, New Mexico (private communication).
41. E. H. HOLT, Electron loss processes in the oxygen afterglow, *Bull. Am. Phys. Soc.*, **4,** 112 (1959).
42. V. G. ISTOMIN, Investigation of the ion composition of the earth's atmosphere on geophysical rockets (1957–1959), *Planet. Space Sci.*, **9,** 179 (1962).
43. G. S. IVANOV-KHOLODNY, Intensity of the sun's shortwave radiation and rate of ionization and recombination processes in the ionosphere, *Geomag. & Aeron.*, **2,** 377 (1962).
44. G. S. IVANOV-KHOLODNY AND G. M. NIKOLSKY, A prediction of solar line emission in the extreme ultraviolet, *Soviet Astron. AJ*, **5,** 632 (1962).
45. J. E. JACKSON AND S. J. BAUER, Rocket measurements of a daytime electron-density profile up to 620 km, *J. Geophys. Res.*, **66,** 3055 (1961).
46. C. Y. JOHNSON, E. MEADOWS, AND J. HOLMES, Ion composition of the Arctic ionosphere, *J. Geophys. Res.*, **63,** 443 (1958).
47. W. H. KASNER, W. A. ROGERS, AND M. A. BIONDI, Electron-ion recombination coefficients in nitrogen and in oxygen, *Phys. Rev. Letters*, **7,** 321 (1961).
48. K. KAWABATA, The relationships between post burst increases of solar microwave radiation and sudden ionospheric disturbances, *Rept. Ionos. Space Res. Japan*, **14,** 405 (1960).
49. V. I. KRASSOVSKY, Energy sources of the upper atmosphere, *Planet. Space Sci.*, **1,** 14 (1959).
50. R. W. KREPLIN, Solar X-rays, *Ann. Géophys.*, **17,** 151 (1961).
51. R. W. KREPLIN, T. A. CHUBB, AND H. FRIEDMAN, X-ray and Lyman alpha emission from the sun as measured from the NRL SR-1 satellite, *J. Geophys. Res.*, **67,** 2231 (1962).
52. M. R. KUNDU, Solar radio emission on centimeter waves and ionization of the *E*-layer of the ionosphere, *J. Geophys. Res.*, **65,** 3903 (1960).
53. M. R. KUNDU AND J. F. DENISSE, Solar radiation on decimeter waves as an index for ionospheric studies, *J. Atmos. Terr. Phys.*, **13,** 176 (1958).
54. G. F. O. LANGSTROTH AND J. B. HASTED, General discussion, *Discussions Faraday Soc.*, **33,** 298 (1962).
55. R. E. LE LEVIER, Determination of the *D*-layer dissociative recombination coefficient from a high altitude nuclear explosion, *J. Geophys. Res.*, **69,** 1469 (1964).
56. S. C. LIN, Ionization phenomenon of shock waves in oxygen-nitrogen mixtures, *Avco-Everett Research Report No.* **33** (1958).
57. A. E. LYTLE AND D. M. HUNTEN, Observations of N_2^+ twilight and sunlit aurora, *Can. J. Phys.*, **40,** 1370 (1962).
58. S. L. MANDELSTAM, I. P. TINDO, YU. K. VORONKO, B. N. VASILYEV, AND A. I. SHURYGIN, Investigations of solar X-ray radiation, *Artificial Earth Satellites No. 10*, 12; *No. 11*, 3 (Moscow, 1961).
59. D. F. MARTYN, The normal *F*-region of the ionosphere, *Proc. Inst. Radio Engrs.*, **47,** 147 (1959).
60. T. M. MULYARCHIK AND P. V. SHCHEGLOV, Temperature and corpuscular heating in the auroral zone, *Planet. Space Sci.*, **10,** 215 (1963).
61. M. NICOLET, Density of the heterosphere related to temperature, *Smithson. Astrophys. Obs. Special Rept. No. 75* (1961).
62. M. NICOLET, Aeronomy, *Handbuch der Physik* (to be published).
63. M. NICOLET AND A. C. AIKIN, The formation of the *D*-region of the ionosphere, *J. Geophys. Res.*, **65,** 1469 (1960).

64. M. Nicolet and W. Swider, Jr., The ionospheric conditions, *Penn. State Univ. Ionos. Res. Lab. Sci. Rept.*, **193** (1963).
65. A. O. Nier, J. H. Hoffman, C. Y. Johnson, and J. C. Holmes, The neutral composition of the atmosphere in the 100–200 km range, *J. Geophys. Res.*, (in press).
66. B. J. O'Brien, Lifetime of outer zone electrons and their precipitation into the atmosphere, *J. Geophys. Res.*, **67**, 3687 (1962).
67. K. A. Pounds and A. P. Willmore, Preliminary report on UK-I satellite (unpublished).
68. J. D. Purcell and R. Tousey (unpublished).
69. J. A. Ratcliffe, A survey of solar eclipses and the ionosphere, *Solar Eclipse and the Ionosphere*, W. J. G. Beynon and G. M. Brown (eds.) (Pergamon Press, 1956).
70. H. Rishbeth, Atmospheric composition and the *F*-layer of the ionosphere, *Planet. Space Sci.*, **9**, 149 (1962).
71. F. Roach (private communication).
72. J. Sayers, Recent laboratory studies of recombination cross sections, *Solar Eclipses and the Ionosphere*, W. J. G. Beynon and G. M. Brown (eds.) (Pergamon Press, 1956).
73. J. Sayers, Ionic recombination, *Atomic and Molecular Processes*, D. R. Bates (ed.) (Academic Press, 1962).
74. E. J. Schaefer, Neutral composition obtained from a rocket-borne mass spectrometer, *Space Research IV* (North-Holland Publishing Co., 1964, in press).
75. L. G. Smith, Rocket measurements of electron density and temperature in the nighttime ionosphere, *Geophys. Corp. Amer. Tech. Rept.*, **62-1-N** (1962).
76. E. V. Stupochenko, I. P. Stakhanov, E. V. Samuilov, A. S. Pleshanov, and I. B. Rozhdestvenskii, Thermodynamic properties of air in the temperature interval from 1000 to 12,000 K and the pressure intervals from 0.001 to 1000 atmosphere, *ARS Journal*, **30**, 98 (1960).
77. Z. Svestka, Spectral anomalies associated with the extraordinary x-ray emission recorded by the SR-1 satellite on August 7, 1960, *Space Research IV* (North-Holland Publishing Co., 1964, in press).
78. D. W. Swift, The effect of solar X-rays on the ionosphere, *J. Atmos. Terr. Phys.*, **23**, 29 (1961).
79. M. W. Syverson, R. P. Stein, T. M. Shaw. M. Scheibe, and R. C. Gunton, Electron-NO^+ recombination in shock heated air, *Bull. Amer. Phys. Soc.*, **7**, 378 (1962).
80. V. L. Talrose, M. I. Markin, and I. K. Larin, The reaction $O^+ + N_2 \rightarrow NO^+ + N$, *Discussions Faraday Soc.*, **33**, 257 (1962).
81. J. Taubenheim, Information on the ionizing radiation of solar flares from the ionospheric absorption effect, *J. Atmos. Terr. Phys.*, **24**, 191 (1962).
82. H. A. Taylor, Jr., and H. C. Brinton, Atmospheric ion composition measured above Wallops Island, Va., *J. Geophys. Res.*, **66**, 2587 (1961).
83. J. O. Thomas, The distribution of electrons in the ionosphere, *Proc. Inst. Radio Engrs.*, **47**, 162 (1959).
84. Upper Atmosphere Rocket Research Panel, Pressures, densities and temperatures in the upper atmosphere, *Phys. Rev.*, **88**, 1027 (1952).
85. H. Volland, On the diurnal propagation of V.L.F. waves at a distance of 1000 kilometers, *Heinrich Hertz Institut Tech. Ber. Nr. 37* (1960).
86. J. Warwick and H. Zirin, *High Altitude Obs. Sci. Rept. No. 7*)1957).
87. K. Watanabe and H. E. Hinteregger, Photoionization rates in the *E* and *F* regions, *J. Geophys. Res.*, **67**, 999 (1962).

CHAPTER 10

THE STRUCTURE OF THE UPPER ATMOSPHERE

M. Nicolet

1. Introduction

Before the International Geophysical Year our knowledge of the upper atmosphere was based on the interpretation of spectroscopic and radio-electric observations made at ground level and on a few rocket results obtained in the United States. Spectroscopic analysis of the night airglow has led to the detection of radiation emitted by atomic oxygen, molecular oxygen, and the OH radical. No emission from the molecular spectrum of nitrogen has been identified. Twilight spectrum results have also been useful. They have shown that N_2^+ bands and OI red line are present up to very high altitude. On the other hand, the general conclusion obtained from studies of the twilight and night airglow was that most excitation processes were due to chemical reactions occurring below 100 km. Auroral spectra exhibit lines and bands of molecular nitrogen which do not occur in the normal airglow spectrum. The spectral behavior of an aurora, including the displaced lines of atomic hydrogen, were conclusive evidence that charged particles are responsible for auroral displays. Some information concerning atmospheric composition was also gained through auroral analysis since the presence of N_2^+ bands in sunlit auroras up to 1000 km clearly indicates the presence of molecular nitrogen at high altitudes. The deduction of an absolute composition of the atmosphere from spectroscopic studies is difficult because of the different excitation processes involved.

Determinations of electron density profiles have often been misleading due to the fact that the actual heights of the ionization peaks were not given. For example, the conception of a maximum of photoionization above 200 km associated with the F_1-peak has led, during the past several years, to a misinterpretation of the atmospheric parameters involved in the analysis of the atmospheric structure.

A major advance in aeronomy occurred when the U.S. Naval Research Laboratory began using rockets for such work. At the end of 1953 [6] when the International Geophysical Year was planned, the ultraviolet solar spectrum was known down to about 2000 Å, and the daytime distribution of ozone had been observed up to 70 km and deduced theoretically up to 90 km. The vertical distribution of molecular oxygen was experimentally and theoretically deduced as being not in photochemical equilibrium but rather almost in diffusive equilibrium. The X-ray solar radiation was detected as being important in the range of 20–60 Å while Lyman α was first detected at altitudes below 75 km. Various pressure measurements were made below 100 km, but only three rocket flights above that height gave densities at 160 km and 200 km. Few rocket observations have been made between 100 and 200 km and the pressure at 100 km is not well known. Adopting a pressure of $(2.5 \pm 1.0) \times 10^{-4}$ mm Hg at 100 km, it is not yet possible to determine the exact range of the real variations. All upper atmospheric models are based on boundary conditions near the 100-km level; hence, any analysis of the upper atmosphere structure is subject to an uncertainty due to the unknown variations of the pressure in the lower thermosphere.

The lack of density observations made by rockets has been compensated for by the large number of satellite launchings which began with the first Sputnik at the beginning of the IGY. The Explorer and Vanguard satellites have made possible the study of the density variation over a height range of more than 500 km. The vertical distribution of thermospheric densities is now interpreted up to the atomic hydrogen belt, with a scale height which continually increases with height. Before attempting to draw a diagram of the neutral atmosphere, it is necessary to emphasize the terminology which was introduced by S. Chapman and which is now adopted by the International Union of Geodesy and Geophysics and the World Meteorological Organization. The vertical distribution of the temperature is the basis of such a nomenclature. Starting from the definition used in meteorology that the lowest atmospheric region is the troposphere heated by the earth's surface and its upper boundary the tropopause where the temperature gradient changes, it is possible to define regions representing alternately negative and positive gradients of the temperature. In this system the stratosphere extends up to a temperature peak in the neighborhood of 50 km where the upper atmosphere studied by physicists and radio engineers begins.

Thus, the atmosphere can be described as follows:

Earth's surface:	Temperature, 273°K ± 20°K.
Troposphere:	Temperature decreases with height.
Tropopause:	Temperature minimum, 210°K ± 20°K, and altitude 13 ± 5 km.

Stratosphere:	Temperature increases with height.
Stratopause:	Temperature maximum, 273°K ± 20°K, and altitude 50 ± 5 km.
Mesosphere:	Temperature decreases with height.
Mesopause:	Temperature minimum, 190°K ± 25°K, and altitude 85 ± 5 km.
Thermosphere:	Temperature increases.
Thermopause:	Beginning of an isothermal region.

The thermosphere temperature and its gradient vary with latitude and season. The variation with time of day and solar activity is remarkable.

The vertical distribution of the temperature depends on the local heat source and is related to the process of heat transport. In the troposphere, the heat source is the earth's surface and convection is the principal process of heat transport. Absorption of solar ultraviolet radiation by ozone and emission of infrared radiation in the stratosphere show that the heat budget involves radiative processes. The mesosphere, in which absorption processes are unimportant compared to heat loss processes, is a relatively unstable region.

Above the mesopause all ultraviolet radiation of wavelength shorter than 1750 Å is gradually absorbed and a fraction of the absorbed energy is used for the heating of the thermosphere. Atomic oxygen can radiate in the infrared at about 63 μ but convection in the lower thermosphere and conduction in the upper thermosphere are the principal processes of heat transport.

Composition must be introduced in the atmospheric nomenclature, for it is necessary to consider two essential divisions: the homosphere in which the composition is uniform despite the presence of minor constituent layers (i.e., ozone), and the heterosphere in which the mean molecular mass varies because such physical processes as molecular dissociation or diffusion of gases alter the composition.

Chapman's terminology is clear and satisfactory. It involves temperature, mean molecular mass, and composition, i.e., all the parameters necessary for defining an atmosphere for which hydrostatic conditions can be used. However, above the thermopause in the *isothermal region,* the mean free path of neutral atoms becomes so large that the hydrostatic law becomes inapplicable. The exosphere begins at a certain altitude called the *critical level.* This is where neutral atoms describe various orbits in the gravitational field of the planet.

Since the earth's atmosphere under static equilibrium is considered as a perfect gas composed of molecules and atoms of which only a small fraction is represented by charged particles, the *ionosphere* includes all atmospheric regions in which the behavior of ions and electrons influenced by the earth's magnetic field is studied. However, above a certain altitude, charged particles are governed primarily by the earth's magnetic field rather than its gravitational field. This outermost region of a planetary atmosphere is called the *magnetosphere*. Its outer boundaries reach out into interplanetary space.

2. The Chemosphere

Nighttime airglow observations [42] made by rockets show that the principal radiations, namely from OI (λ 5577 Å), Na (λ 5892 Å), O_2 bands, and hydroxyl bands, occur at relatively low height with emission peaks below 100 km. The aeronomic processes involved in producing such radiation correspond to chemical processes and cannot be associated with ionospheric processes. The nightglow cannot be caused by particles entering the atmosphere down to 100 km. However, photoelectrons can lead to appreciable airglow emission during the daytime in the ionospheric regions where the electron production is important.

Since Chapman drew attention to the chemical reservoir for the production of the airglow, the basic theories have considered the behavior of atomic oxygen in the mesosphere and lower thermosphere. Photochemical processes in the mesosphere and lower thermosphere are controlled by solar radiation for $\lambda > 1700$ Å. This leads to an atomic oxygen concentration not less than the ozone concentration for daytime conditions [3] at the stratopause. Ozone and oxygen atoms are important constituents in the mesosphere and they cause the introduction of many other chemical processes. A great variety of collision reactions are possible in an oxygen atmosphere (O_2, O, O_3) bathed in ultraviolet radiation and containing minor constituents such as water vapor, methane, and nitrogen oxides.

Free oxygen atoms are subject to reactions such as

$$O_2 + O + M \rightarrow O_3 + M \tag{1}$$

and

$$O_3 + O \rightarrow 2O_2 \tag{2}$$

During the night, atomic oxygen disappears through the rapid formation of ozone in the lower part of the mesosphere where the number of three-body collisions is very large. At the mesopause level, the ozone concentration grows at a smaller rate and the recombination of oxygen atoms by the process

$$O + O + M \rightarrow O_2 + M \tag{3}$$

is always small.

Methane is subject to direct photodissociation by Lyman α in the upper mesosphere. Methane disappears also by the oxidation process [2]

$$CH_4 + O \rightarrow CH_2 + H_2O \tag{4}$$

The presence of water vapor in the mesosphere is therefore not related to an upward transport from the stratosphere but to its production in the stratosphere itself. The photodissociation of H_2O leads to the production of hydrogen atoms. A hydrogen-oxygen atmosphere is very complicated since many important reactions can exist. A single free or combined hydrogen atom reacts with one of the allotropic forms of oxygen as

$$H + O_2 + M \rightarrow HO_2 + M \tag{5}$$

$$H + O_3 \rightarrow OH + O_2 \tag{6}$$

$$OH + O \rightarrow H + O_2 \tag{7}$$

$$HO_2 + O \rightarrow OH + O_2 \tag{8}$$

Other reactions such as

$$OH + OH \rightarrow H_2O + O \tag{9}$$

$$HO_2 + HO_2 \rightarrow H_2O_2 + O_2 \tag{10}$$

$$OH + HO_2 \rightarrow H_2O + O_2 \tag{11}$$

are also important processes. In the lower thermosphere, equilibrium conditions can be found for H, OH, and HO_2. The elements H_2O and H_2 should follow a vertical distribution subject to a departure from photochemical equilibrium conditions in the entire mesosphere. Since the rate of oxidizing reactions falls off rapidly with altitude, hydrogen compounds become less important with height and the element is left in atomic form in the lower thermosphere. Free hydrogen atoms diffuse in the mixing region and the rate of the upward flow controls the escape flow in the exosphere. On the other hand, H_2O is produced at the bottom of the mesosphere and this is an important source of water vapor in the middle atmosphere. (The dissociation of methane is also a source of carbon dioxide which must be subject to a downward transport.)

The production of nitric oxide is related to the production of nitrogen atoms [2, 40] by direct processes such as the predissociation of N_2 or by dissociative recombination of NO^+, an ion produced by reactions like

$$O^+ + N_2 \rightarrow NO^+ + N \tag{12}$$

$$O_2^+ + N_2 \rightarrow NO^+ + NO \tag{13}$$

Two important reactions can be considered as the loss processes of atomic nitrogen, which is a minor atmospheric constituent:

$$N + O_2 \rightarrow NO + O \tag{14}$$

and

$$N + NO \rightarrow N_2 + O \tag{15}$$

Reaction 13 should play a role in the *D*-region while reaction 12 occurs in the *F*-region. As far as nitric oxide is concerned, reactions 14 and 15 control its concentration. At sufficiently low levels, i.e., in the mesosphere, nitric oxide has a very long lifetime. Any NO molecule going downward at mesopause will have the tendency to follow a mixing distribution in the mesosphere. At sufficiently low levels, NO_2 must be considered, keeping in mind such reactions as:

$$NO_2 + O \rightarrow NO + O_2 \tag{16}$$

$$NO + O_3 \rightarrow NO_2 + O_2 \tag{17}$$

$$NO + O \rightarrow NO_2 \tag{18}$$

and

$$NO_2 + h\nu \rightarrow NO + O \tag{19}$$

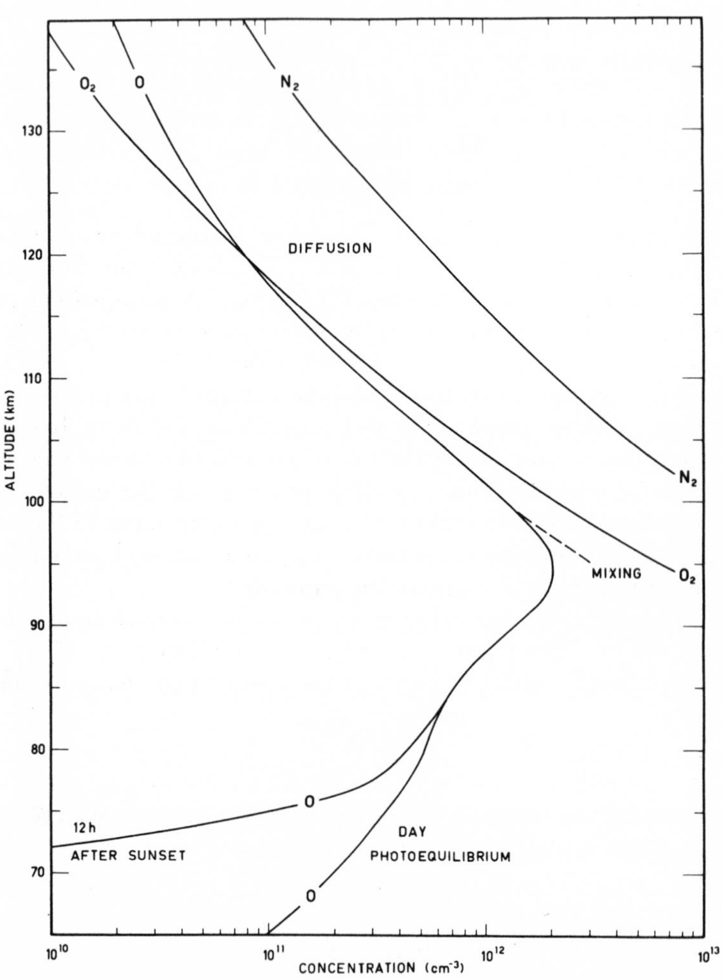

FIG. 1. The vertical distribution of oxygen and nitrogen in the upper mesosphere and lower thermosphere. The absolute values have been determined by assuming a pressure of 3×10^{-4} mm Hg at 100 km. A variation of the pressure at that level may be considered as a variation of the reference height; for example, 100 km ± 5 km.

Evidence supporting several of the preceding deductions can be found through the interpretation of the airglow spectrum and of the ionic constitution of the upper atmosphere.

The fundamental problem of the chemosphere starts from the dissociation of molecular oxygen. This dissociation depends mostly on the absorption of solar radiation of wavelengths less than 1750 Å and corresponds to a rate coefficient of about 5×10^{-6}/sec at zeroth optical depth. In the lower thermosphere with finite optical depth, the dissociation times become very long and diffusion leads to a departure from photochemical conditions. Figure 1 is intended to illustrate the conditions under which the problem of oxygen dissociation must be considered.

It is convenient to consider that the heterosphere, i.e., the atmospheric region where the mean molecular mass decreases with height, begins above the mesopause due to the partial dissociation of oxygen. The structure of this region is still very uncertain (recall the uncertainty in the pressure at 100 km). Therefore, it is necessary to select a reference level for diffusion. We have chosen 120 km as this level because it is almost certain that all the principal constituents are in diffusion equilibrium for steady-state conditions. Also, the introduction of a temperature gradient which increases rapidly can be made because the kinetic energy of a vertical column in this region is of the same order as the total solar ultraviolet energy absorbed in one day.

Thus, the thermosphere can be characterized with order in height by the dissociation of oxygen, the diffusion of all constituents, and the rapid increase in temperature.

3. Density in the Heterosphere

The heterosphere has been studied very extensively since the IGY [5, 32] and much detailed information is available from satellite data. Density determinations have been made by various authors following the initial calculations of the acceleration of the first two satellites (1957α and β, Sputniks I and II) whose perigees were below 225 km. The satellites Vanguard I (1958 β_2), Explorer I (1958 α), Explorer IV (1958 ϵ), and Sputnik III (1958 δ) have made an analysis of the densities possible at altitudes of approximately 650 km, 350 km, 260 km, and 220 km corresponding to the perigees of the above satellites. A synthesis of the results obtained through August, 1958 is given in the Volume XII of the Annals of the IGY [32]. The first Sputnik was launched during the period of maximum solar activity in October, 1957 when the thermopause temperature was a minimum of 2000°K for daytime conditions and greater than 1500°K for nighttime conditions. An approximate value of the density near 230 km is estimated to be 2×10^{-13}, which leads to about 4×10^{-13} gm/cm^3 at 200 km. Exclusive of systematic errors introduced in the determination of the absolute values of the density, various spurious effects [24] were noticed, such as variations of density with latitude which are due to the effect of the earth's equatorial bulge. This effect is only of the order of 5 per cent for Vanguard I, but has reached 40 per cent for Sputnik III. Several previous analyses should be modified to take into account the latitude variation of perigee. A consistent picture of the vertical distribution of air density cannot be obtained if the exact heights above sea level are not used. "Wiggles" or "kinks" in density curves below 300 km have been interpreted as due to peaks in the temperature. Comparison of the results obtained by several authors [52] (King-Hele, Paetzold, Priester and Martin [49]) shows that the method of analysis is involved in these deductions since the peaks do not occur at the same height for the same satellites. For example, a maximum and a minimum of temperature has been deduced near 220 km. Therefore, the available atmospheric density data near 200 km are not yet precise enough to determine the absolute density value and its real variations. Variations of ± 15 per cent cannot be necessarily considered as real modifications of atmospheric conditions, and they can lead to wrong deductions of atmospheric parameters.

A study of the observations from 300 km to 700 km, i.e., over a large range of altitudes, leads to the conclusion that the temperature variation is *not* the only important parameter determining the vertical distribution but that the variation of the mean molecular mass is also a controlling factor. The variation of ρ, the mass-density, which is expressed by

$$\frac{d\rho g}{\rho g} = -\frac{1+\beta}{\beta}\frac{dH}{H} \tag{20}$$

(where $\beta = dH/dr$ is the gradient of the atmospheric scale height H, and g is the gravitational acceleration) indicates that up to the maximum perigee height of Echo I ($\sim$1600 km) the major varying parameter is the mean molecular mass.

Studies of the fluctuations in the accelerations of satellites Vanguard I and Sputnik III, which were found to be in phase by Jacchia [16], showed that this atmospheric variation was correlated with solar radiation (Priester [48]). Furthermore, Jacchia [15] detected another effect. This led to a correlation between the increase of satellite drag and geomagnetic disturbances. Finally, the difference in density between daytime and nighttime conditions was recognized (Jacchia [18]), with a strong diurnal effect at highest altitudes. A diurnal effect can only be explained if the temperature of the isothermal region varies considerably between night and day. Furthermore, the normal heating of the upper atmosphere takes place by electromagnetic radiation and any hypothesis introducing a direct or indirect effect of particle cannot be taken too seriously, excepting auroras. The good correlation between radio-solar fluxes and atmospheric

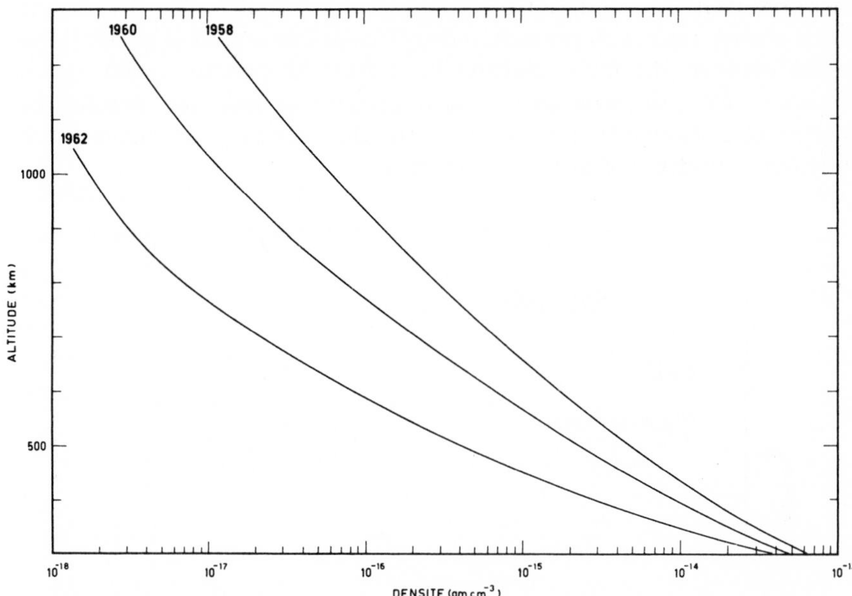

FIG. 2. Average density values for decreasing solar activity from 1958 to 1962. The density variation above 300 km is essentially associated with the temperature variation of the isothermal region.

densities [47] also shows that ultraviolet radiation is responsible for atmospheric heating. Solar activity was at its maximum when the first satellite was launched. Since then there has been a continuous decrease, almost reaching a minimum in August, 1962. Figure 2 illustrates average conditions for 1958, 1960, and 1962, and indicates the large density variation due to the decrease of the ultraviolet heating of the thermosphere during this period.

4. Variation of Solar Activity and Temperature

The solar radio flux is composed of a basic component corresponding to the general emission of the solar disc and of a slowly varying component associated with sunspots. There is a way in which radio observations can be used as indices of solar activity. A choice of radiations in the range of 1000 to 10,000 Mc/sec is justified because they are emitted from that part of the solar atmosphere where the majority of ultraviolet emissions are produced. Furthermore, there is a correlation between the Zurich sunspot number and a particular radio flux when average values are taken over a sufficiently long period [38] such as a 27-day or monthly period. A plot (Fig. 3) of the Wolf number $\bar{R}_{27}$ with the radio flux $\bar{S}_{27}$ (10.7 cm) shows where a linear relationship is valid. It should be noticed that variations of

±10 per cent are significant for average values. Daily values have variations greater than ±20 per cent and are unsuitable as a solar index. Differences between the fluxes emitted from 1000 Mc/sec to 10,000 Mc/sec which occur with variations of solar activity exclude any peculiar behavior at a specific frequency [37]. Certain "effects" can apparently be attributed to drifts of instrumental origin.

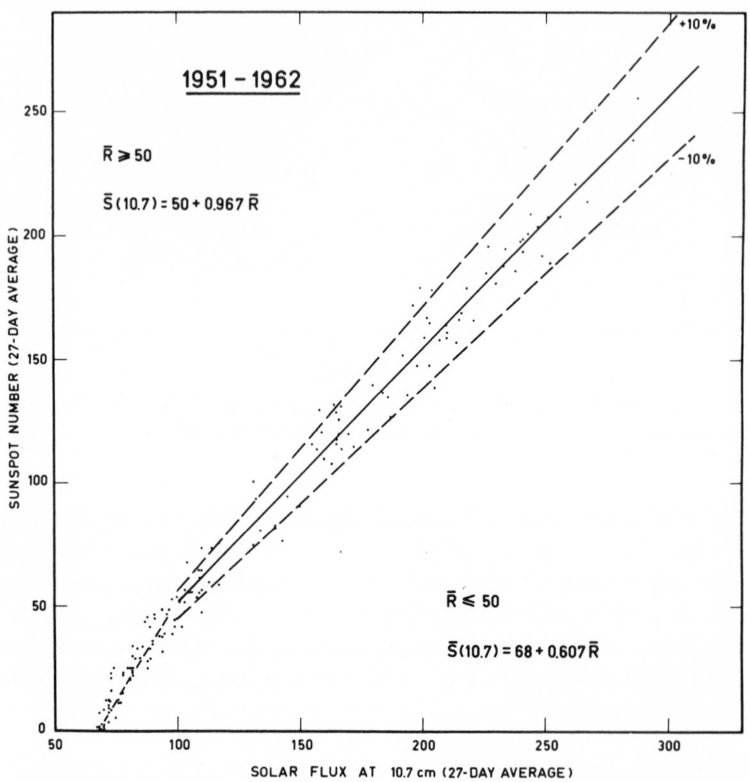

Fig. 3. The relationship between the relative sunspot number and the radio flux at 10.7 cm. A linear relationship cannot be used for the entire solar cycle. From M. Nicolet [38].

A complete analysis shows that the ratio of two solar radio fluxes does not remain constant during an entire solar cycle. A typical example is the flux variation for two wavelengths such as 8 cm and 10.7 cm. Figure 4 shows the gradual difference in the ratio of 27-day mean values. Both fluxes are identical near 200 units while the ratio is reversed for lower and higher values of solar fluxes. The ratios of the maximum 27-day mean value reached in October–December, 1957 and of the minimum 27-day mean value reached in May, 1954 are 3.7 and 4.2 for 8 cm and 10.7 cm, respectively. The same ratios become 1.6 and 4.5 at 3.2 cm and 30 cm, respectively.

The ratios of the minimum daily fluxes during the maximum sunspot of 1957 and of the minima 27-day mean values increase with the wavelength. The ratios are 1.2, 2.2, 2.5, 2.8, and 3.0 for 3.2 cm, 8 cm, 10.7 cm, 15 cm, and 30 cm, respectively. A variation from 1.2 to 3.0 shows that it is difficult to determine the amplitude of the quiet-sun variation as related to the

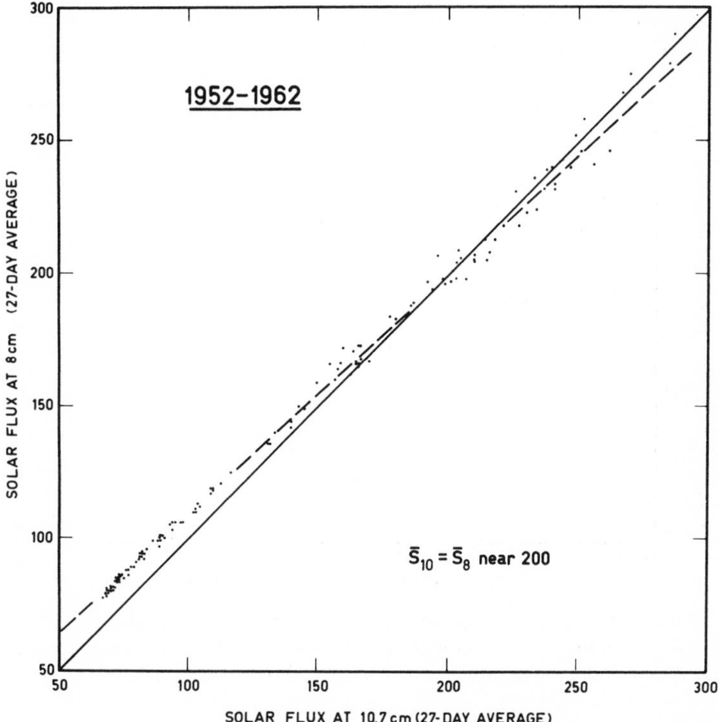

Fig. 4. The relationship between radio fluxes at 8 cm and 10 cm from minimum to maximum solar activity. It shows that the ratio of these fluxes varies with solar activity. From Nicolet [38].

ultraviolet flux. When 27-day mean fluxes are compared over a whole solar cycle (Fig. 5), one finds a departure from a smooth curve. Individual ratios are affected by about ±5 per cent, which corresponds to errors accepted for *good* measurements of the solar radio fluxes.

Finally, the maximum variation which is observed in the solar radio flux from 1000 Mc/sec to 10,000 Mc/sec, i.e., the ratio of the maximum daily flux reached in 1957 and the minimum daily flux reached in 1954 is less than 6. It is less than the change in the X-ray flux absorbed in the ionospheric *E*-layer, which is 7 for a solar cycle [10]. The behavior of the solar radio flux is not a good representation of the solar X-ray flux, but a specific frequency can represent, approximately, the major part of the ultraviolet flux associated with atmospheric heating.

Above a certain altitude, i.e., at the thermopause, the increase of atmospheric scale height with altitude is due to the decrease of the mean molecular mass in an isothermal atmosphere. The variation of thermopause temperature is related to the variation of the ultraviolet heating and conduction cooling. There is a relationship between solar radio flux and thermopause temperature. Jacchia [17], using Nicolet's atmospheric model [39], introduced a linear relationship between the solar flux at 10

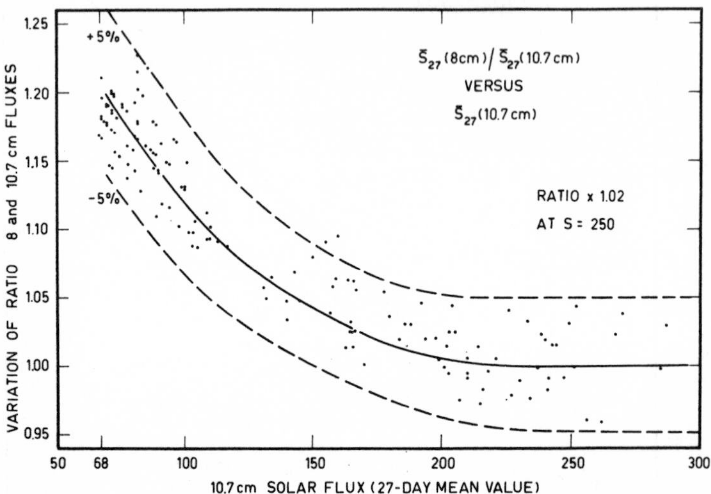

FIG. 5. The ratio of radio fluxes at 8 cm and 10.7 cm from minimum to maximum values of the solar flux. A variation of ±5 per cent for individual ratios being an indication of errors in the temperature determination. From Nicolet [38].

cm and the thermopause temperature. This was adopted also by Harris and Priester [12] and Paetzold [43].

In light of the preceding discussions the form of such an equation for the thermopause temperature may be written as follows:

$$T = T_0 + a\bar{S}_{27} + b\,\Delta S \tag{21}$$

where $\bar{S}_{27}$ is the mean value for a 27-day period and ΔS represents the oscillation during such a period. T_0, a, and b are constants which are obtained from observational analysis. For average nighttime conditions, we write

$$\bar{T}_{\text{night}} = 280°\text{K} + (4°\!.6 \pm 0.25)\,\bar{S}_{27}(8\text{ cm}) \tag{22}$$

in which a variation of ±5 per cent for any average absolute value of the

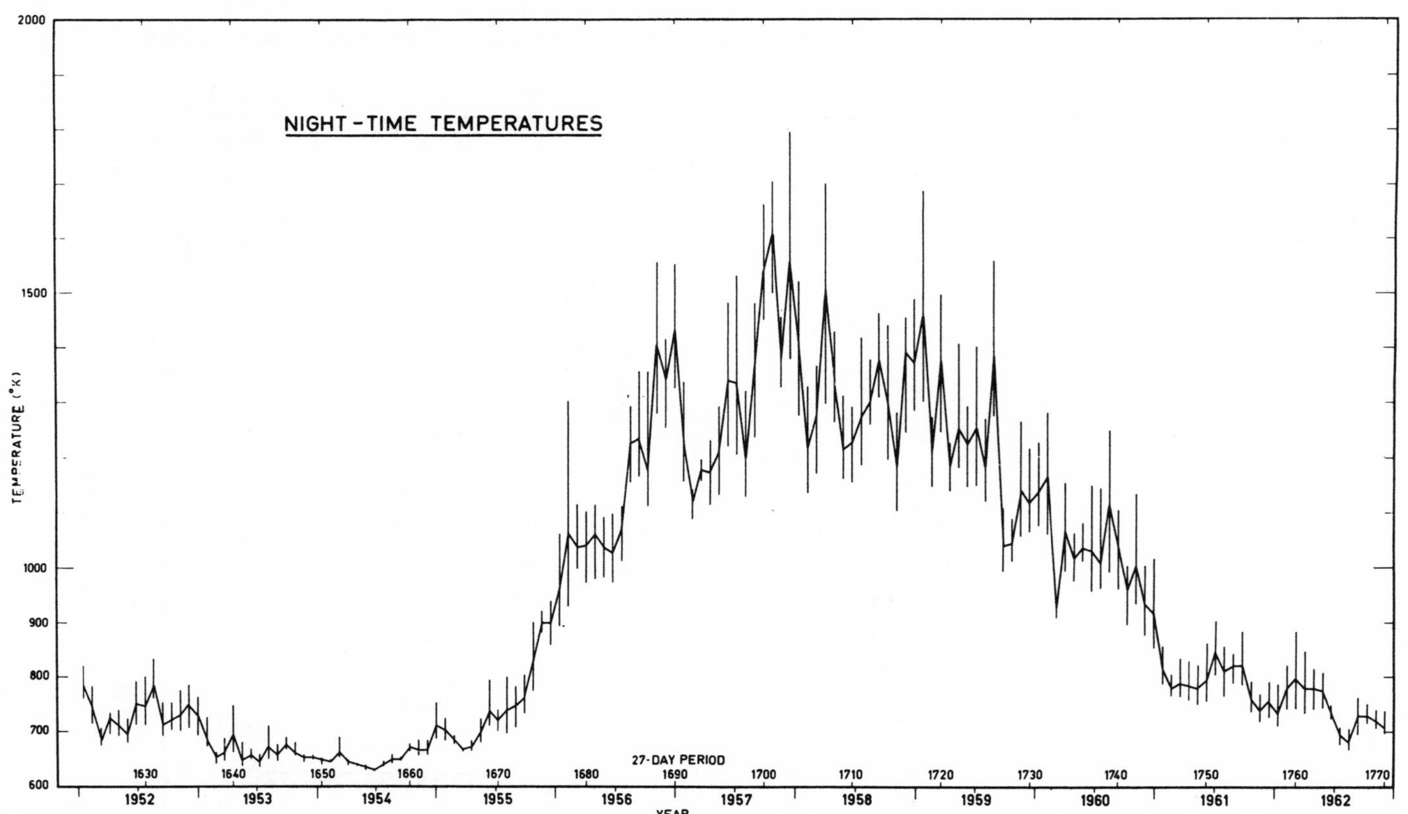

FIG. 6. Average nighttime temperatures (27-day mean values) at the thermopause level and the 27-day maximum temperature range from 1952 to 1962. Magnetic storm effects are not included. From Nicolet [38].

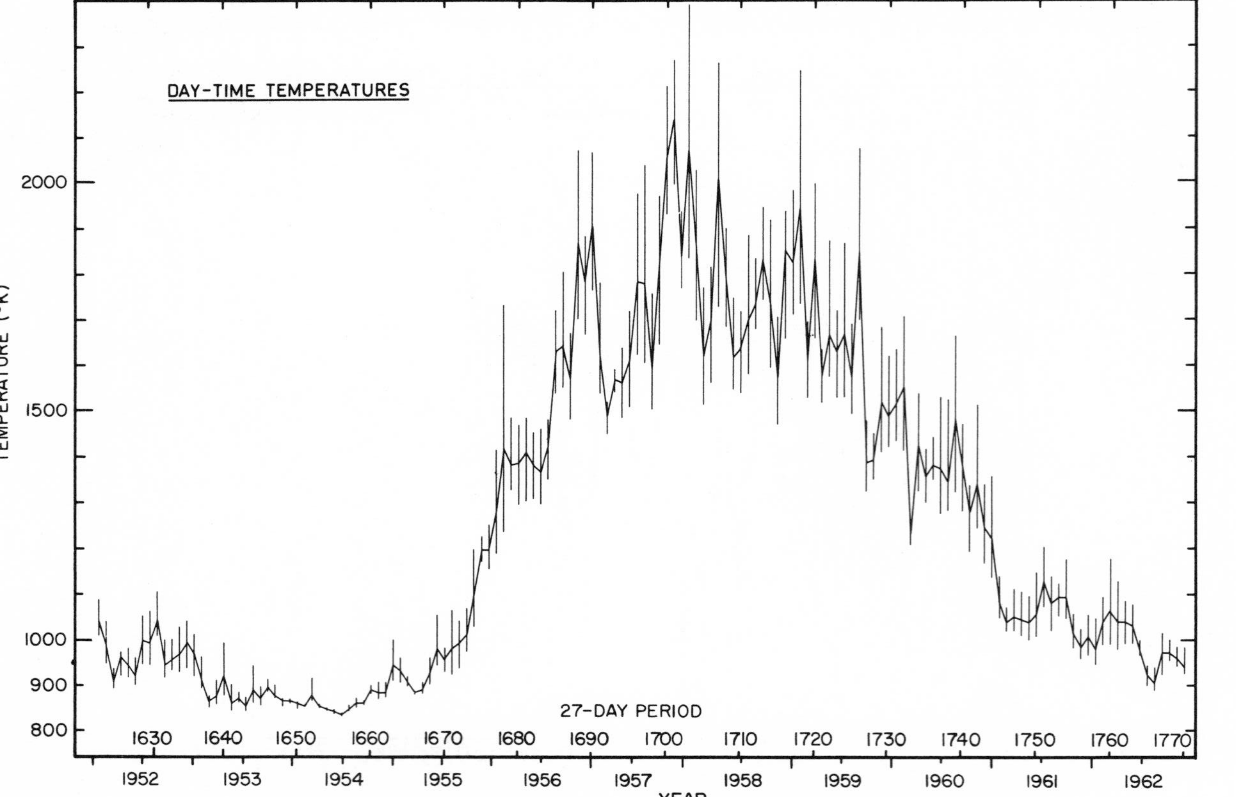

FIG. 7. Average daytime temperatures (27-day mean values) at the thermopause level and the 27-day maximum temperature range from 1952 to 1962. Magnetic storm effects are not included. From Nicolet [38].

solar flux is taken into account by the term $\pm 0.25 S$. This fluctuation indicates an uncertainty of $\pm 50°$K for a solar radio flux of 200 units.

The study of the 27-day oscillation made by Jacchia and Slowey [19] can be expressed by

$$T = \bar{T} + (2°.5 \pm 0.25)\,\Delta S(8\text{ cm}) \tag{23}$$

in which a variation of ± 10 per cent takes into account differences which often occur in the daily fluxes.

The nighttime temperature is given by combining Equations 22 and 23 as

$$T_{\text{night}} = 280°\text{K} + (2°.1 \pm 0.25)\,\bar{S}_{27} + (2°.5 \pm 0.25)\,S \tag{24}$$

$dT/d\bar{S}_{27} = 2°.1 \pm 0.25$ is due only to the ultraviolet radiation and not the solar wind or corpuscular radiation; $dT/dS = 2°.5 \pm 0.25$ represents the contribution of the ultraviolet radiation which is due to the 27-day oscillation and it has a smaller weight then the basic component $\bar{S}_{27}$ which represents the entire solar disk.

In order to obtain the average daytime conditions we use Jacchia's relation

$$\bar{T}_{\text{day}} = 1.3\bar{T}_{\text{night}} \tag{25}$$

It is possible to illustrate the variation of daytime and nighttime temperatures over a whole solar cycle with formulas 24 and 25. Figures 6 and 7 indicate the temperatures reached during the IGY, when the solar cycle was its maximum, and the temperatures which will be observed during IQSY for a quiet-sun period.

5. Diffusion

The composition of the thermosphere is characterized by three principal constituents, namely molecular nitrogen and atomic and molecular oxygen. It is not possible, however, to explain the vertical distribution of density in the whole heterosphere without considering helium and atomic hydrogen. The helium belt, which was introduced by Nicolet [36, 35], is now accepted as explaining the neutral and ionized atmosphere above 500 km (the last objection was given by Paetzold and Zschörner [44]). A complete helium-hydrogen analysis has been made by Kockarts and Nicolet [27, 28] considering a diffusion steady state involving the thermal diffusion effect in the thermosphere. It should be pointed out here that Paetzold [43] and also Harris and Priester [12] have not included thermal diffusion in their computations and thus their atmospheric models must be modified above a certain altitude.

The hydrogen distribution which was determined by Bates and Patterson [4] and Kockarts and Nicolet [27, 28] is based on the following general equation, applicable to a minor constituent in a steady state:

$$\frac{\partial n_1}{\partial r} + \frac{n_1}{H_1}[1 + \beta_1^*(1 + \alpha_T)] + \frac{F_a}{D_1}\left(\frac{a}{r}\right)^2 = 0 \tag{25}$$

In this equation, r is the distance to the earth's center, and $a = r$ is the lower boundary of the region under study. The scale height H_1 of the minor constituent of mass m_1 is

$$H_1 = kT/m_1g \tag{26}$$

with a gradient

$$\beta_1 = \beta_1^* + 2H_1/r \tag{27}$$

The thermal diffusion factor is denoted by the symbol α_T. The last term of Equation 25 expresses the continuity of the flux F

$$F = n_1w_1 = F_a(a/r)^2 \tag{28}$$

where w_1 is the diffusion rate of the minor constituent. The diffusion coefficient is introduced in the following form:

$$D_1 = \frac{3\sqrt{\pi/2}}{8\pi\sigma^2 f}\left(1 + \frac{m}{m_1}\right)^{1/2} \frac{(gH)^{1/2}}{n} \tag{29}$$

where m and H are the mean molecular mass and the scale height of the principal constituent with concentration n; $\sigma f^{1/2}$ represents the effective radius for diffusion. The diffusion flux F_{DM} for mixing conditions is

$$F_{DM} = \frac{n_1}{n}\frac{g}{T^{1/2}}\frac{3\sqrt{\pi/2}}{8\pi\sigma^2 f}\left(1 + \frac{m}{m_1}\right)^{1/2}\left(\frac{m}{k}\right)^{1/2}\left(1 - \frac{m_1}{m} - \beta^*\alpha_T\right) \tag{30}$$

where β^* is defined by a formula like Equation 27 in which H is the atmospheric scale height. For any minor constituent the diffusion flux in mixing conditions depends on the constant ratio n_1/n, is proportional to the product $(a^2/r^2)\,T^{-1/2}$, and is related to the height variation of $\beta^*\alpha_T$. Thus, the escape flux of a minor constituent of small mass m_1 is controlled by diffusion conditions in the mixing region. The escape flux F_c at the critical level r_c is given by

$$F_c = n_cv_E \tag{31}$$

in which v_E denotes the effusion velocity. This velocity depends essentially on the temperature since it is proportional to the exponential factor $[-r_cm_1g/kT]$. The escape flux for a steady state obtained from Equations 30 and 31 is given by the following expression:

$$a^2F_{DM} = r_c^2F_c = n_cr^2v_E \tag{32}$$

Thus, the concentration n_c depends on the diffusion flux in the mixing region.

The last term of Equation 25 is practically negligible for helium and diffusion equilibrium can be applied to a constituent for a constituent of mass $m_1 \geq 4$. In the thermosphere, Equation 32 must be used for atomic

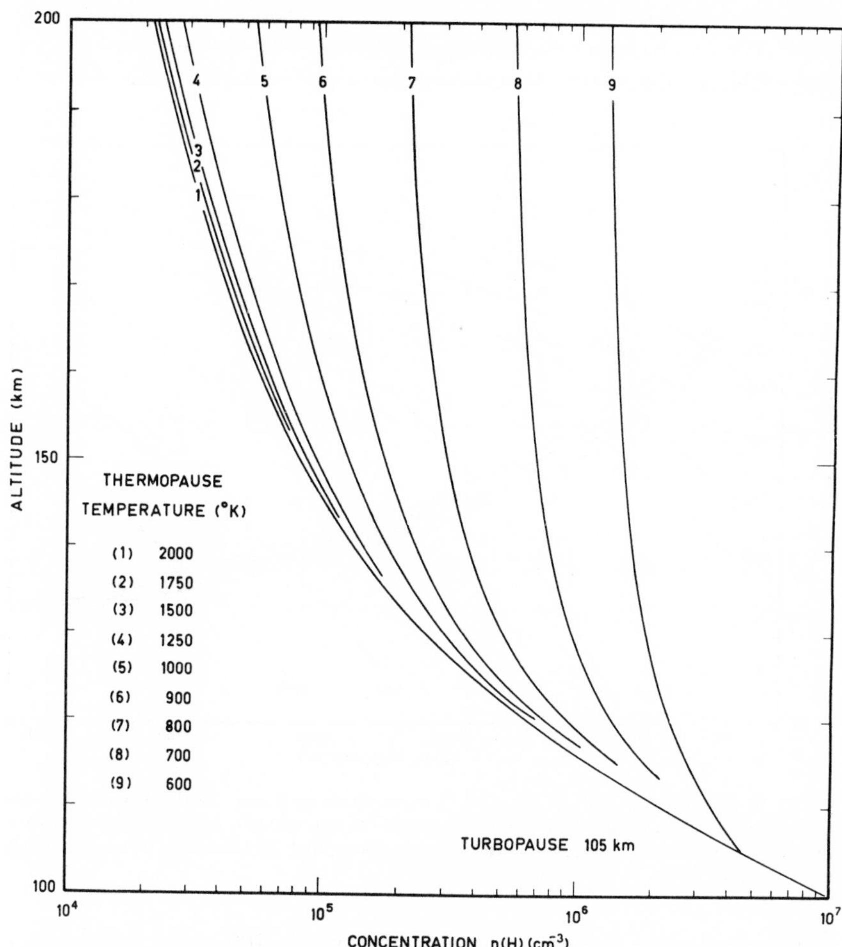

FIG. 8. The vertical distribution of atomic hydrogen between 100 km and 200 km for various thermopause temperatures. At high solar activity (thermopause temperature $T > 1250°$K), very small variation of the density with temperature. At low solar activity ($T < 1250°$K) density variations of an order of magnitude at 200 km. From Kockarts and Nicolet [28].

hydrogen. An illustration of the vertical distribution of atomic hydrogen is presented in Figure 8. The concentration n(H) at 200 km is seen to depend on the thermopause temperature. Variation of temperature from 2000–1000°K leads to an increase of only a factor of 2 in the concentration at 200 km, the variation of temperature from 1000–700°K corresponds to an increase of a factor 10 for the concentration.

Diffusion is very important in the entire heterosphere. In order to illustrate how strongly the lightest constituents can be affected, Figure 9 shows the variation with temperature of concentration of H, He, and O above 1000 km. Helium is the principal constituent for temperatures greater than 1000°K, and at the lowest temperatures (minimum solar activity)

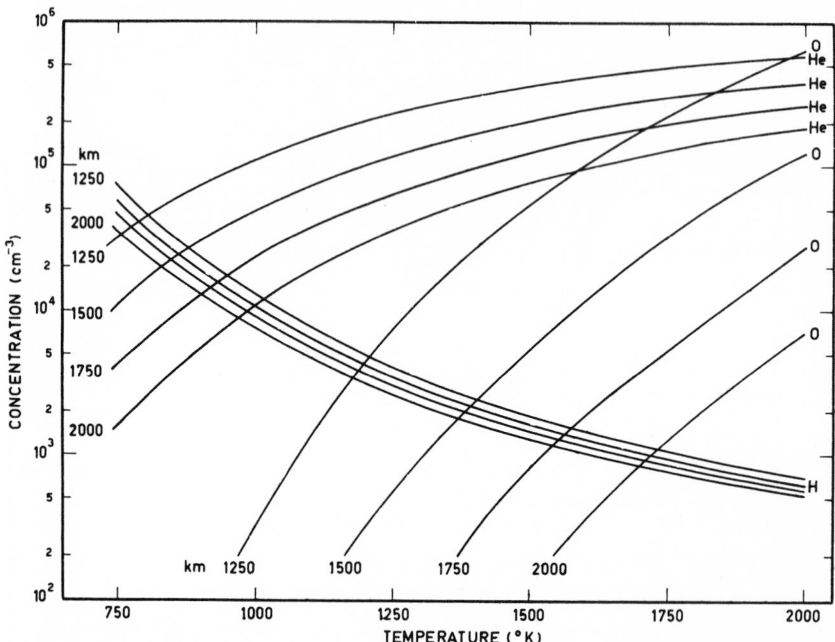

FIG. 9. The variation of H, He, and O concentrations above 1000 km with thermopause temperature. There is a rapid decrease of atomic oxygen and a small decrease of helium while atomic hydrogen increases with decreasing temperature. From Kockarts and Nicolet [28].

atomic hydrogen reaches a concentration about 100 times greater than during maximum solar activity.

6. Thermobalance in the Heterosphere

Diffusion in the heterosphere implies that conduction is also important. It is a normal consequence of the high temperature gradients in the thermosphere. Spitzer [51] has drawn attention to the effect of thermal conductivity as compared with the heating due to absorbed solar radiation. Bates [2] analyzed the thermobalance by considering the energy gained by absorption of ultraviolet absorption and lost through radiation and conduction. Johnson [20] has shown that the temperature cannot increase above a certain height if solar electromagnetic radiation is the sole predominant source. Nicolet [37] demonstrated that all atmospheric models based on an increasing gradient of temperature with height were not acceptable and that the normal tendency for daytime or nighttime conditions is to attain isothermy above a variable height level called the thermopause, even for diurnal temperature variations reaching 500°K.

The flux density of heat,

$$E = -AT^{2/3} \text{ grad } T \tag{33}$$

(A is a numerical factor depending on the atmospheric constitution), can be introduced in the continuity equation:

$$\rho c_v \frac{\partial T}{\partial t} + \text{div } E = P - L \tag{34}$$

where c_v is the specific heat at constant volume with density ρ, and L denotes the radiative loss of heat per unit of time and volume. In the terrestrial atmosphere this loss is due only to Bates' process of emission from atomic oxygen at 63μ. The production of heat P cannot be defined with great precision. If it is taken as directly proportional to the ionizing radiation, conclusions are obtained which are not acceptable for a problem of thermobalance in the heterosphere. For example, Harris and Priester [12] have introduced, in addition to the ultraviolet heating, a peculiar heating of the same amount which according to them derives its energy from solar corpuscular radiation and/or the solar wind. In fact, the vertical distribution of an ultraviolet heat source cannot be simply related to the ionizing fluxes which depend on the solar zenith distances. Various processes such as ionization and excitation are simultaneously involved with chemical reactions so that there is a certain redistribution of the heat source by conduction before the complete transformation of ultraviolet radiations into heating occurs. Even for nighttime conditions an internal heat source cannot be avoided since there are recombination processes. The solution of the time-dependent heat conduction equation is unresolved as yet since it requires perfect knowledge of the vertical distribution of the thermospheric heat source.

Evidence favoring a gradient of temperature associated with thermal conductivity in the upper thermosphere is indicated by the occurrence of pronounced diurnal variations of the density. The exact time variations cannot be obtained from a theoretical analysis since the transformation into heat of all ultraviolet radiations is not accomplished instantaneously.

If the diminution of the temperature gradient with height is given by a law of the form

$$\frac{dT}{dr} \propto \Sigma E_{uv}(1 - e^{-\tau}) \tag{35}$$

for an overhead sun, it is not possible to obtain a clear picture of the variation of the heating effect with solar zenith distance. In other words, the relaxation times controlling the thermobalance with internal heat sources cannot be determined since ionospheric reactions are involved.

7. Composition

In the diffusion region the application of Equation 20 can be applied to all constituents (except hydrogen) in the following form

$$\frac{d\rho_i g}{\rho_i g} = -\frac{1 + \beta_i}{\beta_i}\frac{dH_i}{H_i} \tag{36}$$

where

$$H_i = kT/m_i g \tag{37}$$

For a height range in which β is practically constant, Equation 36 is, after integration,

$$\frac{\rho_i g}{\rho_0 g_0} = \exp\left\{-\frac{(1 + \beta_i)z}{\frac{1}{2}(H_i + H_{0i})}\left[1 + \frac{1}{3}\left(\frac{H_i - H_{0i}}{H_i + H_{0i}}\right)^2 + \cdots\right]\right\} \tag{38}$$

and the total density in the heterosphere is determinable when the vertical distribution of each constituent is known. The boundary conditions must be established at a height where diffusion equilibrium conditions are acceptable. In any case, the mean molecular mass, which is fixed by the expression

$$m = \Sigma\rho_i/\Sigma n_i \tag{39}$$

is determined by the boundary conditions.

It is not possible to describe all the atmospheric models which have been proposed. The background of the problem of standard atmospheres can be found in the introduction of *The ARDC Model Atmosphere* by Minzner and Ripley [30], published before the IGY. It will not be discussed here. Before the availability of knowledge resulting from rocket-borne experiments, several attempts were made to extend the standard atmospheres (applied to the homosphere) into the heterosphere. But important modifications were introduced in order to follow the vertical density distribution deduced from the rate of change of the orbital periods of satellites. A first adjustment was made in 1959 to the ARDC atmosphere by Minzner, Champion, and Pond [31]. This led to an increase of approximately 20 in the density at 600 km. However, the mean molecular mass, about 27.1 at 180 km and decreasing to 17 at 700 km, required a continuous increase of the temperature gradient from 300 km up to 700 km — a gradient rapidly destroyed by conduction in this region.

The Russian model published by Mikhnevich *et al.* [29] corresponded to a temperature gradient only 1°K/km at 250 km and about 7°K/km at 700 km. This is an unacceptable increase of the gradient since it requires a downward heat flow by conduction which is several times greater at 700–500 km than at 250–200 km.

The *COSPAR International Reference Atmosphere* (CIRA) [25] includes references to various proposals made in 1961. It is a matter of fact that there is a tendency among the various authors to adopt isothermal conditions above a certain height, as done by Nicolet [34] who used the same density data deduced from satellite observations as the other workers, contrary to his first proposal [33] of an increasing temperature in the entire heterosphere. In the COSPAR reference atmosphere mean molecular masses are arbitrarily assigned and it is impossible to deduce consistent data for the concentrations. The only parameter deduced from satellite observations (density) does not allow a determination of the

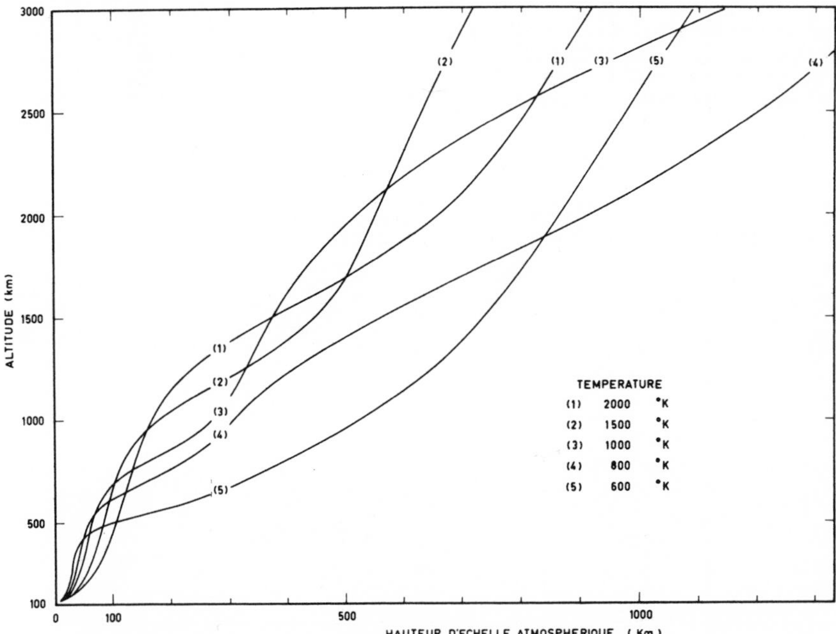

FIG. 10. The atmospheric scale height from 100–3000 km for thermopause temperatures between 600–2000°K. Above 500 km, the variations of the mean molecular mass affect the vertical distribution of the scale height. From Kockarts, to be published in *Bull. Acad. Sciences, Belgium* [26].

composition. Rocket measurements such as those made by the Naval Research Laboratory [9] before the IGY give information about the vertical distribution of molecular oxygen in the thermosphere. More recent measurements using different methods, by Pokhunkov [46], Hinteregger [14], Schaefer and Nichols [50], Jursa *et al.* [23] show that it is still not possible to determine diurnal and/or geographical variations of the density. Factors such as experimental error are too large as yet.

The composition of the heterosphere is certainly affected by varying solar conditions, and boundary conditions cannot be kept constant for a whole solar cycle. For example, if we consider various gradients of the scale height at 150 km with constant boundary conditions at 120 km, i.e., constant density and constant pressure, the density varies by a factor of

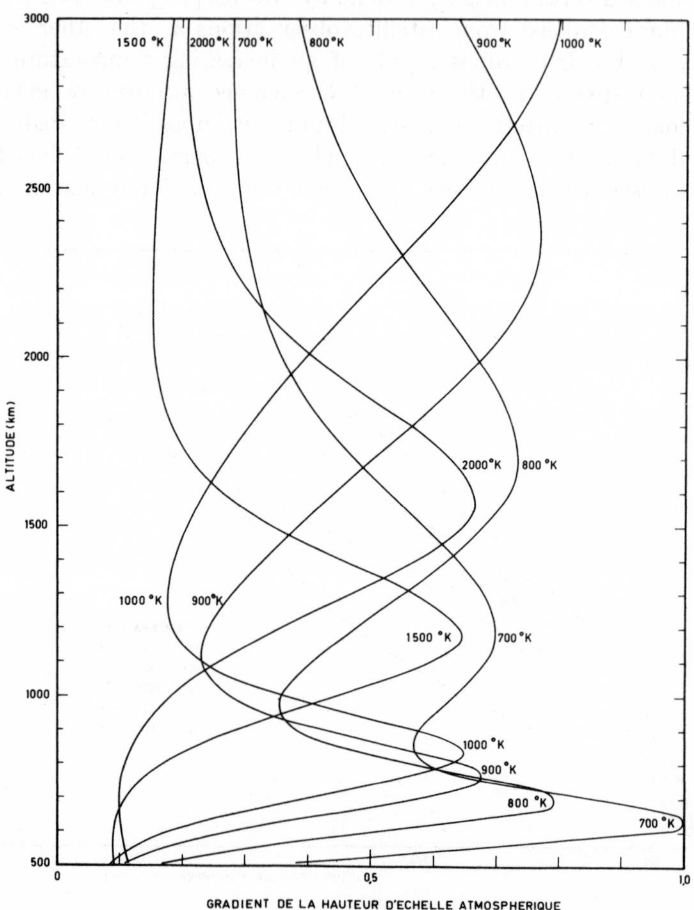

FIG. 11. The scale height gradient from 500–3000 km. Very large variations occur which are often greater than in the thermosphere. From Kockarts, to be published in *Bull. Acad. Sciences, Belgium* [26].

at least 2 at 200 km during a solar cycle. With $\rho = 3.5 \times 10^{-11}$ gm/cm³ and $p = 2.6 \times 10^{-5}$ mm Hg at 120 km, β varying from $\beta = 0.3$ to $\beta = 0.7$ at 150 km, the density ρ at 200 km is $(3.5 \pm 1.0) \times 10^{-13}$ gm/cm³. The same density at 200 km can be obtained by assuming a pressure variation of only ± 10 per cent at 120 km and by changing the gradient β by ± 0.1. In other words, atmospheric models must be adapted to the proper solar and atmospheric conditions by a specific temperature gradient in the thermosphere (near 150 km, for example) and by varying boundary conditions at 120 km (for example, by a pressure variation).

As an example of the atmospheric complexity of a complete solar cycle, a general picture of the vertical distribution of the atmospheric scale

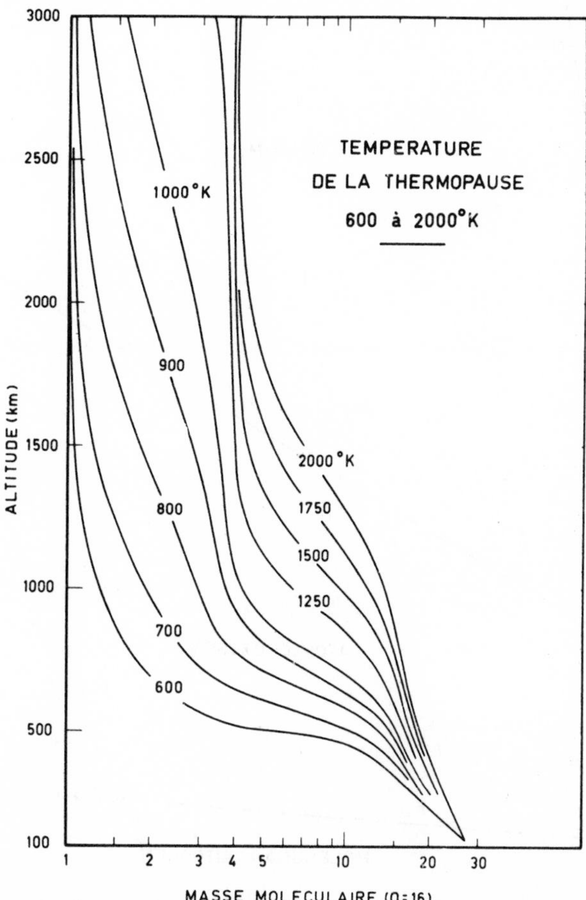

FIG. 12. The vertical distribution of the mean molecular mass from 100 km to 3000 km. For $T \geq 1250$°K, the minimum mean molecular mass, M, is 4, due to helium. For $T \leq 1000$°K, $M < 4$ above 1000 km due to atomic hydrogen. From Kockarts, to be published in *Bull. Acad. Sciences, Belgium* [26].

height and its gradient is given [26] in Figure 10 and 11 for constant lower boundary conditions. The associated variation of the mean molecular mass is shown in Figure 12. The corresponding distribution of N_2, O, He, and H is shown in Figure 13 where the successive belts of atomic oxygen, helium, and atomic hydrogen are indicated by their variation with temperature. Above a certain level, only helium and atomic hydrogen must be

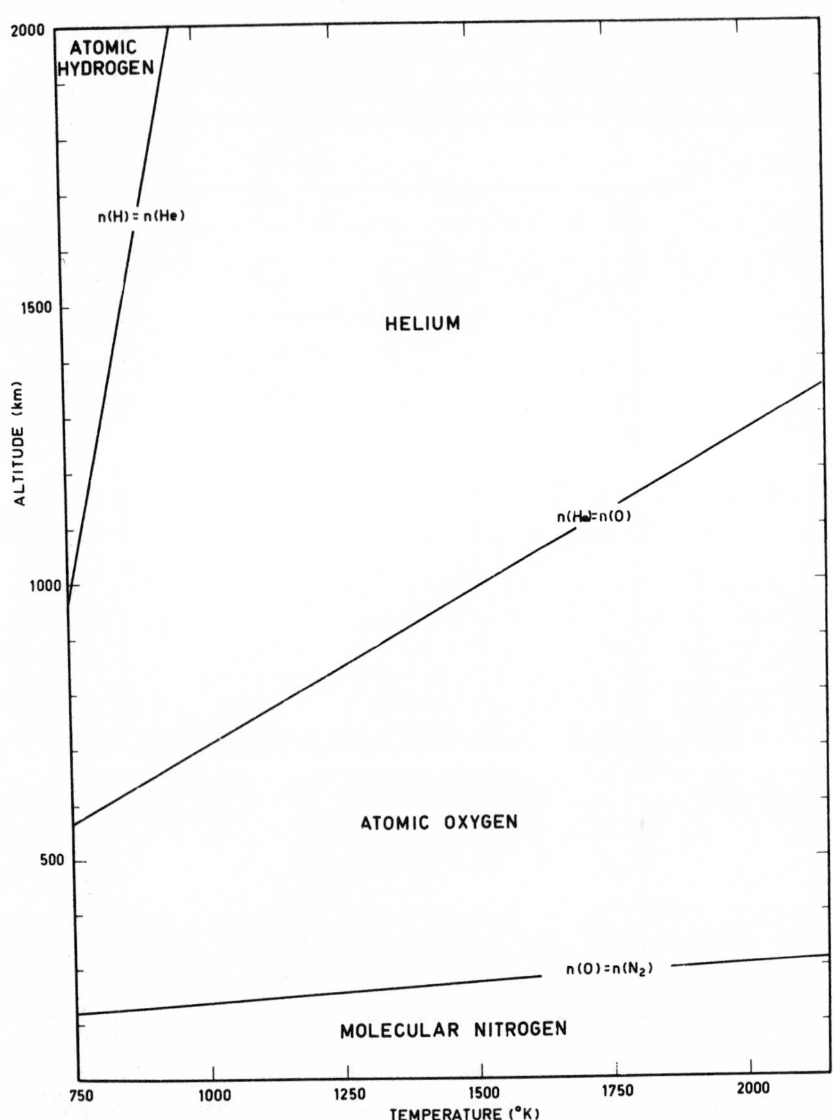

FIG. 13. Distribution of atomic oxygen, helium, and hydrogen belts for thermopause temperatures between 2000–750°K. From Kockarts and Nicolet [28].

considered and a helium-hydrogen atmosphere is subject to special conditions in the exosphere.

This elementary examination of the composition problem of the heterosphere justifies new observational programs for obtaining physical data which cannot be deduced from the analysis of satellite data. The fundamental processes of ultraviolet heating and conductive cooling indicate that atmospheric models for which thermopause temperatures vary between 1000–2000°K are adaptable to daytime conditions. Account must also be taken of the variation of the boundary conditions in order to explain oscillations in the density above the thermopause.

8. Exosphere

Application of Equation 20 above the thermopause leads to

$$\frac{\rho_1}{\rho_{1,a}} = \exp\left[-\left(\frac{a}{r}\right)\frac{r-a}{H_{1a}}\right] \tag{36}$$

where a is the radius at the bottom of the isothermal layer. For a rotating atmosphere, Equation 36 is modified to take into account the effect of the centrifugal force:

$$\frac{\rho_1}{\rho_{1,a}} = \exp\left\{-\left(\frac{a}{r}\right)\frac{r-a}{H_{1,a}}\left[1-\frac{\omega_e^2}{2ag_a}(r+a)r\sin^2\theta_e\right]\right\} \tag{37}$$

where ω_e is the angular velocity of the earth and θ_e represents the colatitude.

Equation 36 leads to a constant density at $r = \infty$, and Equation 37 to a minimum at about 6.6 earth's radii at the equator. The application of 37 is not generally required since the effect of the centrifugal force is unimportant at the bottom of the exosphere (less than 1 per cent at 1000 km). In any case, the application of 36 and 37 is based on the fact that the velocity distribution is a Maxwellian distribution. In the exosphere the density of a neutral constituent must be defined by a gravitational treatment in which contributions to the density come from various different orbits of particles not subject to collisions. This problem has been studied in detail by numerous authors [1, 7, 8, 11, 13, 21, 22, 41]. It is based largely on the distribution of velocities derived from Liouville's or Boltzmann's equation.

At some height in the exosphere the following components can be introduced, in order to cover all possibilities:

a. Particles related to the critical level:
1. An elliptic entry component corresponding to particles leaving the critical level with less than the escape velocity.
2. An elliptic reentry component corresponding to particles returning

to the critical level. In a steady state both components are equal and their density $\rho_1 + \rho_2$ represents a certain fraction $\rho_{\rm I}$ of the total density at the critical level.

3. A hyperbolic escape component consisting of particles with velocities greater than the escape velocity.
4. A hyperbolic incoming component representing particles arriving at the critical level from the interplanetary space. In a steady state where $\rho_3 = \rho_4$ the total density $\rho_{\rm III} = \rho_3 + \rho_4$ would complete the velocity distribution of particles related to the critical level.

b. Particles not reaching the critical level:

5. An elliptic trapped component corresponding to particles in orbits with perigee above the critical level.
6. A hyperbolic component due to particles not in trapped orbits which should be interplanetary particles.

These last two types of particles, fraction $\rho_{\rm II}$ and $\rho_{\rm IV}$ for elliptic and hyperbolic components, respectively, would complete the distribution of particles at any level in the exosphere, i.e.,

$$\rho_{\rm I} + \rho_{\rm III} + \rho_{\rm II} + \rho_{\rm IV} = 1 \tag{38}$$

In order to illustrate the dependence of the exospheric components $\rho_{\rm I}$, $\rho_{\rm III}$, $\rho_{\rm II}$, and $\rho_{\rm IV}$ upon the atmospheric parameters at the critical level, we consider the radius a in Equation 36 as representing the critical level, and we write Equation 36

$$\rho(y) = \rho(1)e^{-E(1-y)} \tag{39}$$

with the following notations used by Öpik and Singer [41]

$$y \equiv a/r \tag{40}$$

leading to $y = 1$ at the critical level and to $y = 0$ at $r = \infty$, and

$$E = a/H_a \tag{41}$$

Assuming a Maxwellian distribution, Equation 39 represents the total density while 38 is the normalization at each altitude of 39: $\rho(y) = 1$. Particles not reaching the critical level are represented by

$$\rho_{\rm II} + \rho_{\rm IV} = (1 - y^2)^{1/2}e^{-Ey^2/(1+y)} \tag{42}$$

and, of course, the particles related to the critical level

$$\rho_{\rm I} + \rho_{\rm III} = 1 - (1 - y^2)^{1/2}e^{-Ey^2/(1+y)} \tag{43}$$

Under the same conditions, elliptic components are expressed by

$$\rho_{\rm I} + \rho_{\rm II} = \Phi(Y) + \tfrac{1}{2}\Phi''(Y) \tag{44}$$

where $\Phi(Y) \equiv \Phi[(Ey)^{1/2}]$ is the error function and $\Phi''(Y)$ its second derivative. Hyperbolic components are expressed by

$$\rho_{III} + \rho_{IV} = 1 - \Phi(Y) - \tfrac{1}{2}\Phi''(Y) \tag{45}$$

Furthermore, the elliptic trapped component ρ_{II} is written

$$\rho_{II} = (1 - y^2)^{1/2} e^{-Ey^2/(1+y)} [\Phi(Z) + \tfrac{1}{2}\Phi''(Z)] \tag{46}$$

where

$$\Phi(Z) \equiv \Phi\left[\left(\frac{Ey}{1 + y}\right)^{1/2}\right], \tag{47}$$

while

$$\rho_{IV} = (1 - y^2)^{1/2} e^{-Ey^2/(1+y)} [1 - \Phi(Z) - \tfrac{1}{2}\Phi''(Z)] \tag{48}$$

Equations 42 to 48 indicate that the components at the critical level are expressed by

$$\rho_I = \Phi(E^{1/2}) + \tfrac{1}{2}\Phi''(E^{1/2}) \tag{49}$$

$$\rho_{III} = 1 - \Phi(E^{1/2}) - \tfrac{1}{2}\Phi''(E^{1/2}) \tag{50}$$

$$\rho_{II} = \rho_{IV} = 0 \tag{51}$$

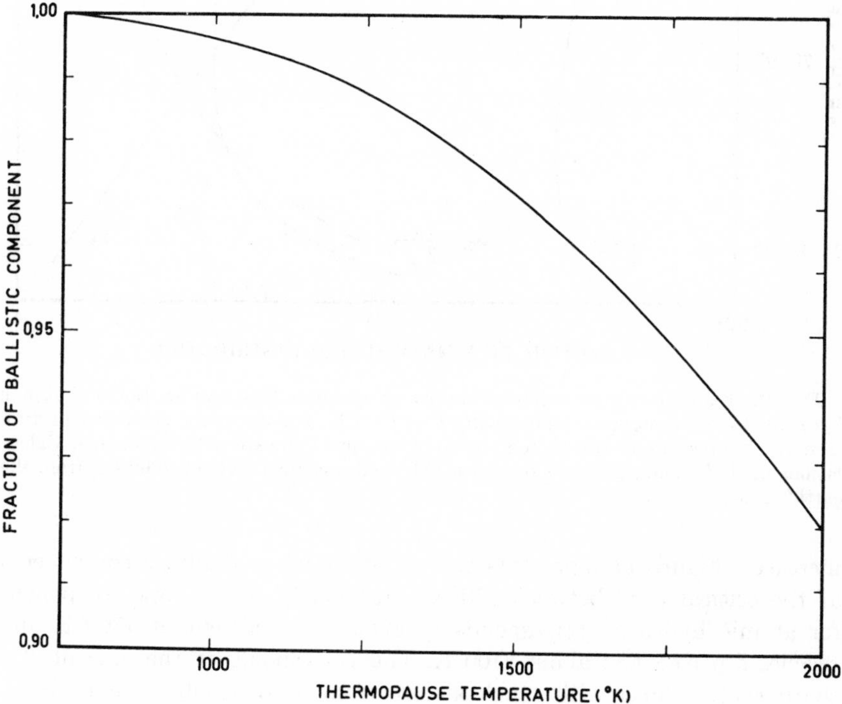

FIG. 14. Density relation of the ballistic component of atomic hydrogen at the beginning of the exosphere, assuming a Maxwellian distribution for the total density $\rho = 1$.

Equations 49 and 50 show that ρ_{III} is practically negligible for a constituent whose escape rate is very small. For example, $\rho_I = 0.9996$ for atomic hydrogen with a thermopause temperature of 750°K or for He^4 with $T = 3000°K$. In other words, the escape component does not play a practical role for helium and heavier atoms in the terrestrial atmosphere. For atomic hydrogen, the effect is not negligible when the temperature

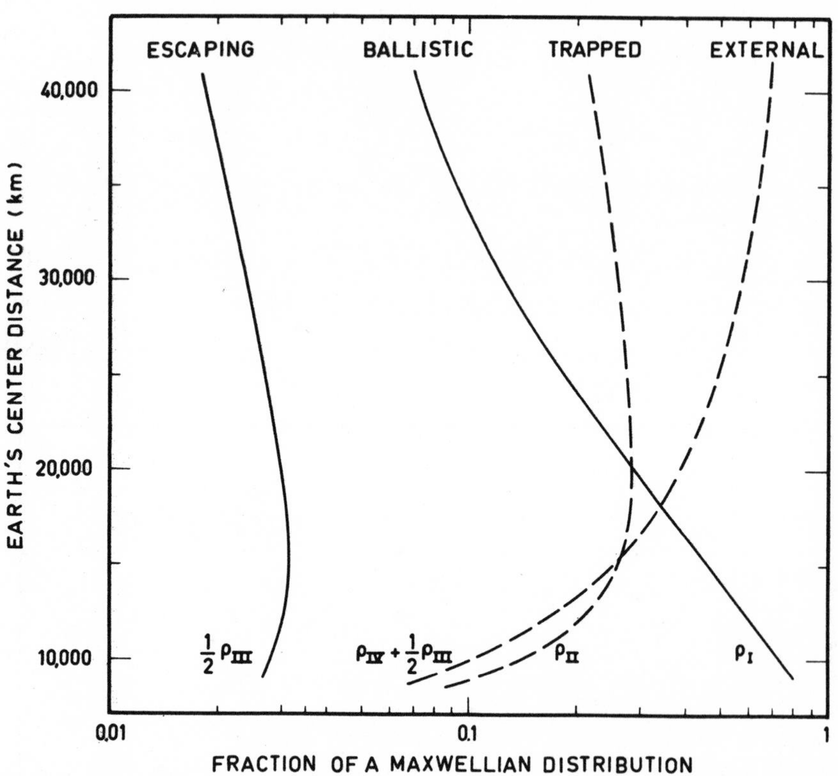

FIG. 15. Exospheric distribution of various components (real and fictitious) of atomic hydrogen for a thermopause temperature $T = 1700°K$. The maximum possible departure from the hydrostatic distribution is shown by trapped and external components. Calculations made in using Godart's formulas [11] and a critical level at 7000 km from the earth's center.

increases. Figure 14 represents the variations of ρ_I (ballistic component) at the critical level between 750°K and 2000°K. The escape component for atomic hydrogen corresponds to about 2.5 per cent at 1700°K and reaches 5 per cent at about 2100°K. This corresponds to the concept of a sharp critical level with no departure from a Maxwellian distribution. Nevertheless, such a concept cannot be accepted since ρ_{III} involves a hyperbolic incoming component which is equal to the escape component.

A Maxwellian distribution therefore cannot be considered as representing real conditions at the critical level. It is useful only as an approximation for determining the escape flux. At $T = 1700°K$, the effusion velocity v_E for a Maxwellian distribution, which is

$$v_E \propto \left(\frac{E+1}{E^{1/2}}\right)e^{-E} \tag{52}$$

leads to

$$v_E(H) \propto 2.5e^{-4} \tag{52a}$$

$$v_E(He^4) \propto 4.25e^{-16} \tag{52b}$$

$$v_E(O) \propto 8.25e^{-64} \tag{52c}$$

for atomic hydrogen, helium, and oxygen, respectively. The approximation is satisfactory when the rate of escape (helium, oxygen) is small but not for atomic hydrogen for which the departure from a Maxwellian distribu-

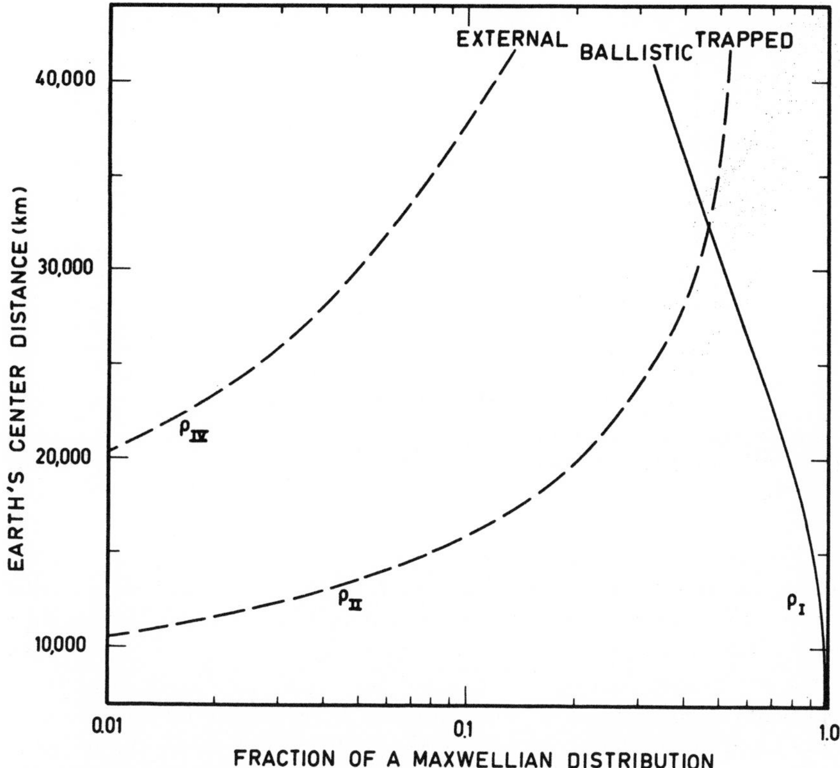

Fig. 16. Exospheric distribution of various components of helium for a thermopause temperature $T = 1700°K$. The ballistic component is relatively more important for helium than for atomic hydrogen.

tion must be introduced in the calculations of the escape flux. There is another aspect which cannot be forgotten for atomic hydrogen: the escape flux is related to the diffusion flux at the bottom of the thermosphere, and the density of atomic hydrogen at the critical level depends on the thermospheric conditions.

It is strictly assumed that there are no collisions in the exosphere; then $\rho_{II} = 0$, i.e., there are no particles in trapped orbits. If no particles are coming from the interplanetary space, $\rho_{IV} = 0$. Under such conditions, Equation 42 would give the fraction of particles which does not enter into

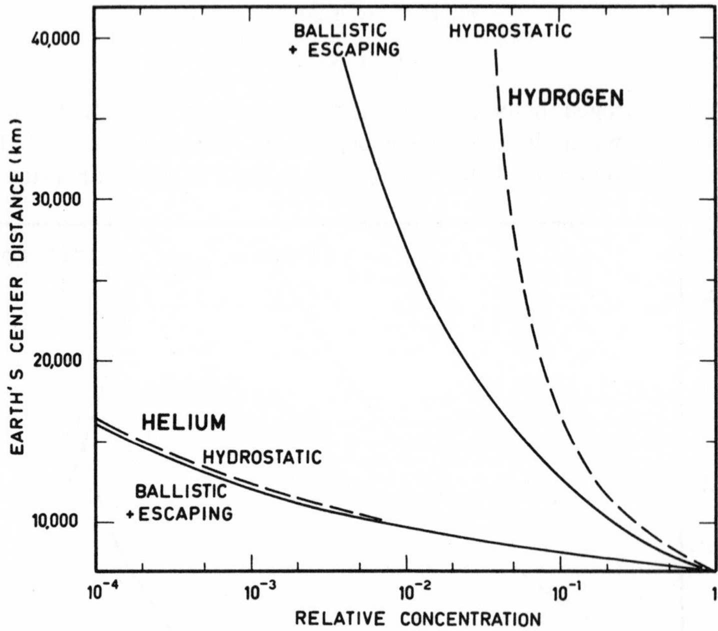

FIG. 17. Relative concentrations of atomic helium and atomic hydrogen in the exosphere at $T = 1700°K$. The hydrostatic distribution and the minimum real distribution are compared.

the hydrostatic equation 39. At $r = \infty$, $\rho_{IV} = 1$, i.e., the total density. Numerical results illustrate (Figs. 15 and 16) the height distribution of the various components in the exosphere for H and He at a thermopause temperature $T = 1700°K$. The escaping component $\frac{1}{2}\rho_{III}$ cannot be neglected for atomic hydrogen but is not important for helium. Figure 17 represents a comparison in the exosphere between the hydrostatic conditions and the minimum density represented by the ballistic and escaping component. Finally, Figure 18 shows the actual distribution when the absolute values of atomic hydrogen and helium concentrations are taken at the critical level. Note that a large variation occurs when the thermo-

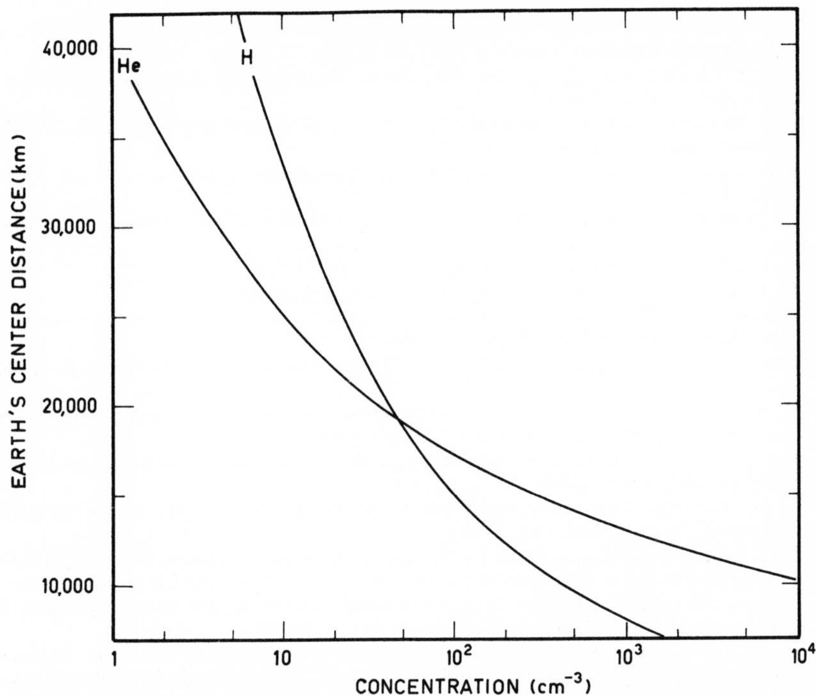

FIG. 18. Absolute concentrations of atomic hydrogen and helium in the exosphere when a Maxwellian distribution is assumed at a critical level corresponding to a distance of 7000 km from the earth's center. There is an identical concentration near 20,000 km for a thermopause temperature of 1700°K.

pause temperature varies since the ratio $n(\mathrm{H})/n(\mathrm{He})$ increases rapidly with decreasing temperature.

The preceding analysis corresponds to an idealization of the exosphere problem. Several physical aspects must be introduced such as the photoionization, and charge exchange processes. In fact, the interaction of the ionized atmosphere with the neutral atmosphere, in addition to the behavior of the superthermal particles, must be considered for the analysis of the transition from the planetary to interplanetary hydrogen [45].

REFERENCES

1. R. E. AAMODT AND K. M. CASE, Density in a simple model of the exosphere, *Phys. Fluids*, **5**, 1019 (1962).
2. D. R. BATES, The physics of the upper atmosphere, *The Earth as a Planet*, G. Kuiper (ed.), Chap. 12 (Chicago Univ. Press, 1954).
3. D. R. BATES AND M. NICOLET, The photochemistry of atmospheric water vapor, *J. Geophys. Res.*, **55**, 301 (1950).
4. D. R. BATES AND T. N. L. PATTERSON, Hydrogen atoms and ions in the thermosphere, *Planet. Space Sci.*, **9**, 959 (1962).

5. L. V. Berkner, G. Reid, J. Hanessian, Jr., and L. Cormier, eds., *Manual on Rockets and Satellites, Annals of IGY, VI* (1958).
6. R. L. F. Boyd and M. J. Seaton, eds., *Rocket Exploration of the Upper Atmosphere* (Pergamon Press, 1954).
7. J. C. Brandt and J. W. Chamberlain, Density of neutral gas in a planetary exosphere, *Phys. Fluids*, **3**, 485 (1960).
8. J. W. Chamberlain, Planetary coronae and atmospheric evaporation, *Planet. Space Sci.*, **11**, 901 (1963).
9. H. Friedman, The sun's ionizing radiations, *Physics of the Upper Atmosphere*, J. A. Ratcliffe (ed.), Chap. 4 (Academic Press, 1960).
10. H. Friedman, Solar radiation, *Astronautics*, **7**(8), 14 (1962).
11. M. Godart, Density of neutral gas in the exosphere, unpublished.
12. I. Harris and W. Priester, Heating of the upper atmosphere, *Space Research III*, 53 (North-Holland Publishing Co., 1963).
13. J. Herring and L. Kyle, Density in a planetary exosphere, *J. Geophys. Res.*, **66**, 1980 (1961).
14. H. E. Hinteregger, Absorption spectrometric analysis of the upper atmosphere in the EUV region, *J. Atmos. Sci.*, **19**, 351 (1962).
15. L. G. Jacchia, Corpuscular radiation and the acceleration of artificial satellites, *Nature*, **183**, 1662 (1959).
16. L. G. Jacchia, Two atmospheric effects in the orbital acceleration of artificial satellites, *Nature*, **183**, 526 (1959).
17. L. G. Jacchia, A working model for the upper atmosphere, *Nature*, **192**, 1147 (1961).
18. L. G. Jacchia, Solar effects on the acceleration of artificial satellites, Smith. Astrophys. Obs., Special Report 29 in Smithsonian Contributions to Astrophysics, **6**, Research in Space Science, Washington, D.C., (1963).
19. L. G. Jacchia and J. Slowey, Accurate drag determinations for eight artificial satellites atmospheric densities and temperatures, Smith. Astrophys. Obs., Special Report 100, Research in Space Science (1962).
20. F. S. Johnson, Temperature distribution of the ionosphere under control of thermal conductivity, *J. Geophys. Res.*, **61**, 71 (1956).
21. F. S. Johnson, The distribution of hydrogen in the telluric hydrogen corona, *Astrophys. J.*, **133**, 701 (1961).
22. F. S. Johnson and R. A. Fish, The telluric hydrogen corona, *Astrophys. J.*, **131**, 502 (1960).
23. A. S. Jursa, N. Nakamura, and Y. Tanaka, Molecular oxygen distribution in the upper atmosphere, *J. Geophys. Res.*, **68**, 6145 (1963).
24. H. Kallmann-Bijl, ed., *Space Research I*, (North-Holland Publishing Co., 1960).
25. H. Kallmann-Bijl, ed., *COSPAR International Reference Atmosphere* (CIRA) (North-Holland Publishing Co., 1961).
26. G. Kockarts, Le problème des hauteurs d'échelle et leurs gradients dans l'hétérosphère, *Bull. Acad. Roy. Sci. Belgique* (1963).
27. G. Kockarts and M. Nicolet, Le problème aéronomique de l'hélium et de l'hydrogène neutre, *Ann. Géophys.* **18**, 269 (1963).
28. G. Kockarts and M. Nicolet, L'hélium et l'hydrogène atomique au cours d'un minimum d'activité solaire, *Ann. Géophys.*, **19**, 370 (1963).
29. V. V. Mikhnevich, B. S. Danilin, A. I. Repnev, and A. V. Sokolov, Certain results in the determination of structural parameters of the atmosphere with the aid of the third Soviet artificial earth satellite, *Iskusstvennye Sputniki Zemli*, **3**, 84 (1959).
30. R. A. Minzner and W. S. Ripley, The ARDC model atmosphere 1956, *Air Force Surveys in Geophysics*, No. 86 (1956).
31. R. A. Minzner, K. S. W. Champion, and H. L. Pond, The ARDC model atmosphere 1959, *Air Force Surveys in Geophysics*, No. 115 (1959).
32. H. E. Newell and L. Cormier, eds., *First Results of IGY Rocket and Satellite Research, Moscow, August 1958*, Annals of IGY, *XII* (1961).
33. M. Nicolet, High atmosphere densities, *Science*, **127**, 1317 (1958).

34. M. Nicolet, Les variations de la densité et du transport de la chaleur par conduction dans l'atmosphère supérieure, *Space Research I*, 46 (North-Holland Publishing Co., 1960).
35. M. Nicolet, Helium, an important constituent in the lower exosphere, *J. Geophys. Res.*, **66,** 2263 (1961).
36. M. Nicolet, Les modèles atmosphériques et l'hélium, *Space Research II*, 896 (North-Holland Publishing Co., 1961).
37. M. Nicolet, Structure of the thermosphere, *Planet. Space Sci.*, **5,** 1 (1961).
38. M. Nicolet, Solar radio flux and temperature of the upper atmosphere, *J. Geophys. Res.*, **68,** 6121 (1963).
39. M. Nicolet, Density of the heterosphere related to temperature, Smithsonian Contributions to Astrophysics, Research in Space Science, **6,** 175 (1963).
40. M. Nicolet, Dynamic effects in the high atmosphere, *The Earth as a Planet*, G. Kuiper (ed.) Chap. 13 (Univ. Chicago Press, 1954).
41. E. J. Öpik and S. F. Singer, Distribution of density in a planetary exosphere, *Phys. Fluids*, **2,** 653 (1959); **3,** 486 (1960); **4,** 221 (1961).
42. D. M. Packer, Altitudes of the night airglow radiations, *Ann. Geophys.*, **17,** 67 (1961).
43. H. K. Paetzold, Solar activity in the upper atmosphere deduced from satellite observations, *Space Research III*, 28, (North-Holland Publishing Co., 1963).
44. H. K. Paetzold and H. Zschörner, The structure of the upper atmosphere and its variations after satellite observations, *Space Research II*, 959, (North-Holland Publishing Co., 1961).
45. T. N. L. Patterson, F. S. Johnson, and W. B. Hanson, The distribution of interplanetary hydrogen, *Planet. Space Sci.*, **11,** 767 (1963).
46. A. A. Pokhunkov, Studies by means of mass spectrometer of parameters of the earth's atmosphere between 100 km and 200 km, *Iskusstvennye Sputniki Zemli*, **7,** 89 (1961).
47. W. Priester, ed., *Space Research III* (North-Holland Publishing Co., 1963).
48. W. Priester, Sonnenaktivität and Abbremsung der Erdsatelliten, *Naturwissenschaften*, **46,** 197 (1959).
49. W. Priester and H. A. Martin, Temperature inversion in the F_1-layer, *Nature*, **188,** 200 (1960).
50. E. J. Schaefer and M. H. Nichols, Neutral composition obtained from a rocket-borne mass spectrometer, *Space Research IV*, 205 (North-Holland Publishing Co., 1964).
51. L. Spitzer, Jr., The terrestrial atmosphere above 300 km, *The Atmospheres of the Earth and Planets*, 213, G. P. Kuiper (ed.) (Chicago Univ. Press, 1949).
52. H. C. van de Hulst, C. de Jager, and A. F. Moore, eds., *Space Research II* (North-Holland Publishing Co., 1961).

CHAPTER 11

STUDIES OF IONOSPHERIC ABSORPTION

W. R. Piggott

1. Introduction

The study of the strength of signals reflected from the ionosphere is the oldest technique for studying the radio-frequency properties of the upper atmosphere. It is a relatively simple measurement—at least qualitatively—and, in addition to important practical applications in ionospheric radio propagation communications, such measurements can in principle be used as a scientific tool for identifying properties and conditions of the atmosphere in the range of heights where absorption takes place. Absorption studies have been carried out since the earliest days of radio science; however, the stimulation and cooperation provided by the IGY has resulted in the best ever world-wide coverage of absorption observations with more than usual attention to consistency of techniques among stations.

Ionospheric absorption can be measured by the pulse reflection method, which in its simplest form involves measuring the strength of the ionospheric echo at vertical incidence, the other important parameters being the angular frequency of the probing pulse ω and the virtual height at which the reflection takes place. The riometer measures absorption from variations in the observed strength of the background of radio waves from extraterrestrial sources; the unabsorbed background is essentially constant in time but will appear to vary in a particular observing configuration as the earth rotates relative to the galaxy. Absorption changes which are above certain minimum values are also given, qualitatively, by the parameter $f_{\min}$, the lowest frequency on which echoes are observed at vertical incidence with a sweep-frequency ionosonde. These methods are described in some detail in the IGY Instruction Manual for the ionosphere discipline [35] together with some discussion and intercomparison of pre-IGY measurements. A further method of getting data on absorption, from the field strength of continuous-wave transmissions over oblique paths, gives essentially comparable data to the first method and will not be discussed separately here.

Programs for measuring absorption by one technique or another were active in many countries before the IGY, and indeed there were some in which identical methods were used for many years over a considerable range of geographic latitude and longitude. It is, however, worthwhile to mention the three features which distinguish IGY effort from that of previous years: (*a*) The building up of a sufficiently dense network of absorption and ionosonde stations to delineate the main features of normal and abnormal absorption phenomena and hence to produce an outline picture of their morphology. (*b*) The development and widespread deployment of the riometer which has greatly simplified the measurement and interpretation of ionospheric absorption. (*c*) The widespread adoption of uniform methods of ionogram reduction which has made it possible, with care and a critical appreciation of the data, to use ionogram parameters as absorption indices.

These advances have made it possible to make morphological studies of absorption phenomena, with a reasonable chance of avoiding the pitfalls inevitable with unreliable or insufficient data. The response has been remarkable: the literature based on IGY observations alone considerably exceeds that obtained in all pre-IGY years. As an example we may mention studies of the Polar Cap Absorption Event (PCA) which was practically unknown before the IGY, but now has an extensive literature. A recent survey by Bailey [5] gives 192 references.

A large quantity of data on ionospheric absorption has reached the IGY World Data Centers, representing 39 stations using the pulse reflection method, 9 stations using field strength methods, 14 riometer stations, and, of course, the more than 160 ionosonde stations reporting $f_{\min}$. Most of the absorption observations are concentrated near local noon, but some give diurnal variations as well, at least for World Days. Few of the riometer stations have, however, produced data about the regular slowly varying absorption, as opposed to special events. Reviewing the published discussions of IGY station observations, for example [1, 10, 24, 30], it is clear that most groups obtained consistent data which confirmed and gave additional confidence in the classical sort of investigations. Rather few studies have made full use of the potential of the IGY data and these have been mainly studies of major absorption excesses, and their physical interpretation and causes, for example [11, 29].

The ionospheric absorption for a given angular working frequency ω is affected by the electron density N and the collision frequency ν of the ionized medium and is particularly large at levels where the refractive index μ is small. The angular gyrofrequency ω_H and the dip angle of the earth's magnetic field can also modify the absorption significantly. In practice, the range of heights for which the absorption may be appreciable is relatively large; from roughly 60 km to near the level of maximum ionization in the E-layer and, for particular bands of frequencies, near the maxima of ionization in the F-region.

In principle, absorption and vertical height measurements over a sufficiently wide band of frequencies can delineate the height variations of electron density and collision frequency, though in general they are not uniquely separable using these techniques alone. The deduction of these functions is one of the major scientific objectives of absorption investigations. With computers available it should no longer be necessary to rely on approximate methods of analysis. A start in this direction has been made by Whitehead [47] and Fejer and Vice [22] though most of the IGY analyses use simple methods. However, even with these aids, it is essential to take a broad view of the available data since it is easy to obtain apparently consistent solutions of limited problems which are demonstrably inconsistent with other known facts.

The same measurements can and have been used for other important scientific purposes; the study of the behavior of the lower ionosphere as the incidence of incoming solar radiation changes, including diurnal, seasonal, geographical, and solar cycle variations. These studies serve not only to describe the absorption phenomena, but allow inferences to be made about atmospheric changes and mechanisms and on many particulars of the ionizing radiation. Some topics in this field will be touched upon later.

It does not seem desirable to attempt to give here a full review of the studies already published on IGY absorption results. Rather it appears to be more valuable to point out some major discrepancies implicit in the data and their interpretation and to note some relatively new points which appear worthy of more attention. However, in Section 2 we mention a few typical results obtained in the IGY. The theories used to interpret the data are discussed in Section 3 along with some methods of estimating crudely whether the absorption is mainly in or below the E-layer. In Section 4 the results of some preliminary tests of these methods are given, and some other outstanding problems are discussed in Section 5. An example of qualitative absorption studies at high latitudes is given in Section 6. Most of the suggestions made are tentative and based on small samples of data—which may or may not be representative—but will be justified if they provoke new work on the subject.

2. Some Particular Results

Many examples of the use of qualitative absorption data have been discussed in other sessions of this symposium and in the 1961 Conference on Earth Storm at Kyoto [29]. Two particular applications are reproduced in

Figures 1 and 2 which show the movement of the zone of maximum blackout activity in the Northern Hemisphere [43] with time during the IGY and some relations [8] between blackout and magnetic activity at different times of day at one station. Qualitative data are also helpful in outlining the regions affected and the morphology of PCA events [5]. Further, the studies of PCA events observed using riometers working at relatively high frequencies (20–50 Mc/sec) and by pulse methods at much lower frequencies [37] show that the relative intensity of different events depends on frequency. This probably means that for some PCA's the extra ioniza-

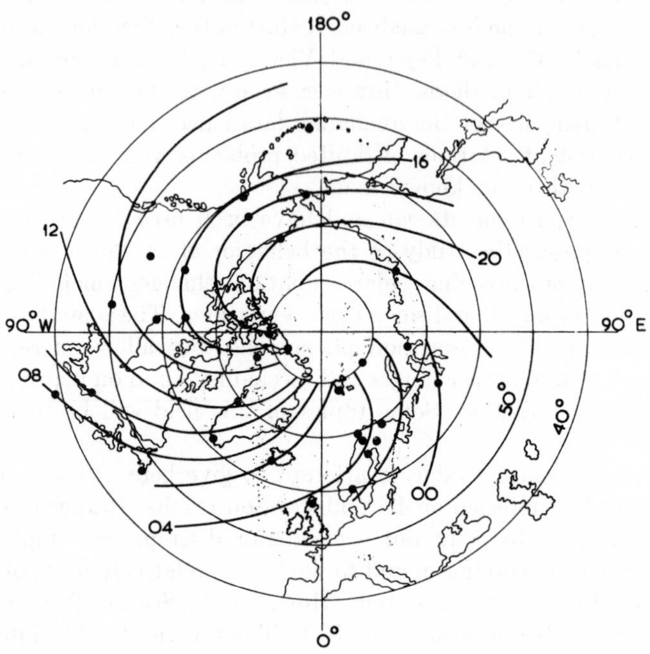

FIG. 1. Isochrons in Universal Time of maximum occurrence of blackout in the IGY showing the concentration in the zone containing the magnetic pole.

tion is formed relatively low in the *D*-region whereas for others it is relatively high, as would be expected if the spectrum of the solar cosmic rays varies from event to event. This type of investigation deserves to be extended in more detail.

There have also been successful investigations based on semiquantitative studies of absorption data. Thus Thomas [44] has studied the winter anomaly in absorption for the Northern Hemisphere. During winter months the absorption in midlatitudes is considerably higher on most days than that near the equinoxes and is very variable from day to day. The highest values can even exceed those found in summer. Thomas has shown the condition of exceptionally high absorption extended over an area of

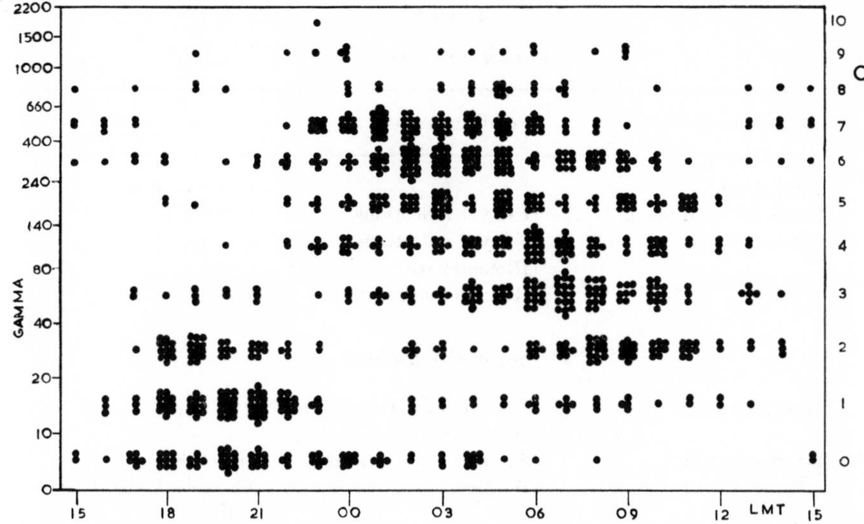

FIG. 2. The occurrence of blackout (ionosonde data, Halley Bay, IGY winter) as functions of local time and the level of magnetic activity. Strong absorption is correlated with weak magnetic activity about 2000 LMT but with strong magnetic activity a few hours later.

at least 10^6 sq km but was regional; days of high absorption over North America tended to show relatively low absorption over Europe or western Russia and vice versa—a clear indication that the absorption was dependent on atmospheric properties which were changing with position.

Turning to quantitative data, there is a very good agreement between results obtained by different workers in the IGY [9, 30]. It is generally agreed that the diurnal variation of absorption $\int K\,ds$, with the solar zenith angle χ, is well represented over most of the earth and in most seasons by

$$\int K\,ds = A[\mathrm{Ch}(R\chi)]^{-n}$$

where $\mathrm{Ch}(R\chi)$ is the Chapman function [17, 48]—$\mathrm{Ch}(R\chi) = \sec\chi$ for $\chi < 75°$. There is normally a lag in absorption relative to noon so that the agreement is better if χ is calculated for a time between 20 and 30 minutes later than the time of observation. In some parts of the world the seasonal variation, at least for some months, may also be represented by a relation of the form $\int K\,ds \propto [\mathrm{Ch}(R\chi)]^{-m}$. Some average values of n and m for different conditions are shown in Table 1.

Near the auroral zone, n is abnormally small [10, 18, 49] and rather variable from day to day and the seasonal variation, when the sun is above the horizon, is usually more dependent on the average magnetic activity than on the value of χ. Another anomaly appears at low latitudes where

TABLE 1

DIURNAL VARIATIONS

Latitude zone	Conditions	
Auroral zone		$n = 0.2$ variable
Temperate and low latitudes	E-layer reflections	$n = 0.8$
	F-layer reflections	$n = 1.0$
	Riometer winter	$n = 0.8$
	Riometer summer	$n = 1.0$
	Seasonal Variations	
Auroral zone	Varies mainly with magnetic activity	
Temperate zone	Summer and equinox	$m = 0.8$
	Winter	Variable high absorption
Low latitudes		$m = 1 - 2$

the seasonal changes, though small, vary with position and the general level of solar activity.

For ground-based experiments it is only possible to measure the integrated absorption up to a certain level, which varies with the working frequency, the absorption is a complicated function of the ionization density, collision frequency, and operating frequency. Despite the complexity of these relations, it is a remarkable fact that accurate absorption measurements made on different days are usually closely correlated provided the frequencies used are not near the critical frequencies of the reflecting layers.

Noon values at nearby stations outside the auroral zone correlate strongly, the correlation falling fairly smoothly with spacing until about half the observations agree within the sampling errors at 1500 km. This at the same time gives confidence in the reliability of the observations and indicates that the phenomena are not controlled by extraterrestrial factors alone. One of the main gaps in the study of IGY absorption data is the comparison of day-to-day changes at widely spaced stations. We shall return to this point later.

Apart from the morphological studies, there were a large number of special studies during the IGY directed to particular problems. These involve both new and old techniques, such as rocket measurements of electron density and collision frequency in the lower ionosphere [16, 27, 41] and ground-based measurements of partial reflection phenomena or wave interaction [16, 20, 21, 23]. In general, the object was to obtain detailed information about the height variation of electron density and collision frequency for particular occasions using methods which would be too expensive to employ in routine studies. Such studies complement the morphological work and clarify its interpretation.

3. Comments on Absorption Theory

The main controversy in the interpretation of $A1$ absorption data is the question of whether most of the absorption is generated in the E-layer or in the region below it. The critical problem is the value of the collision frequencies, ν, through the E-region. This is difficult to determine experimentally with adequate accuracy. The computed absorption for waves reflected in an E-layer model with acceptable values of ν made by Whitehead [47] and others [22, 38] using a full theory show that it is easy to produce an absorption in the reflection zone equal to the total absorption actually observed. In fact unless the values of ν in the E-layer are less than those generally assumed, there can be little significant absorption at lower levels. It is, therefore, important to devise tests to show whether the behavior of the absorption is consistent with the hypothesis that almost all the absorption normally occurs in the E-layer.

The principle of most experimental methods for separating the absorption in the E-layer from that at lower heights is to assume forms for the frequency variations of the absorption in the two regions and then match these with the observed frequency variation of absorption, $L(f)$.

The absorption coefficient k for frequencies appreciably higher than the plasma frequencies corresponding to the electron densities present in the absorbing region is given by:

$$k = \frac{2\pi e^2}{mc} \frac{1}{\mu} \frac{N\nu}{\nu^2 + (\omega \pm \omega_L)^2}$$

where ω is the angular frequency, ω_L is the angular gyrofrequency about the longitudinal component of the magnetic field, μ is the refractive index ($\mu \doteqdot 1$), and N is the electron density. Provided that $\nu^2 \ll (\omega \pm \omega_L)^2$ at all heights at which k is significant, the total absorption is proportional to the value of $\int N\nu \, dh$ through the absorbing region. If significant absorption occurs where this is not true, it is necessary to evaluate it, for example with the aid of riometer data, before attempting to separate E- and D-region absorption. Long-wave propagation analyses [36] show that absorption at levels where $\nu^2 \nless (\omega \pm \omega_L)^2$ is usually small for the frequencies normally used in $A1$ absorption measurements, above about 1 Mc/sec, except during PCA's and a few auroral events. This greatly simplifies the analysis.

In general it is necessary to assume that the absorption in the E-layer is given by a function $F(x)$ of the ratio x of the working frequency f to the critical frequency foE of the E-layer, where $F(x)$ depends on the height variations of the electron density and collision frequency in the layer. For frequencies below foE, the function $F(x)$ varies rapidly with the values of ν and of $1/(dN/dh)$ at the reflection levels. The total absorption is then given by:

$$L(f) = \frac{A}{(f \pm f_2)^2} + B \cdot F(x) \tag{1}$$

where the values of A and B and the form of $F(x)$ determine the relative importance of the absorption below and in the E-layer. The valuable spider-web technique of Bibl *et al.* [14, 15] is a nomogram for solving this expression when data are available for a number of frequencies. The interceptions of the lines joining the values of $(f \pm f_L)^2 L(f)$ and $L(f)/F(x)$ for each measured value, $L(f)$, enable the best values of A and B to be deduced (Fig. 3). The ratio of the total absorption to the absorption below

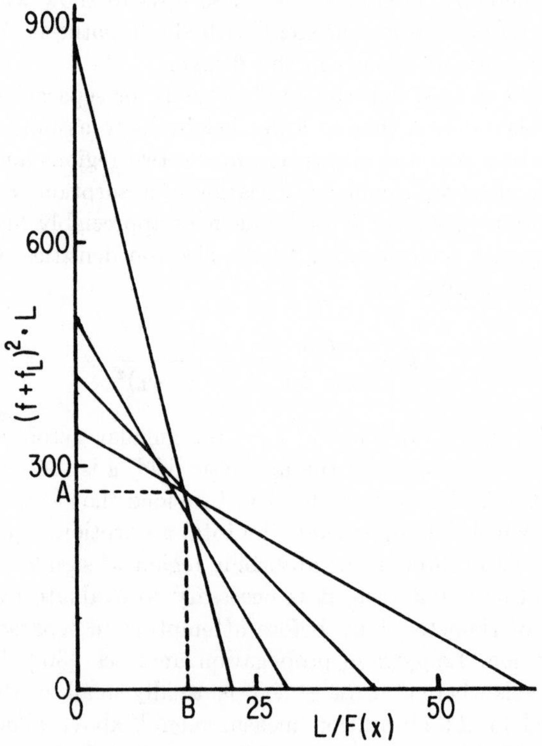

Fig. 3. Example of the spider-web nomogram for solving Equation 1 for A and B using the measured absorption L on each of four frequencies (Inverness, noon, equinox). The resulting values of A and B are related to the absorptions in the D- and E-regions, respectively, and can be used to estimate $\int N\nu\, dh$ for these regions.

the E-layer for each frequency is given by the ratio of the values of $(f \pm f_L)^2 L(f)$ to A. The relative values of $\int N\nu \, dh$ in the E-layer and below it can be readily deduced from Equation 1 by calculating the values of the two terms for a frequency large compared with $f_L = \omega_L/2\pi$ and foE.

Any attempt to split the absorption into two terms at a single station essentially depends on the differences in absorption at different frequencies. The separation of the E-layer term depends critically on whether the frequency variation of the absorption in the model E-layer has been computed correctly.

In practice the height variation of the electron density in the E-layer may be adequately represented by a parabolic expression, $N = N_0[1 - (y/ym)^2]$, where ym is the semithickness of the layer and the height y is measured from the maximum. However, even in this case, analytic forms for the absorption function $F(x)$ are only available when the quasi-transverse approximation of the magnetoionic equation is applicable. This is a serious limitation.

The value of the quasi-transverse approximation may be estimated from the virtual height curves compiled by Shinn and Whale [42], since, to a crude first approximation, the variation of absorption with frequency for a given model follows the variation of group retardation $(h' - h_0)$.

For the no field case the group retardation in a parabolic layer is given by

$$(h' - h_0)/y_m = x \tanh^{-1} x = F(x)$$

where $x = f/foE(f \leq foE)$ or $x = foE/f(f \geq foE)$ and $h_0 + y_m$ is the height of the maximum of the layer. It is therefore convenient to plot $(h' - h_0)/y_m$ against $x \tanh^{-1} x$ [3] as in curve 1, Figure 4. When the field is included [46] the quasi-transverse approximation gives

$$(h' - h_0)/y_m = x \tanh^{-1} x \sec D = F(x) \sec D$$

where D is the angle of dip, curve 2. Shinn and Whale's computations show that the frequency variation of virtual height can be put in the approximate form $(h' - h_0)/y_m = Mx \tanh^{-1} x$ where the factor M is considerably less than sec D. The full theory gives $(h' - h_0)/y_m = F'(x)$, where the form of F' depends on both the angle of dip and on the relative magnitude of ω and ω_H. Curves of these functions for a dip angle of 66°44′ (southern England) when foE is 3.7 Mc/sec are shown in Figure 4, curves 3 and 4, respectively. It is clear that the analytic forms can be seriously misleading and exact computations are needed.

An independent test of whether most of the absorption is in the E-layer is given by the values of n for frequencies above and below foE. The classical analysis of Appleton [2] shows that the absorption for frequencies which penetrate a Chapman-type E-layer should give $n = 1.5$. The apparent value of n can be greater than this if the working frequency is near foE or $foF1$ at noon. The theory due to Jaeger [26] shows that the value of

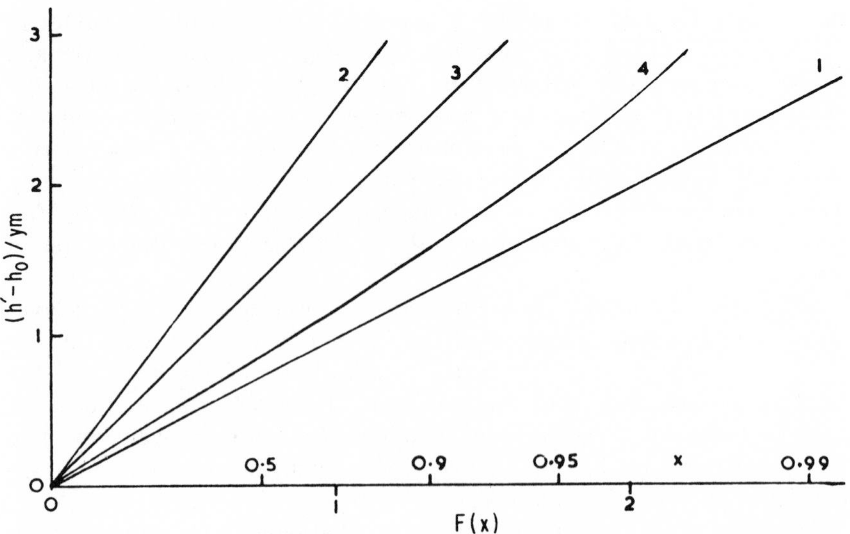

FIG. 4. Effect of different magnetoionic approximations on estimations of group retardation in a parabolic ionospheric layer: the normalized retardation is plotted against $F(x)$, and some values of $x = f/foE$ are indicated. Curve 1 is for no magnetic field. Then, for magnetic dip 66°44′, curves 2 and 3 are the quasi-transverse approximation, with factors sec D and M, respectively, and curve 4 is from the full magnetoionic theory. Note that curve 2 overestimates the retardation many times more than the underestimation of curve 1.

n for frequencies reflected in a Chapman-type E-layer should be near 0.8. The E-layer electron density and height varies with χ in reasonable agreement with the predictions of simple Chapman theory [39]. For any contribution from heights below the E-layer the value of n is the same for frequencies above and below foE. Thus, in principle, if the total absorption for a frequency below and a frequency above foE are determined at two values of χ, χ_1, and χ_2, giving $L_1(\chi_1)$, $L_2(\chi_1)$, $L_1(\chi_2)$, and $L_2(\chi_2)$, respectively, then

$$L_1(\chi_1) = D(\cos \chi_1)^x + E(\cos \chi_1)^y$$

$$L_2(\chi_1) = D(\cos \chi_1)^x + E(\cos \chi_1)^{1.5}$$

$$L_1(\chi_2) = D(\cos \chi_2)^x + E(\cos \chi_2)^y$$

$$L_2(\chi_2) = D(\cos \chi_2)^x + E(\cos \chi_2)^{1.5}$$

giving four equations from which D, E, x, and y may be evaluated.

It is possible to confirm the deductions by studying the absorption with riometers though care must be taken to avoid cases where refraction and absorption in the F-layer is important or where scattering processes may affect the observed cosmic noise intensity. This method has been used particularly by Indian workers [30].

Another method of estimating the importance of absorption in the E-layer is to compare the absorption on a frequency reflected from the F-layer with that found at the same frequency from a totally reflecting sporadic E-layer choosing pairs of days for which the absorption of frequencies below foE is the same.

Since the electron density near the maximum of the E-layer varies only slightly with height over a range of one scale height, the absorption above the level of the sporadic $E(Es)$-layers may be computed with adequate accuracy by assuming that the electron density is constant with height. If ν_0 and H_0 are the collision frequency and scale height of the collision frequency variation with height at the height of the Es-layer, the absorption in decibels L for frequencies above about $1.4foE$ is given by

$$L = 3 \times 10^{-5} \nu_0 H_0 (foE)^2/(f \pm f_L)^2$$

where $f_c = \omega_L/2\pi$. The resulting value at $\nu_0 H_0$ is only an upper limit since there may be some losses during the processes of reflection in the F-layer.

We turn now to another theoretical point which needs attention. This is the question of the variation of collision frequency with height.

In the Appleton–Hartree theory, the dissipation of energy of an electromagnetic wave due to collisions of free electrons with neutral molecules is introduced by a method that implies that the collision frequency of an electron is independent of electron energy, i.e., that the collision cross section of an electron is inversely proportional to its velocity. This assumption is not true in the ionosphere. Recent laboratory measurements [33] show that the collision cross section of monoenergetic electrons with nitrogen is large compared with that for oxygen and varies linearly with electron velocity. The collision frequency for air should be essentially the same as that for the nitrogen present. Thus the variation of ν with height for an atmosphere in static equilibrium should be [31]

$$\nu = \nu_0 \left(\frac{T}{T_0}\right) \exp(-z)$$

where z is the height in terms of the scale height for the nitrogen. At E-region levels, where O_2 dissociates into O, the scale height of ν will be smaller than the scale height for the atmosphere. This will decrease the absorption for waves which penetrate the layer relative to the absorption for waves reflected in it.

4. Some Experimental Tests of Absorption Theory

Systematic experimental errors in the absorption measurements or in the value of ν assumed in analysis can seriously alter the interpretation of the data. We shall therefore try the tests described above on a few examples with the object of establishing whether there is a case for reexamining common assumptions.

We shall first briefly examine the variation of absorption with dip angle by comparing the absorption at the same frequency at stations with different dips but equal value of *foE*. The simplest pair of this type is Slough (51.5°N) and Port Stanley (51.5°S) using noon data in equinox months. The average values of *foE* appear to agree within experimental error. The dip angles are 67° and 47° respectively, giving sec D = 2.53 and 1.46, respectively. The curves of Shinn and Whale [42] suggest that the multiplying factors M should be nearer 1.9 and 1.2, a ratio of 1.6, but the observed ratio of the total absorption is only 1.3. This could imply that at least half of the total absorption occurs below the E-layer. This result is confirmed by the ratio of the absolute values of absorption at equatorial stations, where sec $D \doteqdot 1$, to that found where sec D is large. Again ratios below 1.5 are usually found.

Tests on a few examples show that the consistency of the interceptions in the spider-web analysis is greatly improved when $F(x)$ is computed with a full magnetic field theory and with a modified height variation of ν in the E layer.

Similar conclusions can be drawn from the diurnal variations of absorp-

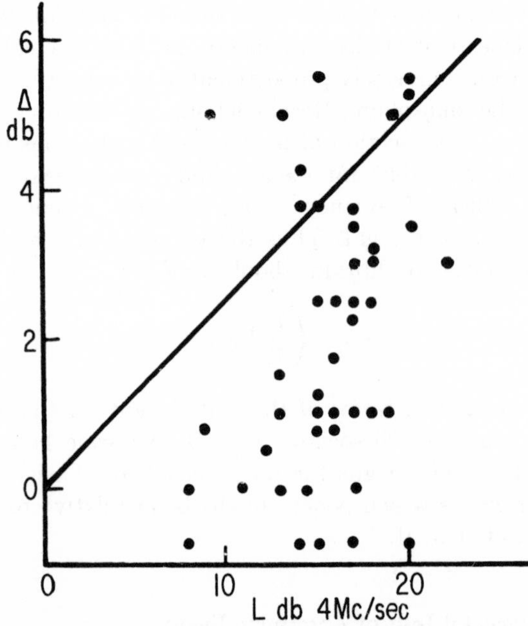

FIG. 5. Test of relation between absorption above and below the height of maximum density of the E-layer, *hmE*. The difference Δ in the absorption for an F-reflection and for an *Es*-reflection is plotted against the latter. Data are from pairs of days matched for identical absorption at lower frequencies and chosen so that *hEs* is very close to *hmE*. The line shows the expected relation were all absorption in the E-layer.

tion summarized in Section 2. The values of n found are mostly below $n = 1$ for E-region reflections and near $n = 1$ for F-region reflection or riometer data. While it is possible to interpret the low values of n for E-region reflections as being due to the changes in reflection level [26], n for the F-region reflections should then be near 1.5; or even higher when the frequency is near foE at noon. In practice, while it is probable that the value of n for F-reflection is greater than that for E-reflections, the difference is much too small to be consistent with the hypothesis that most of the absorption of the E-reflection occurs near the level at reflection. In fact the riometer data, e.g., [13, 40], are consistent with the lower frequency observations if the E-layer contribution is about one-third of the total absorption. This is consistent with our previous estimate.

Turning to the comparison between E- and F-reflections for days on which the absorption is the same for frequencies reflected from the E-layer and for which the variation of vertical height with frequency is small for the F-layer frequency, we find that at Slough the median difference is less than 2 db at 4.0 Mc/sec and the range of difference is between -1 db and

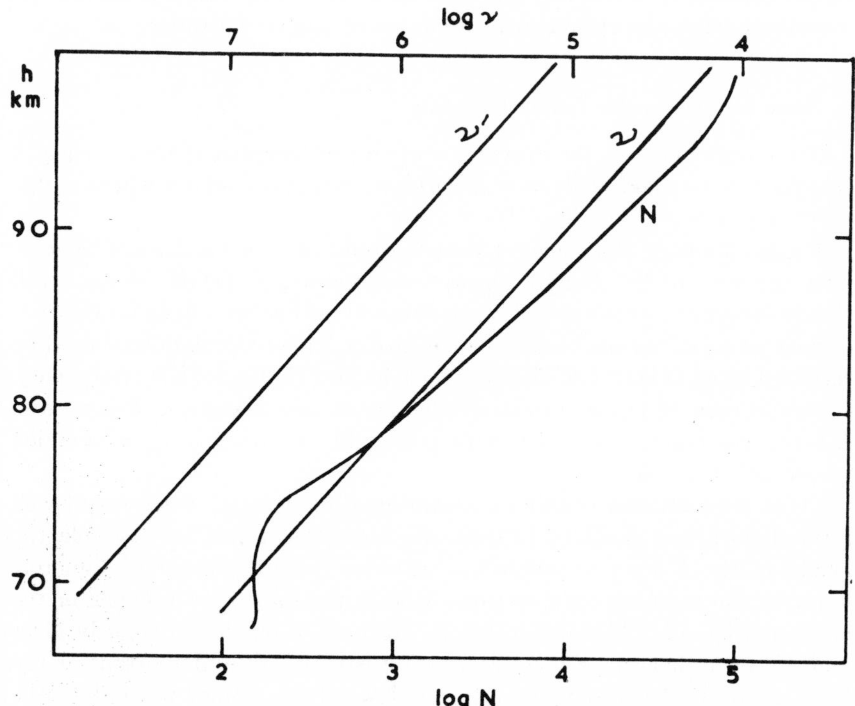

Fig. 6. Height variation of electron density N and collision frequency ν deduced from absorption and partial reflection data (Johannesburg, summer noon, after Vice). Note that the scales of N and ν are opposite. Curve ν' is taken from Nicolet [32].

5 db. If most of the absorption for 4.0 Mc/sec is in the E-layer, the corresponding computed difference, neglecting F-region absorption, should be about 6 db. Furthermore the difference should always be close to one-quarter of the total absorption for the day, as seen at 4.0 Mc/sec, whereas in practice it is found to be uncorrelated with this total absorption, Figure 5.

Thus it appears probable that, as thought by the earliest workers on absorption, a significant part of the absorption is generated below the E-layer, and absorption technique offer methods of studying the variations of electron density and collision frequency in this region even when reflections from the E-layer are used.

The consistency of the IGY absorption data for a given zone suggests that, given an adequate technique of analysis, very valuable data could be obtained both about the variation of collision frequency in the E-layer and the variations of $\int N\nu \, dh$ below this layer with time, position and solar activity. One example is the full theory work of Vice [45] with Johannesburg absorption data. His resulting models of the height variation of electron density and collision frequency are shown in Figure 6. We may note that the values of ν at E-region heights are relatively small compared to values commonly cited [32] but even these values are still too high to be consistent with absorption measurements at higher latitudes.

5. Some Suggestions for Further Research

If the arguments in the previous section are accepted there is clearly a case for a more exact analysis of absorption data, particularly where multi-frequency observations have been made.

The preliminary tests suggest that it would be well worthwhile to compute the form of the E-layer absorption function, $F(f/foE)$, using a full theory for a number of absorption stations, or, as has been done for electron density analyses, at convenient values of dip. These calculations should be repeated using at least two different scale heights for the collision frequency. It should then be possible to study the day-to-day changes in E-layer and D-layer absorption separately with reasonable accuracy using a modified spider-web method.

There are a number of other outstanding discrepancies which might well form the starting point of further investigations. Thus, for example the height of the E-layer at temperate latitudes is usually several kilometers lower in the morning than at times with equal solar zenith angles in the afternoon [4, 12]. The absorption is, however, a maximum slightly after noon. Thus either the E-layer absorption is relatively unimportant or the level of constant collision frequency is lower by a similar amount in the morning. As the height difference is about one-third of a scale height, the effect is not trivial. Similar phenomena can be found when studying day-to-day or month-to-month variations in E-layer height. The relative constancy of the absorption suggests that we may be able to detect changes in the levels of constant pressure in the E-layer, an exciting prospect which would justify serious work on absorption and virtual height relations.

The study of the day-to-day variations in the absorption at different stations suggests that there may be difference in the atmosphere with geographic position. The regional character of the extremes of the winter anomaly has already been mentioned. The magnitude of the normal absorption may be studied in the same way.

The normal absorption is well known to be correlated with the level of solar activity as given by monthly mean sunspot numbers. The sensitivity of the correlation, b in $\int k\, ds = a(1 + bR)$, for long series of data [34] is about 0.004 and is roughly the same for all stations. For shorter periods, b is usually smaller and less consistent among stations, 0.0015 to 0.003 for the IGY. It is also fairly easy to demonstrate [28] significant 27-day variations in absorption data, but the phase appears to differ slightly in the data for different stations. Superposed on these regularities are rather large day-to-day fluctuations which suggest there are important differences in the atmosphere from place to place. This can be shown by seeing whether days of absorption extremes—relatively high or low—correspond for various pairs of stations. Using equinoctial periods for many years, the low-latitude stations Singapore and Ibadan are found to be paired in the same sense at least three times as often as would be expected by chance. However, either of these compared with temperate-latitude stations Slough or Port Stanley are paired in the opposite sense twice as often as by chance, despite the positive correlation of all stations with 27-day solar activity fluctuations. In fact, in the sample examined, no cases were found when peak absorption occurred on the same day at temperate and low latitudes. All this is very suggestive that the lower atmosphere and its sensitivity to changes is significantly different between low and temperate latitudes.

6. The Diurnal Variation of Absorption at High Latitudes

The diurnal variation of absorption at latitudes near the auroral zones differ from that at lower latitudes in three important ways: (*a*) There are large irregular changes of absorption during individual days. (*b*) The average absorption for the midday period varies greatly from day to day and can range between several times the absorption near the subsolar point and a small fraction of this absorption. (*c*) The average change in absorption during the day is small, i.e., the value of n is small, typically about 0.2 in contrast with $n = 0.8$ at temperate latitudes.

Some of these facts have been known for many years [19]. During the IGY, special efforts were made to obtain more accurate measurements of absorption at these latitudes. These show some new features which merit mention. The examples which follow are from data obtained at Halley

Bay [7] though somewhat similar results, using different methods, have also been reported for the Northern Hemisphere from the Soviet Union [10].

At Halley Bay (75°S 30°W) a few degrees outside the auroral zone, there was a well-marked solar-controlled diurnal variation of absorption, Figure 7, even in midwinter when χ was always greater than 95°. The absorption figure increased suddenly when $\chi = 101°$ and was relatively high, though somewhat variable, throughout the period when χ was less than 101°. Normal absorption, associated with photoionization of the type found at lower latitudes was first detected when χ decreased through 92°.

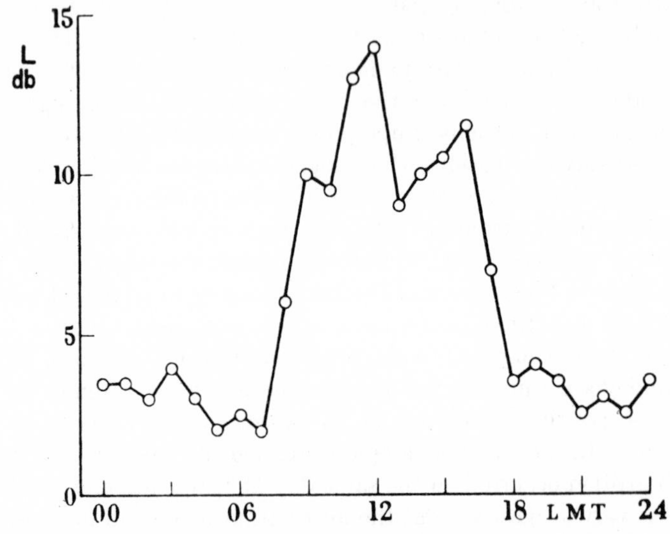

FIG. 7. IGY diurnal absorption results for Halley Bay (75°S) near the winter solstices when the solar zenith angle χ even at noon was greater than 95°. At temperature latitudes absorption becomes appreciable only for χ less than about 92°. Values shown are medians of about 21 measurements.

Despite the absence of solar photoionization, the values of the absorption near noon in winter were surprisingly large, on the average about one-quarter of the values found at low latitudes near the subsolar point. The maximum values found occasionally reached eight times the median value and usually occurred during and after periods of magnetic activity. Absorption was small during prolonged periods of magnetic quiet conditions. Similar relations with magnetic activity, Figure 8, were obtained at Dixon Island [25].

There was often a time lag between magnetic activity and absorption: e.g., selecting the 21 days with highest noon absorption in the winter of 1959, 8 occurred on days which also showed a maximum in the daily average of Kp and 2 in periods of more or less steady magnetic activity. Further studies of the phenomena showed that the absorption occurred mainly at heights a few km above 75 km. For ionization at these heights the critical angle $\chi = 101°$ corresponds to a screening height within 5 km of the surface of the earth and implies a photodetachment process with a negative ion of low dissociation energy. We may note that, when χ is less than 90°, the combination of a photodetachment layer and the normal photoionization process would cause the type of diurnal variation of absorption actually found with n small.

Further work is needed to show whether this winter absorption is associated with more or less continuous particle activity, whether there is

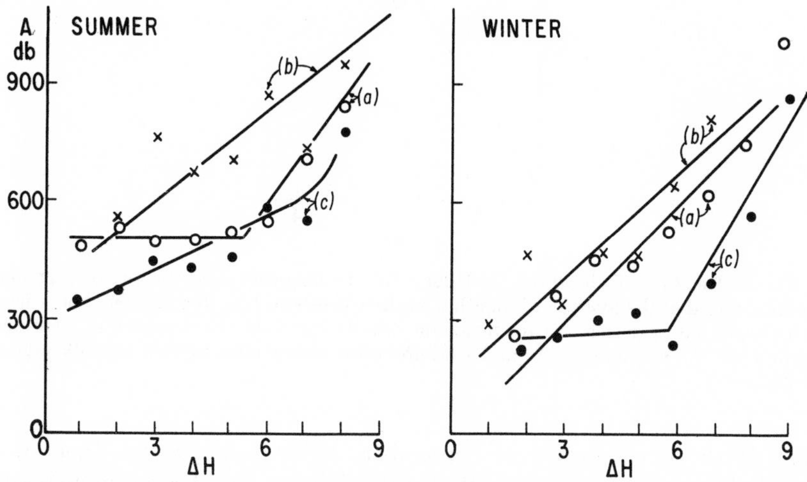

FIG. 8. Relation between absorption, $A = (f + f_L)^2L$, and magnetic activity at Dixon Island (73°N) in winter and summer for (*a*) 00–08, (*b*) 09–16, (*c*) 17–23 hours LMT. The station's magnetic index ΔH is very similar to the K- or Q-indices.

storage of negative ions in the lower atmosphere or whether the absorption is due to other causes. In any event detailed studies of these common but relatively undramatic phenomena are likely to throw a new light on the characteristics of the lower ionosphere near the auroral zone.

The importance of the month-to-month changes in magnetic activity in determining the seasonal variations in absorption can be demonstrated clearly with Halley Bay data, using a composite parameter R_c for the average month-to-month changes in magnetic disturbance in the IGY. This is based on the average Kp, the number of disturbed days per month, and the number of very quiet days per month, and is expressed on a scale of 1 to 5. The average of the median values of $f_{\min}$ for the hours 1000–1400 30° West Meridian Time are shown in Figure 9 as a function of this param-

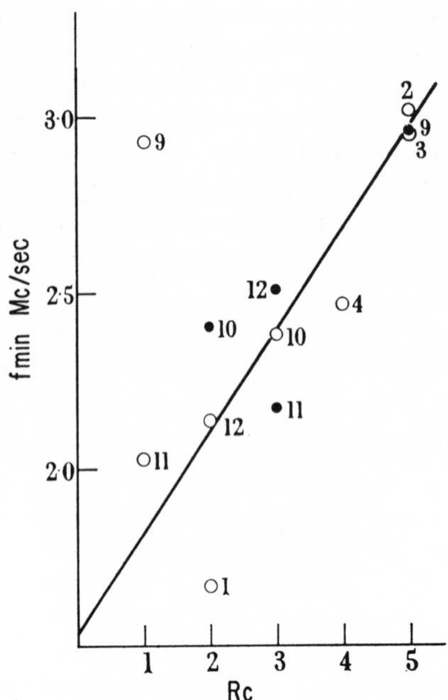

FIG. 9. Relation of absorption at Halley Bay to magnetic activity for summer and equinox months: the average of monthly median values of f_{min} for the five hours near noon is plotted against a relative magnetic activity figure R_c. Each month is identified by number (1 = January, etc.) and solid and open circles refer to 1957 and 1958 data, respectively.

eter. With the exception of September, 1957, during which there was abnormal structure and absorption in the E-layer, the absorption increases with R_c and the midsummer months December (12) and January (1) are by no means the months with most absorption.

7. Conclusions

The absorption measurements made during the IGY have amply confirmed those taken in earlier years and have been sufficiently intensive to allow useful studies of the morphology of absorption phenomena. Widespread use has been made of qualitative data showing the incidence of abnormal absorption. The studies of normal absorption have mostly been classical in type, and further development is needed to test their significance and to use them in new ways. In particular, approximate methods of interpreting absorption data should be replaced by accurate methods. There appear to be no great difficulties in developing these so that useful detailed studies could be made of the properties of the lower ionosphere. It is probable that research on these lines would be fruitful.

ACKNOWLEDGMENTS

The author acknowledges the help and advice of A. H. Shapley in the preparation of this manuscript. The work described above was carried out as part of the program of the Radio Research Board, and this communication is published by permission of the Director of Radio Research of the Department of Scientific and Industrial Research.

REFERENCES

1. Y. Aono, The Ionosphere, *Japanese contribution to the IGY and IGC, III,* Sci. Council of Japan, 35–67 (1961).
2. E. V. Appleton, Regularities and irregularities in the ionosphere-I, *Proc. Roy. Soc. A,* **162,** 451–479 (1937).
3. E. V. Appleton and W. J G. Beynon, The application of ionospheric data to radio communications problems, Part II, *Proc. Phys. Soc.,* **59,** 58–76 (1947).
4. E. V. Appleton, A. J. Lyon, and A. G. Turnbull, Distortion of the *E* layer of the ionosphere by electrical currents flowing in it, *Nature,* **176,** 897–899 (1955).
5. D. K. Bailey, Polar cap absorption, *Planet. Space Sci.* (in press).
6. R. E. Barrington, E. V. Thrane, and B. Bjelland, Diurnal and seasonal variations in *D*-region electron densities derived from observations of cross modulation, *Canad. J. Phys.,* **41,** 271–285 (1963)
7. W. H. Bellchambers, L. W. Barclay, and W. R. Piggott, Ionospheric observations, *Roy. Soc. IGY Expedition Halley Bay II,* 179–289 (1962).
8. W. H. Bellchambers and W. R. Piggott, The ionosphere over Halley Bay, *Proc. Roy. Soc. A,* **256,** 200–218 (1960).
9. N. P. Ben'kova, Ionospheric investigations in the U.S.S.R., *Geomag. and Aeron.,* **1,** 2–17 (1961).
10. N. P. Ben'kova, Informal communication, which included the following references to U.S.S.R. IGY absorption studies:
    (*a*) O. M. Ataev. *Radiotehn. and Electronica,* **5** (1957).
    (*b*) N. P. Ben'kova and M. D. Fligel, Ionospheric disturbances of Nov. 10–17 1960, *Geomag. and Aeron.,* **1,** 731–734 (Engl. Transl.) (1961).
    (*c*) N. P. Ben'kova and L. A. Yudovich, Diurnal variations of blackout occurrence according to IGY data, *Geomag. and Aeron.,* **1,** 641–645 (Engl. Transl.) (1961).
    (*d*) A. S. Besprozvannaya, Abnormal absorption of short radio waves in the polar region, *Ionosph. Res.,* **6,** 58–74 (1961).
    (*e*) A. S. Besprozvannaya and V. M. Driatsky, Abnormal absorption in the polar region according to the observational data obtained with the method of ionospheric vertical sounding, *Ionosph. Res.,* **5,** 7–19 (1960).
    (*f*) P. Danilkin, N. A. Kotchenova, A. M. Svechnikov, S. S. Chavdarov, and A. L. Yarosheva, The state of the ionosphere over Rostov-on-Don at the time of the total solar eclipse of 15 February 1961, *Geomag. and Aeron.,* **1,** 612–615 (1961).
    (*g*) V. G. Dubrobski, *Izvestia ANTSSR,* **1,** 110–112 (1959).
    (*h*) M. D. Fligel, Absorption of radio waves in ionosphere according to the data of the Mirny station, Rep. of Rostov Symp., Rostov Univ., 54–61 (1961).
    (*i*) M. D. Fligel, On the geographical distribution of ionospheric absorption, *Ionosph. Res.,* **10,** 5–13 (1962).
    (*j*) G. N. Gorbushina, Application of the first reflections for the absorption measurements in the ionosphere at Dixon station, *Ionosph. Res.,* **3,** 60–65 (1960).
    (*k*) G. N. Gorbushina, Results of measurements of radio wave absorption in the ionosphere, *Ionosph. Res.,* **5,** 28–40 (1960).
    (*l*) G. N. Gorbushina, To the question of abnormal absorption in the auroral zone, Rep. of Rostov Symp., Rostov Univ., 62–71 (1961).
    (*m*) B. A. Grochotovo, *Annals of SFTI,* **38,** 15–22 (1960).

(n) E. S. Kazimirovsky, V. D. Kokourov, and V. M. Polyakov, Certain results of the ionospheric radio absorption measurements at Irkutsk, *Ionosph. Res.*, **6**, 52–57 (1961).
(o) A. M. Kotchenova, *Izvestia Visch. Utcheln. Zaved., ser. Radiofyz.*, **3** (1960).
(p) I. H. Kuchuberia, The quantitative estimation of the ionospheric absorption by minimum reflection frequency, *Ionosph. Res.*, **5**, 41–49 (1960).
(q) I. H. Kuchuberia, Calculation of intensity of the radio wave field according to the data of the measurement of ionospheric absorption, Rep. of Rostov Symp., Rostov Univ., 75–79 (1961).
(r) G. N. Minasyan, Ionospheric and geomagnetic effects of large chromospheric flares, *Geomag. and Aeron.*, **1**, 675–680 (Engl. Transl.) (1961).
(s) M. P. Rudino, Annals of SFTI (in press).
(t) M. Shirmamedov, About the phenomenon of the concentration in focus in the measurement of absorption, Rep. of Rostov Symp., Rostov Univ., 72–74 (1961).
(u) M. Shirmamedov, *Izvestia ANTSSR*, **6**, 30–35 (1960)
(v) M. Shirmamedov, *Izvestia ANTSSR*, **1**, 13–18 (1961).
(w) O. N. Struin and J. I. Feldstein, Non-deviative absorption in the auroral zone, *Ionosph. Res.*, **3**, 66–76 (1960).
(x) R. A. Zevakina, Geographical distribution of polar absorption, *Ionosph. Res.*, **6**, 35–45 (1961).

11. W. J. G. Beynon (ed.), *Some Ionospheric Results Obtained during the International Geophysical Year*, 1–401 (Elsevier, 1960).
12. W. J. G. Beynon and G. M. Brown, Geomagnetic distortion of region-*E*, *J. Atmos. Terr. Phys.*, **14**, 138–166 (1959).
13. R. V. Bhonsle, Ionospheric absorption using cosmic radio noise on 25 Mc/s. at Ahmedabad, *Proceedings of I.G.Y. Symposium I*, A. P. Mitra (ed.), 117–131 (C.S.I.R., New Delhi, 1962).
14. K. Bibl, A. Paul and K. Rawer, Absorption in the *D* and *E* regions and its time variations, *J. Atmos. Terr. Phys.*, **23**, 244–259 (1962).
15. K. Bibl and K. Rawer, Les contributions des régions *D* et *E* dans les mesures de l'absorption ionosphérique, *J. Atmos. Terr. Phys.*, **2**, 51–65 (1951).
16. R. E. Bourdeau, Ionospheric research from space vehicles, *Space Sci. Rev.*, **1**, 683–728 (1963).
17. S. Chapman, The absorption and dissociative or ionizing effect of monochromatic radiation in an atmosphere on a rotating earth, *Proc. Phys. Soc.*, **43**, part I 26–45, part II 483–501 (1931).
18. K. Davies, A study of 2 Mc/s. ionospheric absorption measurements at high latitudes, *J. Geophys. Res.*, **65**, 2285–2294 (1960).
19. K. Davies and E. L. Hagg, Ionospheric absorption measurements at Prince Rupert, *J. Atmos. Terr. Phys.*, **6**, 18–32 (1955).
20. J. A. Fejer, The interaction of pulsed radio waves in the ionosphere, *J. Atmos. Terr. Phys.*, **7**, 322–332 (1955).
21. J. A. Fejer, The absorption of short radio waves in the ionospheric *D* and *E* regions, *J. Atmos. Terr. Phys.*, **23**, 260–274 (1962).
22. J. A. Fejer and R. W. Vice, The use of full-wave solutions in the interpretation of ionospheric absorption measurements, *J. Atmos. Terr. Phys.*, **16**, 307–317 (1959).
23. F. F. Gardner and J. L. Pawsey, Study of the ionospheric *D*-region using partial reflections, *J. Atmos. Terr. Phys.*, **3**, 321–344 (1953).
24. N. C. Gerson (ed.), Radio wave absorption in the ionosphere, *J. Atmos. Terr. Phys.*, **23**, 1–379 (1962).
25. G. N. Gorbushina, Results of measurements of radio-wave absorption in the ionosphere, *Ionosph. Res.*, **5**, 28–40 (1960).
26. J. C. Jaeger, Equivalent path and absorption in an ionospheric region, *Proc. Phys. Soc.*, **59**, 87–96 (1947).
27. J. A. Kane, Re-evaluation of ionospheric electron densities and collision frequencies derived from rocket measurements of refractive index and attenuation, *J. Atmos. Terr. Phys.*, **23**, 338–347 (1962).

28. G. Lange-Hesse, 27 day variations in the absorption of the D region of the ionosphere over Singapore and Slough, *J. Atmos. Terr. Phys.*, **3,** 153–162 (1953)
29. K. Maeda and O. Minakawa (ed.), Proceedings of the international conference on cosmic rays and the earth storm, Part I, *J. Phys. Soc. Japan*, **17,** *Suppl. A-I*, 1–339 (1962).
30. A. P. Mitra (ed.), *Proceedings of IGY Symposium I*, 1–246 (C.S.I.R., New Delhi, 1962).
31. P. Molmud, Langevin equation and the ac conductivity of non-Maxwellian plasmas, *Phys. Rev.*, **114,** 29–32 (1959).
32. M. Nicolet, The collision frequency of electrons in the ionosphere, *J. Atmos. Terr. Phys.*, **3,** 200–211 (1953).
33. J. L. Pack and A. V. Phelps, Drift velocities of slow electrons in helium, neon, argon, hydrogen and nitrogen, *Phys. Rev.*, **121,** 798–806 (1961).
34. W. R. Piggott, The calculation of the median sky wave field strength in tropical regions, *Radio Research Special Report No.* **27,** *D.S.I.R.*, London (1959)
35. W. R. Piggott, W. J. G. Beynon, G. M. Brown, and C. G. Little, The measurement of ionospheric absorption, *IGY Annals*, **3,** 171–226 (1957).
36. W. R. Piggott, M. L. V. Pitteway, and E. V. Thrane, The numerical calculation of wave-fields, reflection coefficients and polarizations for long radio waves in the lower ionosphere-II, *Phil. Trans. Roy. Soc.* (in press).
37. W. R. Piggott and A. H. Shapley, The ionosphere over Antarctica, *Geophysical Monography No.* **7,** *Amer. Geophys. Un.*, 111–126 (1962).
38. J. A. Ratcliffe, *The Magneto-ionic Theory and its Applications to the Ionosphere* (Cambridge Univ. Press, 1959).
39. B. J. Robinson, Experimental investigations of the ionospheric *E*-layer, *Rep. Progr. Phys.*, **22,** 241–279 (1959).
40. K. A. Sarada and A. P. Mitra, Measurements of cosmic noise absorption at Delhi at 22.4 Mc/s. in: *Some Ionospheric Results Obtained during the IGY*, W. J. G. Beynon (ed.), 270–280 (Elsevier, 1960).
41. J. C. Seddon, Summary of rocket and satellite observations relating to ionosphere, In: *Ionospheric Radio*, W. J. G. Beynon (ed.), 86–126 (Elsevier, 1962).
42. D. H. Shinn and H. A. Whale, Group velocities and group heights from the magneto-ionic theory, *J. Atmos. Terr. Phys.*, **2,** 85–105 (1952).
43. L. Thomas and W. R. Piggott, Some aspects of the incidence of polar blackout during the IGY, In: *Some ionospheric results obtained during the IGY*, W. J. G. Beynon (ed.), 61–71 (Elsevier, 1960).
44. L. Thomas, The winter anomaly in ionospheric absorption, *J. Atmos. Terr. Phys.*, **23,** 301–317 (1962).
45. R. W. Vice, Informal communication.
46. J. D. Whitehead, The quasi-transverse (Q.T.) approximation to Appleton's magneto-ionic equation, *J. Atmos. Terr. Phys.*, **2,** 361–362 (1952).
47. J. D. Whitehead, The absorption of short radio waves in the *D*-, *E*- and *F*-regions of the ionosphere, *J. Atmos. Terr. Phys.*, **16,** 283–290 (1959).
48. M. V. Wilkes, A table of Chapman's grazing incidence integral (ChX, χ), *Proc. Phys. Soc. B*, **67,** 304–308 (1954).
49. J. Yasuda, Analysis of world-wide data on ionospheric absorption, *J. Radio Res. Lab. Japan*, **9,** 325–337 (1962).

CHAPTER 12

IONOSPHERIC MOVEMENTS AND IRREGULARITIES

Colin O. Hines

The study of ionospheric movements and irregularities has been widespread and intensive in recent years. Many results of the IGY and post-IGY period have become available in monograph collections [e.g., 4, 52, 59] and survey articles [e.g., 18, 38, 49, 53]. Bearing these surveys in mind and in view of other chapters in this volume, I shall consider the following topics: the movement of equatorial (Section 1) and auroral (Section 2) sporadic-E ionization irregularities, the formation of field-aligned F-region irregularities at low and high latitudes (Section 3), E-region winds (Section 4), ionization "drifts" (Section 5), magnetoshear sporadic E (Section 6), traveling ionospheric disturbances (Section 7), midlatitude spread F (Section 8), atmospheric gravity waves (Section 9) and, finally, the relatively new field of turbulence low in the E-region (Section 10).

1. Equatorial Sporadic *E* [4, 49]

To me, one of the most fascinating and potentially important studies that have emerged from the IGY–IGC era is the VHF radar backscatter investigation of equatorial sporadic-E ionization — q-type E_s, or E_s-q — by Bowles and his colleagues [8, 9, 17]. This investigation complements earlier and contemporary studies of the same phenomenon by vertical-incidence HF returns [e.g., 42, 58], but it provides information of a new and most valuable kind. This comes in the form of Doppler-shift measurements and their variation with angle of elevation of the radar beam, and it permits the resolution of motions that were beclouded in the form of fading rates and apparent drifts in the more conventional observations.

The Doppler-shift data have proved to be incompatible with a commonly adopted model of the drift measurements, in which ionization irregularities are taken to be embedded within a horizontally moving layer and to be transported therewith. Instead, quite a different model has emerged: the irregularities are caused by waves which propagate through the ambient ionization, perturbing the latter as they progress, and the speeds of propagation are comparable to the speed of sound in the ionized gas. This statement applies regardless of the direction of wave propagation, although only a limited range of directions can be observed at a given time. The wave normals are confined almost exclusively to a plane perpendicular to the local magnetic field — in effect, to the magnetically East-West vertical plane at the equator — and exhibit a spread within that plane that is centered on the westward horizontal direction. The intensity of the waves and their vertical spread of propagation directions increased with the strength of the equatorial electrojet (as revealed by surface magnetograms), thereby echoing the behavior of E_s-q intensity observed by standard ionosondes. Equatorial slant sporadic E, E_s-s, has been found to be a further consequence of the wave system [17].

The waves have been interpreted by Farley [22] with great success, as a manifestation of a plasma instability in the electrojet. (A similar theory has been developed, but not applied in detail by Buneman [15]; a closely related theory by Whitehead [63] describes the phenomenon as a stable manifestation of the electrojet, but derives very similar conditions for its occurrence.) The generation mechanism may be thought of physically as a consequence of the westward flow of electrons that constitutes the eastward electrojet. When the speed of electron flow relative to ion flow exceeds by a certain (small) margin the relevant speed of sound, unstable wave disturbances are generated within the plasma. The propagation directions of these waves are confined closely to the plane perpendicular to the magnetic field, for all pertinent electron speeds, and are inclined to the direction of electron flow (which is itself horizontal and normal to the field) at angles such that the horizontal trace speed of a phase front is comparable to the electron speed. These qualities are clearly consistent with the observed features listed above, and the quantitative agreement obtained by Farley is even more striking.

It is still too early to know whether the radar-revealed characteristics and their interpretation account fully for the properties of E_s-q as observed with ionosondes, and indeed even the radar technique exhibits a class of horizontal stratifications that apparently escape explanation on the basis just outlined. Nevertheless, the further elucidation of the wave component of E_s-q promises to provide a fascinating study for the coming years.

Nor is interest in that component confined to it for its own sake. It has a considerable potential as a diagnostic in the study of the electrojet and thence in the study of the whole quiet-day system of E-region currents and in the interpretation of lunar and storm-time modifications thereof

[48]. It provides for the first time a direct measure of the speed of electron motion within those currents, and this speed can be converted with little error into a measure of the (nearly vertical) electric polarization field that drives the equatorial electrojet. Through the chain of dynamo theory, the induction emf's and the large-scale horizontal polarization fields may be inferred and compared with deductions made by other means. This chain has been followed in the past, but never before with the electron speeds and the electric fields separated so clearly from the ionization densities and integrated conductivities.

2. High-Latitude E_s-Movement [18, 52]

It is widely held, and recent observations of various types support the view, that sporadic-E ionization at high latitudes is created as a direct consequence of some storm-associated phenomenon, be it the precipitation of energetic charged particles (as is most commonly assumed) or a local discharge mechanism. This being so, a discussion of the generation process would be out of place in the present context (but see the end of Section 7). On the other hand, a few comments on the motion of irregularities within high-latitude E_s seem highly pertinent if only because of a close similarity to E_s-q that has been noted in the radar observations.

It had been found before the IGY, and was confirmed more extensively during that period, that the motion of irregularities in auroral luminosity and related ionization tended to move westward in the late evening hours and eastward in the early morning hours [41, 45]. These conclusions pertained, however, to latitudes at or below the conventional auroral zone. The IGY–IGC period produced results for higher latitudes, where it was found that the sense of movement was reversed during the stated time intervals, and that continuity of flow was apparently maintained by an equatorward motion near midnight and (for the ionization irregularities at least) a poleward motion by day [13, 19]. Thus each polar region appeared to contain two circulatory loops, comparable in form but opposite in sense to the flow of the high-latitude *Ds*-current system.

It was noted by Bowles *et al.* [9] that the VHF radar scattering properties of aurorally associated E-region ionization are similar in many respects to those of the equatorial E_s, and they suggested accordingly that the wave phenomenon of the latter might be equally operative in auroral conditions. A close correlation between the occurrence of radar echoes and the strength of the auroral current system has now been reported [60], duplicating that at the equator. Further, the stringent geometrical conditions subsequently implied by the theory are said to be met in the case of the auroral ionization. And, finally, the central direction of propagation in the wave instability should match the direction of electron motion, and a reversal of the *Ds*-pattern of flow should then indeed be found. The relevance of the instability process would appear to be established with a high degree of plausibility, if not virtual certainty (provided the electron speeds are adequate, as they are believed to be, in the auroral electrojet at least).

It is not at all clear, however, that this process is the one most often met. Its relationship to irregularities of luminosity is as yet vague; it would not account readily for many radar returns, which do not exhibit strong aspect-sensitivity [e.g., 13], nor would it produce any substantial irregularity except in company with high electron speeds. A second process may then be necessary to account for many if not most of the observations, and may yield place of prominence to the instability mechanism only when the geophysical and observational circumstances so dictate.

Such a process is indeed available through the action of electrostatic fields, as has been recognized by many authors [18]. Perhaps the most pertinent discussion for present purposes is that given by Axford and me [3], in which we point out the close connection that should exist between the pattern of movements and the *Ds*-current system, provided the movements are indeed electrodynamically controlled. This connection arises not only when local irregularities are being transported by the action of fields at ionospheric levels, but — and this point is often overlooked — even if the ionospheric irregularity is caused by the precipitation of energetic charged particles from above; the electrodynamic drifts may therefore be equally applicable to the luminosity irregularities. (In the case of the precipitation process, the connection may be established as a consequence of the "frozen field" theorem of hydromagnetics, which indicates that a source of precipitating particles high in the magnetosphere would move from one geomagnetic field line to another, in such a fashion that it remains always magnetically connected to a specific group of electrons moving in the *E*-region. The argument is valid, however, only if the irregularity that acts as source comprises particles which are not themselves too energetic.) Whether local transport or precipitation is involved, but for different reasons, the instantaneous motion of an irregularity will depart from the instantaneous current direction (reversed) to some extent, and only statistical agreement should be expected; this alone is found (cf. wide "instantaneous" departures from any cohesive pattern, as illustrated by Bullough [14]).

With two competing, or complementary, theories available, and perhaps others about to spring forth, a period of sorting out necessarily lies ahead. With respect to the instability mechanism, we should witness the application to auroral latitudes of the technique and analysis that have been devised for equatorial regions, and we should foster a closer collaboration between researchers employed on VHF radar measurements and those who detect irregularities in other ways. Tests of electrodynamic drifts may be made with the aid of rocket-released ionic tracers, preferably accompanied by molecular tracers as well, although suitable techniques and facilities for such experiments are not yet available; for the present, less direct tests dependent on further consequences of the electric fields must be devised.

3. Field-Aligned *F*-Region Irregularities [4, 52]

Observations of "spread-*F*" returns on conventional ionograms, and of radio-star and satellite scintillations, are commonly attributed to field-aligned irregularities of ionization in the *F*-region. An exception (arising at middle latitudes) will be discussed subsequently, but for the present this interpretation will be adopted.

The irregularities are observed most frequently near the equator at night and at polar latitudes during local winter [57]. There is a clear minimum in their occurrence near 30° magnetic latitude [46, 57], which tends to separate them conceptually into two distinct classes, and this tendency is strengthened by the fact that the equatorial irregularities correlate negatively with magnetic activity while the higher latitude irregularities correlate positively [46]. It is difficult at present to judge whether two distinct origins (or more) should be sought, or whether a single mechanism might be operative.

There was at one time a hope that the irregularities at all latitudes could be explained by turbulence in the *F*-region, but this has vanished. The *E*-region turbulence, with effects carried upward by means of electrostatic fields, was also contemplated as a source, but it appears to produce *F*-region irregularities that are too weak to be detectable save possibly at low latitudes [21].

High shears associated with a theoretically suggested nonrotating polar ionosphere have been proposed for the high-latitude irregularities [35], and have recently been given some measure of support through the detection [27] of a consistent westward velocity of irregularities (at speeds that actually exceed the eastward rotational speed of the earth at auroral latitudes!), but these observations conflict with others [50] and cannot yet be accepted as conclusive. Precipitation of energetic particles is frequently invoked for the high-latitude irregularities, and, while this begs the question of the origin of the irregularities, it permits their motion at times of magnetic disturbance to be explained in terms of the electrodynamic convection process previously mentioned. The latter process in turn raises the possibility that the high-latitude irregularities have their origins far out in the magnetosphere, perhaps at the surface of contact with the solar wind, and that they are then carried inward [3]; obviously it also implies a positive correlation with magnetic activity, in agreement with the high-latitude observations.

The remarkable success achieved by the plasma instability process at lower levels, in the explanation of somewhat similar irregularities, might raise the hope that an extension to F-region heights would account for the observations there. It must be noted however that the relative electron-ion speeds decrease in the F-region and that the strong equatorial electric fields responsible for supersonic speeds are confined to the E-region.

Quite a different point of view was brought to bear on the subject of these irregularities by Martyn [47], who advanced arguments for suggesting that the underside of the F-layer might be unstable with respect to the growth of small irregularities if the ionization were rising. He related this supposed instability to the apparent rise of the equatorial F-layer at sunset, more or less coincident with the onset there of spread-F conditions, despite the fact that tidal dynamo theory leaves unmistakable the implication that the ionization of the F-layer is descending at that time.

Considerable attention has been paid to Martyn's hypothesis in the subsequent analysis of observational data, but without conspicuous success (e.g., [43]). A complementary process has been proposed by Calvert [16], in which the same instability is invoked but its operation is attributed to a descent of the neutral gas due to the nighttime cooling of the F-region. In neither case is the geometry suitable for explaining high-latitude irregularities.

It should be stressed that the arguments originally advanced by Martyn were by no means complete, and that the theoretical likelihood of an instability of the type he inferred is far from being established. At the moment it stands as a hypothesis only, however plausible. It has led me to a further line of thought, however, and one that might be found equally plausible; for examination reveals that both low-latitude and high-latitude spread F occur primarily at times when the magnetically connected magnetospheric ionization — the ionization of the F-region and above, that extends along the associated geomagnetic field lines — is undergoing compression and inwards convection under the influence of the electrodynamic forces of the Sq- and Ds-current systems [33], and that the negative correlation with magnetic activity that is found at low latitudes can be attributed to a decreased convection there when the Ds-system opposes the Sq-system [3, 33]. It seems reasonable then to search for an instability in the compressional process.

The instabilities sought by Martyn and Calvert, and perhaps that just proposed, differ significantly from the wave instability previously discussed in that they concern a net transport of ionization in irregular formations across magnetic field lines. It has been argued by Dougherty [20] that such movements would be inhibited by dissipation in associated E-region currents, and this point is undoubtedly true. However it appears appropriate to remark that the times of major occurrence of the irregularities, indicated at the start of this section, are those during which solar illumination is absent and E-region conductivity a minimum.

The study of these irregularities is now being extended by means of satellite observations, and new data of great value are being accumulated. These show, for example, that high-latitude spread F occurs above the peak of the F-layer at all times [51]; it descends to or through that level only on occasion, when it can be observed by ground-based sounders. With the theoretical picture in such a state of uncertainty, and novel information being derived, the coming years should be active ones in this field of investigation.

4. *E*-Region Winds [38, 53]

Strong shearing winds have been detected just below and within the E-region, first by the study of meteor-trail deformations, and more recently with the aid of rocket-released vapor trails. The most extensive data available so far have been provided by radio-meteor studies at Jodrell Bank [e.g., 24, 25], although the rocket technique is rapidly adding to those data and extending them to higher levels [e.g., 5, 55]. This latter technique, whose application expanded to major proportions during the IGY–IGC period, has become one of the most useful available for the study of upper atmospheric motions; its continued development promises to supply the solution to many problems now confronting us.

The meteor observations have revealed appreciable winds in a general circulation pattern, primarily zonal in nature but with some meridional component. Rocket data provide an indication that the latter becomes increasingly important at greater heights, although the evidence is as yet scanty. While these winds have an important bearing on some ionospheric studies, their relevance to other topics in the present discussion is rather remote and they will not be pursued here.

Of greater concern are the tidal oscillations. These have been revealed clearly by the meteor studies [e.g., 25] with speeds of the order 30 m/sec. There is some evidence that their amplitude increases and their phase lags as we go upward through the meteor height range, in qualitative agreement with tidal theory (if the energy input occurs predominantly at lower levels), but in other respects the detailed observations provide new and intriguing problems [38].

These cannot yet be studied effectively with the aid of rocket-released vapor trails, for until recently the detection of such trails was confined to twilight periods and so referred always to a fixed phase of the tide (or to two fixed phases, in the case of the diurnal component). New techniques have opened the way to a better coverage of the tidal phenomenon, however, and early results [55] can be interpreted again in a qualitatively if not quantitatively acceptable fashion: a tidal wave with vertical wavelength λ_z of the order 20 km and horizontal wind speeds as high as 100 m/sec or more sweeps down through the E-region — the height range 95 to 115 km was under observation — at a speed V_z of the order 1.5 km/hr, which corresponds to a period $\lambda_z/V_z \sim 12$ hours. (The downward progression of phase corresponds to an upward propagation of energy.) The amplitude at the higher levels was increased at night, consistent with the view that ohmic losses limit the height to which tidal energy can penetrate by day. The further application of these new techniques, and the extension of the old to the month-long twilight of high latitudes, should greatly expand our understanding of the tidal system at high altitude.

Superimposed on the tides are winds of comparable magnitude but somewhat smaller vertical and temporal scale (e.g., [5, 24]). Early data on these "irregular" winds were frequently discussed in terms appropriate to turbulence, and indeed often reduced with the aid of relations applicable specifically to a Kolmogoroff type of turbulence (isotropic, with a broad inertial subrange). Turbulence dissipation rates of 10 watts/kg and more have been inferred on this basis, but they would correspond to a heating of the atmosphere at a rate exceeding 1000°K/day and are clearly untenable. It became apparent a few years ago that some other basis of interpretation must be found [39].

Within the turbulence concept, it was argued that a strong gravitational influence might be acting and that new formulas appropriate thereto would be needed [7, 34]. Within this same concept, it has more recently been pointed out that the spectral distribution of irregularities whose vertical scale is less than 6 km obeys the Kolmogoroff distribution [64]; but this agreement applies only to the vertical scales and takes no account of the anisotropies that are known to be present.

A totally different point of view was introduced with the recognition that internal atmospheric gravity waves could account not only qualitatively but also quantitatively for many of the observed characteristics [36]. These waves, which may be thought of as the low-frequency equivalents of sound waves or the small-scale counterparts of the global tides, were conceived to constitute a broad spectrum at meteor heights, in order to account for the highly irregular wind pattern. They were believed to originate partly *in situ*, from nonlinear interactions within the tidal system, and probably more strongly in the underlying regions where energetic dynamical phenomena are always in progress. In the latter case the waves would amplify as they propagated upward, as a consequence of the diminishing gas density that they would encounter. At the heights of observation they would be subject to appreciable nonlinearities, but it was apparent that substantial agreement with observation could be obtained even if a linearized theory were retained. It remains for further study to examine the full role of nonlinearities, and so to distinguish more clearly between the wave and turbulence aspects.

The conclusive identification of these winds as internal gravity-wave oscillations, if such they be, should proceed apace when detailed comparisons are available between their spectra and the vertical profiles of temperature, density, and/or pressure. For it is one of the advantages of a wave theory that these various parameters are related by a very explicit set of equations, as regards both amplitude and phase, and the combined observations must be consistent with those equations or the theory cannot survive. Available measurements of temperature fluctuations, of the order $\pm 10°K$ over height intervals of a few kilometers at the base of the E-region, are consistent with what we know of typical wind speeds at the same level, but much more stringent tests can be made with suitable instrumentation on individual rocket flights. It is to be hoped that the IQSY will witness the institution of such a program.

5. Ionization "Drifts" [4, 38, 52, 53]

The study of "drifting" irregularities of ionization in the E- and F-regions, by means of three closely spaced receivers operating in conjunction with a single radio transmitter, was well established before the IGY, and extensive plans for global coverage went into effect during that period. A preliminary report on the F-region results has been presented by Briggs [12]. In it, he notes that the pattern of East-West "drifts" that emerged was fairly consistent with the pattern of F-region motions that is implied by tidal dynamo theory: the drift velocity at midnight was about 100 m/sec toward the East at the equator and toward the West at high latitudes, with smaller speeds and obviously a reversal of direction between. The North-South component was only marginally in agreement with theory, and exhibited a reversal in sense when compared with earlier data obtained at a time of sunspot minimum. It was considered possible, then, that such agreement as was obtained in the case of North-South motions might be fortuitous.

It should be noted that tidal motions of ionization in the F-region are subject to a severe constraint, in that they must follow closed equipotential contours [33]. The East-West and North-South components of motion are then confined to an intimate relationship with one another and one which does not appear to enjoy the flexibility attributed to the drift data. It must then be questioned, whether or not the latter do indeed reveal the ambient wind.

This is a question that has always plagued the study of "drifts." An empirical answer appeared to have been provided by measurements of Jones [40], in which E-region "drifts" revealed a tidal component that was consistent with an upward extrapolation of meteor-height data. Apart from other questions, now to be raised, it should be noted that the agreement in this case was with the tide in the neutral gas, whereas the F-region comparison undertaken by Briggs related to the tidal motion of the ionization; the two are not the same.

The question comes back to the basic nature of the irregularities that are detected. When the irregular winds of meteor levels were attributed to turbulence, it was reasonable to conceive of the ionization irregularities as a further manifestation of this same phenomenon and to expect them to be borne along with the ambient wind. In present circumstances, however, a new explanation seems to be in order.

It is natural first to enquire whether the internal gravity waves might account for the irregularities, and the answer is to date unquestionably in the affirmative: a number of properties of the observations find qualitative and quantitative explanation if these waves are taken to be operative [36]. The irregularities of ionization may be caused by the wind shear that the waves provide, operating in conjunction with the magnetic field, or by the transport of ionization from one level to another where a different background intensity is to be found; or, in the presence of ionizing radiation, they may result directly from the density fluctuations that are imposed on the neutral gas. In any event, with the fixed-frequency method of observation that is commonly employed, the irregularities would appear to move horizontally with the horizontal trace speed of the phase fronts, and the observed "drifts" would then represent an oblique projection of a phase speed rather than a true wind speed.

It seems plausible, but is not yet established, that a superimposed tidal wind might be revealed even in these circumstances, and the observations of Jones could then be explained. (It will be difficult to account for them on any but a wave theory, incidentally, for ionization should not move with the neutral wind at the relevant heights.) It is equally plausible, but this must be explored, that tidal winds can selectively reflect or transmit certain modes of the wave system as the latter propagate upward, and so implant a spurious tide-like component on the phase velocities detectable at higher levels [38]. Herein may lie a basis for explaining the somewhat awkward conclusions that Briggs encountered.

The resolution of these questions will come most directly from the intercomparison of "drift" measurements and rocket-revealed wind systems, and it is to be hoped that the program planned for the IQSY period will be adequate for the purpose. A very preliminary result already reported [55] has revealed a "drift" measurement in the same direction as, but appreciably exceeding, the corresponding wind measurement. If this conclusion is confirmed in further tests, it would seem that, whatever else they may be, "drifts" are not indicative of irregularities borne by the local wind.

6. Temperate-Latitude Sporadic *E* [4, 59]

IGY data have fully confirmed [44] what was previously supposed: that the rather anomalous enhancement of sporadic *E* in Southeast Asia extends in the Northern Hemisphere toward the Mediterranean Sea, and has its counterpart in the Southern Hemisphere over the eastern Pacific area. The enhancement has been associated with the relative locations of the geographic and geomagnetic equators, and points immediately to some role for the geomagnetic field to play in the production of sporadic-E ionization at temperate latitudes.

A basis for explaining this role had already been laid by Dungey; it has now been extended for application to the E-region by Whitehead [61, 62], and with various refinements by Axford [2], while Storey and his colleagues have independently and concurrently pursued very similar lines. This development seems to me to be one of the major advances since the IGY, in the field of studies here under review, theoretical though it may be; the IQSY will provide a valuable opportunity for testing it experimentally in some of its more detailed aspects.

In essence, the mechanism depends upon the conversion of a horizontal transport of the neutral gas into a partially vertical motion of the embedded ionization, through the influence of the geomagnetic field. A vertical shear in the horizontal wind then leads to a height variation of the vertical motion, and so to a convergence or divergence of the ionization. While North-South winds are more effective in the F-region, East-West winds control the vertical motion in the E-region and so dominate the production of sporadic E by this "magnetoshear" mechanism. The specific conditions required for convergence have been stated incorrectly in some of the literature, so they bear explicit restatement: the sense of shear most conducive to the formation of a magnetoshear sporadic-E layer is that provided by an underlying wind which is directed toward the East, in company with an overlying wind directed toward the West.*

Probe measurements [e.g., 56] of sporadic E reveal characteristics of layer thickness ($\sim$1 km) that are consistent with the magnetoshear theory, and vertical spacings of successive enhancements that are comparable to the vertical scale of the wind pattern ($\sim$6–12 km). More recently, a sporadic-E layer has been found to lie almost exactly at the height of maximum shear, with the shear in the appropriate sense [55]. (Here the "appropriate sense" is taken to be that specified above. My comment applies, then, to the upper of the two layers reported, unless I have mistaken the terminology employed for wind direction; a lower layer, where

* It seems advisable at this point to comment on the schism between meteorologists and ionospherists in the matter of nomenclature for wind directions. Despite certain international recommendations to the contrary, I see no hope that in practice the two factions can be brought to a common terminology, nor do I even consider it advisable. But at least we should be able to agree to disagree in an unambiguous fashion. Thus, a wind may be said to be "a west wind" or even "a westerly," if need be, but surely it should not be said to "blow in a westerly (or is it easterly?) direction" nor to "have a westerly (?) component." Similarly, the same wind may be said to be directed "toward the east" or "eastward," but it should not be said to "blow east (?)" nor to constitute "an east (?) wind component." Attention to this small point will save many a man-hour misspent in confused interpretation of published data, even when the convention adopted by the author is supposedly stated once and for all in the course of a paper.

the sense of shear was reversed, was embedded in a turbulent region and will be mentioned in that context subsequently.)

The winds responsible for the magnetoshear sporadic *E* may be largely of tidal origin, although the likelihood of internal gravity waves playing a similar role has also been recognized [36]. Indeed, individual sporadic-*E* layers often exhibit fluctuations on spatial and temporal scales of 200 km and 1 hour [32, 53], and these receive a natural interpretation as modifications imposed by internal gravity waves [37]. So too do the sheets of "sequential sporadic *E*," which, when observed at a single station, appear to sweep downward through the *E*-region at speeds well in excess of the vertical tidal progression. These sheets would be expected to be tilted from the horizontal by a few degrees of arc, and such tilts should be looked for particularly in rocketprobe measurements.

In those sheets, incidentally, the ionization can be convected downward with the wave front much as a surfboard is carried along by an ocean wave [1], and the process can act partially even when no strong sheet is formed [2]. Herein may lie the explanation of the "night-*E* layer," which King associates with transport from the *F*-region. (See p. 219 of [59]. If King's arguments are followed further, we are led to question whether auroral sporadic-*E* ionization might not also be carried down from the *F*-region by internal gravity waves. Presumably the waves in this case would be generated in the *E*-region by auroral heating of the atmosphere; their downward phase progression corresponds to an upward energy flow.)

7. Traveling Ionospheric Disturbances [29, 38, 53]

Large-scale traveling ionospheric disturbances (TID's), whose intensive study was pioneered by Munro a decade ago, constituted a class apart in the IGY–IGC program. Comparisons have nevertheless been made between their properties and the "drifts" revealed by smaller-scale *F*-region irregularities. In one case a certain degree of agreement was obtained between the short-term variations of horizontal velocity exhibited by the two classes of irregularity, but this was largely offset by discrepancies between the horizontal velocities themselves and between the mean diurnal variations of these velocities [26; Fig. 8 of this paper, which is here relevant, is to be found over the caption of Fig. 6]. In another comparison [29], little by way of agreement was found, save only for the general order of magnitude of the speeds. In both cases, it was suggested that different origins must be sought.

On the other hand, a somewhat unexpected type of correlation has been revealed: sporadic-*E* patches have been found in conjunction with, and moving at the same speed as, *F*-region deformations caused by TID's [10, 30]. In view of this correlation it is likely that the point will be pursued during the IQSY, and indeed a further study of the conditions for correlation would seem to provide profitable scope. It would be unfortunate, in my opinion, if the rather negative results obtained in the comparison with "drifts" were to inhibit a similar pursuit of that topic.

The TID's are almost always attributed to some wavelike phenomenon, with periods usually in the range 15–50 minutes and with horizontal and vertical trace speeds, the latter invariably directed downward, in the range 100–200 m/sec. They travel over great horizontal distances, often without substantial loss of amplitude or change of form, on broad fronts that may reach 1000 km or more in length. Their observed properties have been summarized recently by Heisler [29].

Various types of wave have been proposed to account for TID's, but almost all can be rejected on one score or another. The sole exception is provided by internal gravity waves, and these appear to be adequate in every respect [36, 38]. The observed temporal and spatial scales almost exactly match the scales permitted to internal gravity waves in the F-region, the vertically downward trace speed may be associated with the upward flow of energy that is to be expected, and the propagation to great distances without serious attenuation may be attributed to a ducting of wave energy below the mesopause, that results from the temperature decline of the mesophere. When such ducting occurs, the energy that reaches the F-region must be interpreted as a leakage energy; but large amplitudes can nevertheless be achieved because of the amplification with height that accompanies the decrease of gas density.

Other points of contact with the observed characteristics of TID's may be made, but they need not be repeated here. It seems appropriate, however, to comment on the recent observations that are outlined in the opening paragraphs of this section, in the light of the gravity-wave theory.

The lack of agreement between the motion of TID's and that of "drift" irregularities is not surprising if the former are ascribed to waves and the latter to some other process, but if the latter are taken to be a manifestation of the same type of wave some accounting must be made. This is readily done. For, as I have stressed elsewhere [36], a broad spectrum of waves must be present in the ionosphere, and the different methods of detection are subject to various types of observational selection such that different parts of the spectrum will be revealed preferentially by each in turn.

A similar point has been made more recently by Heisler [29] from the purely observational point of view, but the theoretical approach has the further advantage of explaining quantitatively some of the variations (e.g., an observed increase of speed with height). In order to account for discrepancies in the observed directions of travel, as between the small-scale and large-scale irregularities, it is necessary only to assume that the observed waves have two or more energy sources, variable with scale size. This is hardly a disagreeable assumption, and it is mitigated in any event by the fact that waves in the neutral gas will automatically introduce an observational selection (when detection is confined to the ionization) which is dependent on scale sizes and orientation of the propagation vector. These are points that will warrant intensive theoretical investigation in the coming years, and they account for my above-stated hope that the intercomparison of TID and "drift" data will not soon be abandoned.

My comments on the connection between TID's and sporadic E have a much more obvious path to follow, since the internal gravity wave that produces the TID is taken to propagate through the E-region as well, on ascending from the mesosphere, and it need only have adequate amplitude there in order to account for a sporadic-E formation. The connection must be somewhat more subtle, however, for the TID's tend to propagate meridionally, and their oscillatory winds would tend to be North-South, whereas the East-West winds are more important to magnetoshear sporadic E; and, further, the peaks of sporadic E have been associated with both upward and downward displacements of isoionic contours in the TID's. These facts suggest once again an observational selection, imposed by the redistribution of ionization itself or by the method of detection, but its nature is not yet clear. Interactions with tidal shears must also be examined in this connection.

A somewhat competitive view should be mentioned. According to it, the link between E_s-patches and TID's is effected electrodynamically, along geomagnetic field lines, and indeed the slope of the TID wavefront is similarly controlled [10, 11, 31]. The mechanism whereby this type of influence is supposed to be exerted has not been described in the literature, so its relevance is difficult to assess. Certainly there are simple arguments that strongly suggest electrodynamic forces would not be adequate for the purpose proposed, but a mathematical theory supporting the contention may yet be produced. If it is, it will have to accommodate the fact that the slope of TID's remains in the "forward" direction even for TID's that propagate across the magnetic meridians (and even, I understand, on rare occasions when a TID moves away from the equator).

If, on the other hand, the frontal surface is determined at all heights by the local action of an internal gravity wave, the tilt is adequately explained and its similarity to the dip angle is more or less fortuitous. In this latter case, however, an observational enhancement of suitably oriented frontal surfaces would undoubtedly occur — specifically, for example, TID's moving toward the equator, with wave fronts inclined parallel to the magnetic field, should produce the greatest ionization deformations — and may account for some magnetic influence which has been directly inferred [11].

8. Midlatitude Spread F

Bowman [11] has shown that much midlatitude spread-F occurrence can be attributed to "ripples" of ionization in the F-layer, of a wavelike nature quite comparable to TID's. My purpose in discussing it separately is to draw attention to the contrast between it and the field-aligned spread-F ionization previously described. Bowman himself points out that his observations do exhibit a magnetic influence, but in the sense that a continuous front rather than a succession of irregularities appears to be extended along the field lines. He notes, too, that such a frontal irregularity might be mistaken for a field-aligned irregularity in certain types of observations.

It seems doubtful that all the spread-F previously discussed can be attributed to irregularities of the type described by Bowman — although spread-F observations at all latitudes should be examined with this point in mind — and the separation by section that I have adopted here reflects my own guess as to the ultimate division of types. Such a division, in which midlatitude spread F is distinguished from high-latitude spread F, despite the fact that there is no clear minimum of occurrence between, may account for a transition in the behavior of radio-star scintillations (or for the appearance of two distinct types) at slightly subauroral latitudes [28]. Further support is gained from recent satellite data [51] which reveal that field-aligned irregularities at the height of the satellite ($\sim$1000 km) are normally present at latitudes of 65–72°N, but are rarely seen at latitudes below 55°N, the transition from no spread to extreme spread occurring usually within 4° of latitude. Further examination should be made during IQSY of the distinction between midlatitude and high-latitude spread F.

9. Internal Atmospheric Gravity Waves [36, 38]

While much of what should be said about internal gravity waves has already been stated, there remains more. I could comment at length about the strong temperature fluctuations detected by rockets in the mesosphere, with a vertical scale of a few kilometers; or the ionization strata similarly located and similarly scaled; or the clearly defined waves revealed by noctilucent clouds. But these topics carry us somewhat beyond the scope of this survey, and they would serve only to amplify a point already implicit in what has gone before.

That point should be clear. Even with my personal bias fully unleashed, I cannot of course state without reservation that all midlatitude irregularities heretofore discussed are necessarily manifestations of internal gravity waves. But I can state, and do, that these waves are capable of accounting at one stroke for a wide variety of midlatitude irregularities, both qualitatively and quantitatively, both individually and in combination. Further, that other mechanisms that have been proposed for the explanation of one or other of these irregularities are by and large invalid, and, if not, they are at best ad hoc (save for the tides, whose role has been recognized in the foregoing when relevant). Finally, that these facts should be taken into account in the future analysis of data and in the planning of experiments. It is on this last point that I wish to dwell briefly, for a great deal of research time is at stake during the IQSY and beyond.

The problems that must be faced in the analysis of data are nowhere more severe than in the "drift" studies, and their case will serve for illustration. Initially the data were reduced by the "method of similar fades," which was suitable for quantitative estimates of drift if the pattern of irregularity were sufficiently large and sufficiently unchanging as it moved. But it was found often to be inadequate, and much labor has been expended in the development and application of correlation techniques, which are said to yield both a mean drift and an estimate of the random fluctuations of the pattern of irregularity. I do not wish to belittle this effort, nor to advocate its abandonment. But I feel I must point out that it was derived with a particular model of irregularities in mind — a turbulence plus wind model — and that that model cannot now find theoretical justification. On the other hand, the one theory that claims adequate justification — the theory of internal gravity waves — has as yet found no counterpart in the analysis of data. (Indeed, it seems to me doubtful that the drift data can yield any useful information as to direction and speed of motion except when the method of similar fades is clearly adequate, and not always then.) This may well be only a matter of time, but while we wait for the appropriate time much precious effort may be wasted in useless analysis. Nor is the problem one which can be left to the theorists alone, for, as I have indicated, observational selection is strong, and close collaboration with the experimenter will be required. It is to be hoped that the IQSY will witness a careful reexamination of data reduction techniques in the light of theoretical developments.

In the planning of experiments for IQSY, considerable emphasis has been placed on the intercomparison of data acquired by various means. I submit that this emphasis should be increased in future years, and extended with the aid of theoretical inferences. Thus, as indicated previously, various relationships can now be predicted between temperature, pressure, density and wind fluctuations, and their spatial and temporal correlations; these should be exploited, and confirmed or denied. Additional phenomena should be considered with the wave interpretation in mind, and analyzed accordingly. A specific example is provided by airglow cells, which exhibit scale sizes of 100 km and horizontal motions at speeds of 50 m/sec or so [54], quite consistent with "drift" irregularities. The link here might be found through the density fluctuations of the waves, for amplitudes of the order ± 10 per cent are to be expected and the strength of airglow emissions is believed by most to be highly density-dependent.

New sources of the ionospheric disturbances can be inferred, but interdisciplinary studies will have to be encouraged to test them. The latter may on occasion require new observational arrangements, but they too should be facilitated. For example, it is reasonable now to look for an association between major TID's, which are strongest in winter and propagate toward the equator, with origins in the stratospheric "polar night jet"; but the TID's are studied primarily in Australia and the polar stratosphere in the Arctic. This impact of theory on experimental planning is again undoubtedly a matter of time, but it must certainly take place, and hopefully soon.

10. Turbulence [38]

While much that was previously considered to be turbulence has here been discussed in other terms, there remain some observations whose natural interpretation is based on the operation of a true turbulence system. The rapid expansion of meteor trails [23] and of rocket-released vapor trails [6] have indicated a turbulence dissipation of about 10^{-2} watt/kg at the 90–100 km level, with sudden termination shortly above. The data are open to some question, and they pose some difficulty of acceptance in view of the degree of static stability of the atmosphere, but this difficulty does not seem severe and a substantial assimilation into standard turbulence theory can be achieved [6, 38]. What is more important to the present discussion, the turbulence is adequate [38] to account for the spatial scales of ionization irregularities observed by VHF scattering from the D-region. It appears to be generated by wind shears, moreover, and so its enhancement at a level of high wind shear is to be expected. Turbulence has often been advocated as a means of producing sporadic E, and a recent observation [55] of sporadic E at a height where turbulence and high shear combine must be met with considerable interest.

Small-scale turbulence in the neutral gas of the upper atmosphere has come under direct study only since the IGY. Its relation to larger scale wind structure, whether the latter be caused by true turbulence or by systematic wave motions, provides a fascinating problem in fluid mechanics. Its relation to ionospheric scatter irregularities holds no less fascination, and indeed carries a high degree of practical significance as well. Both topics will merit much fuller examination in the years that lie ahead, and many of the relevant studies are already planned for IQSY. As in other areas, however, definitive results can be obtained only through the simultaneous application of several techniques. In this respect, much remains to be done.

References

1. W. I. Axford, Note on a mechanism for the vertical transport of ionization in the ionosphere, *Can. J. Phys.*, **39,** 1393 (1961).
2. W. I. Axford, The formation and vertical movement of dense ionized layers in the ionosphere due to neutral wind shears, *J. Geophys. Res.*, **68,** 769 (1963).
3. W. I. Axford and C. O. Hines, A unifying theory of high-latitude geophysical phenomena and geomagnetic storms, *Can. J. Phys.*, **39,** 1433 (1961).
4. W. J. G. Beynon (ed.), *Some Ionospheric Results Obtained During the International Geophysical Year* (Elsevier Publishing Company, 1960).
5. J. E. Blamont and J. M. Baguette, Mesures déduites des déformations de six nuages de métaux alcalins formés par fusées dans la haute atmosphère, *Ann. Géophys.*, **17,** 319 (1961).
6. J. E. Blamont and C. de Jager, Upper atmospheric turbulence near the 100 km level, *Ann. Géophys.*, **17,** 134 (1961).
7. R. Bolgiano, Turbulent spectra in a stably stratified atmosphere, *J. Geophys. Res.*, **64,** 2226 (1959).
8. K. L. Bowles and R. Cohen, A study of radio wave scattering from sporadic E near the equator, *Ref. 59*, p. 51.
9. K. L. Bowles, R. Cohen, G. R. Ochs, and B. B. Balsley, Radar echoes from field-aligned ionization above the magnetic equator and their resemblance to auroral echoes, *J. Geophys. Res.*, **65,** 1853 (1960).
10. G. G. Bowman, Some aspects of sporadic-*E* at mid-latitudes, *Planet. Space Sci.*, **2,** 195 (1960).
11. G. G. Bowman, Further studies of spread-*F* at Brisbane, *Planet. Space Sci.*, **2,** 133 and 150 (1960).
12. B. H. Briggs, A preliminary report on horizontal drifts in the *F* region during the IGY, *Ref. 4*, p. 297.
13. K. Bullough, The radio aurora in high latitudes, *Ref. 52*, p. 151.
14. K. Bullough, Radio-echo observations of the aurora in Terre Adélie, *Ann. Géophys.*, **17,** 195 (1961).
15. O. Buneman, Excitation of field-aligned sound waves by electron streams, *Phys. Rev. Letters*, **10,** 285 (1963).
16. W. Calvert, Instability of the equatorial *F* layer after sunset, *J. Geophys. Res.*, **68,** 2591 (1963).
17. R. Cohen, K. L. Bowles, and W. Calvert, On the nature of equatorial slant sporadic E, *J. Geophys. Res.*, **67,** 965 (1962).
18. K. D. Cole, Motions of the aurora and radio-aurora and their relationships to ionospheric currents, *Planet. Space Sci.*, **10,** 129 (1963).
19. T. N. Davis, The morphology of the polar aurora, *J. Geophys. Res.*, **65,** 3497 (1960).
20. J. P. Dougherty, Magnetohydrodynamics of the small-scale structure of the *F* region, *J. Geophys. Res.*, **64,** 2215 (1959).
21. D. T. Farley, A theory of electrostatic fields in the ionosphere at nonpolar geomagnetic latitudes, *J. Geophys. Res.*, **65,** 869 (1960).
22. D. T. Farley, A plasma instability resulting in field-aligned irregularities in the ionosphere, *J. Geophys. Res.*, **68,** 6083 (1963).
23. J. S. Greenhow, Eddy diffusion and its effect on meteor trails, *J. Geophys. Res.*, **64,** 2208 (1959).
24. J. S. Greenhow and E. L. Neufeld, Large-scale irregularities in high altitude winds, *Proc. Phys. Soc.*, **75,** 228 (1960).
25. J. S. Greenhow and E. L. Neufeld, Winds in the upper atmosphere, *Q. J. Roy. Met. Soc.*, **87,** 472 (1961).
26. V. D. Gusev, J. V. Kushnerevsky, and S. F. Mirkotan, Comparison of results of observations of large-scale and small-scale inhomogeneities in the F2 layer, *Ref. 4*, p. 322.
27. L. Harang, Drift of the ionosphere at high latitude determined from radio star scintillations, *J. Atmos. Terr. Phys.*, **25,** 107 (1963).

28. T. R. HARTZ, Radio star scintillations and ionospheric disturbances, *Can. J. Phys.*, **37,** 1137 (1959).
29. L. H. HEISLER, Observation of movement of perturbations in the *F*-region, *J. Atmos. Terr. Phys.*, **25,** 71 (1963).
30. L. H. HEISLER AND J. D. WHITEHEAD, *F*-region traveling disturbances and sporadic-E ionization, *J. Geophys. Res.*, **65,** 2767 (1960).
31. L. H. HEISLER AND J. D. WHITEHEAD, The phase speed of a travelling disturbance in the *F* region of the ionosphere and its comparison with group velocity, *Aust. J. Phys.*, **14,** 481 (1961).
32. L. H. HEISLER AND J. D. WHITEHEAD, Rapid variations in the sporadic-*E* region, *J. Atmos. Terr. Phys.*, **24,** 753 (1962).
33. C. O. HINES, Geomagnetism and the ionosphere, *Ref. 52*, p. 103.
34. C. O. HINES, Turbulence at meteor heights, *J. Geophys. Res.*, **64,** 939 (1959).
35. C. O. HINES, Motions in the ionosphere, *Proc. Inst. Rad. Engrs.*, **47,** 176 (1959).
36. C. O. HINES, Internal atmospheric gravity waves at ionospheric heights, *Can. J. Phys.*, **38,** 1441 (1960)
37. C. O. HINES, Ionization irregularities in the *E*-region, *J. Atmos. Terr. Phys.*, **25,** 305 (1963).
38. C. O. HINES, The upper atmosphere in motion, *Q. J. Roy. Met. Soc.*, **89,** 1 (1963).
39. International symposium on fluid mechanics in the ionosphere, *J. Geophys. Res.*, **64,** 2037 (1959).
40. I. L. JONES, The height variation of drift in the *E* region, *J. Atmos. Terr. Phys.*, **12,** 68 (1958).
41. J. A. KIM AND B. W. CURRIE, Further observations of the horizontal movements of aurora, *Can. J. Phys.*, **38,** 1366 (1960).
42. R. W. KNECHT AND R. E. MCDUFFIE, On the width of the equatorial E_s belt, *Ref. 59*, p. 215.
43. B. V. KRISHNAMURTHY AND B. RAMACHANDRA RAO, Effect of magnetic activity and F region height changes on equatorial spread-*F*, *Ref. 52*. p. 310.
44. H. I. LEIGHTON, A. H. SHAPLEY, AND E. K. SMITH, The occurrence of sporadic *E* during the IGY, *Ref. 59*, p. 166.
45. G. F. LYON AND A. KAVADAS, Horizontal motions in radar echoes from aurora, *Can. J. Phys.*, **36,** 1661 (1958).
46. A. J. LYON, N. J. SKINNER, AND R. W. WRIGHT, The geomorphology of equatorial spread-*F*, *Ref. 4*, p. 153.
47. D. F. MARTYN, The normal *F* region of the ionosphere, *Proc. Inst. Rad. Engrs.*, **47,** 147 (1959).
48. S. MATSUSHITA, Interrelations of sporadic *E* and ionospheric currents, *Ref. 59*, p. 344.
49. S. MATSUSHITA AND E. K. SMITH, Concluding remarks, *Ref. 59*, p. 376.
50. A. MAXWELL, Investigation of *F* region drift movements by observations of radio star fading, *The Physics of the Ionosphere* 166 (The Physical Society, 1955).
51. L. E. PETRIE, Top-side spread echoes, *Can. J. Phys.*, **41,** 194 (1963).
52. *Proceedings of the International Conference on the Ionosphere* (The Institute of Physics and the Physical Society, 1963).
53. K. RAWER, Ionospheric irregularities and movements, and Summary — irregularities and drifts, *Ref. 52*, pp. 239 and 370.
54. F. E. ROACH, Variations of [OI] 5577 Å emission in the upper atmosphere, *Ann. Géophys.*, **17,** 172 (1961).
55. N. W. ROSENBERG, H. D. EDWARDS, AND J. W. WRIGHT, Ionospheric winds: motions into night and sporadic *E* correlations (*COSPAR Meeting*, Warsaw, Poland, June, 1963).
56. J. C. SEDDON, Sporadic *E* as observed with rockets, *Ref. 59*, p. 78.
57. T. SHIMAZAKI, The diurnal and seasonal variations of the occurrence probability of spread *F*, *Ref. 4*, p. 158.
58. N. J. SKINNER AND R. W. WRIGHT, The reflection coefficient and fading characteristics of signals returned from the E_s layer at Ibadan, *Ref. 59*, p. 37.

59. E. K. Smith and S. Matsushita (eds.), *Ionospheric Sporadic E* (Pergamon Press, 1962).
60. C. D. Watkins, Auroral radio-echoes and magnetic disturbances, *J. Atmos. Terr. Phys.*, **20,** 131 (1961).
61. J. D. Whitehead, The formation of the sporadic-*E* layer in the temperate zones, *J. Atmos. Terr. Phys.*, **20,** 49 (1961).
62. J. D. Whitehead, The formation of a sporadic-*E* layer from a vertical gradient in horizontal wind, *Ref. 59*, p. 276.
63. J. D. Whitehead, Theory of equatorial sporadic-*E*, *J. Atmos. Terr. Phys.*, **25,** 167 (1963).
64. S. P. Zimmerman, Upper atmospheric turbulence near the 100 km level, *Ann. Géophys.*, **18,** 116 (1962).

CHAPTER 13

WHISTLERS AND VLF EMISSIONS

R. A. Helliwell

1. Background

The purpose of this paper is to review the present status of research on whistlers and VLF emissions and to mention some of the problems before us. This field of research was practically unknown prior to the initiation of IGY planning. The very rapid growth of interest in this field is illustrated by the fact that the relevant literature contains over 500 entries of which less than 10 per cent were available before the year 1956. A detailed discussion of research results and a comprehensive bibliography are in press [7]. Review papers covering the background and some of the IGY results are available [6, 8].

Whistlers are produced by the electromagnetic impulses from lightning and are observed mainly in the range of frequencies from 300–30,000 cycles. Much of the energy of the impulse is reflected from the ionosphere back to the ground, where it is the main source of interference to radiocommunication from very low to high frequencies. Some of the energy enters the ionosphere, where it is guided by the earth's magnetic field into the opposite hemisphere. Dispersion in the ionosphere stretches the original impulse into a gliding tone (order of one second in duration) which is called a whistler. A whistler often echoes several times between the path end points, with the echo time increasing directly with the number of traverses of the path. A typical whistler path is shown in Figure 1, and the associated spectra which would be observed at the two ends of the path are sketched in the figure inserts. An actual recording is shown in Figure 2. Whistler paths appear to be fixed in the ionosphere at any given time, and often two or more such paths can be observed simultaneously, giving rise to what is known as the multiple-path whistler. The shape of the frequency vs. time curve of the whistler is determined by the dispersion, which is

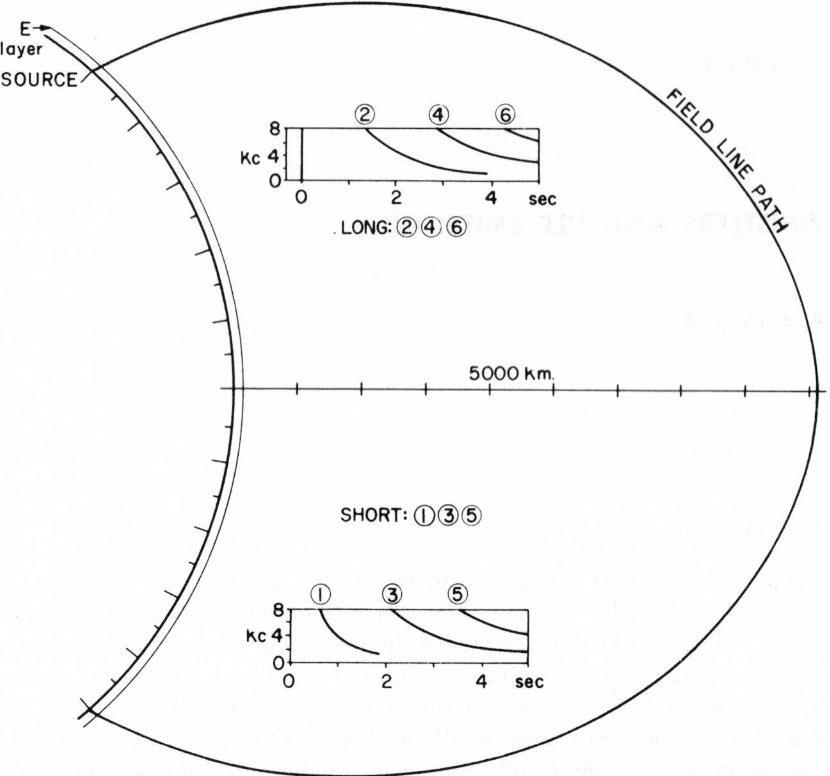

FIG. 1. Field-line path followed by whistler. Inset diagrams show idealized spectra of whistler-echo trains received at northern and southern terminations of path.

controlled by the electron density and the earth's magnetic field. Details of the dispersion and guiding of whistlers are treated elsewhere [7, 11].

VLF emissions are a second class of phenomena observed at whistler frequencies and include steady noise, called hiss, as well as a variety of discrete forms of a generally musical character [6]. They are believed to arise from the excitation of whistler-mode waves by streams of charged particles which follow the earth's magnetic field.

Before the beginning of the IGY our understanding of whistlers and related phenomena was relatively limited. Whistlers were first described by Barkhausen [1] in 1919, who heard them while eavesdropping on Allied telephone communications at the front lines during World War I. In 1928, Eckersley [5] in England reported an association between whistlers and lightning and also between whistlers and solar activity. The first evidence of VLF emissions was reported by Marconi workers, who heard and described the so-called "dawn chorus" in 1931. Measurements of the dispersion of a whistler were reported by Burton and Boardman in 1933

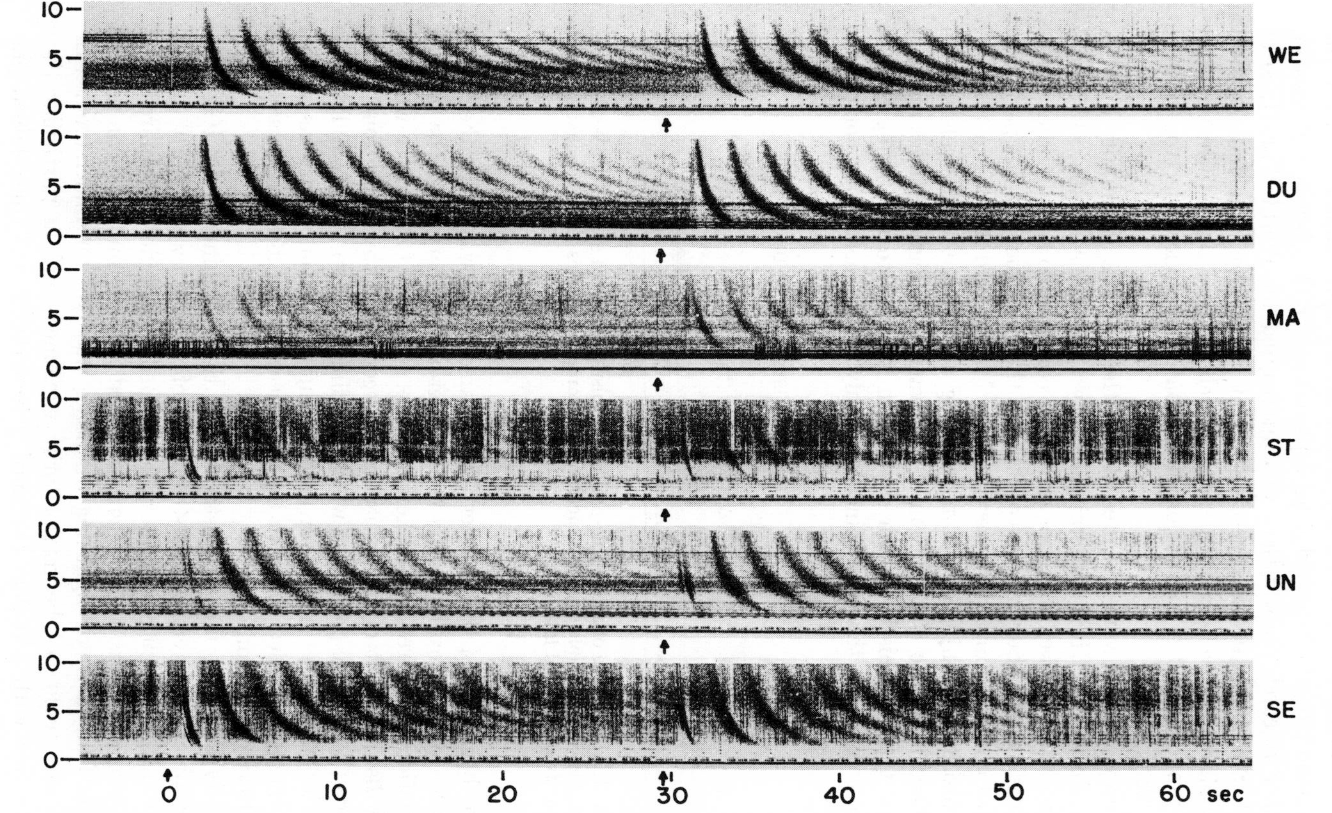

Fig. 2. Whistler trains received both in the Southern Hemisphere (upper three spectra) and the Northern Hemisphere (lower three spectra). The two causative lightning impulses from the Southern Hemisphere are indicated by arrows. These spectra were prepared from tape recordings made at Wellington and Dunedin, New Zealand; Macquarie Island, Antarctic Ocean; Stanford, California; Unalaska, Aleutian Islands; and Seattle, Washington.

[3], following which Eckersley published an approximate form of the dispersion law which provided an explanation for the observed dispersion. Further research on whistlers was interrupted by World War II, after which Storey began his investigations at Cambridge, England. In 1953 he published his well-known paper in which the field-aligned whistler path was proposed and a calculation of the outer-ionosphere electron density was made.

Storey's results were first presented to the scientific community by J. A. Ratcliffe at the URSI General Assembly (Sydney, Australia, 1952) and stimulated a number of groups in various countries to begin studies of this fascinating topic. Several tests of Storey's theory of the field-line path were carried out, including the observation by Morgan and Allcock in 1956 [9] of whistlers at conjugate points, showing approximately the relationship sketched in Figure 1. Extension of observations to high latitudes revealed a new type of whistler which showed, in addition to the falling tone, a rising component that was joined smoothly to the descending component

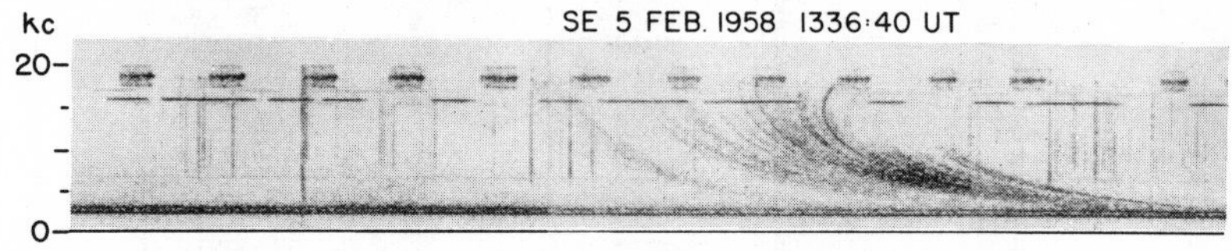

Fig. 3. An example of a multiple-path nose whistler recorded at Seattle, Washington. The presence of multiple spectral traces in this example indicates that propagation paths were active at several latitudes.

at the beginning of the whistler. This strange shape was called the "nose" whistler and was explained by the magnetoionic theory after the limiting restrictions of Storey and Eckersley were removed. Later, nose whistlers were discovered at middle latitudes in accord with the predictions of the theory. A multiple-path nose whistler is illustrated in Figure 3. The nose whistler provided a means for determining the latitude of the associated field-line path, called the path latitude, necessary in using dispersion data for study of electron density.

Many questions faced investigators at the beginning of the IGY. The geographical and temporal distributions of whistlers were poorly defined, and the IGY synoptic program was designed to provide the required data. The fine structure of whistlers exhibited by the multiple components arising from a single lightning discharge was not yet understood. VLF emissions could not be satisfactorily explained, and in particular their connection with whistlers remained a remarkable and unexplained phenomenon. Finally, although Storey had estimated the electron density in the outer ionosphere from whistlers, there was yet no method for determining a profile of electron density throughout the magnetosphere. These were some of the questions which occupied the minds of experimenters planning synoptic programs for the IGY.

2. Results of the IGY–IGC Period

From the IGY-IGC data the gross features of the distribution of whistlers were defined. It was found that the distribution tends to be related to geomagnetic latitude, with very few whistlers being heard on the geomagnetic equator. The peak in whistler activity lies near 50° geomagnetic latitude, and activity tapers off toward the polar regions with occurrence rates being relatively low near the geomagnetic poles. Temporal variations of whistlers are complicated, but to a first order are characterized by a tendency for whistlers to occur most frequently during nighttime, probably because of reduced *D*-region absorption at night. However, at some stations daytime maxima are observed, and these effects have yet to be explained. Whistlers show a tendency to occur most frequently during seasons when thunderstorm activity at the conjugate point or in the vicinity of observation is a maximum. Solar cycle variations in whistler occurrence will probably not be well defined until the IQSY data are analyzed.

Analysis of the fine structure of whistlers showed that the dispersion of particular whistler components was the same at spaced stations and from one whistler to the next. In addition, the equivalent one-hop time delays were the same regardless of whether the source was in the hemisphere of the observer or in the opposite hemisphere. Furthermore the travel times of whistler echoes were generally in integer ratios. These facts taken together indicated that the path of a particular whistler component was fixed in the ionosphere and was not affected by the location of either the source or the receiver. This fixed path was called a "duct." It was suggested that a duct might consist of an enhancement of electron density aligned with the earth's magnetic field. It was shown by application of ray theory that enhancements of about 10 per cent with respect to the background density were capable of trapping whistler energy at middle latitudes. Although the theory provided a natural explanation for the observed fine structure, there was no direct test of the existence of the postulated enhancements of electron density.

Study of VLF emissions during the IGY was concentrated on the classification of different types. Periodic emissions, now an important new type, were recognized. The common occurrence of emissions triggered by whistlers was also noted during the IGY period.

IGY whistler data were applied to the study of the electron density in the magnetosphere. Methods for converting whistler dispersion data to electron density were developed. These studies resulted in a description of the equatorial profile out to five earth radii, a curve for which is shown in Figure 8.

Sounding of the magnetosphere at very low frequency using man-made whistler-mode signals was first carried out during the IGY. Whistler-mode signals on 15.5 kc/sec were successfully sent from station NSS to a receiving station located at Cape Horn, South America. The basic theory of Storey was further confirmed by this experiment and a new technique for study of the magnetosphere was introduced.

3. Post-IGY Results

The promising results from the IGY studies led to a continuation of most of the experimental programs, and new experiments were initiated following the IGY, including the observation of whistlers in rockets and satellites.

The first satellite to observe whistlers carried a magnetometer whose bandwidth permitted the observation of frequencies up to 10 kc [4]. Spectrographic examination of the magnetometer telemetry tapes showed the frequent occurrence of very short whistlers that were explained on the basis of existing dispersion theory and the short path to the satellite when it was at a relatively low altitude. In addition, longer whistlers were heard when paths of appropriate length were excited. Interpretation of these whistler observations gave results consistent with those obtained by other methods. Later observation of whistlers in the Alouette satellite by Canadian workers [2] showed that whistlers are often observed in the satellite when nearby ground stations are recording no whistlers. These observations support predictions that whistlers may be launched along nonducted paths and be totally reflected back into the ionosphere at the lower boundary of the ionosphere.

Nuclear detonations produced electromagnetic impulses of sufficient intensity to excite whistlers. Characteristics of nuclear-excited whistlers were found to be essentially the same as those of natural whistlers, and certain conclusions about the mechanism of generation and the path of propagation of nuclear whistlers were drawn.

Following the IGY a number of studies were made of middle-latitude whistlers observed in polar and equatorial regions. It was shown that many whistlers observed in polar regions resembled middle-latitude whistlers, from which it was concluded that whistlers emerging from middle-latitude ducts propagated poleward in the earth-ionosphere waveguide to the receiver. Observations on the equator showed for the most part a complete absence of whistlers. However, in an experiment on the *Eltanin* it was found that on occasion whistlers could be observed while the ship was on the equator, but that these whistlers were characteristic of middle-latitude paths. These observations support the idea that whistlers exit from a particular small region in the ionosphere and propagate great distances in the earth-ionosphere waveguide. The results suggested that the favored direction of propagation was toward the polar regions.

Consideration of the temperature of the ionospheric plasma showed that absorption might occur as a result of gyroresonance between electrons and the whistler-mode signal. It was shown that the upper cutoff of whistlers which normally occurs below 6/10ths of the minimum gyrofrequency along the path could be explained in terms of a kind of Landau damping in the hot magnetospheric plasma.

Dispersion theory was extended to include the effect of ions which become important at the lower whistler frequencies. It was found that ions could produce a detectable change in the dispersion law and that measurements of this effect might provide a measure of the concentration of protons along the path of propagation.

Following the ideas of interaction between waves and electrons, a proposal was developed for the controlled acceleration of relativistic electrons. Termed the "geocyclotron," this mechanism could be used for the purpose of producing artificially a belt of energetic electrons somewhat similar to that produced by the Argus nuclear tests.

The study of VLF emissions accelerated greatly during the post-IGY period as a result of the excellent collection of quantitative data obtained in the IGY synoptic recording program. It was discovered that periodic emissions at conjugate points have the expected antiphase relation. An example is shown in Figure 4.

During examination of whistler tape recordings taken during and after the IGY, it was discovered that discrete emissions are sometimes triggered by the transmissions from Morse-code VLF stations. In the cases examined it was found that the emissions were triggered almost entirely by the Morse-code dashes (150 msec duration) and seldom by the dots. An example is shown in Figure 5. This discovery showed that the medium was capable of generating an emission whenever the proper stimulus was applied, and that the stimulating signals must exceed a certain minimum duration before any effect could be observed.

Periodic emissions were found in several cases to be related to whistlers and it was shown that the emission process required the presence of a whistler-mode wave packet which would trigger the emission. From these new data it was possible to distinguish between two postulated mechanisms for the generation of VLF emissions. One theory required the prior existence of bunches of charged particles which would radiate coherently when they passed through the "interaction" region. In the other theory the emissions resulted from the organization of particles in existing streams by a passing whistler-mode wave. Closely related to the discovery of the relation between periodic emissions and whistlers was the identification of so-called multiphase periodic emissions. Here the phenomenon consisted of the superposition of several sets of periodic emissions. An example of a three-

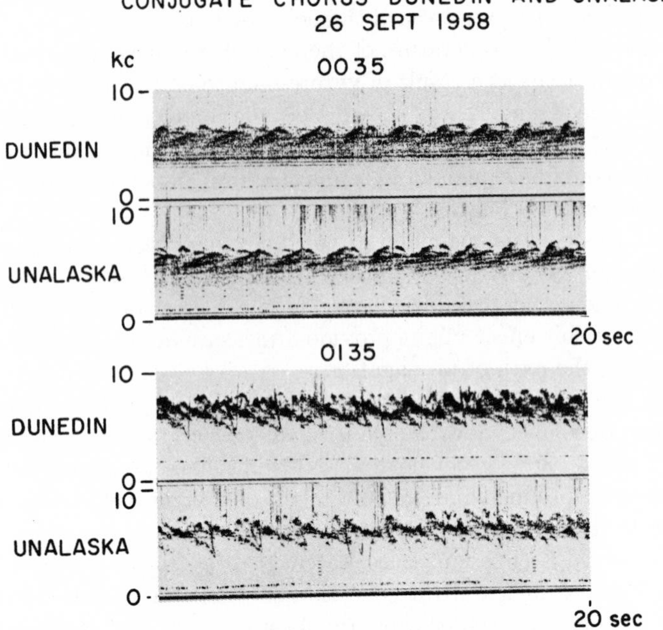

Fig. 4. Periodic emissions recorded at conjugate stations. Emissions demonstrate antiphase relationship at opposite hemispheres.

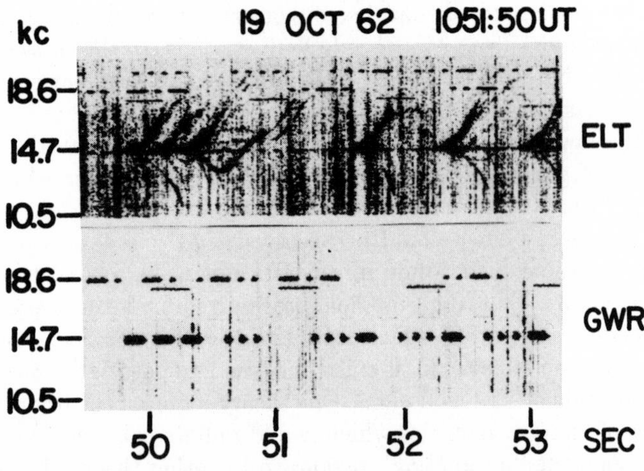

Fig. 5. Emissions triggered by a VLF station at 14.7 kc. Top record shows the emissions received on board the U.S.N.S. *Eltanin* while it was cruising at 50°S geomagnetic latitude. The lower record shows, for comparison purposes, the 14.7-kc transmissions from station NAA in Maine, received at Great Whale River, Quebec. The lower record has been shifted to the right by approximately 1.2 sec with respect to the upper record to compensate for the one-hop whistler-mode delay. Transmissions of other VLF stations appear on both records.

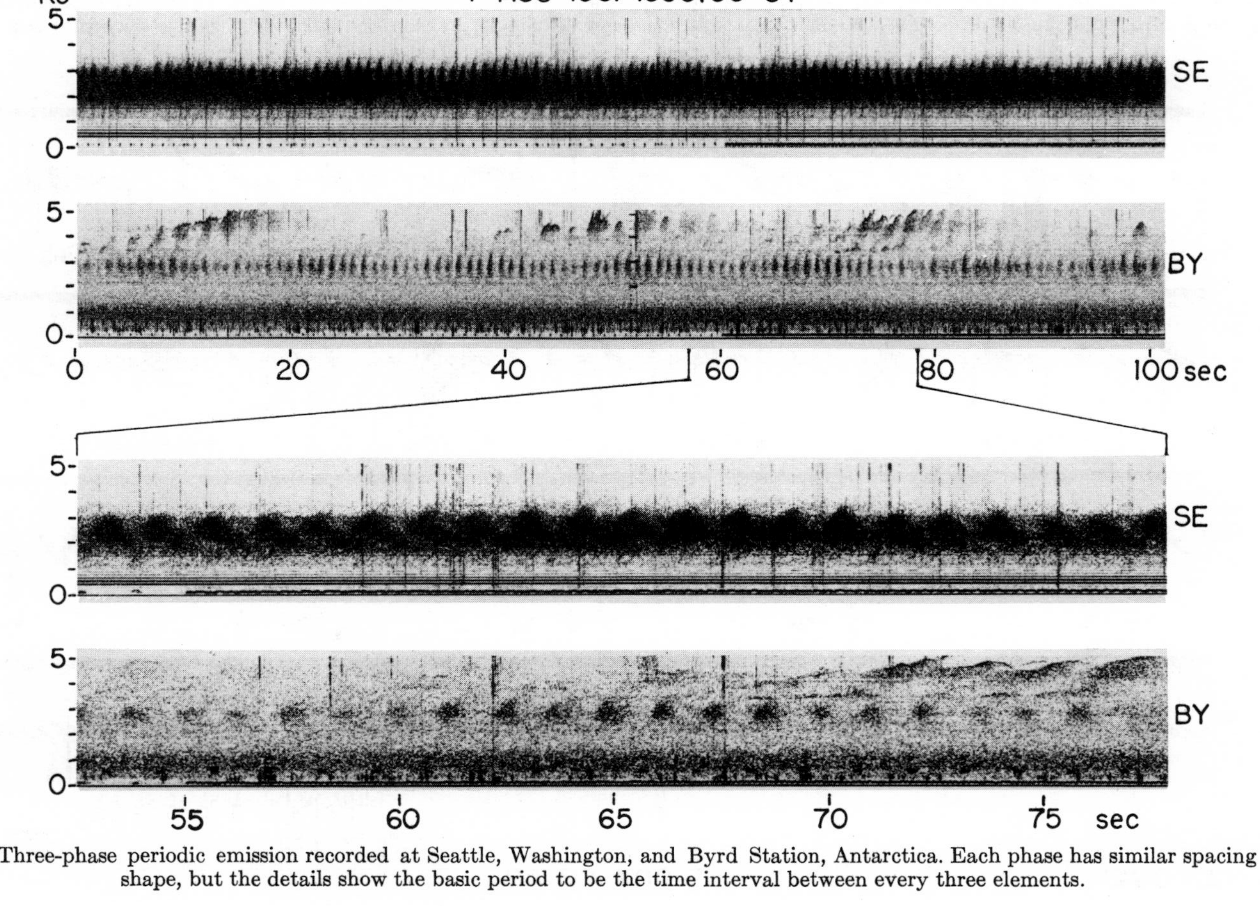

FIG. 6. Three-phase periodic emission recorded at Seattle, Washington, and Byrd Station, Antarctica. Each phase has similar spacing and shape, but the details show the basic period to be the time interval between every three elements.

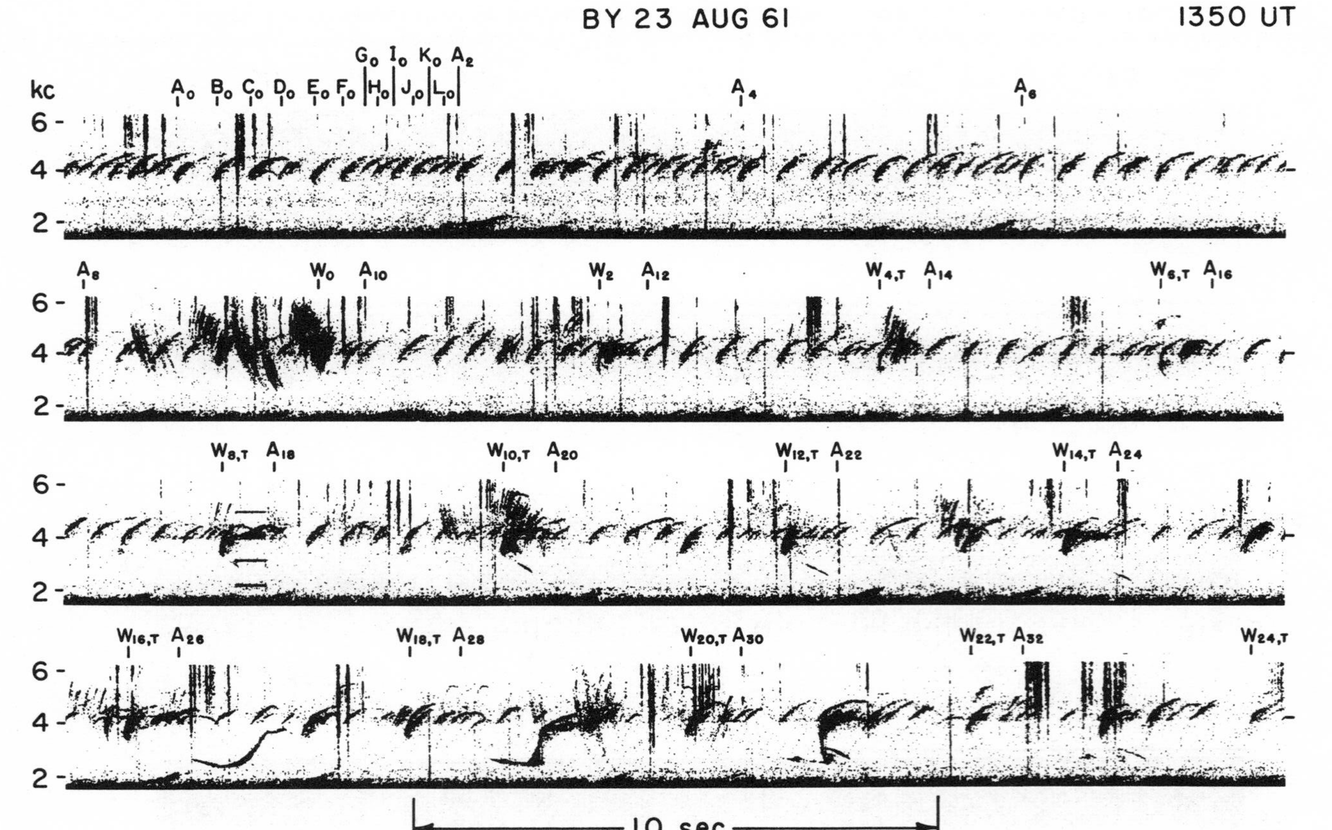

FIG. 7. Chorus consisting of a 12-phase periodic emission. The four panels are consecutive spectra of a recording made at Byrd Station, Antarctica. Each phase is labeled by a letter whose subscript represents the relative number of hops, but after the first occurrence, the labeling of the separate phases is omitted. The letter *W* represents the successive hops of a whistler.

phase periodic emission is shown in Figure 6. When the number of sets exceeded half a dozen or so, the result was classed as a type of chorus. An example of this type of chorus is shown in Figure 7.

A particular type of VLF emission known as "hiss" was found to correlate closely with visual aurora in studies conducted at Byrd Station, Antarctica. These studies indicated an intimate connection between the two phenomena, suggesting that the source of the hiss might lie in the lower ionosphere.

Most of the IGY work was limited to frequencies below approximately 30 kc, but occasional measurements made at higher frequencies indicated that VLF emissions, particularly hiss, often extend above 50 kc and may on occasion extend to frequencies as high as several hundred kc.

Studies of electron density distribution using whistlers made rapid progress following the IGY. The discovery was made that during magnetic storms the electron density of the magnetosphere tends to be depressed. Normally the values are limited to 80 per cent of the quiet-day values, but during very severe storms, depressions to as low as 10 per cent of quiet-day values were observed. Some correlation was found between the depressions in magnetospheric density as determined by whistlers and reductions in the *F*-region density determined by Faraday rotation measurements on signals from satellites.

As more quantitative data on dispersion and path latitude became available, a new phenomenon was discovered. This consisted of a sharp decrease in electron density, called the "knee," with geomagnetic latitude. The position in latitude of this knee would move equatorward with increasing disturbance. The results obtained in this study were consistent with previously puzzling electron-density measurements made on the Lunik satellite. They provided a basis for more clearly defining the nature of storm-associated electron density changes in the magnetosphere.

Because much whistler data were obtained during the IGY, it was possible to get statistically significant measures of diurnal variation of the electron density even though whistler data were sparse during daytime. It was found from these studies that the diurnal variation was of the order of 30 per cent or less and could be attributed almost wholly to variations in the normal *F*-region. These results indicated that the magnetosphere electron density was nearly constant, implying relatively weak coupling between the ionosphere and magnetosphere.

Intensive study of whistler data obtained from Byrd Station yielded a number of whistlers with nose frequencies as low as 1 kc or less. From these observations the electron-density profile was extended to a geocentric distance of eight earth radii. These results also showed that the very high latitude whistler paths were generally observed only during the daytime.

Comparison of whistler-derived electron densities with incoherent backscatter measurements made in Peru indicated consistency of results.

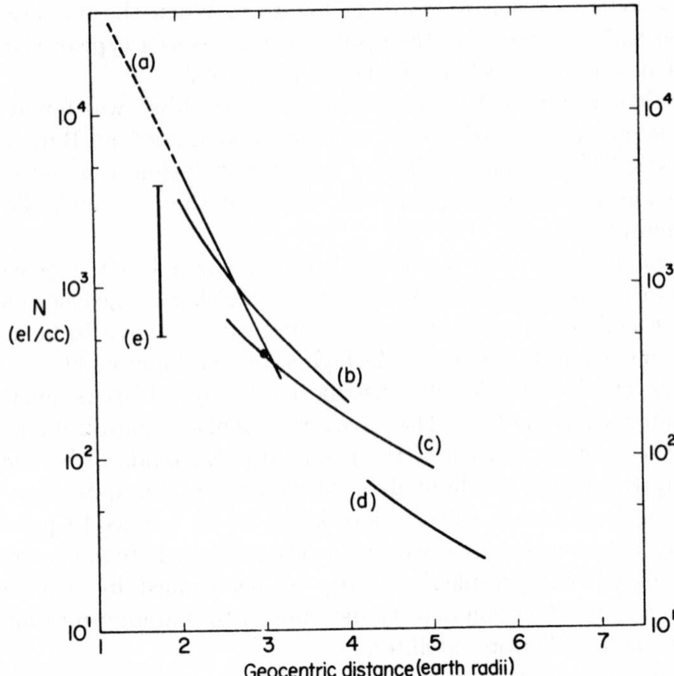

FIG. 8. Electron density as a function of geocentric distance. Curves (*a*)–(*d*) represent measurements derived from various studies of whistlers. The dot represents early measurements by Storey [11]. Incoherent backscatter measurements are represented by (*e*), where the vertical line represents the range of uncertainty.

However, the scatter in the data was insufficient to determine whether there were significant differences in the two methods. Results of various electron-density measurements using whistlers are summarized in Figure 8.

A new experiment was performed very recently using a VLF rocket receiver. The phase path of station NSS was measured in the rocket over its entire trajectory. From the variations in phase, the electron-density profile was computed and found to be in good agreement with results obtained by other methods. In addition, the method was found to be sensitive to small variations and showed promise of becoming an important new tool in the study of the *D*- and *E*-region electron-density profiles.

Extensions of the fixed-frequency magnetospheric-sounding method, first developed during the IGY, yielded interesting new data. Marked diurnal variations were found in which the echoes predominated at night in accordance with the expectations based on absorption calculations. In addition it was found that the diurnal variation often contained two peaks at night indicating for the first time that propagation factors were of primary importance in producing the diurnal variations.

Results from the fixed-frequency-sounding experiments showed that whistler-mode signals were subject to regular deep fading that could not be explained by the known fading effects in the earth-ionosphere waveguide. Fading periods from 20 seconds to over one minute were observed on both one-hop and two-hop signals traveling in the whistler mode. The depth of the fading was great and the fading was quite regular, suggesting a model in which two relatively stable signals were beating together with a progressive change in relative phase. It was suggested on the basis of the data that two whistler-mode paths were present during the observation of such fading, and that the number of wavelengths in these paths were changing relative to one another.

In the course of fixed-frequency studies of the magnetosphere, a new method of sounding was developed based on frequency modulation of a VLF station. Station NPG was frequency-modulated over a range of ± 50 cycles using a saw-tooth pattern of frequency variation with a two-second period. The whistler-mode echo was mixed with the transmitted signal and the difference frequency was recorded so as to provide a measure of the group delay. This method was found to be more sensitive than the pulse method previously used.

In the course of studies of whistler-mode propagation other new and interesting propagation results were obtained. It was found that round-the-world echoes from station NAA could be observed regularly at Stanford. It was also found that nuclear detonations produced marked changes in the amplitude of VLF signals received over various paths. An effect of a solar eclipse was detected in the normal propagation of VLF signals. Whistler tapes have been used to develop an improved detector of SID's [10].

4. Problems

Although much progress has been made in this field, some old and many new problems remain to be solved. For example, the nature of the ducts within which whistlers propagate has not been determined. Are these ducts in reality field-aligned enhancements of ionization as supposed or are they something else? The theory of the coupling of whistler-mode signals between the earth-ionosphere waveguide and the magnetosphere has yet to be laid out in proper quantitative form. This theory is needed in order to calculate the transmission loss between a point on the earth and a point in the ionosphere. Observations in satellites are showing whistlers whose trace shapes are not readily explained in terms of the field-aligned ducts that have been successful in accounting for ground-based observations. These results require careful review of the assumptions on which the present theory is based.

Much remains to be done in the field of VLF emissions. The observable characteristics are probably not yet adequately defined, especially at conjugate points. More theoretical work is needed before we can hope to be able to explain VLF emissions quantitatively. Consideration might be given to suitable laboratory plasma experiments in this work.

The relation between VLF emissions and other phenomena such as the aurora, X-rays, micropulsations, and ionospheric absorption should be investigated on a thorough and quantitative basis. The discovery of artificially stimulated emissions suggests the need for a source of VLF energy with which emissions could be produced on a controlled basis. A suitable high-power sweep-frequency VLF transmitter may be required for this type of experiment.

The physical location of the emitting regions for VLF emissions is still not known. It may be possible with the use of satellite and rocketborne receivers to locate approximately the position of the emitting regions and relate these to streams of charged particles trapped on the lines of force of the earth's magnetic field. The characteristics of VLF emissions as functions of latitude should be studied in a satellite, since many emissions are observed in satellites, particularly at low latitudes, which are not observable on the ground.

Electron-density studies using whistlers have proceeded with considerable speed, but even so, many questions remain unanswered. For example, we do not yet know the solar-cycle variation of electron density in the magnetosphere, but we suspect that it is much smaller than that in the *F*-layer. There is some suggestion that the magnetospheric density may be a function of longitude, and this possibility can only be investigated with the aid of good synoptic data taken at different longitudes. The distribution of electron density along the field lines is still not well defined by any method. Possibilities exist for extending this knowledge by means of rockets and satellites. Although the middle region of the magnetosphere is well covered with existing whistler data, the inner and outer regions are still not too well understood and should be investigated thoroughly.

VLF methods arising from the study of whistlers can be applied to surveys of the electron content within the ionosphere. With the aid of ground-based VLF transmitters, rockets can be used for obtaining vertical profiles and satellites for variations in the electron content with position. Both of these methods could be usefully employed to increase our knowledge of the distribution of electrons in the ionosphere.

Interaction between whistler-mode waves and charged particles provides a basis for a number of interesting experiments. One is the creation of an artificial belt of high-energy electrons using the geocyclotron. Another is the possibility of removal of energetic electrons from the existing radiation belts by means of an inversion of the geocyclotron process. And finally, we should investigate the possibility that whistlers may play a role in the production and decay of the radiation belts.

References

1. H. Barkhausen, Zwei mit Hilfe der neuen verstärker entdeckte Erscheinungen, *Physik. Zeitschr.*, **20**, 401 (1919).
2. R. E. Barrington and J. S. Belrose, Preliminary results from the very-low-frequency receiver aboard Canada's Alouette satellite, *Nature*, **198**, 651 (1963).
3. E. T. Burton and E. M. Boardman, Effects of solar eclipse on audio frequency atmospherics, *Nature*, **131**, 81 (1933).
4. J. C. Cain, I. R. Shapiro, J. D. Stolarik, and J. P. Heppner, A note on whistlers observed above the ionosphere, *J. Geophys. Res.*, **66**, 2677 (1961).
5. T. L. Eckersley, Letter to the editor, *Nature*, **122**, 768 (1928).
6. R. M. Gallet and R. A. Helliwell, Origin of 'very low frequency' emissions, *J. Res. NBS*, **63D**, 21 (1959).
7. R. A. Helliwell, *Whistlers and Related Ionospheric Phenomena*, Stanford University Press, Stanford, Calif. (in press) (1964).
8. R. A. Helliwell and M. G. Morgan, Atmospheric whistlers, *Proc. IRE*, **47**, 200 (1959).
9. M. G. Morgan and G. McK. Allcock, Observations of whistling atmospherics at geomagnetically conjugate points, *Nature*, **177**, 30 (1956).
10. E. T. Pierce, Very-low-frequency atmospherics due to lightning flashes, *Final Report Contract AF33(657)-7009*, Stanford Research Institute, Menlo Park, Calif. (1962).
11. L. R. O. Storey, An investigation of whistling atmospherics, *Phil. Trans. Roy. Soc.*, **A246**, 113 (1953).

CHAPTER 14

MORPHOLOGY OF STORMS IN THE IONOSPHERE

Tatsuzo Obayashi

1. Introduction

Historically, it has long been recognized that the earth's ionosphere is greatly affected by solar disturbances, such as the appearance of sunspots, solar flares, and corpuscular streams which are observed on the earth's surface as geomagnetic storms. As early as 1932–1933, on the occasion of the Second Polar Year, it was discovered by the British Polar Expedition that the polar ionosphere was disturbed during geomagnetic storms. They also noted polar blackout phenomena and auroral E-echoes which are now described as abnormal ionization at lower ionospheric heights due to incoming energetic particles. Later, Berkner and his colleagues found that ionospheric disturbances were associated with geomagnetic storms in lower latitudes too, even notably at the equator. Meanwhile, remarkable ionospheric radio fadeouts followed by bright solar flares were discovered independently by Mögel and Dellinger, which have since been known as sudden ionospheric disturbances. These early studies necessarily employed limited observations; nevertheless, they showed conclusively that E-region disturbances were mainly due to enhanced ionization, while the F-region was affected in such a way that the electron density decreased generally.

Sudden ionospheric disturbances are associated with solar flares. It has been generally believed that an excess of solar ultraviolet radiation produces increased ionization in the D-layer of the ionosphere causing strong absorption for radio waves passing through. Extensive investigations made during the IGY and thereafter, particularly by rocket and satellite observations, revealed the important source of this type of disturbance; an outburst of solar X-rays of 1–10 Å range at the time of a solar flare. Since the effects of sudden ionospheric disturbances are relatively well understood now and extensive surveys are available [27, 118], they will be excluded in the present discussion.

One of the outstanding disturbances in high latitudes is a polar blackout. The blackout, referred to as the "no-echo" condition of ionospheric radio soundings, is apparent on ionograms as an increase of f_{min}, often extending to complete disappearance of radio echoes. This effect is due to a temporary formation of a strong absorbing region in the lower ionosphere, which appears frequently near the auroral zone associated with geomagnetic activities and auroras. Because of the importance of its disturbance effect on radio communications, a number of studies have been carried out since the time of its earliest discovery. This was particularly true throughout the IGY and the IGC. In fact, the discovery of a new type of polar blackout was made during the IGY, giving a completely new insight into the problem of solar-terrestrial relationships.

Intense polar blackouts have been found, which are apparently associated with neither geomagnetic disturbances nor auroras, but occur after a large solar flare. This type of blackout is clearly distinguishable from that of a sudden ionospheric disturbance, since it covers only the polar cap region and often continues for several days. The earliest indication of this phenomenon was reported by Bailey [7, 8], and Shapley and Knecht [109] during the great solar event of February 23, 1956, which revealed strong absorption of radio waves on high-latitude links of VHF forward scatter and a prolonged blackout condition at some polar cap stations. An extensive investigation of polar blackouts was initiated by Hakura *et al.* [33] using IGY world-wide ionospheric data of f_{min}. Obayashi and Hakura [82, 83] have since then concluded that energetic solar protons are ejected at the time of an intense flare and impinge upon the polar cap ionosphere, thereby producing a severe ionospheric blackout, which they called a polar cap blackout in contrast to the usual auroral blackout. Independently, such an enhanced ionization in the polar ionosphere was found by several groups measuring VHF cosmic radio noise absorption [41, 56, 95]. The existence of energetic solar particles impinging upon the polar ionosphere has been detected by direct measurements with high-altitude balloons [3] and by satellites [102].

The next major development was the result of a remarkable interdisciplinary cooperative study by many groups working on polar cap disturbance events. More important investigations of polar cap disturbances have since been made, notably by ionospheric workers (see survey papers [17, 43, 58, 100, 120]). Some recent works have included studies of the close relationship with solar radio outbursts and numerous satellite and rocket observations of solar particles. A more detailed description of polar cap blackouts as well as auroral blackouts will be given later.

The disturbance effect in the $F2$-layer is remarkable during a geomagnetic storm. Systematic morphological studies on F-region disturbances were initiated by Appleton and Piggott [5], Martyn [63], Obayashi [76–78], and Sinno [111, 112]. The average features obtained by the earlier workers may be summarized as follows: In high latitudes, a marked depression of the peak electron density ($foF2$, the critical frequency of the $F2$-layer) occurs, the largest effect being centered near the auroral zone, and having a pronounced diurnal variation. In low latitudes, however, an increase of the electron density is very common, and a depression is rather rare, being noted only during a very severe storm. The variation in middle latitudes shows a marked diurnal control as well as an over-all depression except for occasional increases during the winter season. Because of such a pronounced diurnal component of the disturbance superposed on the simultaneous world-wide effect, the time variation of $F2$-storms has been separated into the disturbance diurnal variation Ds and the storm-time variation Dst, employing the same method as in the case of geomagnetic storms.

Recently, Matsushita [65, 67, 68] carried out a more extensive statistical analysis, using world-wide ionospheric data obtained during the past ten years. He not only confirmed the above-mentioned general characteristics of $F2$-storms, but also found from his analysis of N-h profiles that the total number of electrons below the $F2$-peak (subpeak electron content) behaves in the same way. Furthermore, it has become apparent, from satellite information on the electron content above the peak, that during a geomagnetic storm the total electron content in the whole ionosphere above the 200-km level appears to change in the same sense; i.e., the electron content decreases at middle latitudes and increases at equatorial stations.

These new results have an important implication on the theory of $F2$-storms, suggesting that the storm changes in the F-region do not represent a redistribution of the electrons in that layer, but real decreases and increases in the total electron content. Although no completely satisfactory theory of $F2$ ionospheric storms has as yet appeared there have been several promising attempts. Martyn [63] suggested that vertical drift motions of electrons would play an important role in the large diurnal part of the changes in the $F2$-layer. The vertical drift would result from the interaction of the geomagnetic field and the electric field associated with the geomagnetic Ds current system. This drift theory has successfully been applied by Sato and Maeda [62] to explain the average storm features of the Ds part of ionospheric storms in middle latitudes, though some incompleteness of their theory has recently been pointed out. On the other hand, there is another school of thought, notably of Yonezawa [126] and Matsuura [69], which explains the storm variations in terms of an entire temperature change in the $F2$-region during geomagnetic storms. Their idea has found some support from the satellite drag data, which indicate a large temperature rise above the 200-km level during severe geomagnetic storms. They showed that an increase in the F-region temperature would produce changes in the electron production and loss rates as well as the diffusion rate, leading to substantial electron density variations. However, their assumed processes of photochemical reactions depend rather critically on the model of the ionosphere, and this thermal heating theory may need to await a further comprehensive study.

There are some other disturbance phenomena which are very important for a future study. A feature of many recent studies of ionospheric disturbance phenomena in the polar region has been the evidence for spiral-like or curved precipitation patterns for the two main ionospheric phenomena, polar blackouts and polar sporadic E, and for related geophysical phenomena. As has been suggested by Axford and Hines [6], this effect would be connected to large-scale convective and rotational motions in the earth's magnetosphere. The interrelation between ionospheric phenomena and the precipitation of auroral particles is extremely complex and may be linked closely with conditions in the radiation belts [90]. Knecht and McDuffie [53] have shown marked increases in the electron density of the $F2$-region on several occasions associated with solar flares, accompanied by sudden sea-level cosmic-ray increases. This indicates that in addition to the emission of solar cosmic-ray particles these flares were also unusual in their photon radiation. Finally, the effects of ionospheric disturbances from an artificial origin should be mentioned [87]. Nuclear explosions at high altitudes produce various remarkable disturbances; in particular, artificial ionospheric and geomagnetic storms accompanied by brilliant auroral displays. It has also been found that a strong blast wave propagates over the world through the ionosphere, thereby inducing severe disturbances in the F-region. Since these phenomena exhibit artificial effects under controlled conditions, they should provide important information on the nature of upper atmospheric disturbances.

2. Disturbances in the *E*-Region

A strong enhancement of ionization is the main effect of disturbances in the lower ionosphere. In polar regions, in addition to sudden ionospheric disturbances which are due to solar flare X-rays, polar blackouts are the most significant disturbance. This blackout effect is apparent on ionograms as an increase of f_{min}, and also on the record of absorption measurements by riometer (relative ionospheric opacity meter). The latter measures the integrated absorption of cosmic radio noise passing through the whole ionosphere, though the major absorption occurs at heights below the E-region.

Studies of the polar ionosphere made by these methods especially during the IGY have shown that polar blackouts may be classified into two main categories: auroral zone blackouts and polar cap blackouts [81, 95]. Auroral zone blackouts have been known for many years. They appear near the auroral zone, and their occurrence is correlated with auroras and local geomagnetic disturbances. Ionospheric absorption is very variable in time and in space — it may last for periods of minutes or hours. The lower latitude boundary of this blackout zone, like that of the auroral zone itself, may shift equatorward as the main phase of a geomagnetic storm develops. On the other hand, polar cap blackouts (or, as they are more commonly called polar cap absorption, PCA) occur in polar cap regions within geomagnetic latitudes approximately 60°. Unlike auroral zone blackouts they may exist without simultaneous magnetic disturbances, and are directly related to intense solar flares.

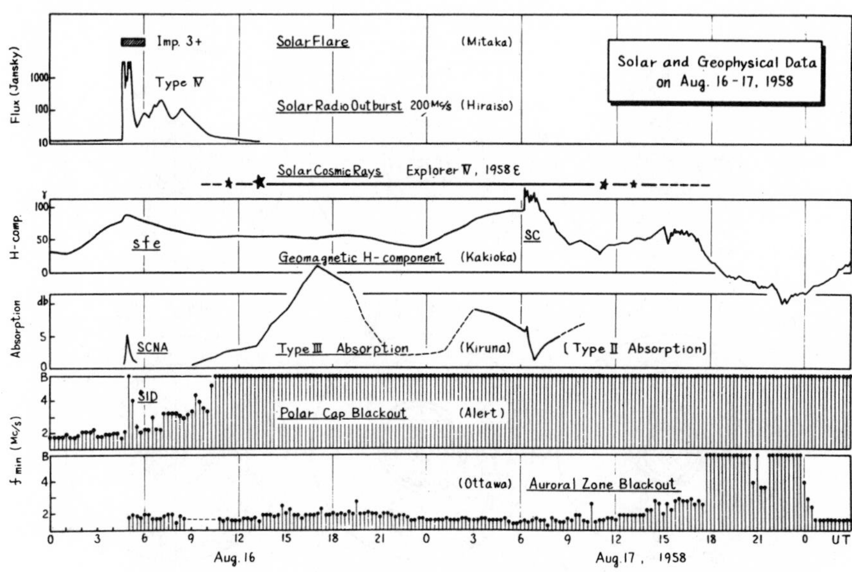

FIG. 1. The polar cap blackout event and associated solar geophysical data, 16–18 August 1958.

It is now generally accepted that polar cap absorption is caused by enhanced ionization in the lower ionosphere due to incoming solar cosmic-ray protons having subrelativistic energies. In order to show the general aspect of this phenomenon, a typical example, observed on August 16–17, 1958, is illustrated in Figure 1. A solar flare of importance 3+ was observed at 0440 UT on August 16, and was followed by an intense sudden ionospheric disturbance (SWF, SCNA, and geomagnetic crochet). It is important to note that this flare was accompanied by a strong solar radio outburst of Type IV, known as synchrotron radiation. Within several hours after the flare, an outstanding increase in absorption was indicated both on the ionograms and the riometer data at the polar cap stations, though there was no appreciable change at the subauroral zone stations.

Concurrently, an incidence of energetic protons of 10–100 Mev was detected by Explorer IV in its orbit. The onset of a geomagnetic storm followed about a day later, and during the main phase of the storm, an abnormal absorption was observed even at subauroral zone stations. The global patterns of the enhanced ionization and, hence, the precipitation of solar protons, for respective stages after the flare are shown in Figure 2. During the period before the onset of the geomagnetic storm, solar protons were impinging upon the polar cap region confined within geomagnetic latitudes of about 65°, causing radio blackouts indicated by the hatched area. At the outbreak of the geomagnetic storm, the region of enhanced

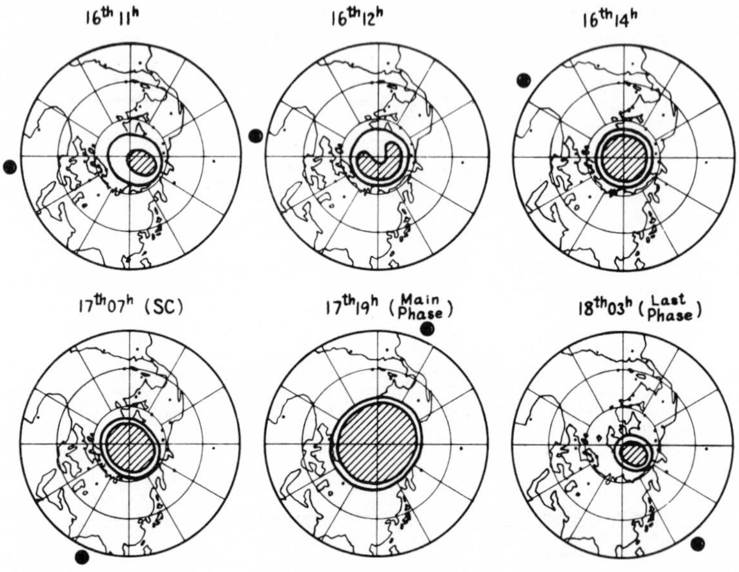

FIG. 2. World-wide patterns of polar blackout deduced from ionograms for the event of 16–18 August 1958 (the hatched areas indicate complete blackout, ● the position of the sun).

ionization spread over a larger area, and, particularly at the main phase of the storm, the outer edge of the region shifted toward low latitudes. It has been noted, however, that during the period of a geomagnetic storm the precipitation pattern may be affected considerably by the existence of an auroral-type absorption. In fact, on many occasions, enhanced ionization appears only along the auroral zone during the main phase of geomagnetic storms, as shown in Figure 3 which illustrates the well-distinguished pattern of a polar cap blackout and of an auroral zone blackout [82, 83].

The general nature of such enhanced ionization in the polar ionosphere has been firmly established in the past few years [19, 22, 35, 37, 46, 57]. The absorbing region formed at the time of polar cap events is found to be situated at rather low altitudes of 50–80 km [30, 42], and this is consistent with the effect on VLF radio propagation [10, 92] and also with polar glow auroras, particularly the enhancement of the molecular nitrogen band 3914 Å [104]. Polar cap absorption events provide important information about solar cosmic-ray particles, which helps in understanding the structure of interplanetary magnetic fields. An extensive survey of this problem will be given elsewhere [88], but will not be discussed here. Auroral absorptions are often associated with X-ray bursts which may presumably be produced by the bremsstrahlung from dumping energetic electrons [119]. It is also found that a sudden increase of absorption of short duration begins at the same time as the geomagnetic sudden commencement, accompanied with simultaneous bursts of X-rays detected at balloon altitudes [15, 66].

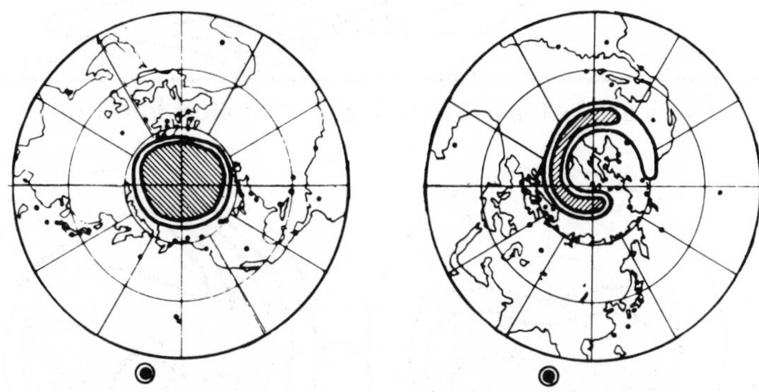

Fig. 3. Typical patterns of polar cap blackout (left) and auroral zone blackout (right) during the event of 12–13 September 1957.

In order to derive a general morphological picture of these disturbances, Hakura [36] carried out a statistical analysis to obtain average patterns of polar cap and auroral blackouts. During the period of the IGY 1957–1958, ten typical and isolated events of polar cap blackouts were selected. Using data from a number of ionospheric stations in North America, at each station all events are superposed with respect to geomagnetic storm time (i.e., time reckoned from the sudden commencement of the geomagnetic storm, SC) and also with respect to local time. The storm-time variation and the local-time variation thus derived are expressed as the percentage occurrence of abnormal absorption ($f_{\min} \geq 4$ Mc/sec or B) for each two-day period before and after the SC of the geomagnetic storm. These results are summarized in Figure 4 as follows: (*a*) the storm-time variation of the planetary magnetic *Kp*-index averaged for all events used in this analysis; (*b*) the pattern of storm-time variation of polar blackouts, and (*c*) the average local-time variations of polar blackouts both for the pre-

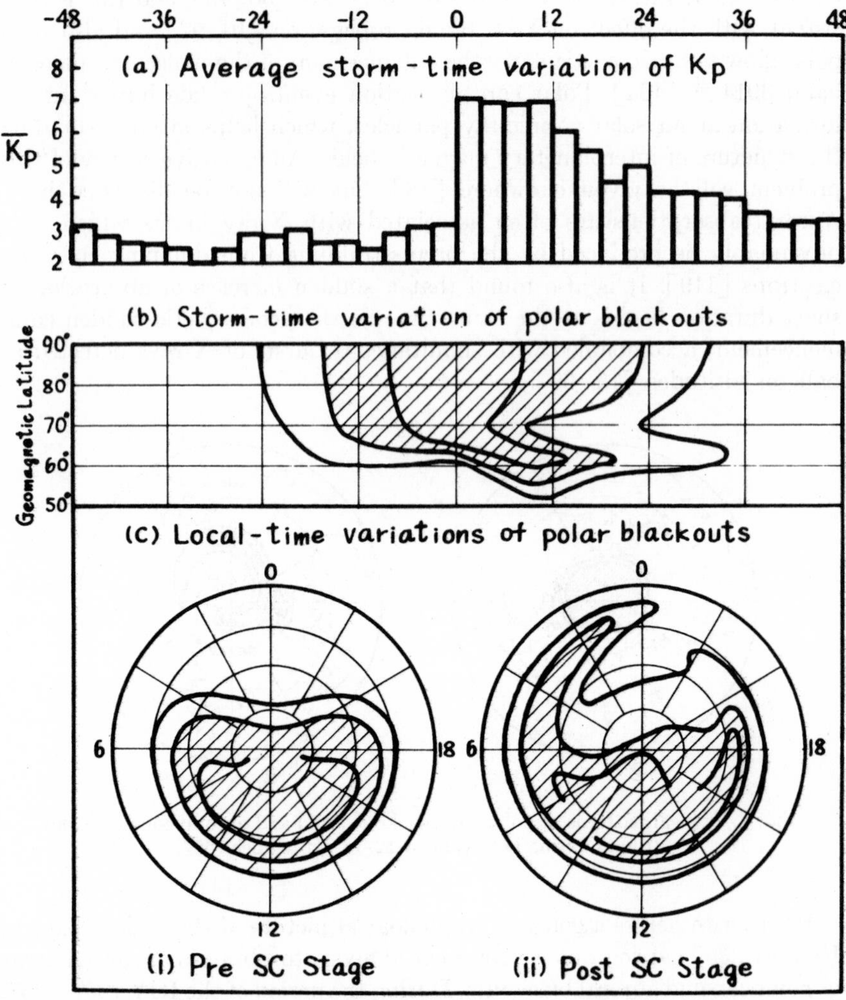

FIG. 4. Average global features of polar blackouts associated with geomagnetic storms. (*a*) the average storm-time variation of the K_p-index; (*b*) the pattern of storm-time variation of polar blackouts; (*c*) patterns of the local-time variation of polar blackout both for the pre-SC and the post-SC period. Contour lines are shown as the occurrence probability of abnormal absorption ($f_{\min} > 4$ Mc/sec, or blackout) in 20 per cent steps (after Hakura [35]).

SC and the post-SC period, which are presumably the polar cap blackout and a combination of polar cap and auroral zone blackouts, respectively. These variations are drawn on the map in geomagnetic coordinates.

It is shown that a polar cap blackout starts well before the onset of a geomagnetic storm. Since the average time delay between a solar flare and the SC of a storm for the events under study is about 30 hours, energetic solar particles which produce the absorption effect arrive at the earth within several hours. The polar cap blackout is confined within geomagnetic latitude 60° during the pre-SC period. Although the enhanced absorption covers in general the whole polar cap, it reveals a strong solar control in its diurnal variation, being much more intense during the day than at night. This accords with the results obtained by riometer measurements, which give more quantitative values of absorption. During the period of a geomagnetic storm, the blackout region expands toward lower latitudes. It is evident that the auroral zone blackout develops and its tail extends from the morning to the night hemisphere. However, the effects of polar cap blackouts are still persisting during the post-SC stage. It has been shown that the southernmost extent of blackouts is proportional to the depression of the geomagnetic field during a storm. The auroral-zone blackout disappears as the geomagnetic activity diminishes, while the polar cap blackout is, in most cases, independent of geomagnetic activity, and decays gradually after two or three days.

Another interesting feature of ionospheric disturbances in the polar region is the evidence for spirallike or curved precipitation patterns for polar blackouts and polar sporadic *E*. The latitude variations in the former exhibit a sort of spiral pattern on the morning side of the pole [11, 50, 117] while for *Es* a differently directed spiral pattern on the evening to night side of the geomagnetic pole is found [32, 49, 116]. These patterns are closely linked up with the maximal line of polar geomagnetic agitations [40, 75] and the precipitation of auroral protons [73]. Although the originally invoked interpretation in terms of a Störmer's spiral is no longer valid [1], a mechanism which involves convective and rotational motions in the magnetosphere has been suggested by Axford and Hines [6].

A peculiar absorption in the lower ionosphere in middle latitudes is known to be associated with geomagnetic storms. This phenomenon was reported originally by Lauter and Sprenger [54] and confirmed by Belrose [10]. The absorption of VLF radio waves persists for several days after the geomagnetic storm, and may be called "*D*-region after effect." A similar persistent absorption effect has also been noted during the events caused by the high-altitude nuclear explosions over Johnston Island in the Pacific, reviewed by Obayashi [87]. Radio noise intensities on LF and MF frequency ranges observed at Hawaii and eastern Australia showed an abrupt drop after the explosion and a subsequent depressed diurnal variation, which apparently persisted for a few weeks. Although these effects need further elucidation, it might be possible to postulate chemical changes in the atmosphere, or the dumping of particles from the radiation belt, which is known to become "over-full" after a storm or nuclear explosion and to remain so for a time of this order [94].

3. Disturbances in the F-Region

Disturbances in the F-region of the ionosphere that are associated with geomagnetic storms are the most striking phenomena, and are commonly called "ionospheric storms." Many important systematic average features of ionospheric storms have been derived on the basis of statistical studies [5, 59, 63–65, 74, 76–78, 105, 106, 111, 112]. In much of the earlier work the ionospheric parameters used were $foF2$ and $h'F2$ (the critical frequency and the virtual height of the $F2$-layer). It has been found that at high latitudes, a marked depression of $foF2$ (or the peak electron density) occurs, the maximum effect being centered at noon or somewhat earlier. At low

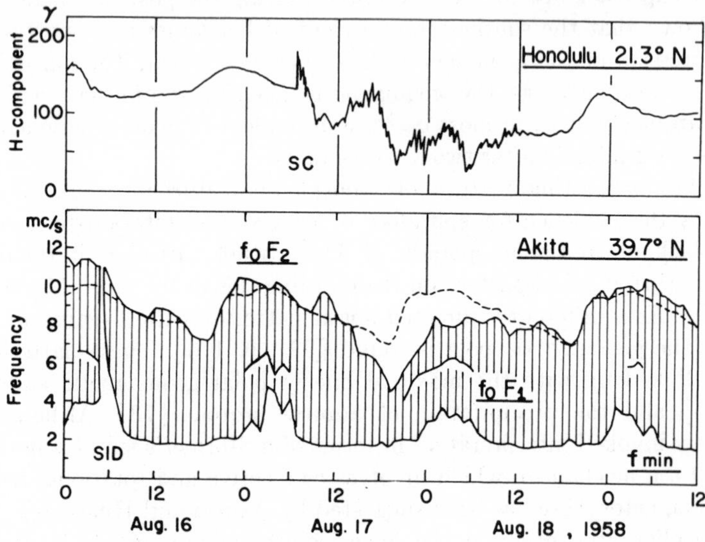

FIG. 5. Ionospheric variation associated with the geomagnetic storm of 17 August 1958. The f-plot data at Akita, Japan ($foF2, foF1, f_{min}$, and a dotted curve showing the monthly median variation of $foF2$).

latitudes, including the equator, the depression is rare, and $foF2$ is increased at all seasons. At middle latitudes there may be a depression or an increase of $foF2$ depending upon the time of day and season. The change in $h'F2$ is upward in most cases. However this height parameter contains considerable group retardation effects due to the lower ionospheric regions, and hence it is unreliable for deducing height changes during storms. A typical example of such an ionospheric storm is illustrated in Figure 5, the f-plot data at Akita, Japan, during the period August 16–18, 1958, which has been discussed earlier. It clearly shows that a large depression of $foF2$ occurs during the main phase of the geomagnetic storm. The storm variation is apparently included in the local-time control, being depressed a great deal in the morning and less appreciably in the afternoon. This is very common in middle latitudes, but the variations are rather different at other latitudes, as has been stated earlier.

In order to obtain a more sophisticated view of ionospheric storms, Martyn and Japanese workers, following a similar procedure to that used by geomagneticians, obtained the storm-time variation *Dst* and the disturbance diurnal variation *Ds*, both for *foF*2 and *h'F*2. The storm-time variation is the average over all longitudes, and hence of the local time around each circle of latitude, and is reckoned with respect to storm time, i.e., from the SC of a geomagnetic storm. The disturbance diurnal variation, on the other hand, is the diurnally varying part or the disturbance local-time inequality. Figure 6 gives the *Dst*(*F*2)-variation expressed by the percentage deviation of the peak electron density, as derived by

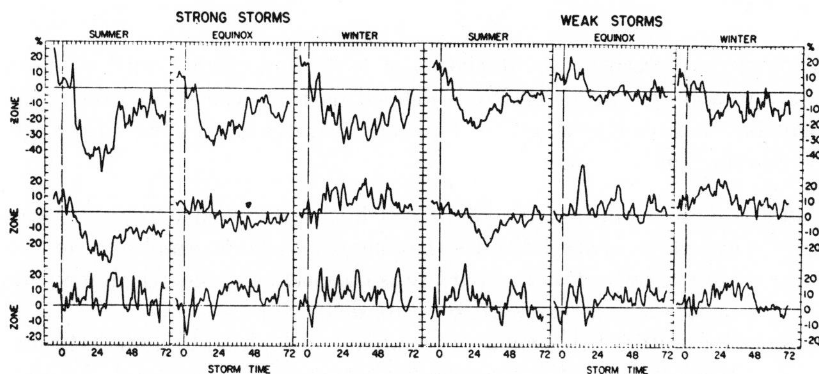

FIG. 6. Average *Dst*(*NmF*)-variations for strong and weak storms. Reading from the top: middle latitudes, $\Phi = 50$–$55°$; low latitudes, $\Phi = 25$–$30°$; and equatorial latitudes, $\Phi < 10°$ for summer, equinoxes, and winter seasons (after Matsushita [65]).

Matsushita [65] from the data from many ionospheric storms, collected during the period 1946–1955 at a number of stations over the world. The storms are classified as strong and weak, depending on their geomagnetic activity. The *Dst*-variation for each season is shown for three representative zones: middle latitudes, $\Phi = 50$–$55°$; low latitudes, $\Phi = 25$–$30°$; and equatorial latitudes, $\Phi < 10°$. The figure shows that an initial short increase in the electron density is followed by a prolonged large depression at middle latitudes particularly during summer, whereas an increase is evident at equatorial latitudes.

The composite patterns of the *Dst*-, *Ds*-, and *D*- variations are shown in Figures 7 and 8, which are drawn on a map viewed from above the geomagnetic North Pole (local time is used instead of longitude). Results are obtained by averaging nine typical storms during the period 1950–1951, using data from 40 ionospheric stations in the Northern Hemisphere [78].

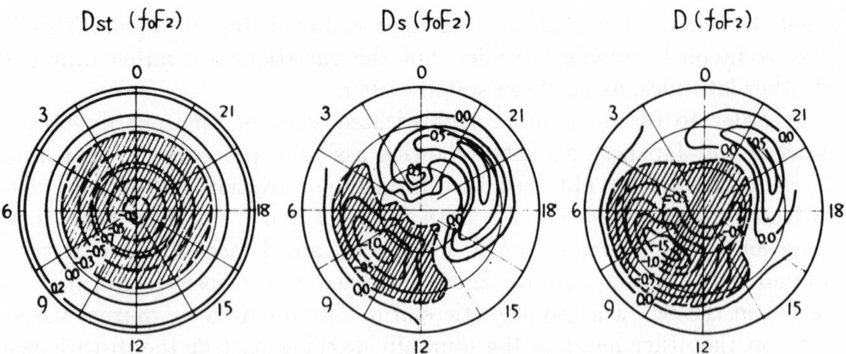

FIG. 7. Average *Dst*(*foF*2), *Ds*(*foF*2), and *D*(*foF*2) variations in the Northern Hemisphere during the main phase ($K_p \geq 5_o$) of geomagnetic storms. Contour lines are deviations of *foF*2 from normal values in Mc/sec; depression (negative) areas indicated by hatching.

They are expressed by the deviation of *foF*2 from normal quiet values in Mc/sec, and the storm period is defined as that when the geomagnetic planetary indices *Kp* exceed 5*o*. The main features of these variations may be described as follows:

Dst: a depression of *foF*2 (indicated by the hatched regions) prevails except in lower latitudes, having a maximum amplitude in subauroral latitudes. The pattern is essentially symmetrical about the earth's axis as expected from its definition.

Ds: the diurnal behavior is predominant in high and middle latitudes. It decreases in the forenoon hemisphere and increases in the afternoon hemisphere. The phase seems to change somewhat with respect to latitude, being a minimum at about 9–12h in the auroral zone and at about 6–9h in middle latitudes.

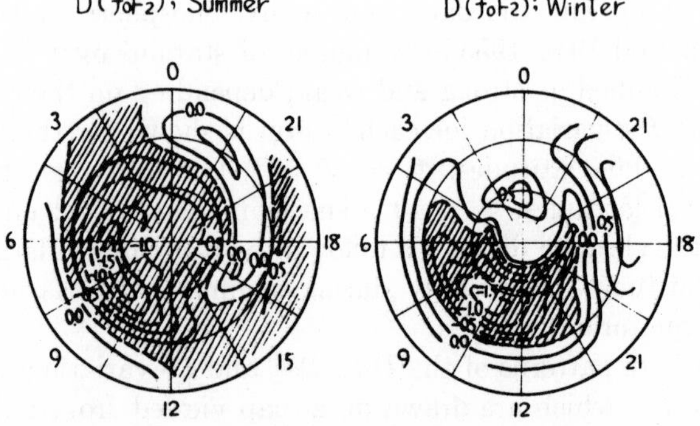

FIG. 8. Seasonal variations of *D*(*foF*2) for the northern summer and winter. Contour lines are deviations of *foF*2 from normal values in Mc/sec; depression areas indicated by hatching.

D: the pattern is the combined disturbance $D = Dst + Ds$, and represents the actual distortion of the $F2$-region during geomagnetic storms. A seasonal change in the D-variation is apparent; the depression is confined to a smaller area during the winter season, so that the increase is accentuated, whereas during the summer the depression covers almost an entire hemisphere except at low latitudes.

The development of ionospheric storms is illustrated in Figure 9, with average patterns of $D(F2)$ at successive three hourly intervals measured

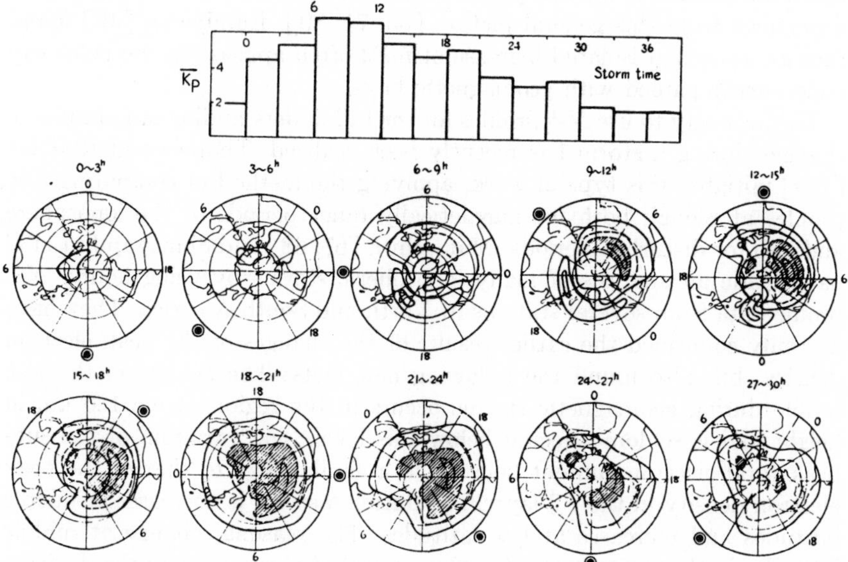

FIG. 9. Average pattern of the development of an ionospheric storm. $D(foF2)$ patterns for the successive stages of a geomagnetic storm, showing the growth and decay of the negative (dotted lines) and positive (continuous lines) regions. The position of the sun is indicated by ⊙.

from geomagnetic storm time. The figure is shown as an idealized situation, the geomagnetic storm commencing at 0000 UT. The upper diagram represents the change in the magnetic activity Kp with respect to storm time, averaged for all the storms used. The patterns are shown by contour lines of the percentage deviation of $foF2$ from its normal value in 10 per cent steps. In the early phase of a geomagnetic storm, a somewhat increased region of $foF2$ appears in high latitudes. This is then followed by a large depression situated in the forenoon side and an increase in the afternoon side. This pronounced Ds-variation during the main phase of a geomagnetic storm is very stable, and the disturbance pattern moves progressively from East to West, keeping a position fixed relative to the sun. In the last phase, however, the entire high-latitude region becomes depressed with a more diffused disturbance effect. The phase of the *Ds* is also retarded gradually, i.e., the disturbance pattern does not move around the earth with the sun but remains in particular localities. In other words, during the active phase of a storm, disturbances may be considered to show a real *Ds*-variation, while later disturbances appear to be a sort of after effect.

The general nature of ionospheric storms is thus characterized mainly by the combination of the *Dst*- and *Ds*-variations mentioned above. However, it should be emphasized that these represent the average behavior based on conditions for many storms, and sometimes there are significant departures from this general picture [55, 71, 80]. Kamiyama [49] found that an abnormal isolated increase of *foF*2 often appears in the polar cap region accompanied with geomagnetic bays.

The necessity to use *N-h* profiles for the full understanding of ionospheric changes during a storm has recently been realized. Thomas and Robbins [115] initiated this type of work, applying the method of computing *N-h* profiles at Slough both for magnetically quiet periods of the ionosphere and also for disturbed periods. Matsushita [67, 68] and Somayajulu [113] have made an analysis of many ionospheric storms by using hourly *N-h* profile data from several stations in North and South America. They have not only confirmed the earlier results of the changes of the peak electron density, but also found the following new facts: The change in the *N-h* profile during geomagnetic storms occurs in the region above 180 km in height and is seldom affected below this level. The variation of the subpeak total electron content behaves in a similar way to that of the peak electron density in the *F*2-layer, i.e., during a storm it decreases at middle latitudes and increases at low latitudes. The seasonal change at middle latitudes is also remarkable. In summer and at the equinoxes the decrease of electron density occurs at all levels higher than about 180 km, while in the winter season an increase is predominantly above the 300 km level having a slight decrease below it. The peak height of the *F*-layer and the semithickness of the layer generally increase during a storm both in summer and winter, though an occasional decrease may appear in winter. A somewhat schematic picture of these changes of *N-h* profile during an increase (positive) and decrease (negative) phase during storms is illustrated in Figure 10, which is mainly based on the results given by Matsushita [67, 68].

It is interesting to note that recent satellite information on the total electron content up to 1000 km appears to show a similar variation to that of the subpeak electron content during a storm [28, 122]. Furthermore evidence is presented by Carpenter [18] from his whistler analysis that the depressions in whistler delays during geomagnetic storms may be interpreted as a substantial reduction in electron density in the magnetosphere. If these facts are confirmed, it means that ionospheric storm changes at middle and high latitudes represent real removal of ionization at all levels above 200 km to greater heights beyond the ionosphere. For the storm effect at lower latitudes evidence is reported by Bowles [13] from his experiment of incoherent radio scatter soundings at Lima, Peru, that the electron density at all levels above 400 km shows an increase during a geomagnetic storm.

It is generally believed that no appreciable simultaneous effect in the $F2$-layer is associated with most solar flares, despite their significant ionization effect in the lower ionosphere. However, on a few occasions marked increases in electron density of the $F2$-layer have been reported in the literature. Dieminger [25] reported that a large solar flare on November 19, 1949, had significant effect on the F-region over Lindau. A similar effect was also observed at Okinawa on February 23, 1956 [110]. Two additional cases have been observed recently accompanying the large solar flares that occurred on November 12 and 15, 1960 [53]. As shown in Figure 11, large increases in the peak electron density are evident, which undoubtedly exceed statistical fluctuations. One of the most significant features of these particular solar flares distinguishing them from others was that these flares were known to be associated with intense solar cosmic-ray increases at sea level. It has been shown that, for the observable increase of the electron density, the height of the $F2$-layer at the time of the flare is also an important controlling factor, which must be lower than a certain critical height $h_{max} \sim 300$ km. The increase of subpeak electron content and its simultaneity with flare wave radiations indicates that these

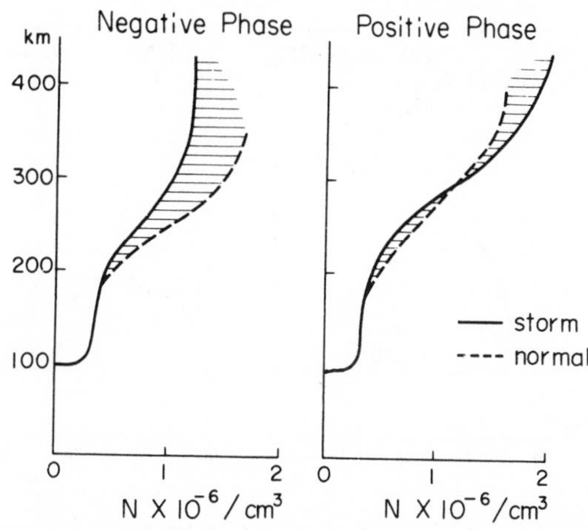

FIG. 10. Idealized typical N-h profiles for two types of disturbed condition; negative and positive variations of the peak electron density. Dotted curve represents the profile for the normal condition.

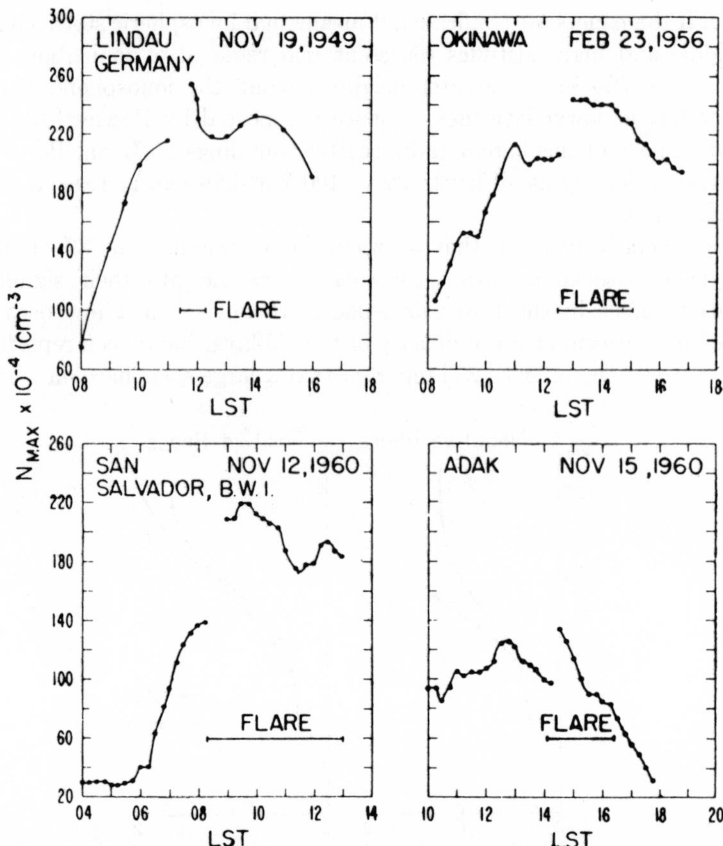

Fig. 11. Variations in the *F*2-peak electron density during four solar flares that were associated with sea-level increases in cosmic-ray intensity (after Knecht and McDuffie [53]).

cosmic-ray flares are in some way unusual in their photon radiation as well as in their high-energy particle emission.

Another type of outstanding ionospheric disturbance is the result of nuclear explosions in the high atmosphere, which has been demonstrated by several experiments in the past [87]. Intense ionizing radiations and energetic particles are released at nuclear detonations and spread over a considerable distance and ionize the air in the ionosphere. Ionospheric disturbances also result from generated shock waves due to explosive blasts. Since these effects arise from an artificial source under controlled conditions, the origin of the disturbances and the environmental conditions are known. These phenomena are, therefore, of value in providing information on the nature of disturbances in the upper atmosphere. The most spectacular *F*-region disturbance produced by nuclear explosions is the

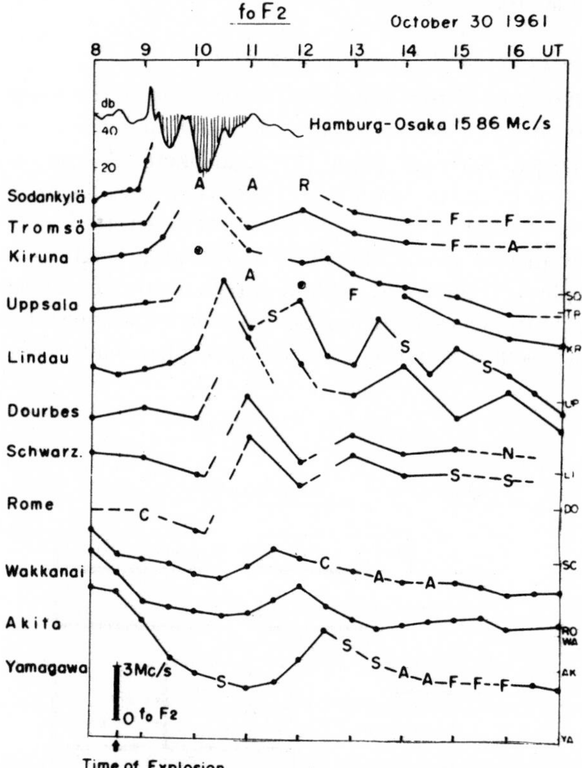

FIG. 12. Time variations of *foF*2 and the field strength of DGP-862 (15.86 Mc/sec) during the period of a nuclear explosion, 30 October 1961. A large increase and subsequent fluctuations of *foF*2 spread over an area of several thousands of kilometers at average speeds of 250–1000 m/sec.

effect of traveling pressure waves. Both the tests in the Pacific and at Novaya Zemlya produced a remarkable surge of disturbances which spread out some thousands of kilometers over the world [86, 91]. The effects of the event on October 30, 1961, on the variations of *foF*2 at several key stations in Europe and in Asia are reproduced in Figure 12. It is evident that an anomalously large increase with subsequent fluctuations of the electron density was delayed progressively from near to distant stations with an average speed of 400 m/sec. More specifically, there are two different types of disturbance waves; a sudden increase with subsequent oscillatory fluctuations traveling with a speed of 1000 m/sec, while violent turbulences follow, spreading out with a slower speed of about 250 m/sec. These traveling disturbances are explained as the propagation of pressure waves (acoustic-gravity waves) in the high atmosphere excited by intense blast, the main energy of the waves being ducted in the lower ionosphere.

4. Theoretical Interpretations

Abnormal Ionization in the Lower Ionosphere

It is well recognized that enhanced ionizations in the lower ionosphere are produced either by bursts of solar radiation or by the precipitation of energetic charged particles upon the ionosphere. A general scheme of major disturbances in the lower ionospheric region is illustrated in Figure 13. An excess of solar X-rays of a few Å range emitted at the time of a solar flare produces a strong ionization at *D*-region heights over the entire sunlit hemisphere. This could explain satisfactorily the effects of sudden ionospheric disturbances including several accompanying phenomena. An enhanced corpuscular radiation upon the ionosphere causes polar blackouts

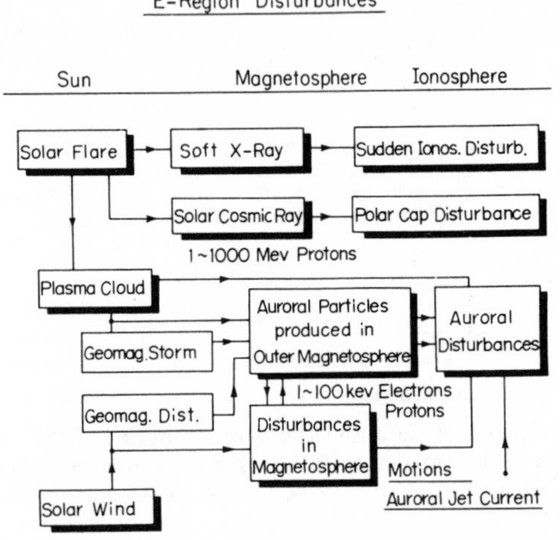

FIG. 13. The source and mechanism producing major *E*-region disturbances.

and associated geophysical disturbances. There are two types of energetic particles. Solar cosmic-ray particles, emitted occasionally from an intense solar flare, produce polar cap blackouts. On the other hand, auroral particles, which are presumably energetic electrons and protons, are the source of auroral blackouts and many other related disturbances in the polar regions.

The accumulated evidence of recent years indicates that solar cosmic rays ejected from flares consist of a wide spectrum, ranging from a few Mev up to relativistic energies. The mechanism producing such high-energy protons is still unknown. However, the observed close connection of solar cosmic-ray bursts with Type IV radio outbursts of synchrotron radiation indicates the existence of some effective acceleration processes taking place near the flare region [93, 114]. At any rate, these energetic solar protons impinge upon the polar atmosphere thereby producing ionization. Theoretical computations of the electron density profile and the specific radio absorption produced by such ionization have been made on the basis of recent data of the solar proton spectrum and of an appropriate atmospheric model [8, 14, 97]. The result shows a fair agreement with the observed absorption, including marked differences of absorption between day and night conditions which may be explained in terms of the formation of negative ions during the night and subsequent photodetachment after sunrise.

The confined precipitation of solar protons inside the polar cap region is to be expected because of the effect of the geomagnetic field. Applying an improved version of Störmer's theory, Obayashi [81, 84] and Rothwell [102] showed independently that the observed outermost boundary of polar cap blackouts may be explained by assuming a slight deformation of the geomagnetic dipole field which might be caused by the prevailing conditions of the outer geomagnetic field. Their theory also predicts successfully the equatorward expansion of particle precipitation during geomagnetic storms, as an effect of a decrease in the magnetic cutoff energy for incoming particles due to the depression of the geomagnetic field. Further extensive studies on this problem have been made by Winckler and his colleagues [120].

At the time of SC's of geomagnetic storms, polar cap absorption sometimes decreases and the absorbing region recedes towards higher latitudes [42, 84]. This is explained as a temporal increase of the cutoff energy, viz., the displacement of the allowed latitude for precipitating particles during the initial phase of the storm. On the contrary, it is also known that on many occasions SC's are accompanied by a sudden increase of absorption of short duration. Brown *et al.* [15] showed evidence that this effect is due to bremsstrahlung from energetic electrons dumped along the auroral zone.

It is known that auroral absorption is closely related to local geomagnetic activity [16]. Auroral absorption is generally associated with visible auroral displays; however, the detailed correlation between them on a short time scale is often poor and may differ considerably depending on the type of auroras. On the other hand, auroral X-ray events observed by high-altitude balloons coincide with auroral absorption. Thus some of the auroral particles may be identified as high-energy electrons of 20–100 kev. However, McIlwain [70] showed from his rocket experiments that the energy of precipitating particles responsible for visible auroras is different, being less than 10 kev. With regard to the origin of auroral particles, it was earlier thought that they might be dumped electrons from the outer radiation belt which would be a huge reservoir of trapped particles. This view has been criticized by O'Brien [89], who advocates strongly that auroral electrons are not the result of an occasional leak from the reservoir of trapped particles but are fresh particles created by some rapid acceleration process taking place near the magnetospheric boundary. Furthermore the direct entry of solar particles as the origin of auroral particles is still another possibility. No attempt will be made, however, to assess these controversial ideas, which must await further study.

The theory has been advanced by Axford and Hines [6], that polar ionospheric disturbances, including geomagnetic perturbations and auroras, are closely connected with the earth's magnetospheric motions. As has been described earlier, polar blackouts show a spirallike pattern on the morningside, while polar *Es* and Hα auroral emissions are strong along a loop which descends from high to low latitudes on the premidnight side. On the other hand, auroral motions are westward before midnight and eastward after midnight in the auroral zone, and these motions are reversed in the polar cap [23]. Thus, the pattern of observed loops of circulation is very similar, but in approximately the opposite direction, to the *Ds*-currents flowing in the polar ionosphere. These facts may be explained consistently by a convective system in the magnetosphere, which is set up by a viscous-like interaction between the magnetosphere and solar plasma streams. The postulated convective motions are such as to carry the outer ionization of the magnetosphere toward the region of the tail, and to establish a return path for the flow down to the interior of the magnetosphere. Turbulence at the outer boundary is also carried into and through the interior, the ionization being energized during the inward convection. These motions and the turbulent regions are then communicated downward along geomagnetic field lines, which would be observable at ionospheric heights as drifting disturbances, *Ds*-currents, and precipitating energetic particles indicated by radio blackouts or sporadic *E*.

Theories of Ionospheric Storms in the F-Region

The mechanism of disturbances in the *F*-region is very controversial and no satisfactory theory that explains the major features of storms has appeared yet. One of the reasons for this is the complexity of the *F*-region formation itself even during quiet conditions. The *F*2-layer shows neither a simple solar control such as is the case in the *E*- and F_1-regions nor an immediate response to the source of disturbances except for some exceptional phenomena. It is now hoped, however, that the vast amount of observational data obtained during the last few years and, particularly, the recent intensive efforts made to acquire detailed *N-h* profiles during storms will provide the opportunity to formulate a sound theory of ionospheric storms, which is consistent also with our recent knowledge of other related geophysical phenomena.

Two main theories of ionospheric storms have been proposed in the past; one is based on the electrodynamic drift motions of electrons, and the other attributes the changes to electron loss rate by an enhanced thermal effect in the F-region. In 1953, Martyn suggested that vertical drift motions of electrons would play an important, if not a dominant, part in the changes that occur in the F-region during geomagnetic storms. This vertical drift would result from the interaction of the geomagnetic field and the electrostatic field associated with currents flowing in the ionosphere during a storm. This theory was later developed by Maeda [61], Hirono [39], and Sato [106]. The electric field in the dynamo region is estimated from the observed geomagnetic Ds-variations, which in turn interacts with the geomagnetic field and drives the drift motions of the electrons in the F-region. The continuity equation of electrons is then solved using the estimated drift velocities and an assumed atmospheric model of the electron production and loss rates. The result obtained by Sato and Maeda [62] gives a reasonable agreement between the calculated and observed Ds-variations in middle and low latitudes, though the effect of diffusion has been neglected in their computation. In support of this drift theory, a recent analysis made by Rishbeth [99] indicates that, at middle-latitude stations, geomagnetic storms which produce opposite changes of F-region electron density variation also have different phases in the local magnetic Ds-variation. It is also well known that such electromagnetic drift motions due to dynamo currents are important in explaining the distortion of the D-region of the ionosphere [12].

Although the drift theory has many attractive features, nevertheless, it has some difficulties in applying the actual ionospheric parameters to compute the electron density variations. In fact, the height distribution of the electron loss rate assumed by Sato and Maeda is rather different from that which is accepted now from observations. Using the known decreasing electron loss rate with height, Yonezawa [123], Rishbeth and Barron [98] showed that the upward drift yields an increase of the peak electron density as well as its height and, conversely, the downward drift yields a decrease of density and of its height. This result suggests that the typical effect of storms, showing a decrease of the peak electron density accompanied by an increase in its height, cannot be explained by the drift theory alone.

In recent years, it has become evident that the temperature in the F-region increases considerably during geomagnetic storms. From observations of satellite drag, Jacchia [44] and Groves [31] infer that there is a general heating of the atmosphere from 200 to 700 km during a geomagnetic storm. An increase in the F-region temperature would result in substantial changes of electron equilibrium in terms of photochemical processes as well as gas dynamical motions. Yonezawa [126] has studied changes in the height and the peak electron density in the $F2$-region during a severe storm in terms of changes in scale height and in the attachment coefficient, both of which are ascribed to changes of temperature. In his theory, the rate of chemical reactions in the charge exchange process is shown to be sensitive to temperature change. Thus, the rate of electron loss is enhanced as the temperature increases and this results in the reduction of the peak electron density, though Bates has commented on the insensitivity to temperature changes that is to be expected for the effective attachment coefficient. From his study of N-h profiles during an intense ionospheric storm, Matsuura [69] showed that the main processes which control electron density variations during storms are predominantly those of loss and ambipolar diffusion. He calculated the temperature dependence of these terms, solving numerically the continuity equation, and concluded that the electron loss and diffusion rates change appreciably, only a fractional change of temperature being necessary to account for the observed electron density variations.

There are some other theories which account for gas dynamical motions in the F-region. Nagata [74] proposed that the thermal expansion of the atmosphere caused by the heating due to particle bombardments would produce a depression of the electron density in the auroral zone. On the other hand, Seaton [108] suggested that the enhanced mixing in the F-region during disturbances would increase the concentration of neutral molecules O_2 provided by transportation from the lower ionosphere, thus causing a rise of electron attachmentlike charge exchange processes. A similar idea to an increased loss rate was proposed by Kamiyama [47], in which he assumed the transport of ions by vertical drifts.

There are thus good reasons to believe that the changes produced by geomagnetic storms in the F-region are probably due to a combination of photochemical changes, heating of the atmosphere, and electromagnetic movements. It is worthwhile to review here the present state of knowledge of these mechanisms.

(*i*) *Continuity Equation.* The changes of the electron density in the ionospheric region are determined by the continuity equation,

$$\frac{\partial N}{\partial t} + \operatorname{div}\,(N \cdot \mathbf{V}) = Q - L$$

where N is the electron density, Q and L the rates of electron production and electron loss per unit volume, respectively, and $\mathbf{V}$ the effective drift velocity of the electron gas which may include the effects of ambipolar diffusion and electromagnetic movements. We may discuss possible processes taking place during storms and evaluate their relative importance in the continuity equation under the prevailing conditions.

(*ii*) *Ionization* (Q) *and Loss* (L). Solar radiation produces an ionization maximum at about 160 km corresponding to the F_1-peak, which ionizes N_2 and O. The N_2^+-ions rapidly recombine with electrons by a dissociative recombination process. The O^+-ions lead to a loss of electrons by a combination of ion-atom interchange and dissociative recombination processes

TABLE 1

ELECTRON LOSS PROCESSES

	Reaction	Rate
(a)	$N_2^+ + e \rightarrow N' + N''$	$\alpha = 2 \times 10^{-6}$ cm³/sec
(b)	$O^+ + O_2 \rightarrow O_2^+ + O$	$\beta = 2 \times 10^{-11}$
	$O_2^+ + e \rightarrow O' + O''$	$\alpha = 2 \times 10^{-8}$
(c)	$O^+ + N_2 \rightarrow NO^+ + N$	$\beta = 1 \times 10^{-12}$
	$NO^+ + e \rightarrow N' + O'$	$\alpha = 5 \times 10^{-9}$
(d)	$O^+ + e \rightarrow O + h\nu$	$\alpha = 1.5 \times 10^{-12}$

and also by a radiative recombination process. These are shown in Table 1 with approximate values of the reaction rates [124].

The rate of electron loss L by these processes may approximately be represented by

$$L = \sum_i \frac{\alpha_i \beta_i N n_i}{\alpha_i N + \beta_i n_i} N$$

where N and n_i are the electron density and density of the ith particle, respectively. The most effective process may be (*b*), since otherwise the process (*a*) is too rapid to contribute significantly to the observable electrons. However, other processes may well be important under some conditions, and it is not yet known how these vary with latitude. In any case the loss rate of electrons decreases with height, and its magnitude is determined by the concentrations of O_2 and possibly of N_2, leading to an attachmentlike loss rate proportional to N.

A change of temperature alters all these production and loss processes, because the concentration of atmospheric constituents with height is very sensitive to the temperature. As has already been mentioned, Yonezawa even thinks that the change of charge exchange rate itself is due to an increase of temperature.

(*iii*) *Effect of Electron Drifts.* Under the condition that the assumption of horizontal uniformity is approximately fulfilled, only the vertical velocity of the ionized gas is important for the variation of electron density. Following Matsuura [69] the vertical velocity of the ionized gas in the F-region will be caused by three mechanisms: For ambipolar diffusion, the velocity is given by

$$V_1 = -D_a \sin^2 I \left(\frac{1}{N} \frac{\partial N}{\partial z} + \frac{1}{T} \frac{\partial T}{\partial z} + \frac{1}{2H} \right)$$

where Da, the ambipolar diffusion coefficient, $8.5 \times 10^{17} T^{1/2}/n$, I is the geomagnetic dip angle, and T and H are the temperature and scale height, respectively. For the drag due to neutral atmospheric gas motion, the velocity is given by

$$V_2 = -\frac{\mathbf{u} \cdot \mathbf{B}}{B} \sin I$$

where $\mathbf{u}$ is the neutral gas velocity, and B the total geomagnetic field. These two velocities V_1 and V_2 have their directions predominantly parallel to the geomagnetic field lines. The drift motion due to the electric field in the geomagnetic field has its direction perpendicular to them. The vertical drift velocity is given by

$$V_3 = \frac{E}{B} \cos I$$

where E is the east component of the electric field.

All of these velocities may have typical values of the order of 10–50 m/sec. However the diffusion coefficient is inversely proportional to the total number density of the atmosphere and its effect is more appreciable at higher levels, whereas the drift motion due to the electric field will be independent of height above at least 150 km, where the electric field is constant with respect to height. The difference in the preferential direction of motions with respect to the geomagnetic field may be important in distinugishing between these three mechanisms, but no clear observational evidence has been reported as yet.

(*iv*) *Relative Importance of* Q, L, *and* D. The relative importance of the ionization Q, the loss L, and the effect of diffusion $D = V_1 \partial N/\partial z$ has been calculated by Matsuura [69] for an appropriate atmospheric model in which the temperature increases with height as

$$T = T_0 + \Gamma(z - z_0)$$

where $\Gamma = 2°\text{K/km}$ and $z_0 = 150$ km. The temperature dependence of these three terms is reproduced in Figure 14 for various values of T_0, where the effect of a temperature increase above the reference value ($T_0 = 700°\text{K}$) is indicated by a shaded area. This value of the reference temperature has been chosen as the best fit for the quiet ionosphere. The effect of temperature variation on L and D is remarkable — the temperature rise resulting in an increase of L and also a decrease of D. The former is due to an increase of the molecular density (O_2 or N_2) and the latter mainly to an increase of the total atmospheric density which appears in the ambipolar diffusion coefficient. It is to be noted that the effect is dominated by diffusion at heights above 250 km, by electron loss due to photochemical reactions at 200–300 km, and by electron production below 180 km, though the last has very little effect on the temperature change.

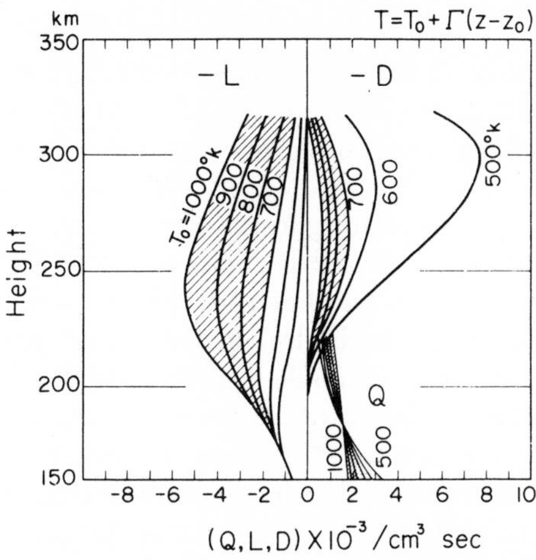

FIG. 14. Temperature dependence of electron production-rate Q, loss-rate L, and diffusion-rate D (after Matsuura [69]).

(*v*) *Comparison with Observed Dst* (*F*2) *Variation.* From the above considerations, it can be seen that a temperature rise will ultimately result in a decrease of the electron density in the whole of the F-region above 200 km, provided that the effects of V_2 and V_3 are neglected. This result is certainly consistent with the average features of the ionospheric *Dst*-variation in middle latitudes. Since the order of magnitude of $\partial N/\partial t$ is about 500 cm^{-3} sec^{-1} or less at the 250-km level, the required temperature change of T_0 may be estimated to be only 100 or 200°K, the corresponding change of atmospheric densities being a factor of 2 or 3. Such density variations were observed by satellite drag experiments. In Yonezawa's theory of the change of the chemical reaction rate, the required temperature change is several hundred degrees, and there may be need of a more detailed investigation including both effects.

The *Dst*-variation in lower latitudes, which shows an increase in the electron density during storms, remains unexplained. In fact the situation in low latitudes is very different; the diffusion or drift of electrons along geomagnetic field lines would cause quasi-horizontal motions, which would distort the electron density distribution appreciably. Nevertheless, a promising idea has been put forward by Yonezawa [125] for an explanation of the storm effect in terms of temperature change. He presumes a temperature increase also, but the loss process involved may be totally different from the one described above. The height of stratification of the F2-peak near the equator is extremely high, being around 400 to 500 km. At these greater heights there are very few molecular particles, and hence, the only electron loss mechanism is the radiative recombination process (*d*). The recombination coefficient is temperature-sensitive, and is inversely proportional to it, i.e., $\alpha \propto T^{-n}$, where $n = \frac{1}{2} \sim \frac{3}{4}$. Therefore, an increase in temperature results in an increase of the electron density at the $F2$-peak, though at low heights the electron density may decrease as in middle latitudes. This explanation accords well with the observed N-h profile for the positive phase of ionospheric storms as has been shown in Figure 10.

(*vi*) *Heat Source.* The heating of the F-region may come from several sources: the impinging of auroral particles or energetic trapped particles [45]; heat conduction from the hot solar plasma surrounding the earth [20]; the effect of heating by hydromagnetic waves passing through the ionosphere [2, 24, 69]; and by Joule heat dissipation of *Ds*-currents [21]. Of these the most appropriate heat source contributing to such a temperature rise during a geomagnetic storm may be that due to hydromagnetic waves. Matsuura showed that the heating effect is appreciable for waves in the frequency range 1 to 0.01 cps, and may be sufficient to attain the required temperature. It is to be noted that the heat source from hydromagnetic waves is first impressed on ions and the relaxation time between ions and neutral particles is about 100 $\sim$ 1000 seconds in the ionosphere. Therefore the effect of heating ions may precede somewhat that of an increase of the atmospheric scale height. Another advantage of hydromagnetic wave heating is that its effect may be expected even at the equator, which is difficult to achieve by any other mechanism. However, as has been suggested by Cole, in high latitudes Joule heating by strong *Ds*-currents may be important as well as the effect of energetic particle precipitation.

(*vii*) *Comparison with Observed Ds* ($F2$)*-Variation.* It seems that thermal effects in the ionosphere during storms may be the dominant cause of ionospheric storms at least in the middle-latitude zones. The thermal heating theory would, therefore, be appropriate for the ionospheric *Dst*-part, provided that such heat sources do really exist. However, for the ionospheric *Ds*-part, there is no reliable evidence suggesting a similar variation of the source or condition of the ionosphere with respect to local time as well as latitude. In this regard, the electrodynamical drift theory cannot be ruled out, because of the over-all similarity between ionospheric and geomagnetic *Ds*-variations. It has been indicated by Garriott and Thomas [29] that even during the quiet nighttime an effect of upward drifts must be assumed of sufficient strength to nearly balance downward diffusion. Undoubtedly in any future study the effect of horizontal drifts must be taken into account which may reach a velocity of a few hundred m/sec during disturbed periods [60]. In this respect, it is strongly recommended that the electromagnetic drift theory must be reexamined in the light of the new atmospheric model of the F-layer formation, including other terms such as the effect of diffusion.

(*viii*) *Interaction with the Exosphere.* An interesting suggestion has been made by Rothwell [103] that ionospheric F-layers at magnetic conjugate points in opposite hemispheres may be coupled by diffusion of ions along geomagnetic lines of force, if many hydrogen ions in the exosphere originate in the F-layer from the charge exchange reaction

$$H + O^+ \rightarrow H^+ + O$$

Her argument is that, since ion–ion diffusion times are strongly temperature-dependent, the diffusion rate from the summer to the winter hemisphere may be speeded up during geomagnetic storms. Thus, ions from the summer hemisphere diffuse faster to the winter hemisphere during storms than during quiet periods. This would be more efficient by day than by night, and the daytime storm electron density should be relatively lower in summer and higher in winter, until equilibrium is reestablished. Since the effectiveness of this process is dependent on the rate of charge exchange

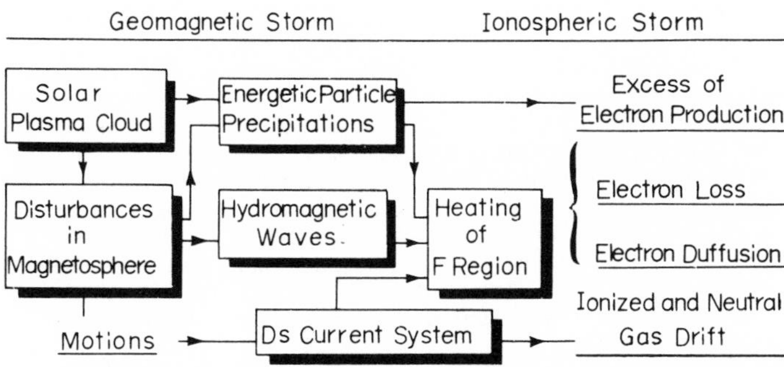

Fig. 15. The possible source and mechanism producing ionospheric storms in the F-region.

that could be expected in the upper F-layer, it is necessary to prove quantitatively that this is sufficiently high to permit the satisfactory working of the process to explain the many observed features.

(*ix*) *Unexplained Problems.* There are some other puzzling phenomena whose cause remains unknown. A temporary abnormal increase of electron density in the polar cap F-region is one of them. Another type of increase is sometimes noted at low-latitude stations during the recovery phase of geomagnetic storms, which is generally formed at lower altitudes near the height of the F_1-peak. A somewhat similar result was obtained statistically by King [52], who showed that the increases of electron density seem to be correlated with low-lying prestorm F-layers and vice versa. These may be difficult to explain by any known mechanisms, but it may be suggested that some new ionizing process or strong drift motions could account for the behavior. To summarize the theory of ionospheric F-region storms, a general picture of storms and their possible mechanisms is illustrated in Figure 15, though this is still tentative and may need further confirmation.

Acknowledgments

The major part of this report has been written at the Institute of Earth Sciences, University of British Columbia, Vancouver, Canada. I wish to express my gratitude to Professor J. A. Jacobs for his hospitality there. I am also much indebted to Dr. N. Matsuura and Dr. Y. Hakura for their valuable discussions during the preparatory period of this work.

References

1. V. Agy, Spiral patterns in geophysics, *J. Atmos. Terr. Phys.*, **19,** 136–140 (1960).
2. S. I. Akasofu, On the ionospheric heating by hydromagnetic waves connected with geomagnetic micropulsations, *J. Atmos. Terr. Phys.*, **18,** 160–173 (1960).
3. K. A. Anderson, R. Arnoldy, R. Hoffman, L. Peterson, and J. R. Winckler, Observation of low energy solar cosmic rays from the flare of 22 August 1958, *J. Geophys. Res.*, **64,** 1133-1147 (1959).
4. K. A. Anderson, Relation of balloon X rays to visible aurorae in the auroral zone, *J. Phys. Soc. Japan,* **17,** Suppl. A-1, 237–241 (1962).
5. E. V. Appleton and W. R. Piggott, The morphology of storms in the *F*2 layer of the ionosphere, *J. Atmos. Terr. Phys.*, **2,** 236–252 (1952).
6. W. I. Axford and C. O. Hines, An unifying theory of high latitude geophysical phenomena and geomagnetic storms, *Can. J. Phys.*, **39,** 1433–1464 (1961).
7. D. K. Bailey, Disturbances in the lower ionosphere observed at VHF following the solar flare of 23 February 1956 with particular reference to auroral-zone absorption, *J. Geophys. Res.*, **62,** 431–463 (1957).
8. D. K. Bailey, Abnormal ionization in the lower ionosphere associated with cosmic-ray flux enhancements, *Proc. Inst. Radio Eng.*, **47,** 255–266 (1959).
9. J. S. Belrose, Some investigation of the lowest ionosphere (Ph.D. Thesis, Cambridge Univ., 1956).
10. J. S. Belrose and D. B. Ross, Observations of unusual low-frequency propagation made during polar cap disturbance events, *J. Phys. Soc. Japan*, Suppl. A–1, 126–130 (1962).
11. N. P. Benkova and L. A. Yudovich, Daily variation of blackout appearances, *J. Phys. Soc. Japan*, **17,** Suppl. A-1, 143–146 (1962).
12. W. J. G. Beynon, Disturbance in the ionospheric region, *J. Phys. Soc. Japan,* **17,** Suppl. A-1, 320–324 (1962).
13. K. L. Bowles, Profiles of electron density over the magnetic equator obtained using the incoherent scatter technique, *US-NBS Rept. 7633* (1962).
14. R. R. Brown and R. S. Weir, Ionospheric effects of solar protons, *Arkiv för Geophys.*, **3,** 523–529 (1961).
15. R. R. Brown, T. R. Hartz, B. Landmark, H. Leinbach, and J. Ortner, Large scale bombardment of the atmosphere at the SC of a geomagnetic storm, *J. Geophys. Res.*, **66,** 1035–1041 (1961).
16. W. H. Campbell and H. Leinbach, Ionospheric absorption at times of auroral and magnetic pulsations, *J. Geophys. Res.*, **66,** 25–34 (1961).
17. H. Carmichael, High energy solar particle events, *Space Sci. Rev.*, **1,** 28–61 (1962).
18. D. L. Carpenter, New experimental evidence of the effect of magnetic storms on the magnetosphere, *J. Geophys. Res.*, **67,** 135–146 (1962).
19. J. H. Chapman, The solar radio blackout of the ionosphere of 7 July 1958, *Can. J. Phys.*, **38,** 1195–1212 (1960).
20. S. Chapman, Notes on the solar corona and the terrestrial ionosphere, *Smithsonian Contribution Astrophys.*, **2,** No. 1 (1957).

21. K. D. Cole, Variation of upper atmosphere densities with solar activity, *Proc. Phys. Soc., Japan*, **17,** Suppl. A-1, 183–187 (1962).
22. C. Collins, D. H. Jelly, and A. G. Matthews, High frequency radio wave blackout at medium and high latitudes during a solar cycle, *Can. J. Phys.*, **39,** 35–52 (1961).
23. T. N. Davis, The morphology of the auroral displays of 1957–1958, I and II, *J. Geophys. Res.*, **67,** 59–110 (1962).
24. A. J. Dessler, Ionospheric heating by hydromagnetic waves, *J. Geophys. Res.*, **64,** 397–401 (1959).
25. W. Dieminger and K. H. Geisweid, Beobachtungen der Ionosphäre der Zustand der Ionosphäre während der Mögel-Dellinger Effektes, *J. Atmos. Terr. Phys.*, **1,** 42–48 (1950).
26. K. W. Eriksen and B. Landmark, Some results concerning the behaviour of long distance VLF circuit during polar cap absorption events, *Arkiv för Geophys.*, **3,** 489–496 (1961).
27. H. Friedman, Ionospheric constitution and ionizing radiations, *Proc. Int. Conf. The Ionosphere*, 3–18 (Inst. Phys. and Phys. Soc., London, 1963).
28. O. K. Garriott, Determination of ionospheric electron content and distribution from satellite observations. *J. Geophys. Res.*, **65,** 1139–1158 (1960).
29. O. K. Garriott, and J. O. Thomas, The continuity equation for electrons in the *F* region of the ionosphere and the calculation of electromagnetic drift velocities. *Proc. Int. Conf. The Ionosphere* (Inst. Phys. and Phys. Soc., London, 1963).
30. J. B. Gregory, Ionospheric reflection below 50 km. during polar cap absorption, *J. Geophys. Res.*, **66,** 2575–2577 (1961).
31. G. V. Groves, Correlation of upper atmosphere air density with geomagnetic storm activity (*Rep. Univ. College*, London, 1961).
32. E. L. Hagg, D. Muldrew and E. Warren, Spiral occurrence of sporadic E, *J. Atmos. Terr. Phys.*, **14,** 345–347 (1959).
33. Y. Hakura, Y. Takenoshita, and T. Otsuki, Polar blackouts associated with severe geomagnetic storms on Sept. 13, 1957 and Feb. 11, 1958, *Rep. Ionos. Res. Japan*, **12,** 459–468 (1958).
34. Y. Hakura and T. Goh, Pre-SC polar cap ionospheric blackout and type IV solar radio outburst, *J. Rad. Res. Lab., Japan*, **6,** 635–650 (1959).
35. Y. Hakura and T. Goh, Ionospheric blackout in the polar region during July 1959 events, *Rep. Ionos. Space Res. Japan*, **15,** 235–244 (1961).
36. Y. Hakura, Polar cap blackout and auroral zone blackout, *J. Rad. Res. Lab., Japan*, **7,** 583–597 (1960).
37. G. E. Hill, Ionospheric disturbances following a solar flare, *J. Geophys. Res.*, **65,** 3183–3207 (1960).
38. C. O. Hines, Ionospheric disturbances at auroral latitudes, *J. Phys. Soc. Japan*, **17,** Suppl. A-1, 308–313 (1962).
39. M. Hirono, Effect of gravity and ionization pressure gradient on the vertical drift in the *F*2 region, *Rep. Ionos. Res. Japan*, **9,** 95–104 (1955).
40. E. R. Hope, Low latitude and high latitude geomagnetic agitation, *J. Geophys. Res.*, **66,** 747–776 (1961).
41. B. Hultqvist, On the interpretation of ionization in the lower ionosphere occurring on both day and night side of the earth within a few hours after some solar flares, *Tellus*, **11,** 332–343 (1959).
42. B. Hultqvist and J. Ortner, Strongly absorbing layers below 50 km, *Planet. Space Sci.*, **1,** 193–204 (1959).
43. B. Hultqvist, Studies of ionospheric absorption of radio waves by the cosmic noise method. *Radio Astronomical and Satellite Studies of the Atmosphere*, J. Aarons (ed.), 163 (North-Holland Publishing Co., 1963).
44. L. G. Jacchia, Satellite drag during the events of November 1960, *Space Research II*, 747–753 (North-Holland Publishing Co., 1961).
45. R. Jastrow, Geophysical effects of the trapped particle layer, *Space Research I*, 1009–1018 (North-Holland Publishing Co., 1960).

46. D. H. Jelly, Polar cap absorption events identified HF vertical ionosonde data, *J. Phys. Soc. Japan*, **17**, Suppl. A-1, 122–126 (1962).
47. H. Kamiyama, Ionospheric changes associated with geomagnetic bays, *Sci. Rep. Tohoku Univ. Geophys.*, **7**, 125–135 (1956).
48. H. Kamiyama, Morphology of ionospheric storms, *J. Phys. Soc. Japan*, **17**, Suppl. A-1, 306–308 (1961).
49. H. Kamiyama, The spiral distribution of the polar *Es* ionization. *Sci. Rep. Tohoku Univ. Geophys.*, **14**, 120–127 (1962).
50. I. Kasuya, Statistical study in occurrence of polar blackouts, *J. Rad. Res. Lab. Japan*, **7**, 451–465 (1960).
51. P. J. Kellogg and J. R. Winckler, Cosmic ray evidence for a ring current, *J. Geophys. Res.*, **66**, 3991–4001 (1961).
52. J. W. King, Some relationships between magnetic and ionospheric variations. *Proc. Int. Conf. The Ionosphere*, 116–119 (Inst. Phys. and Phys. Soc., London, 1963).
53. R. W. Knecht and R. E. McDuffie, Solar flare effects in the *F* region of the ionosphere, *J. Phys. Soc. Japan*, **17**, Suppl. A-1, 280–285 (1962).
54. E. A. Lauter and K. Sprenger, Nächtlich Ionisationsstörungen der tiefen Ionosphären, *Z. Meterol.*, **6**, 161 (1952).
55. R. S. Lawrence, Continental maps of four ionospheric disturbances, *J. Geophys. Res.*, **58**, 219–222 (1953).
56. H. Leinbach and G. C. Reid, VHF radio wave absorption in northern latitude and solar particle emissions, *Proc. URSI/AGI*, Brussels, 281–292 (1959).
57. H. Leinbach and G. C. Reid, Polar cap absorption during the solar cosmic ray outbursts of July, 1959. Symposium on the July 1959 events, *IUGG Monograph No. 7*, 145–150 (1960).
58. H. Leinbach, Interpretations of the time variations of polar cap absorption associated with solar cosmic ray bombardments, *Geophys. Inst., Univ. Alaska. Sci. Rep. No. 3, NSF-Gl-4133* (1962).
59. R. P. Waldo Lewis and D. H. McIntosh, Diurnal and stormtime variations of geomagnetic and ionospheric disturbances, *J. Atmos. Terr. Phys.*, **3**, 186–193 (1953).
60. H. Maeda, World-wide pattern of ionization drifts in the ionospheric *F* region as deduced from geomagnetic variations, *Proc. Int. Conf. The Ionosphere*, 187–190 (Inst. Phys. and Phys. Soc., London, 1963).
61. K. Maeda, Theoretical study on the geomagnetic distortion in the *F*2 layer, *Rep. Ionos. Res. Japan*, **9**, 71–85 (1955).
62. K. Maeda and T. Sato, The *F* region during magnetic storms, *Proc. Inst. Radio Eng.*, **47**, 232–238 (1959).
63. D. F. Martyn, The morphology of ionospheric variations associated with magnetic disturbances, *Proc. Roy. Soc. A.*, **218**, 1–18 (1953).
64. S. Matsushita, Ionospheric variations associated with geomagnetic disturbances, *J. Geomag. Geoelect.*, **5**, 109–135 (1953).
65. S. Matsushita, A study of the morphology of ionospheric storms, *J. Geophys. Res.*, **64**, 305–321 (1959).
66. S. Matsushita, Increase of ionization associated with geomagnetic sudden commencements, *J. Geophys. Res.*, **66**, 3958–3961 (1961).
67. S. Matsushita, Ionospheric variations during geomagnetic storms, *Proc. Int. Conf. The Ionosphere*, 120–127 (Inst. Phys. and Phys. Soc., London, 1963).
68. S. Matsushita, Equatorial ionospheric variations during geomagnetic storms, *J. Geophys. Res.*, **68**, 2595–2602 (1963).
69. N. Matsuura, Thermal effect on the ionospheric *F* region disturbance, *J. Rad. Res. Lab. Japan*, **10**, 1–35 (1963).
70. C. E. McIlwain, Direct measurements of particles producing visible auroras, *J. Geophys. Res.*, **65**, 2727–2747 (1960).
71. J. H. Meek, Ionospheric disturbances in Canada, *J. Geophys. Res.*, **57**, 177–190 (1952).
72. J. H. Meek, Correlation of magnetic, auroral, and ionospheric variations at Saskatoon, Canada, *J. Geophys. Res.*, **58**, 445–456 (1953).

73. R. Montalbetti and D. J. McEwen, Hydrogen emissions and sporadic *D* layer behaviour, *Proc. Phys. Soc. Japan*, **17,** Suppl. A-1, 212–215 (1962).
74. T. Nagata, Ionospheric storms in high latitudes, *Rep. Ionos. Res. Japan*, **8,** 39–44 (1954).
75. A. P. Nikolski, On the high latitude geographic distribution of anomalous absorption of radio waves in the ionosphere, *Dok. Akad. Nauk. SSSR*, **112,** 628–631 (1957).
76. T. Obayashi, Some characteristics of ionospheric storms, *Rep. Ionos. Res. Japan*, **6,** 79–84 (1952).
77. T. Obayashi, On the world morphology of ionospheric disturbances, *Rep. Ionos. Res. Japan*, **8,** 135–142, 165–170 (1954).
78. T. Obayashi, On the world-wide disturbance in *F*2 region, *J. Geomag. Geoelect.*, **5,** 41–50, and **6,** 57–67 (1954).
79. T. Obayashi, Polar ionospheric disturbances associated with a severe magnetic storm, *J. Geomag. Geoelect.*, **10,** 28–35 (1958).
80. T. Obayashi, Geomagnetic storms and ionospheric disturbances, *J. Rad. Res. Lab. Japan*, **6,** 375–512 (1959).
81. T. Obayashi, Entry of high energy particles into the polar ionosphere, *Rep. Ionos. Space Res. Japan*, **13,** 201–219 (1959).
82. T. Obayashi and Y. Hakura, Enhanced ionization in the polar ionosphere caused by solar corpuscular emissions, *Rep. Ionos. Space Res. Japan*, **14,** 1–40 (1960).
83. T. Obayashi and Y. Hakura, Solar corpuscular radiation and polar ionospheric disturbances, *J. Geophys. Res.*, **65,** 3131–3142 (1960).
84. T. Obayashi, Geomagnetic storm effects on charged particles, *J. Geomag. Geoelect.*, **13,** 26–32 (1961).
85. T. Obayashi, Propagation of solar corpuscles and interplanetary magnetic fields, *J. Geophys. Res.*, **67,** 1717–1729 (1962).
86. T. Obayashi, Widespread ionospheric disturbances due to nuclear explosions during October 1961, *Nature*, **196,** 24–27 (1962).
87. T. Obayashi, Upper atmospheric disturbances due to high altitude nuclear explosions, *Planet. Space. Sci.*, **10,** 47–63 (1963).
88. T. Obayashi, Streaming of solar flare particles through interplanetary space, *Space Sci. Rev.* (in press).
89. B. J. O'Brien, Lifetimes of outer zone electrons and their precipitation into the atmosphere, *J. Geophys. Res.*, **67,** 3687–3706 (1962).
90. T. Oguchi, Inter-relation among the upper atmosphere disturbance phenomena in the auroral zone. Japanese Antarctic Research Expedition 1956–1962, *JARE Sci. Ser. A. No.* **1,** 1–82 (1963).
91. J. Oksman and E. Kataja, Geophysical effects of nuclear explosions at Sodankylä, *Ann. Acad. Sci. Fennicae, Helsinki, Ser. A, VI Physica*, No. 115 (1962).
92. J. Ortner, A. Egeland, and B. Hultqvist, *IRE Trans. Antennas Propag., AP*-**8,** 621 (1961).
93. E. N. Parker, Acceleration of cosmic rays in solar flares, *Phys. Rev.*, **107,** 830–836 (1957).
94. J. A. Ratcliffe, Some aspects of ionospheric storms, *Proc. Phys. Soc. Japan*, **17,** Suppl. A-1, 274–279 (1962).
95. G. C. Reid and C. Collins, Observation of abnormal VHF radio wave absorption at medium and high latitudes, *J. Atmos. Terr. Phys.*, **14,** 63–81 (1959).
96. G. C. Reid and H. Leinbach, Low-energy cosmic ray events associated with solar flares, *J. Geophys. Res.*, **64,** 1801–1805 (1959).
97. G. C. Reid, A study of the enhanced ionization produced by solar protons during a polar cap absorption event, *Proc. Phys. Soc. Japan*, **17,** Suppl. A-1, 130–135 (1962).
98. H. Rishbeth and D. W. Barron, Equilibrium electron distributions in the ionospheric *F*2-layer, *J. Atmos. Terr. Phys.*, **18,** 234–252 (1960).
99. H. Rishbeth, Ionospheric storms and the morphology of magnetic disturbances, *Planet. Space Sci.*, **11,** 31–43 (1963).
100. D. C. Rose and S. Ziauddin, The polar cap absorption effect, *Space Sci. Rev.*, **1,** 115–134 (1962).

101. P. Rothwell, Magnetic cutoff rigidities of charged particles in the earth's field at times of magnetic storms, *J. Geophys. Res.*, **64,** 2026–2028 (1959).
102. P. Rothwell and C. McIlwain, Satellite observations of solar cosmic rays, *Nature*, **184,** 138–140 (1959).
103. P. Rothwell, Diffusion of ions between *F* layers at magnetic conjugate points, *Proc. Int. Conf. The Ionosphere*, 217–221 (Inst. Phys. and Phys. Soc., London, 1963).
104. B. P. Sandford, Polar glow aurora in polar cap absorption events, *J. Atmos. Terr. Phys.*, **24,** 155–171 (1962).
105. T. Sato, Disturbances in the ionospheric *F*2 region associated with geomagnetic storms, I, *J. Geomag. Geoelect.*, **8,** 129–135 (1956).
106. T. Sato, Disturbances in the ionospheric *F*2 region associated with geomagnetic storms, II and III, *J. Geomag. Geoelect.*, **9,** 1–22, 94-106 (1957).
107. T. Sato, Morphology of the ionospheric *F*2 disturbances in the polar region, *Rep. Ionos. Space Res. Japan*, **13,** 91–104 (1959).
108. M. J. Seaton, A possible explanation of the drop in *F* region critical densities accompanying major ionospheric storms, *J. Atmos. Terr. Phys.*, **8,** 122–123 (1956).
109. A. H. Shapley and R. W. Knecht, Ionospheric effects of the great solar cosmic ray event of February 23, 1956, *US-NBS Report No. 5596* (1958).
110. A. H. Shapley and R. W. Knecht, Ionospheric effects of the great solar cosmic ray event of February 23, 1956, *IRE Trans. Antennas Propag.*, *AP*-**5**, 326 (1957).
111. K. Sinno, On the variation of the *F*2 layer accompanying geomagnetic storms I and II, *Rep. Ionos. Res., Japan*, **7,** 7–14 (1953) and **8,** 127–133 (1954).
112. K. Sinno, On the disturbances in *F*2 layer associated with geomagnetic disturbances, *Rep. Ionos. Res. Japan*, **9,** 166–173 (1955).
113. Y. V. Somayajulu, Changes in the *F* region during magnetic storms, *J. Geophys. Res.*, **68,** 1899–1922 (1963).
114. T. Takakura, Solar radio outbursts and acceleration of electrons, *J. Phys. Soc. Japan*, **17,** Suppl. A-2, 243–248 (1962).
115. J. O. Thomas and R. Robbins, The electron distribution in the ionosphere over Slough on disturbed days, *J. Atmos. Terr. Phys.*, **13,** 131–139 (1958).
116. L. Thomas, The temporal distribution of storm-type sporadic *E* in the northern hemisphere, *Proc. URSI/AGI*, Brussels, 172–180 (1959).
117. L. Thomas and W. R. Piggott, Some aspects of the incidence of polar blackout during the IGY, *Proc. URSI/AGI*, Brussels, 61–72 (1959).
118. C. S. Warwick, Sudden ionospheric disturbances. *Radio Astronomical and Satellite Studies of the Atmosphere*, J. Aarons (ed.), 457 (North-Holland Publishing Co., 1963).
119. J. R. Winckler, Balloon study of high altitude radiations during the IGY, *J. Geophys. Res.*, **65,** 1331–1359 (1960).
120. J. R. Winckler, Geomagnetic and interplanetary effects on solar cosmic rays, *J. Phys. Soc. Japan*, **17,** Suppl. A-2, 353–359 (1962).
121. K. C. Yeh and H. Chow, Variations of ionospheric electron content during disturbances, *Elect. Eng. Res. Lab., Univ. Illinois, NSG-24-59*, (1961).
122. K. C. Yeh and G. W. Swenson, Ionospheric electron content and its variations deduced from satellite observations, *J. Geophys. Res.*, **66,** 1061–1067 (1961).
123. T. Yonezawa, On the influence of electron-ion diffusion exerted upon the formations of the *F*2 layer, *J. Rad. Res. Lab. Japan*, **5,** 165–187 (1958).
124. T. Yonezawa and H. Takahashi, On the electron and ion density distributions from the lower up to the upper most part of the *F* region, *J. Rad. Res. Lab., Japan*, **7,** 335–378 (1960).
125. T. Yonezawa, Private communication, June 1962.
126. T. Yonezawa, The characteristic behavior of the *F*2 layer during severe magnetic storms, *Proc. Int. Conf. The Ionosphere*, 128–133 (Inst. Phys. and Phys. Soc., London, 1963).

CHAPTER 15

THE AURORA

Sydney Chapman and Syun-Ichi Akasofu

1. A Summary of Pre-IGY Auroral Research

Auroral research has a long history. By the end of the eighteenth century it was well begun. The name *aurora borealis* had been given to it in the previous century by the French astronomer Gassendi (1592–1655), in the course of a description of the great display of 12 September 1621. The first record of a Southern Hemisphere aurora was made by Captain Cook (17 February 1773); he gave to it the name *aurora australis,* later at times wrongly applied to auroras seen by northern observers to their south.

The English astronomer Halley published in the Royal Society's *Philosophical Transactions* an account of the great aurora of 1716; he also proposed that it was due to magnetic particles arising from within the earth. In 1731 the French Academy of Sciences published the first great treatise on the aurora, by de Mairan; it ran to a second edition, revised, in 1754. In 1741 Celsius of Uppsala in Sweden found that the aurora is associated with geomagnetic disturbance,* which had been discovered by Graham in London in 1722; by correspondence in 1741 Graham and Celsius found that magnetic disturbance is not merely local.

In 1770 Wilcke of Stockholm found that the auroral rays lie along the magnetic field lines. Cavendish in 1790 published a good determination of the height of an aurora seen in England in 1784. Another famous scientist of that time, Dalton, the father of the atomic theory in chemistry, was so much interested in the aurora that he observed it regularly for many years. In his *Meteorological Essays*, published in 1793, he devoted 70 pages to the aurora, and 27 more in the second edition of 1834. He suggested that the aurora is an electrical phenomenon. Gauss in 1838 likewise wrote that

* This discovery was not made by Halley, as incorrectly stated in *Geomagnetism* (Chapman and Bartels, p. 471; also quoted by Störmer, *The Polar Aurora*, p. 18).

"there is every appearance that electricity in motion plays a principal part."

The nineteenth century naturally made considerable contributions to auroral knowledge. The sunspot cycle, discovered about 1840 by the German apothecary Schwabe, was found to manifest itself also in magnetic disturbance and the aurora—pointing to intrinsic changes on the sun as the prime cause. Magnetic observatories were set up, increasing our knowledge of *magnetic storms*—a name due to Humboldt. In 1838 Gauss made the first spherical harmonic analysis of the earth's surface magnetic field, thus determining the dipole component and its axis, which have since assumed so much importance in auroral theory.

Muncke about 1840 recognized the existence and rough position of the auroral zone, which was first drawn by Loomis of Yale University in 1860. The Austrian physicist Fritz in 1873 published a great auroral catalog, and a year later his chart of isochasms—lines of equal average frequency of auroral visibility. Ångström in 1867 pioneered in auroral spectroscopy. The First International Polar Year, 1882–1883, added greatly to our knowledge of the aurora, and of the intense magnetic disturbance experienced near the auroral zone.

The discovery of the electron led the Norwegian physicist Birkeland in 1896 to propose the first rational theory of the aurora and magnetic storms. He ascribed them to the action of fast electrons emitted by the sun, which, impinging on the geomagnetic field, were deflected by it to polar latitudes and to the night side of the earth. He made model experiments to support his theory.

Coming to the present century, auroral knowledge was greatly advanced by the Norwegians Störmer and Vegard. Störmer put our knowledge of auroral heights and geographical location on a firm basis by simultaneous photography from two or more places. Vegard was a great leader in auroral spectroscopy. He identified nitrogen bands, and later the atomic hydrogen lines. The famous yellow-green line 5577 long remained mysterious; its origin was found by the Canadian physicist McLennan in 1925. Babcock (1923) applied the interferometer to determine an upper limit to its width, with a view to Doppler interpretation. Rayleigh, son of the great mathematical physicist, measured its photometric intensity and inferred the number of atomic transitions per sq cm column (1930).

Our knowledge of magnetic storm morphology also advanced greatly; Moos of Bombay was the pioneer, followed by Chapman, Vestine, Sugiura, and others. It was inferred (Chapman 1935) that magnetic disturbance is often partly due to electric current flowing in the ionosphere, especially strong in the polar caps, where it has a recurrent pattern; this includes intense laterally limited currents called electrojets, flowing along each auroral zone. Their circuit is completed mainly over the polar caps, but also partly over the great belt between the two auroral zones.

Maunder (1904) and Chree (1922, 1927) established the 27-day recurrence tendency in magnetic storms, which pointed to the influence of the rotation of the sun, and of solar corpuscular streams, in causing such storms and the accompanying auroras.

Daily character figures of magnetic disturbance were introduced, and international days, five per month, of magnetic calm and disturbance, were chosen. Solar flares, first seen in 1859 by Carrington and Hodgson, became familiar, owing to advances in solar observing techniques, in which Hale and Deslandres were pioneers. They indicated a connection between solar eruptions and nonrecurrent storms; they also gave the speed of the solar gas on its way to the earth, as of order 1000 km/sec.

Störmer developed Birkeland's theory of the aurora by mathematical studies of the motion of a single charged particle in a dipole magnetic field. He found some general results, especially that there are certain regions around the earth that are inaccessible to particles projected from infinity—or the sun—with given speed and direction. He was naturally most interested in the regions that are accessible to the particles, and in their latitude and mode of entry into the atmosphere; he did not speculate about particles that might be trapped in the forbidden regions.

Schuster criticized Birkeland's theory, and other cruder theories, that postulated streams of electrically charged particles of one sign only; he pointed out the strong electrostatic repulsion in such a case, that would disperse the stream. Lindemann in 1922 disproved a new one-sign theory advanced by Chapman in 1918; and he added a constructive suggestion, namely that the solar agent must be neutral ionized gas, such as is now called a plasma (Langmuir, 1928). This is the basis of almost all present-day theories of magnetic storms and the aurora, though the ultraviolet light theory of Hulburt is an exception.

Chapman and Ferraro around 1930 [3] inferred that solar plasma impinging on the geomagnetic field would compress and confine it, causing increased intensity at the earth's surface. This is observed during the early stages of magnetic storms, which often begin suddenly, within a time of the order of a minute, all over the earth. Often the polar electric current systems complicate the magnetic variations at the sudden commencement and later.

The Second International Polar Year of 1932–1933 added much to our magnetic and auroral knowledge, and for the first time the polar ionosphere was studied by the methods of radio exploration devised by Breit and Tuve, namely by vertical pulsed beams [2].

It was found that during strong auroras there is intense ionization overhead, along at least part of the auroral zone. Not long afterward (1938) Harang and Stoffregen [6] found that radio beams could be reflected by the auroral sheets.

Bartels exhibited the time characteristics of solar and geomagnetic disturbance by means of improved time patterns, and with Heck and Johnston introduced the important 3-hour *Kp*-indices of magnetic disturbance.

Progress was halted during World War II, but after it ended the rate of advance in this field of science was much accelerated. This was partly due to advances in techniques developed during the war, especially in rockets and radio including radar; radio astronomy grew rapidly, and its methods were applied also to the aurora. Interest in geomagnetism increased greatly, notably in Japan and the United States.

Auroral spectroscopy also advanced rapidly, with improved optical apparatus. More and more lines and bands in the auroral spectrum were identified. Gartlein in 1950 [5] showed that the lines of atomic hydrogen have a special character, being Doppler-broadened, in spectra of auroras seen sideways. This indicated random speeds to and from the observer of order hundreds of km/sec. Later in 1950 Meinel [10] found that when the aurora is viewed *along* the field lines, the hydrogen lines are notably displaced to the violet, indicating speeds of descent of 2000 km/sec or more. This was the first clear proof of the corpuscular theory of the aurora. A few years afterward Van Allen and his colleagues [11] used balloon-launched rockets to explore cosmic rays in the upper atmosphere. They found unexpectedly that in auroral latitudes, below auroral levels, the counters registered what were later interpreted as bremsstrahlung X-rays, from electrons descending through the atmosphere; the X-rays penetrate further than the electrons themselves can. Thus before the IGY the entry of particles of both sign was indicated. The excitation of the auroral spectrum was discussed, but the share of the protons and electrons was not yet clear.

Visual observation of the aurora began to be more extensive; Gartlein in the United States, and Paton in the United Kingdom and elsewhere in Western Europe, organized such observations. Gartlein also applied the all-sky camera, devised for cloud studies, to auroral photography.

Vestine [13] used auroral observations made after the publication of Fritz's catalog to improve the chart of isochasms; he used magnetic disturbance data also for this purpose. Intermittent antarctic records of the aurora enabled Davies *et al.* [14] and others to draw tentative sketches of the southern auroral zone. Heppner in 1954 [7] used the records made at College, Alaska to study the time and space relations of auroral activity during magnetic bays—that is, during the development and decay of the ionospheric current system already mentioned.

There was no agreement as to the mechanism of the aurora and magnetic storms. Chapman and Ferraro [3] sought to explain the second, main phase of storms by a toroidal electric current encircling the earth, with a radius of order 10 earth radii, but they could not see how such a current could grow. Martyn [9] used this conception to add some ideas on the cause of the polar ionospheric current system.

Alfvén in 1944 [1] proposed a theory of magnetic storms and the aurora in which stress was laid on the presence of the solar magnetic field in the plasma streams, out to the earth's distance from the sun, and of an inferred electric field in the plasma, ascribed to the action of the solar magnetic field.

Hoyle [8] and Dungey [4] proposed that the plasma transports away from the sun some of the magnetic fields observed near the sun's surface, and that the combination of such a field in the plasma with the geomagnetic field results in the presence of neutral points in the field. They suggested that near these points the particles could be accelerated to greater energies than those with which they came from the sun, and that accelerated particles find their way to the auroral zone.

Singer, whose initiative in 1954 led to the adoption of space exploration by artificial satellites as part of the IGY program, in 1957 anticipated one of the particle results of this program—namely, the presence and form of a belt of trapped charged particles in the magnetosphere. He attributed the main phase of magnetic storms to the electric current conveyed by these particles.

2. The IGY Plans for Auroral Research

The auroral plans for the IGY naturally included as their main feature enhanced visual, photographic, photometric, and spectroscopic observations. In each participating country where there was even a slight chance of the aurora becoming visible, an auroral reporter was appointed wherever possible, who undertook to stimulate and organize visual and other types of auroral observation. The program of visual observation was very successful. As an example, in Mexico three auroras were observed during the IGY; this is the same as the number of auroras recorded as seen there during all the past years (the dates of the three previously recorded were 1789, 1859, and 1872). The IGY Calendar Record gives for each IGY quarter-day the greatest angular distance from the nearer end of the magnetic dipole axis, at which aurora was seen overhead (that is, within 30° of the zenith); out of the 549 days of the IGY there were 123 on which this distance was from 35° to 40°—well beyond the auroral zones—and 31 on which it equaled or exceeded 40°; these auroras were classified as respectively "outstanding" and "very outstanding." The three IGY auroras seen from Mexico occurred on 13 and 29 September 1957 and 11 February 1958; the angular distances in their cases were respectively 54°, 57°, and 51°. Without the efforts of the national auroral reporters and the observers whose aid they enlisted, we should know far less about the world distribution of the many remarkable auroral events of the IGY.

In the higher latitudes the all-sky cameras recorded the auroras whenever weather and darkness permitted, with a completeness that visual observers in many cases could not match—the auroras were too extensive, and often rapidly changing. Plans were made, and well executed by Dr. Stoffregen with the aid of the auroral world data centers, for a graphic summary of the occurrence of the aurora overhead in different latitudes, based on these camera data. The diagrams are called ascaplots (*asca* is an abbreviation of *a*ll-*s*ky *ca*mera).

Based on the visual auroral watch, covering a greater area than that of the all-sky camera network, diagrams called *visoplots* summarizing the geographical distribution of the aurora in both hemispheres in successive 3-hour intervals have been published in a volume of the *IGY Annals*. The *Annals* will also include synoptic auroral maps, and a narrative summary of the auroral history of the IGY. Volume 16 gives a briefer indication of the IGY events, solar and geophysical, in the *IGY Calendar Record.*

The ascaplots and visoplots are of great value in themselves, for purely auroral studies, and perhaps still more for use with other data, solar and geophysical, namely magnetic, ionospheric, and cosmic-ray; at this date these auroral publications are not complete. But they will far from exhaust the full wealth of asca and visual data available at the auroral world data centers.

The pre-IGY morphological studies of the aurora were seriously limited by the inability of an observer at any one place to see more than a small fraction of an auroral display. The sky area open to view, or to the all-sky camera, at a place with unobstructed horizon, for auroras at the usual minimum height of about 100 km, is very extensive—its radius is 1138 km; but even this great area is but a fraction of that over which many an auroral display extends. Often during the active phase of a great display individual large folds in the auroral curtains cover a major part of the sky. The observer cannot know what lies beyond his horizon—how far the aurora continues in its usual East-West direction.

Even during the IGY the all-sky arctic cameras left great sky areas unobserved—partly because of the polar sea, though there were all-sky cameras on one or two ice islands in that sea, and partly because of budgetary and logistic limitations. But the fields of view overlapped to some extent, so that it is possible by detailed laborious study of the store of ascafilms at the world data centers to obtain at least a partial synoptic picture of the changing auroral distribution over very considerable parts of the polar cap.

3. Auroral Morphology

The aurora has three main forms. Two have notable structure; they are thin luminous sheets, inclined to the vertical along the direction of magnetic dip. Their extent in height is of the order of a hundred or a few hundred kilometers. Their maximum horizontal extension is not yet known, but is certainly often several thousands of kilometers. Their thickness is very small by comparison with these dimensions. The two sheet forms, called arcs, differ in thickness and motion. Those of the first form, quiet arcs, are rather uniform in brightness, slow moving, and about 3-km thick. Those of the second form, rayed arcs, are striated along the field lines, and are wavy or folded; they often move rapidly, sometimes waving like great draperies in the sky, and their thickness is of order 300 meters, about one-tenth of that of quiet arcs.

The third form consists of diffuse patches, apparently lying horizontally, often resembling a dappled or mackerel sky, and often pulsating. Its thickness and full lateral extent are not yet known.

Stagg [20], leader of the British (Second) Polar Year Expedition to Fort Rae in Canada, near the auroral zone, reported that the aurora was visible there at some time on every adequately clear dark night, although the epoch was sunspot minimum, and the magnetic conditions were mostly quiet. The aurora was usually faint, diffuse, and slow-moving–namely of the first form—and generally lay to the north. This suggests that the flow of solar plasma is almost perpetual, though at times feeble—but this inference was not explicitly drawn at that time. Not until nearly 20 years later did Biermann [16] reach this conclusion from cometary evidence, leading Parker [19] to his theoretical studies of what he has aptly called the *solar wind*. On this general outflow from the sun are superimposed the *solar streams* associated with recurrent storms, and the *solar shells* that proceed from flares.

As seen by an individual observer or all-sky camera in or near either auroral zone, there may be one or more "cycles" of auroral development on an aurorally active night. These cycles may be separated by intervals without aurora in the field of view, or only quiet auroras. Each cycle begins with the first form, a quiet arc. It may rise slowly from the poleward horizon, and may or may not attain or pass beyond the zenith. It may be followed by one or more parallel quiet arcs, all lying nearly along the East-West direction. At some epoch the form may change to the second type, the arc or arcs becoming rayed and wavy or folded, with more rapid and more irregular motion. The change may occur in only a few minutes, or even one minute. This process is called the breakup. Later the arcs may fade, or move out of view across the horizon, and be succeeded by the diffuse form, and later by absence of auroral light.

The active part of such a cycle is found to coincide with the growth and decline of the polar ionospheric current system, whose changing magnetic field shows on the observatory records as a magnetic bay, or, if it occurs during a magnetic storm, as an irregularity imposed on the main course of the storm changes. It is then called a polar *substorm*. During a great magnetic storm there may be several auroral cycles and associated polar substorms.

The IGY auroral program made it possible for the first time to approach a world synoptic view of such an auroral cycle, by piecing together the records from many observing stations in different latitudes and in different longitudes relative to the noon meridian containing the sun, that is, at different local times. Davis in 1960 and 1962 [17, 18] and Akasofu in 1962–1963 [15] studied the voluminous ascafilm records collected at the IGY World Data Center A for such records, located at the Geophysical Institute, College, Alaska. Akasofu found that the local breakup is the local manifestation of a general change in the aurora, which may be called an auroral *substorm*. The change is simultaneous, or nearly so, over the whole auroral distribution, arctic and antarctic. But its local character varies according to local time and the situation relative to the auroral zone.

4. A Typical Auroral Cycle

An auroral cycle is here described as it affects the arctic region. The same description would serve for the simultaneous cycle in the antarctic, if *North* and *South* are interchanged.

An auroral cycle begins with the appearance of one or more quiet arcs or bands in the auroral region, extending along the direction of the auroral zone. They may move slowly, perpendicular to their direction of extension. The active phase is marked by a brightening of the display, and arcs scarcely or not visible before may become evident. Rays appear in the arcs. New arcs may appear to the north of those already present. This may occur within a few minutes. In the succeeding minutes the more northerly arcs move northward, while those more southerly move south; the motion is especially active on either side of a central meridian, which is usually near to midnight. Thus the area of auroral display expands in latitude, and may cover a wide belt during great displays. The northward and southward motion is accompanied by drifts of irregularities ("surges") along the arcs, extending outward from the central meridian, so that on the morning (eastern) side of the meridian it is eastward, and on the evening (western) side it is westward. The surges may develop into folds, sometimes complicated, folds within folds. The process is seen locally as the breakup. The range of this breakup extends further to the east than to the west, so that the breakup is a common occurrence on the late morning side—toward the dawn—whereas it is rather rare in the early evening. The drifts correspond to an outward flow from the central meridian, usually near midnight; thus there is an expansion in longitude as well as in latitude. The changes are most active, sometimes even violent, around the central meridian (Fig. 1).

This first phase of expansion is followed by a second phase of contraction in latitude and longitude; this occurs usually, though not always, more slowly than the first phase. Drift motion continues in the *same direction*, outward from the central meridian, but its pace decreases, and may cease to be perceptible. The aurora may become fainter. New faint arcs may still

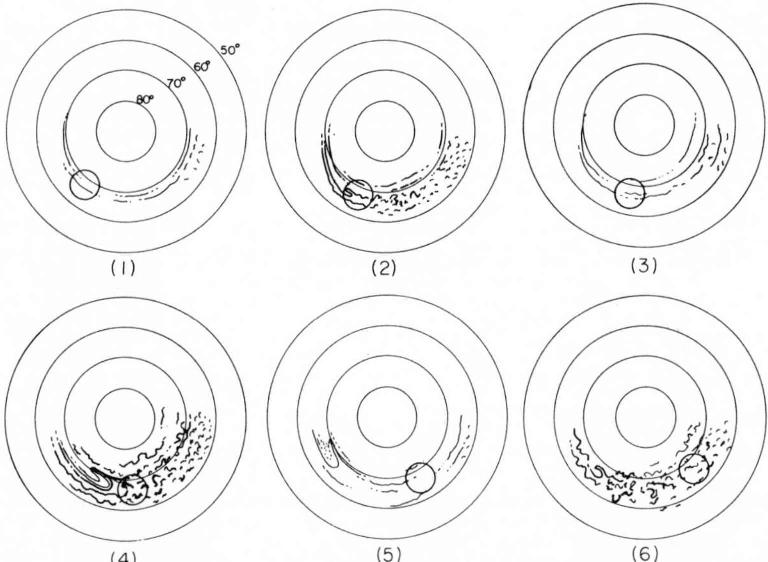

FIG. 1. A model distribution of the auroras over the northern polar region (the sun is toward the top of the diagram). Three successive substorms occur while an all-sky camera station (of which the field of view is indicated by a circle) is in the darkness.

appear, and share in the northward or southward motion of contraction in latitude. The arcs reach limiting latitudes and then remain fairly quiet.

Lastly, they may fade away altogether, and for a time there may remain only diffuse auroral patches, over a considerable area. This may contract, as the patches fade into invisibility; or the pulsation may cease, and the sky for a time may be covered by a uniform glow of auroral light. After an interval, a new cycle may begin with the appearance of new quiet arcs. Figure 1 shows schematically the distribution of the auroras over the northern polar region: three successive substorms are shown as occurring while an all-sky camera station (the field of view is indicated by a circle) is in the darkness.

Heppner [22] described the local appearance of such a cycle of auroral development as seen from College, Alaska, from shortly before to about two hours after midnight, during the growth and decline of the auroral electrojet and its ionospheric current system associated with a magnetic bay. The bay lasted for about two hours. The whole synoptic picture of the typical cycle of auroral development has become clear only as a result of the IGY all-sky camera data.

The orientation of the whole display may change somewhat from one case to another; that is, the central meridian from which the drift motions diverge eastward and westward may be the midnight meridian, or on either side of it, more often after than before.

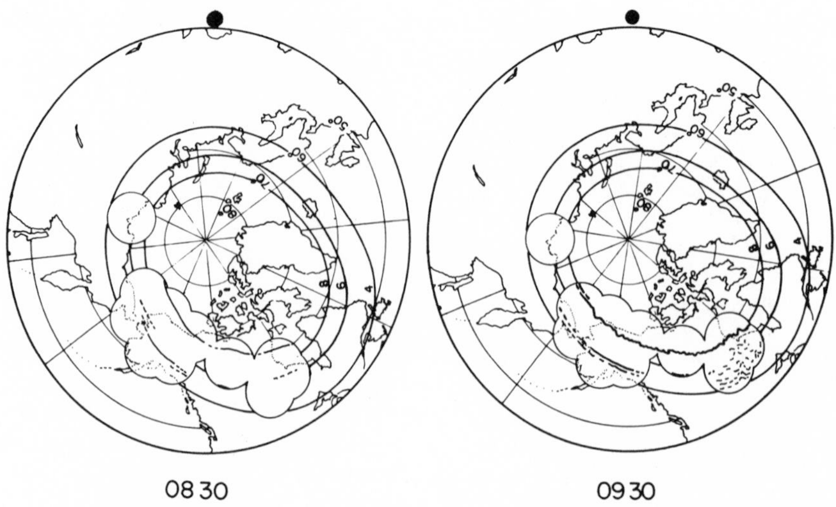

Fig. 2. The distribution of the auroras at 0830 and 0930 UT on 24 March 1958.

The possible full horizontal extent of auroral arcs has long been a matter of uncertainty and speculation, and even now is not settled. But in North America (Canada and Alaska) there was a chain of IGY all-sky camera stations with overlapping fields of view extending over about 5000 km along the auroral East-West direction. Figure 2 shows the combined field of view of these cameras, and also of a U.S.S.R. camera operating at the same time during the display of 24 March 1958, at 0830 and 0930 UT. The latter showed an arc extending up to the eastern limit of the area, but perhaps broken near the western limit; it was at least 5000 km long. Many difficulties beset the large-scale synoptic study of the aurora, even when there is so large a chain of camera stations; often it is effectively broken by areas of bad weather, and at times by malfunctioning at some stations.

The particles that cause the aurora travel downward in the atmosphere along the field lines. It has long been thought that the particles may have a source near the equatorial plane, from which they may travel northward to the Arctic or southward to the Antarctic; consequently some similarity of the events at the two ends of a field line was expected. This expectation was enhanced when it came to be thought that many of the auroral particles may have oscillated to and fro across the equatorial plane before finally plunging into the ionosphere. These expectations have now been verified by comparison of the ascafilms from conjugate regions, that is, regions at the ends of the same field line. DeWitt [21] has shown such similarity at the conjugate pair Farewell (gm. latitude 61.4°N, in Alaska) and Campbell Island (gm. latitude 57.3°S); the course of the auroral cycle is nearly simultaneous at the two stations.

5. The Distribution of the Aurora

5.1. Auroras in the Auroral Zones

The all-sky camera records have also greatly improved statistical studies of the distribution of the aurora over the polar region. It has become possible through such records to draw isoaurores (isolines of equal frequency of *overhead* auroras). A detailed study of the isoaurores in the Northern Hemisphere by Feldstein [27] has corrected the location of the auroral zone over Hudson Bay, which was thought to lie about 4° north of the location now inferred from studies of the ascafilms. Davis [26] made a detailed study of the distribution of the aurora over the Alaskan sky. The visual observations of the aurora made under the leadership of Gartlein and Sprague (United States), [29], Paton, McInnes, and Robertson (United Kingdom), [32], and Lange-Hesse (Germany) [31] will enable Feldstein's isoaurores to be improved.

In the antarctic region, however, there are discrepancies among different estimates of the location of the auroral zone (Vestine and Snyder [35]; Gartlein and Sprague [29]; Feldstein [27], Bond and Jacka [25]). Schneider [34] has summarized and discussed in detail our present knowledge of the southern auroral zone. The discrepancies are primarily due to the paucity of all-sky camera data in the Southern Hemisphere. It is hoped that a more extensive network will be set up in future to determine accurately the location of the southern isoaurores.

5.2. The Distribution of Auroras during Great Magnetic Storms

The aurora of 11 February 1958 provided a rare opportunity to study an auroral display during a great magnetic storm [23].

As the ring current grew and the main phase developed, both the northern and southern borders of the zone in which overhead auroras were seen, moved equatorward. A remarkable feature of the morphology was the occasional absence of overhead aurora over a large region on the poleward side of the zone. During some quiet intervals between intermittent polar substorms, the aurora was completely absent from the region of the auroral zone, where normally it is most frequent and intense (Fig. 3). The relationships between the intensity of the main phase of magnetic storms and the equatorward shift of the latitude of main auroral activity have been discussed by Akasofu and Chapman [24].

Another important feature of the 11 February 1958 aurora was a remarkable and intermittent poleward expansion of the zone. An example of the expansion that started at 1030 GMT on 11 February 1958 is shown in Figure 3.

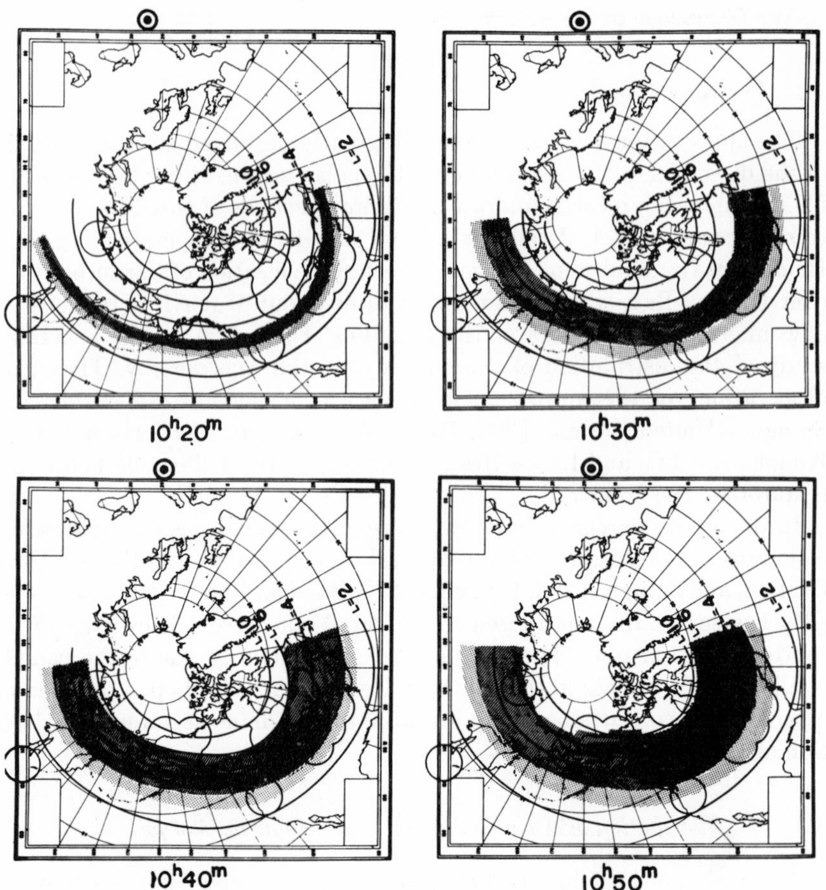

Fig. 3. The distribution of the auroras between 1020 and 1050 UT on 11 February 1958.

5.3. The Theoretical Auroral Zone

Developments of our knowledge of the geomagnetic field [28] and of the nature of auroral primary particles has spurred attempts to infer the approximate location of the auroral zone on a theoretical basis. Quenby and Webber [33] and Hultqvist [30] calculated the positions of the auroral zones, on the assumption that the aurora is produced by energetic charged particles entering the auroral ionosphere, along the earth's magnetic field lines, from a circular arc in the equatorial plane. In the Northern Hemisphere, the projection thus obtained is oval, with its longest diameter approximately in the plane containing the 170° and 350° gm. meridians. Hultqvist's curve agrees well with Vestine's maximum isochasm, except over the region of Hudson Bay, Canada; Feldstein's maximum isoaurore confirmed Hultqvist's result.

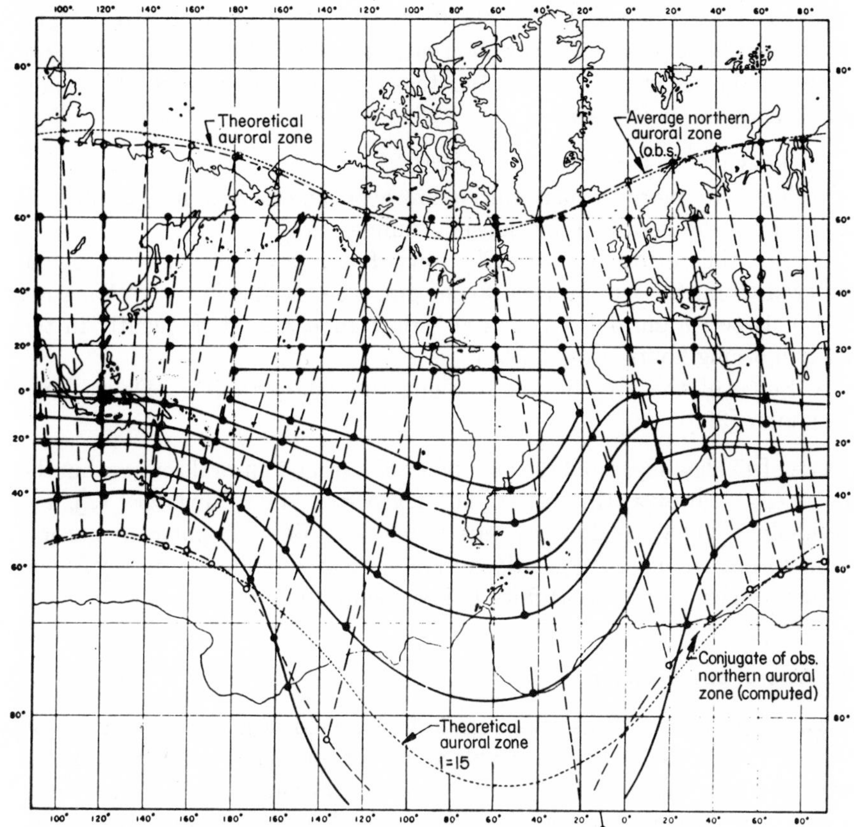

FIG. 4. The theoretical and observed auroral zones, together with pairs of the geomagnetic conjugate points.

Vestine and Sibley [36] calculated the position of the auroral zone by means of the longitudinal invariant I for the motion of trapped particles in the earth's field. By choosing $I = 15.7$ (the unit being the earth's radius) they reproduced fairly well Vestine's maximum isochasm in the Northern Hemisphere (Fig. 4); they confirmed also Feldstein's maximum isoaurore.

On the other hand, in the Southern Hemisphere, none of the observed isoaurores agrees so well with those calculated by Hultqvist or Vestine and Sibley as in the Northern Hemisphere. This may be due partly to the lack of auroral data in the Southern Hemisphere, and partly to uncertainty as to the geomagnetic field over the antarctic region.

6. The Polar Cap Aurora

Auroral observations over the cap enclosed by the auroral zone have been made mainly during the three international efforts, the International Polar

Years I (1882–1883) and II (1932–1933) and, most of all, the IGY. The IGY visual and all-sky camera observations indicate important differences between the polar cap auroras and those in the auroral zone. The main differences are as follows:

1. They are, in general, much fainter.
2. They are more frequent during low geomagnetic activity [15, 27, 38] and during the period of low sunspot number [37].
3. The time of occurrence shifts towards the late morning side, as one proceeds from the auroral zone to the gm. pole (Feldstein and Solomatina [40]). Between gm. lat. 75° and 80°, they appear most frequently in the early morning hours (Lassen [43]).
4. Some of the arcs lie nearly along the sun-earth line (Davis [38]; Denholm [39]).

Lassen [43] has suggested the possibility of a second auroral zone within the polar cap. However, Hatherton [41], Hatherton and Midwinter [42], and Denholm [39] have doubted this conclusion. Because polarcap auroras tend to appear more frequently during sunspot minimum, the IQSY will provide an excellent opportunity to investigate their nature.

7. Auroral Spectroscopy

Great progress has also been made in the field of auroral spectroscopy during the IGY/C. The remarkable activity of the sun provided important opportunities to study special types of the aurora, which appear most frequently during high solar activity. Several new lines were discovered, and by rockets the spectrum was extended far into the ultraviolet [50, 54]. Further, artificial auroras associated with high-altitude nuclear explosions have added important information as to the mechanism of the excitation of auroral lines and bands.

7.1. Special Types of Auroras

(*a*) *Type A Aurora* (*High-Altitude Red Arc*). Detailed studies of high-altitude red arcs have been made by Belon and Clark [48] and by Vallance Jones [60] for the great red aurora of 10–11 February 1958, and by Rees and Deehr [80] for the red arc of 27 November 1959. The red arc is characterized by intense OI 6300–6364 doublet lines and by N_2^+ ING bands. Its height is estimated to be of order 350 km, but Clark and Belon [48] reported an altitude as great as 1100 km during the 10–11 February red aurora. After detailed examination of several plausible processes, Rees [79] concluded that protons of energy of order a few kev and with a flux of order $10^{10}/\mathrm{cm}^2/\mathrm{sec}$ are responsible for the excitation of such arcs.

(*b*) *Type B Aurora* (*Purplish-Red Lower Border*). An active aurora is often characterized by a purplish-red lower border. This is due to the enhancement of N_2IPG bands around the lower border of the common yellowish-white aurora. Malville [63] proposed that this particular emission is related to the mutual neutralization of a negative oxygen atom or molecule and an ionized nitrogen molecule, produced by direct impact of high-energy electrons penetrating down to 80 km in height.

(*c*) *Subvisual Red Arc.* In 1958 Barbier [45] reported a rather stable and persistent subvisual red arc over Haute Provence (gm. lat. 40°N) during large magnetic storms. Later Roach and Marovich [82] reported a red arc extending over the nothern United States, which seemed to be an extension of the arc discovered by Barbier.

A most characteristic feature of the subvisual red arc is its large intensity ratio: I (6300)/I (5577) $\sim$ 80; another important feature is that the N_2 + ING bands are not seen in its spectrum. Roach and Marovich [82/ state that the arc is not affected by the breakup of the common yellowish-white

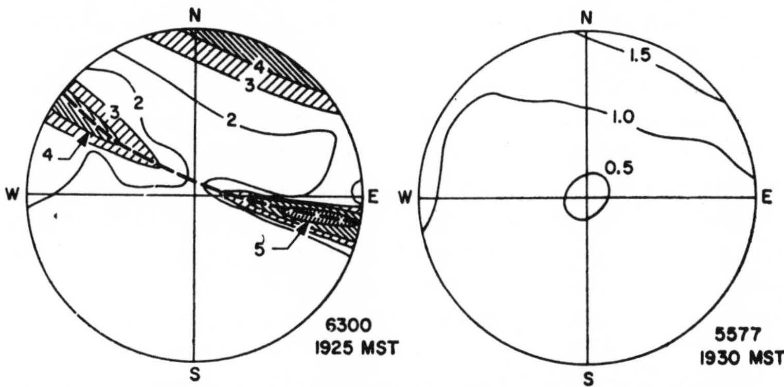

FIG. 5. The isointensity contours for λ 6300 Å and λ5577 Å at Rapid City at 1930 MST on the night of 22 October 1958.

aurora to the north. Figure 5 shows the photometric data obtained on the night of 22 October 1958.

Isointensity contours in a meridian cross section of a red arc were obtained by Tohmatsu and Roach [93]. The height of the brightest portion is of order 380 km; its width in latitude is of order 400 $\sim$ 500 km. A detailed summary of present knowledge of the red arc is given by F. E. and J. R. Roach [83].

Because of the large ratio I(6300)/I(5577), the excitation of the arc must operate preferentially to populate $O(^1D)$, but not $O(^1S)$. Energetic particles are not likely to be involved, because of the absence of the N_2^+ ING bands. Several processes have been proposed (King and Roach [61]; Megill *et al.* [68]), but further detailed study seems to be necessary to reveal the nature of the red arc.

In addition to the above subvisual red arc, Barbier *et al.* [47] and Barbier

[46] discovered red arcs over Tamanrasset (gm. lat. 25.4°N). They found an empirical relation between the intensity of the red arc and the characteristics of the *F*-layer of the ionosphere.

(*d*) *Red Veil during Great Magnetic Storms.* During intense magnetic storms, some of the atomic oxygen lines, particularly λ6300[OI], are greatly enhanced; in low latitudes it is seen as a dark red luminosity covering the northern half sky (cf. Manring and Pettit [65]. During the IGY such an enhancement was observed three times, even as far south as Mexico (gm. lat. 30°N), on the nights already mentioned.

It is not yet certainly known whether such luminosity is the uppermost part of bright bands located far to the north. It has often been reported, as from Mexico on 11 February 1958, that yellowish-white rays are seen in the red luminosity. The enhancement of the λ6300[OI] line seems to be associated with the breakup phase of the aurora to the north [44]. Seaton [87] suggested that this light is produced by accelerated ionospheric electrons, Hikosaka and Yano [58] suggested a direct bombardment of the ionosphere by protons.

(*e*) *Polar Cap Glow Auroras.* The sun produces not only energetic cosmic ray particles, but also a great number of subcosmic-ray particles. Leinbach and Reid [62] found from the simultaneous riometer records from Thule (gm. lat. 88°N), Barrow (gm. lat. 70°N), and College (gm. lat. 64.7°N) after a large solar flare that the ionosphere was heavily bombarded by subcosmic-ray particles guided by the earth's magnetic field towards the polar region. Because of their impact in the lower part of the ionosphere, radio waves are seriously absorbed there (polar cap absorption).

Sandford [85, 86] has shown that during polar cap absorptions an intense glow appears over the polar cap, below an altitude of 100 km (down to 60 km), primarily excited by such solar protons. The intensity of the N_2^+ ING bands is of order 10 kr. Montalbetti and McEwen also [71] observed the Hα glow during polar cap absorption.

(*f*) *Artificial Auroras.* It has been demonstrated that high-energy electrons ejected from nuclear bombs produce an aurora-like luminosity. The artificial aurora associated with the explosion "Teak" over Johnston Island in the Pacific on 1 August 1958 was studied in detail by Steiger and Matsushita [91], Cullington [51], and Malville [64].

The Argus I, II, and III explosions in August–September 1958 were studied by Newman [75]. A brilliant artificial aurora was also produced at Christchurch after another explosion over Johnston Island on 9 July, 1962; Neff [74] showed that over Christchurch (close to the conjugate point of the explosion) the peak intensity of λ6300[OI], λ5577[OI], and λ4278 (from N_2^+ ING bands) was of order 200, 20, and 1 kr, respectively; he showed also that the decay rate of the intensity of λ6300 was 0.0087/sec, which is close to the theoretical value of 0.0092/sec.

7.2. The Excitation of Auroral Luminosity

(*a*) *Hydrogen Glow.* Romick and Elvey [84] and Galperin [55] following Fan and Schulte [53] noticed that the auroral hydrogen emissions are seen in the early phase of the aurora (quiet arcs), but not in the active rayed forms. After extensive calculation of the intensity ratio $I(3914)/I(H\beta)$, Chamberlain [49, p. 256] concluded that protons are not the main cause of auroral arcs.

Later observations have shown that the hydrogen emissions appear in a large part of the auroral sky, but are not necessarily associated with visible auroras [56, 72, 78, 81, 92].

A diagram by Omholt, Stoffregen, and Derblom is reproduced here as Figure 6. Rees *et al.* [81] summarize the main features of the hydrogen glow as follows:

1. The hydrogen emissions appear in a broad diffuse arc, barely visible

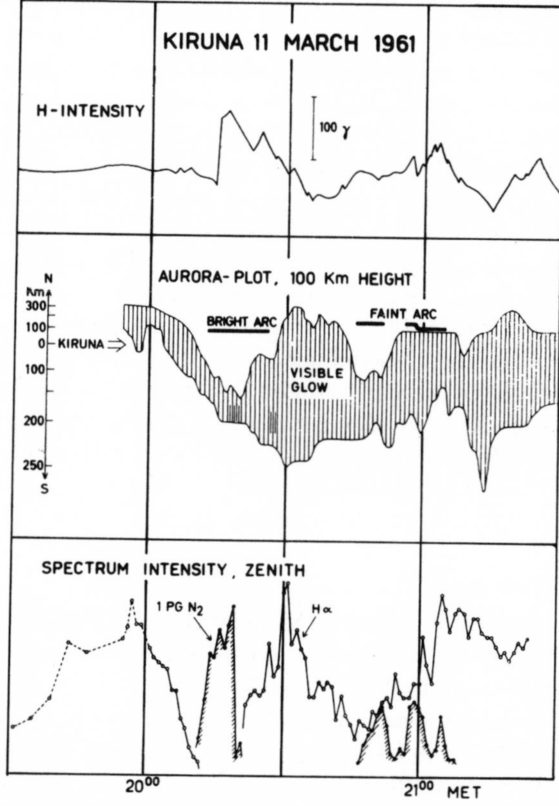

FIG. 6. The distribution of the glow excited by the proton bombardment and of visible auroras, together with magnetic and spectral data.

to the eye—very different from the ordinary thin arcs, which are excited mainly by electrons.

2. Before midnight, the hydrogen arc is located to the south of distinct auroral forms, but after midnight it is to their north (see also Montalbetti and Vallance Jones [70]).

3. During magnetically quiet periods equatorward and poleward movement seems to be a regular feature.

4. At the time of onset of polar magnetic storms, the broad arc seems to shift rapidly equatorward.

(*b*) *Low-Energy Electrons; Rocket Studies.* In 1958 the first direct study of auroral primary particles was made by Meredith *et al.* [69]. Their rockets launched at Fort Churchill detected an intense flow of electrons within visible auroras. On the other hand, the protons were detected over a wide band, and did not seem to be confined within visible auroras; this agrees with the conclusion in (*a*) that visible auroras are not necessarily produced by incoming protons. These conclusions were later confirmed by McIlwain [67] and McDiarmid *et al.* [66].

Further joint and simultaneous observations were recently made by satellite and on the ground [52]. When a satellite passed northward over Alaska, approximately along the 156° geographic meridian, a stable homogeneous arc was located approximately over Fort Yukon. The photometers located at College and Fort Yukon scanned the sky and "triangulated" the aurora. Electrons of energy less than 20 kev were detected within the auroral form by counters carried on the satellite. The energy spectrum is expressed by $E^{-3.6}$, E being the energy of electrons in kev. A calculated luminosity-height profile of the aurora, based on the above energy spectrum, seems to reproduce the observed one.

It seems likely from the above studies that most of the auroral luminosity is produced by electrons. By direct impact they ionize nitrogen molecules in excited states, resulting in the N_2^+ ING bands and others. Secondary electrons thus produced contribute greatly to the excitation of the [OI] lines, such as λ5577 and the λ6300 doublet lines.

7.3. Other Spectral Studies

(*a*) *New identification.* Shefov [88 to 90] has reported that an emission at λ10830 in the sunlit atmosphere is due to fluorescent scattering of solar radiation by HeI atoms in the metastable state.

Infrared regions of the auroral spectrum, particularly the Meinel bands, have recently been extensively explored by the Canadian group [57 to 59, 77]; Fastie, Crosswhite, and their colleagues by rocket studies have explored the ultraviolet region [50, 54].

(*b*) *Upper Atmospheric Temperatures from Auroral Spectra.* The determination of the atmospheric temperature from auroral spectra has greatly advanced by use of the Fabry-Perot interferometer [73, 76, 94, 95]. The temperature at 100-km level determined from the thermal Doppler broadening of atomic lines is found to be of order 300°K; the temperature determined from λ6300[OI] always indicates a higher temperature than that from λ5577[OI].

8. Auroral Particles and the Radiation Belt

Since the radiation belts were discovered, the relationships between the auroral and energetic particles circulating there have been intensively studied. Particle detectors carried by balloons, rockets, and satellites have proved to be powerful tools for the exploration of the origin of auroral particles, which certainly proceed from the radiation belts. Unfortunately the energy of the particles responsible for the major auroral luminosity is close to or below the threshold energy of most of the present detectors carried by balloons and satellites. Thus it is still difficult to draw final conclusions from them as to the origin of the auroral primaries.

8.1. The Balloon Studies

In 1957 Anderson [96] observed a soft radiation by an apparatus carried by balloons at Churchill (gm. lat. 68.7°N) during the magnetic storm of 29–30 August 1957. Winckler *et al.* [107] also observed intense X-ray bursts by an ionization chamber carried by a balloon at an altitude of 30 km over Minneapolis (gm. lat. 55.5°N); the bursts occurred at the time when a bright rayed band passed over the balloon. They were produced by primary electrons with energy sufficient to enable them to penetrate down to about 80–100 km. The photons themselves can travel down to a height of 30–40 km, where they are observed by various balloonborne detectors [106]. Using various X-ray detectors, it is possible to infer the energy spectrum of the primary electrons (Fig. 7). The minimum energy thus far observed is about 25 kev.

Such X-ray bursts have been mainly studied by two groups, of Minnesota and Berkeley; some of the earlier results are summarized by Winckler [105, 106]. Figure 8 gives an excellent example of X-ray bursts and associated cosmic radio noise absorption and magnetic data [107].

It has been established that in the subauroral zone there is a close relation between X-ray bursts and auroral and magnetic activity. However, this correlation is not always found in the auroral zone [97, 101]. This may be partly because auroral zone auroras are mainly produced by electrons of energy less than 25 kev, and partly due to geometrical complexities [102, 103]. Further detailed study is necessary to examine this point. However, the close relation between X-ray bursts and auroral activity in the subauroral zone indicates that there is an association between the primary auroral electrons and the more energetic electrons that generate the X-rays.

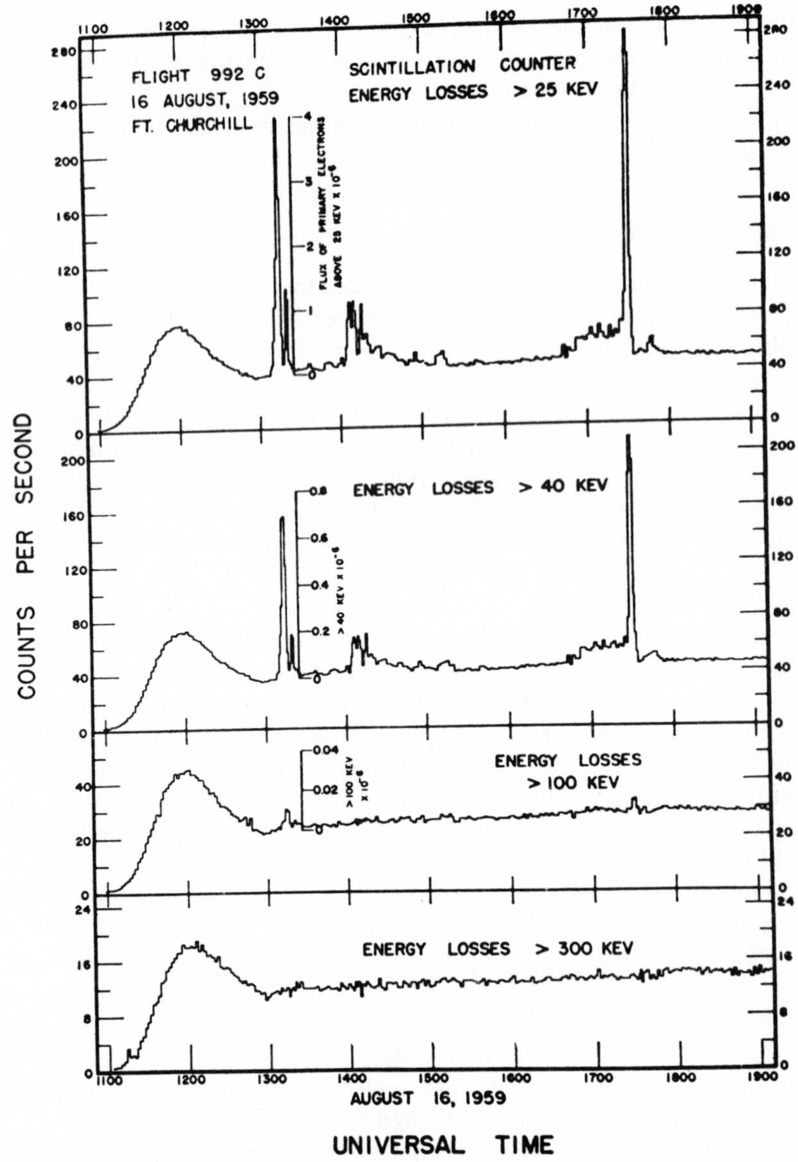

FIG. 7. An example of the X-ray bursts observed in four energy ranges.

Winckler *et al.* [108] made the interesting and important discovery that the X-ray bursts occur in series, each burst being short, of order 0.1 sec duration. They also estimated that the total number of electrons entering the atmosphere during the magnetic storm of 29–30 September 1961 exceeded the number stored in the outer radiation belt by at least a factor of

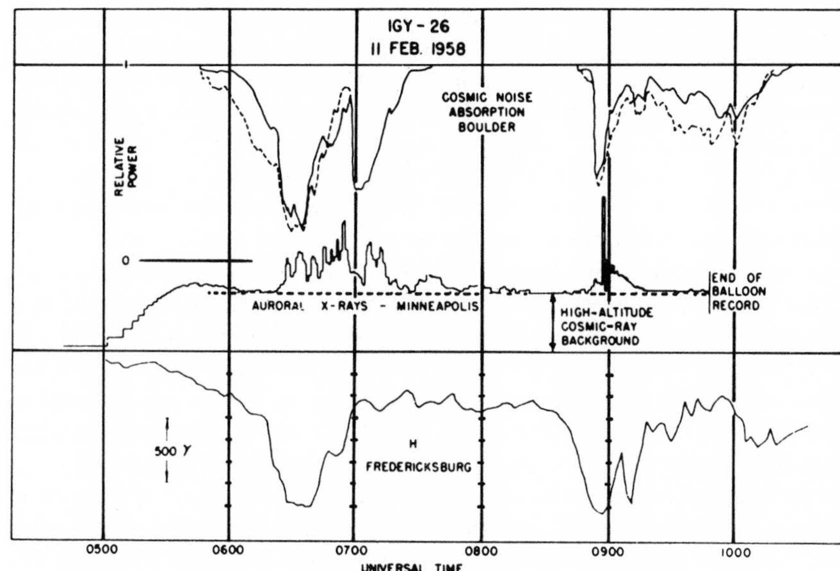

FIG. 8. Simultaneous observations of the cosmic radio noise absorption, X-ray bursts and geomagnetic field on 11 February 1958.

10. This implies that the outer belt is not simply a reservoir of electrons which, once filled, can provide the particles that produce the auroral displays of such a storm; there must be a replenishment of the store during the course of the storm.

Anderson *et al.* [98] observed auroral electron precipitation (by its X-ray bursts) at the conjugate stations College, Alaska, and Macquarie Island in the Antarctic.

8.2. Satellite Studies

The early exploration of the outer radiation belt was made by satellite geiger counters whose threshold energy for electrons was of order 1.5 Mev. Such electrons penetrated directly into the counter, but the counts were misinterpreted; it was thought that they represented X-rays caused by the impact on the counter of electrons whose energy was of order 100 kev, implying that the electrons were 1000 times more numerous than the counts, because only about one electron gives up its energy in bremsstrahlung. Improved counters carried on the Injun I and Explorer XII satellites revealed the error. They showed also that the auroral electrons, of energy 40 kev or less, constitute a quite different belt, extending between about 2 and 10 earth radii.

(*a*) *The Aurora in Relation to High-Energy Electrons* (>1.5 Mev). Arnoldy *et al.* [99] found the first definite indication that the "classical" outer belt of highly energetic electrons changes greatly in intensity during magnetic storms. During the main phase of the storm of 16 August 1959, counters carried by the Explorer VI satellite indicated a remarkable reduction of the counting rate, over a large part of the belt. Then, during the recovery phase of the storm, the flux began to increase rapidly; eventually it exceeded the prestorm counting rate. Arnoldy *et al.* [100] showed also that a rapid decrease in the counting rate coincided with a strong breakup of the aurora seen at Fargo (gm. lat. 56.7°N). The satellite was about 4.6 earth radii away from the earth's center.

It does not seem likely that such high-energy electrons contribute much to the auroral luminosity. Nevertheless, it is important that the production process of auroral primaries affects such high-energy electrons.

(*b*) *Auroral Electrons, of Energy of Order 40 kev.* The main part of the auroral light appears to be produced by electrons of energy much less than that of the outer belt electrons (e.g., 1.5 Mev). Such moderately energetic electrons, registered by the geiger counter 213 on Injun I during one of its northbound passes, gave the counting rate shown in Figure 9 as a function of time, and alternatively as a function of magnetic axis latitude, and of McIlwain's length L. The satellite was at a height of about 1000 km; the detector was pointing at right angles to the magnetic field. It registered electrons whose mirror point was about 1000 km above the earth's surface.

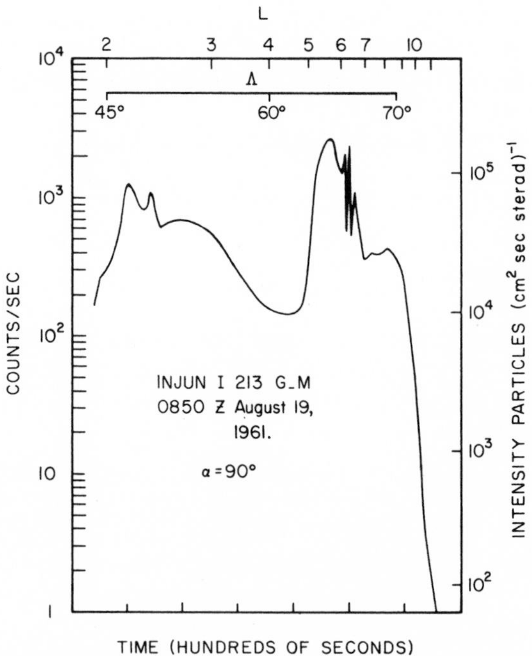

FIG. 9. The distribution of the counting rate observed by the Injun I satellite. Note an anomalous intensity over the auroral zone.

Figure 9 shows that their flux had a peak, with irregularities, in auroral latitudes.

Such electrons would not contribute to the aurora, being turned back high above the F-layer. O'Brien [104] was able to measure the pitch angle distribution of the electrons, and so to determine what proportion of the low-energy electrons would penetrate (or be "dumped" into) the atmosphere. His diagram here shown as Figure 10 shows that whereas the total density of trapped electrons is nearly uniformly distributed across the belt,

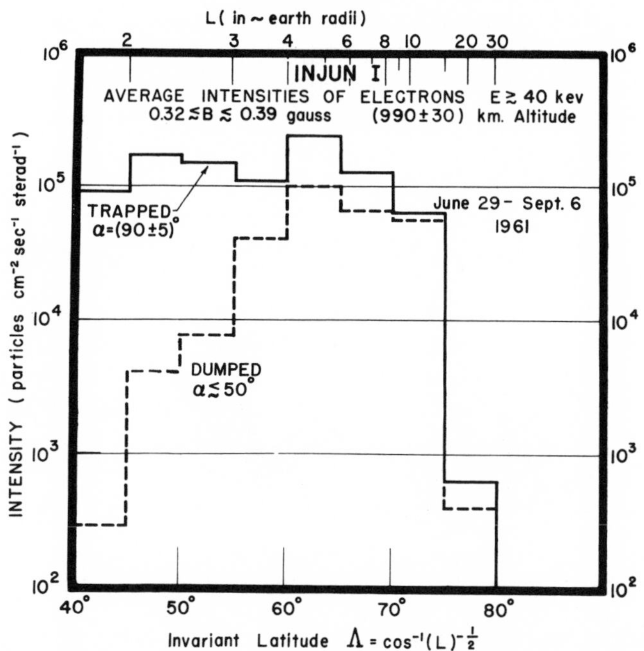

FIG. 10. Average intensities of trapped and dumped electrons (From O'Brien [104]).

the proportion that can be "dumped" increases toward the outer part of the belt. Maehlum and O'Brien found that the radius (from the earth's center) of the outer boundary of the belt decreases during the main phase of a magnetic storm. Electrons that enter the atmosphere from there would consequently reach the earth in a lower latitude than usual—as is observed during storms. O'Brien suggested that the electrons of small pitch angle, able to penetrate the atmosphere and cause auroras, are continuously produced in and lost to the belt.

9. Radio Studies of the Aurora

During the IGY/C, various radio techniques were extensively used to investigate the aurora; they included auroral radar, riometers, and ionospheric sounders. Booker [111] summarized some of the earlier studies. The relation between visible auroras and *radio* or *radar auroras* is not yet clear. Different instruments see different features of the aurora, depending on their characteristics and on the response of the aurora.

9.1. The Radar Studies of the Aurora

The mechanism of radio wave reflection from the aurora has been much discussed. Kaiser [117] interpreted auroral echoes as coming from the surface of an arc lying along a parallel of geomagnetic latitude. However, Unwin [126], Seed [125], Pogorelov [124], and Baker *et al.* [109] demonstrated that the echoes are reflections from aspect sensitive "columns" aligned along the geomagnetic field lines (Fig. 11). The latter's argument

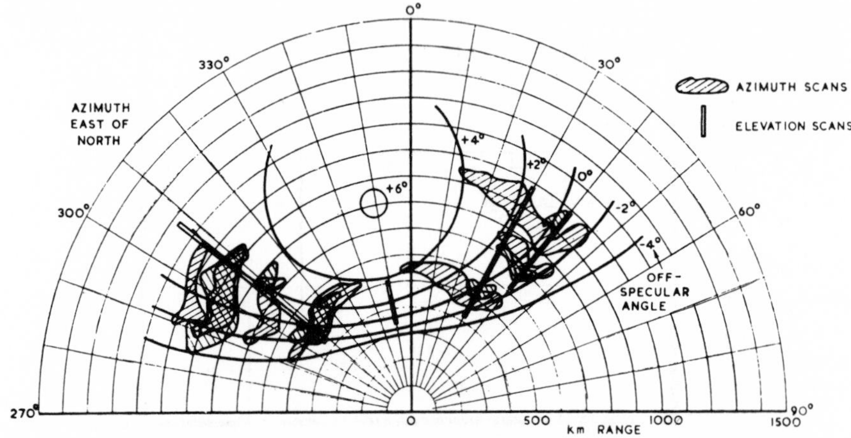

FIG. 11. The locations of auroral echo regions detected at 500 Mc/sec.

was based on Chapman's calculation [112] on the geometry of the aspect-sensitive reflection from aurora; for this particular mechanism the radar echoes are strongest when the ionized "column" is seen perpendicularly by radar beams. Recent workers seem to agree that this is the most important mechanism of reflection, although no definite relation has been found between the visual ray structure of the aurora and the echoes [116]. A further critical study was made by the Canadian group [115].

Both Unwin [126] and Leonard [119] studied radar echoes in detail. The former examined and classified the types of the echoes; the latter contributed greatly to our knowledge of the morphological features of radar auroras. Further extensive studies were made by the Stanford and Canadian groups, including Leadabrand, Presnell, Berg, and Dyce [118], Lyon and Kavadas [123], Forsyth [114], and Lyon and Forsyth [122].

9.2. The Riometer Studies of the Aurora

Our knowledge of the absorption of radio waves caused by the aurora was greatly advanced by the riometer, introduced by Little [120]; see Little and Leinbach [121]. It is a device that records the intensity of cosmic radio noise at relatively high frequencies; thus it can measure absorption that is too great to be determined by ordinary ionospheric sounders. The Alaskan riometer data have been used by Basler [110] to find the daily variation of auroral absorption at College for the five magnetically disturbed and five quiet days. He showed that during the winter and equinoxes the absorption has a rather broad maximum between 0600 and 1300, and a minimum between 1900 and 2200 local time. During the summer months, however, there seems to be no such marked daily variation, and the absorption is less, on the average, than in winter. Chapman and Little [113] discussed the theory of such nondeviative absorption, and the electron density distributions that could produce the observed absorption by day and by night.

10. The Problems of Auroral Physics

The period of initiation, planning, and execution of the IGY enterprise saw the rise of a new generation of researchers in geomagnetic and auroral science. Many of the leaders in observational studies by balloon, rocket, and satellite, which have so greatly advanced the science, have already been mentioned here. Among the principal pioneers in theoretical and interpretative studies in this field, Dessler, Fejer, Hines, Parker, Piddington, and Singer were prominent. They brought new life, criticism, and ideas to the theories developed earlier.

A basic problem of auroral physics is the origin of auroral primary electrons (of energy of order 5 kev). In order to maintain an aurora of medium intensity, there must be an electron flux of order $10^{10}/\text{cm}^2$ sec in a narrow ribbonlike structure. Such low-energy electrons are not likely, however, to be directly injected into the auroral zone from the solar plasma through the magnetospheric boundary. Hence it is suspected that an acceleration process operates within the magnetosphere. If so, it must be very effective, giving thermal electrons sufficient energy to enable them to penetrate deep into the auroral ionosphere. One possibility is a direct acceleration of thermal electrons in the magnetosphere by an electric field (E). This process can be effective in the undisturbed magnetosphere only if E has a component along the lines of force (the component perpendicular to the magnetic field H produces only a drift velocity $v = E \times H/H^2$). It is not certain, however, that a sufficient electric field along the field line can be created and maintained for as long as auroral arcs sometimes remain in one location. An alternative hypothesis is that at the source of the electron flux the magnetic field intensity is close to zero, in a narrow region around the equatorial plane; thermal electrons can be accelerated by an electric field along such a region. On this basis Akasofu and Chapman [128] proposed a neutral line discharge theory. They suggested that the ring current reverses the direction of the earth's field within a limited equatorial strip; several workers have urged that such a reversal is impossible. But a reduction of the field to a very low value may serve instead.

Axford and Hines [130] propose that there is large-scale convective motion within the magnetosphere. They consider that solar particles will be transported by the convective motion into the magnetosphere and will eventually be accelerated. It has not yet been demonstrated whether such large-scale convective motion can be set up by interaction between the solar plasma flow and the magnetosphere. Their argument relies partly on the observed or inferred motions of auroras and ionospheric irregularities over the polar cap.

Chamberlain [131] has suggested that inhomogeneity of the plasma density in the magnetosphere will result in a charge separation around the boundary of the inhomogeneity, and that particles projected into such a boundary layer will gain increased speed along the lines of force. The effectiveness of this process has been questioned by Cole [132] and others.

Thus at present there is no agreed and satisfactory theory to explain the production of auroral primaries. There is also no agreed explanation of the thin ribbonlike structure. The great East-West extension of arcs must also be explained; single arcs have a planetary scale, and therefore cannot be produced merely by small-scale local irregular features in the magnetosphere. The multiplicity of auroral arcs is yet another fundamental feature, of which the theory by Akasofu and Chapman [128] offers an explanation.

Another important feature of the aurora is the substorm, which disrupts quiet and homogeneous arcs and leads to brilliant auroral displays. A detailed examination of all-sky camera records shows that the substorm starts and becomes most intense around the midnight sector where quiet arcs preexist; then the activity spreads in both directions. The magnetospheric region connected by the field lines to the midnight sector of the auroral zone is fairly well "protected" by the earth's magnetic field from particle invasion from the solar plasma. Further, there is no optical evidence to show that before the substorm solar plasma particles penetrate the magnetospheric boundary toward that region. It may be that some "invisible" process such as hydromagnetic waves is associated with the substorms. But it is not certain whether such wave energy can converge to a rather limited region of the magnetosphere, where the substorm first takes place. Various dynamical features associated with the aurora must be examined in detail to explore further the nature of the substorms. It is known [129] that a simple increase of the solar plasma pressure, such as is manifested by the storm's sudden commencement and the initial phase, does not necessarily lead to auroral and magnetic polar substorms. Thus at present the nature of the energy of activation, and the way in which it enters the magnetosphere, are not understood. Further observations by satellites and space probes will provide valuable light on these problems.

The existence of the auroral zones of maximum occurrence frequency is another essential feature. Satellite studies have shown that the auroral zones are located approximately along the lines of intersection of the outer boundary of the outer radiation belt with the auroral ionosphere. Therefore auroral primaries are likely to be produced near the outer boundary of the outer radiation belt. It has in fact been found that during great magnetic storms the outer boundary of the belt moves nearer to the earth, and the active zone of the aurora shifts toward the equator.

The auroras that appear within the auroral cap present a number of interesting problems; often they differ from the auroral zone auroras in many ways. In particular, unlike the zone auroras, those in the auroral cap which appear in the early morning tend to be negatively correlated with magnetic disturbances. The alignment of the arcs along the sun-earth line [17, 18] is another interesting feature to be investigated further.

The excitation mechanism of the usual yellowish-white auroras has become clearer during the last few years; it is found that electrons of energy below 10 kev play the most important role. However, agreement has not been reached as to the excitation of special types of aurora, such as those of Type A, subvisual red arcs, and red veils. In all these cases, the preferential excitation of the $\lambda 6300$ (OI) line, compared with that of the $\lambda 5577$ (OI) line, is the most serious problem.

The hydrogen glow, often present on the equatorial side of visible evening auroras, has been supposed to play an important role in the generation of the auroral electrojet and polar magnetic substorms; Kern [135] and Chamberlain [131] inferred that there will be an electrostatic field between the visible aurora and the hydrogen glow, which impels an electric current flow in the ionosphere.

Several workers have proposed that dynamo action is the cause of the polar magnetic substorms. The basic idea is that anomalous ionization in the auroral zone during magnetic storms produces additional current, which supplements the *Sq*-variation. Cole [133] attaches importance to a wind system generated by Joule heating by the auroral electrojets.

The striking similarity of polar magnetic storms at geomagnetically conjugate points suggests, however, that the electrojets are governed by something other than the wind system; there is no simple reason why the wind pattern should be closely similar in the conjugate areas. (see Wescott *et al.* [136]). Axford and Hines [130] and Piddington [135] suggested that auroral jets are related to the supposed magnetospheric convective motion. Whichever of these different ideas may be right, it seems certain that a strong westward electrojet would be produced by an equatorward electric field in the ionosphere [127].

Acknowledgments

We express our thanks to Dr. C. T. Elvey for his comments on the draft of this paper, and to Drs. D. Barbier, A. Vallance Jones, C. W. Gartlein, M. Huruhata, F. Jacka, V. I. Krassovskii, G. Lange-Hesse, J. Paton, F. E. Roach, O. Schneider, and W. H. Ward for their help in the preparation of this report. This study was in part supported by a grant from the National Aeronautics and Space Administration (No. NsG 201–62).

Bibliography

(*a*) IGY-IGC Publications

Abhandlungen der Akademie der Wissenschaften in Göttingen, Mathematisch-Physikalische Klasse: Beiträge zum Internationalen Geophyikalischen Jahr, Heft Nr. 1: "A simple elevometer for auroral observations," and "A twenty-one year series of geomagnetic activity data, in relation to appearance of aurora in low latitudes," by S. Chapman and J. Bartels (1958); Nr. 6: "German visual aurora observations during the IGY and IGC, 1957–1959," by G. Lange-Hesse (1961).

Annals of the International Geophysical Year, **4**, part 2: "The aurora in middle and low latitudes," and "Visual aurora observation," by S. Chapman; "Auroral photography by all-sky camera," by C. T. Elvey and W. Stoffregen (1958). **20,** parts 1 and 2: "IGY Ascaplots," by W. Stoffregen (1962–1963). **20,** part 3: "The dynamical morphology of the aurora polaris," by S.-I. Akasofu (1963).

Année Géophysique Internationale Participation Française, Série 4, fasc. 1: Aurores et ceil nocturne (Centre National de la Recherche Scientifique, Paris, 1961).

Aurora and Airglow: Results of Research on Section IV of IGY Program (USSR Academy of Sciences, Moscow, 1959–1963). [Nos. 1–6 of this series have the title, "Spectral, Electrophotometrical and Radar Researches of Aurorae and Airglow."]

British Antarctic Survey Scientific Reports, No. 37: "Analysis of auroral observations, Halley Bay, 1959," by M. A. Sheret (1963).

Expédition Antarctique Belge 1957–1958: Résultats Scientifiques, **4**: "Aurores," by J. Loodts, G. de Gerlache de Gomery, and P. Doyen (1963).

Expéditions Polaires Françaises, Publication No. 220: "Terre Adélie 1959, observations visuelles des aurores," by B. Groznykh (1961).

Geofysiske Publikasjoner, Geophysica Norvegica,**20–23** (1957–1962).

Geophysical Institute, University of Alaska, Contributions.

Instituto Antartico Argentino (Buenos Aires), Contribucions.

IGY General Report Series (IGY World Data Center A, U.S. National Academy of Sciences, 1958–1963) especially No. 12: "Report on IGY visual auroral observations," by C. W. Gartlein and G. C. Sprague (1960).

Japanese Contribution to the International Geophysical Year 1957/8 and the International Geophysical Cooperation 1959, **1-5**: Section IV, Aurora and airglow (Science Council of Japan, Tokyo, 1958–1963).

Kiruna Geophysical Observatory (Sweden), Contributions.

New Zealand IGY Antarctic Expeditions, Scott Base and Hallett Stations, by T. Hatherton (New Zealand Department of Scientific and Industrial Research, Bulletin No. 140, 1961). [See section on "Aurorae," p. 66–88.]

Royal Society International Geophysical Year Antarctic Expedition, Halley Bay, Coats Land, Falkland Islands Dependencies, 1955–1959, **1**: "Visual and photographic auroral observations," by S. Evans and G. M. Thomas, p. 27–54 (1960).

Theoretical Interpretation of Upper Atmosphere Emissions, D. R. Bates (ed.) (Papers delivered at the International Astronomical Union Symposium No. 18, Paris, June 1962; Pergamon Press, 1963. Reprinted from *Planetary and Space Science*, **10,** 1963).

(*b*) General

H. Alfvén, *Cosmical Electrodynamics* (Clarendon Press, 1950).
J. W. Chamberlain, *Physics of the Aurora and Airglow* (Academic Press, 1961).
S. Chapman and J. Bartels, *Geomagnetism* (Clarendon Press, 1940).
C. deWitt, J. Hieblot, and A. Lebeau (eds.), *Geophysics; The Earth's Environment* (Gordon and Breach, 1963).
J. W. Dungey, *Cosmic Electrodynamics* (Cambridge Univ. Press, 1958).
C. T. Elvey, Problems in auroral morphology, *Proc. Nat'l Acad. Sci., U.S.*, **43,** 63 (1957).
E. N. Parker, *Interplanetary Dynamical Processes* (Interscience, 1963).
J. A. Ratcliffe (ed.), *Physics of the Upper Atmosphere* (Academic Press, 1960).
C. Störmer, *The Polar Aurora* (Clarendon Press, 1955).

[Note: Some of the early papers mentioned in Section 1, that are listed in the second and third books listed above, (*b*) General, are omitted from the following list of references.]

References

Section 1

1. H. Alfvén, *Cosmical Electrodynamics* (Clarendon Press, 1950).
2. E. V. Appleton, R. Naismith, and L. J. Ingram, British radio observations during the Second International Polar Year, 1932–33, *Phil. Trans. Roy. Soc.*, **A236,** 191 (1937).
3. S. Chapman and V. C. A. Ferraro, A new theory of magnetic storms, *Terr. Mag. Atmos. Elect.*, **36,** 77 (1931).
4. J. W. Dungey, Conditions for the occurrence of electrical discharges in astrophysical systems, *Phil. Mag.*, **44,** 725 (1953).
5. C. W. Gartlein, Aurora spectra showing broad hydrogen lines, *Trans. Amer. Geophys. Un.*, **31,** 18 (1950).
6. L. Harang and W. Stoffregen, Scattered reflections of radio waves from a height of more than 1000 km, *Nature*, **142,** 832 (1938).
7. J. P. Heppner, Time sequences and spatial relations in auroral activity during magnetic bays at College, Alaska, *J. Geophys. Res.*, **59,** 329 (1954).
8. F. Hoyle, *Some Recent Researches in Solar Physics* (Cambridge Univ. Press, 1949).
9. D. F. Martyn, The theory of magnetic storms and auroras, *Nature*, **167,** 92 (1951).
10. A. B. Meinel, Doppler-shifted auroral hydrogen emission, *Astrophys. J.*, **113,** 50 (1951).
11. L. H. Meredith, M. B. Gottlieb, and J. A. Van Allen, Direct detection of soft radiation above 50 kilometers in the auroral zone, *Phys. Rev.*, **97,** 201 (1955).
12. J. A. Van Allen, Direct detection of auroral radiation with rocket equipment, *Proc. Nat'l. Acad. Sci., U. S.*, **43,** 57 (1957).
13. E. H. Vestine, The geographic incidence of aurora and magnetic disturbance, northern hemisphere, *Terr. Mag. Atmos. Elect.*, **49,** 77 (1944).
14. F. W. G. White and M. Geddes, The Antarctic zone of maximum auroral frequency, *Terr. Mag. Atmos. Elect.*, **44,** 367 (1939).

Section 2

(No references)

Section 3

15. S.-I. Akasofu, The dynamic morphology of the aurora polaris, *J. Geophys. Res.*, **68,** 1667 (1963).
16. L. Biermann, Kometenschweife und solare Korpuskularstrahlung, *Z. Astrophys.*, **29,** 274 (1951).

17. T. N. Davis, The morphology of the auroral displays of 1957–1958, 1. Statistical analyses of Alaska data, *J. Geophys. Res.*, **67**, 59 (1962).
18. T. N. Davis, The morphology of the auroral displays of 1957–1958, 2. Detail analyses of Alaska data and analyses of high-latitude data, *J. Geophys. Res.*, **67**, 75 (1962).
19. E. N. Parker, Dynamics of the interplanetary gas and magnetic fields, *Astrophys. J.*, **128**, 664 (1958).
20. J. M. Stagg, *British Polar Expedition, Fort Rae, N.W., Canada, 1932–33, I.* (Royal Society, London, 1937).

Section 4

21. R. N. deWitt, The occurrence of aurora in geomagnetically conjugate areas, *J. Geophys. Res.*, **67**, 1347 (1962).
22. J. P. Heppner, Time sequences and spatial relations in auroral activity during magnetic bays at College, Alaska, *J. Geophys. Res.*, **59**, 329 (1954).

Section 5

23. S.-I. Akasofu and S. Chapman, Large-scale auroral motions and polar magnetic disturbances, IV. The aurora and magnetic storm of 11 February 1958, *J. Atmos. Terr. Phys.*, **24**, 185 (1962).
24. S.-I. Akasofu and S. Chapman, The lower limit of latitude (U.S. sector) of northern quiet auroral arcs and its relation to *Dst* (H), *J. Atmos. Terr. Phys.*, **25**, 9 (1963).
25. F. R. Bond and F. Jacka, Distribution of auroras in the southern hemisphere, *Aust. J. Phys.*, **13**, 611 (1960).
26. T. N. Davis, The morphology of the auroral displays of 1957–1958, 1. Statistical analyses of Alaska data, *J. Geophys. Res.*, **67**, 59 (1962).
27. Y. I. Feldstein, Geographical distribution of aurora and azimuth of auroral arcs, In: *Aurora and Airglow No. 4*, 61 (Section IV of IGY Program, Acad. Sci. USSR, Moscow, 1960).
28. J. F. Finch and B. R. Leaton, The earth's main magnetic field epoch 1955.0, *Geophys. Suppl. Mon. Not. Roy. Astron. Soc.*, **1**, 314 (1957).
29. C. W. Gartlein and G. C. Sprague, Report on IGY visual auroral observations, *IGY Gen. Report No. 12* (U.S. Nat'l Acad. Sci., Washington, 1960).
30. B. Hultqvist, Auroral isochasms, *Nature*, **183**, 1478 (1959).
31. G. Lange-Hesse, German visual aurora observations during the International Geophysical Year and the International Geophysical Cooperation 1957–1959, *Abhandl. Akad. Wissen. Göttingen, Math.-Phys. Klasse No. 6* (1961).
32. B. McInnes and K. A. Robertson, Latitude distribution and seasonal variation of aurora over the British Isles during 1957 and 1958. *J. Atmos. Terr. Phys.*, **19**, 115 (1960).
33. J. Quenby and W. R. Webber, Cosmic ray cut-off rigidities and the earth's magnetic field, *Phil. Mag.*, **8**, 90 (1959).
34. O. Schneider, Indices de actividad auroral, *Contribucion del Instituto Antartico Argentino No. 56* (Buenos Aires, 1961).
35. E. H. Vestine and E. J. Snyder, The geographic incidence of aurora and magnetic disturbance, southern hemisphere, *Terr. Mag. Atmos. Elect.*, **50**, 105 (1945).
36. E. H. Vestine and W. L. Sibley, The geomagnetic field in space, ring currents, and auroral isochasms, *J. Geophys. Res.*, **65**, 1967 (1960).

Section 6

37. F. T. Davies, Visual auroral observations in Canada, *ATME Bull. No. 13*, Trans. Oslo Meeting (1948).
38. T. N. Davis, Negative correlation between polar-cap aurora and magnetic activity, *J. Geophys. Res.*, **68**, 4447 (1963).
39. J. V. Denholm, Some auroral observations inside the southern auroral zone, *J. Geophys. Res.*, **66**, 2105 (1961).

40. Y. I. Feldstein and E. K. Solomatina, Some problems of the geographic distribution of aurorae in the northern hemisphere, *In, Aurorae and Airglow No. 7*, 51 (Section IV of IGY Program, Acad. Sci. USSR, Moscow, 1961).
41. T. Hatherton, Geometry of the southern auroral zone and the evidence for the existence of an inner zone, *Nature*, **186**, 288 (1960).
42. T. Hatherton and G. G. Midwinter, Observations of the aurora australis at New Zealand Antarctic stations during IGY, *J. Geophys. Res.*, **65**, 1401 (1960).
43. K. Lassen, Local aurorae in the morning hours at Godhavn, Greenland, *Det Danske Met. Inst.* (1959).

Section 7

44. S.-I. Akasofu, Large-scale auroral motions and polar magnetic disturbances, II, *J. Atmos. Terr. Phys.*, **24**, 723 (1962).
45. D. Barbier, L'activité aurorale aux basses latitudes, *Ann. Géophys.*, **14**, 334 (1958).
46. D. Barbier, L'émission de la raie rouge du ciel nocturne et les propriétés de la couche *F* de l'ionosphère, *C.R. Acad. Sci.*, **252**, 3315 (1961).
47. D. Barbier, G. Weill, and M. Fafiotte, Les arcs émis par la raie rouge du ciel nocturne en Afrique, *C.R. Acad. Sci.*, **252**, 3102 (1961).
48. A. E. Belon and K. C. Clark, Spectroscopic observations of the great aurora of 10 February 1959-II, Unusual atomic features, *J. Atmos. Terr. Phys.*, **16**, 220 (1959).
49. J. W. Chamberlain, *Physics of the Aurora and Airglow* (Academic Press, 1961).
50. H. M. Crosswhite, E. C. Zipf, and W. G. Fastie, Far-ultraviolet spectra, *J. Opt. Soc. Amer.*, **52**, 643 (1962).
51. A. L. Cullington, A man-made or artificial aurora, *Nature*, **182**, 1356 (1958).
52. J. E. Evans and A. E. Belon, Preliminary results from coordinated measurements of Auroras, *IGY Bulletin No. 77* (Nat'l Acad. Sci., Washington, 1963).
53. C. Y. Fan and D. H. Schulte, Variations in the auroral spectrum, *Astrophys. J.*, **120**, 563 (1954).
54. W. G. Fastie, H. M. Crosswhite, and T. P. Markham, Auroral spectra with a rocket Ebert spectrophotometer, *Ann. Géophys.*, **17**, 109 (1961).
55. Y. I. Galperin, Hydrogen emission and two types of auroral spectra, *Planet. Space Sci.*, **1**, 57 (1959).
56. Y. I. Galperin, Proton bombardment in aurora, *Planet. Space Sci.*, **10**, 187 (1963).
57. A. W. Harrison and A. Vallance Jones, Measurements of the absolute intensity of the aurora and night airglow in the 0.9–2.0 μ region, *J. Atmos. Terr. Phys.*, **11**, 192 (1957).
58. T. Hikosaka and K. Yano, Low latitude red aurora and low energy protons in Van Allen Belt, *J. Phys. Soc. Japan*, **17**, Suppl. A-I, 233 (1962).
59. D. M. Hunten, Recent work at the University of Saskatchewan on auroral and night sky spectra, *Ann. Géophys.*, **14**, 167 (1958).
60. A. Vallance Jones, Analysis of a spectrogram of the red aurora of February 10/11, 1958, in the wavelength range 7300–8700 Å, *Can. J. Phys.*, **38**, 453 (1960).
61. G. A. M. King and F. E. Roach, Relationship between red auroral arcs and ionospheric recombination, *J. Res. NBS*, **65D**, 129 (1961).
62. H. Leinbach and G. C. Reid, Ionization of the upper atmosphere by low-energy charged particles from a solar flare, *Phys. Rev. Letters*, **2**, 61 (1959).
63. J. M. Malville, Type B aurora in the Antarctic, *J. Atmos. Terr. Phys.*, **16**, 59 (1959).
64. J. M. Malville, Artificial auroras resulting from the 1958 Johnston Island nuclear explosions, *J. Geophys. Res.*, **64**, 2267 (1959).
65. E. R. Manring and H. B. Pettit, Photometric observations of the 5577 Å and 6300 Å emissions made during the aurora of February 10–11, 1958, *J. Geophys. Res.*, **64**, 149 (1959).
66. I. B. McDiarmid, D. C. Rose, and E. Budzinski, Direct measurement of charged particles associated with auroral zone radio absorption, *Can. J. Phys.*, **39**, 1888 (1961).

67. C. E. McIlwain, Direct measurement of protons and electrons in visible aurorae, *Space Research*, 715 (North-Holland, 1960).
68. L. R. Megill, M. H. Rees, and L. K. Droppleman, Electric fields in the ionosphere and the excitation of the red lines of atomic oxygen, *Planet. Space Sci.*, **11,** 45 (1963).
69. L. H. Meredith, L. R. Davis, J. P. Heppner, and O. E. Berg, Rocket auroral investigations, *IGY Rocket Rept. No. 1*, 169(Nat'l. Acad. Sci., Washington, 1958).
70. R. Montalbetti and A. Vallance Jones, H emissions during aurorae over west-central Canada, *J. Atmos. Terr. Phys.*, **11,** 43 (1957).
71. R. Montalbetti and D. J. McEwen, Hydrogen emissions during the period November 9–16, 1960, *Can. J. Phys.*, **39,** 617 (1961).
72. L. E. Montbriand and A. Vallance Jones, Studies of auroral hydrogen emissions in west-central Canada I. Time and geographical variations, *Can. J. Phys.*, **40,** 1401 (1962).
73. T. M. Mulyarchik and P. V. Scheglov, Temperature and corpuscular heating in the auroral zone, *Planet. Space Sci.*, **10,** 215 (1963).
74. S. H. Neff, Photometric observations of an artificial aurora, *J. Geophys. Res.*, **68,** 587 (1963).
75. P. Newman, Optical, electromagnetic, and satellite observations of high-altitude nuclear detonations, Part I, *J. Geophys. Res.*, **64,** 923, (1959).
76. J. A. Nilson and G. G. Shepherd, Upper atmospheric temperatures from Doppler line widths — I, Some preliminary measurements of OI 5577 Å in aurora, *Planet. Space Sci.*, **5,** 299 (1961).
77. J. F. Noxon and A. Vallance Jones, The infrared spectrum of the night airglow 1.4 μ to 4.0 μ, *J. Atmos. Terr. Phys.*, **16,** 246 (1960).
78. A. Omholt, W. Stoffregen, and H. Derblom, Hydrogen lines in auroral glow, *J. Atmos. Terr. Phys.*, **24,** 203 (1962).
79. M. H. Rees, Excitation of high altitude red auroral arcs, *Planet. Space Sci.*, **8,** 59 (1961).
80. M. H. Rees and C. S. Deehr, The aurora of 27 November 1959 at College, Alaska, including observations of a high altitude red arc, *Planet. Space Sci.*, **8,** 49 (1961).
81. M. H. Rees, A. E. Belon, and G. J. Romick, The systematic behavior of hydrogen emission in the aurora, *Planet. Space Sci.*, **5,** 87 (1961).
82. F. E. Roach and E. Marovich, A monochromatic low-latitude aurora, *J. Res. NBS (D)*, **63,** 297 (1959).
83. F. E. Roach and J. R. Roach, Stable 6300 Å auroral arcs in mid-latitudes, *Planet. Space Sci.*, **11,** 523 (1963).
84. G. J. Romick and C. T. Elvey, Variations in the intensity of the hydrogen emission line H during auroral activity, *J. Atmos. Terr. Phys.*, **12,** 283 (1958).
85. B. P. Sandford, Polar-glow aurora in polar cap absorption events, *J. Atmos. Terr. Phys.*, **21,** 117 (1961).
86. B. P. Sandford, Optical studies of particle bombardment in polar cap absorption events, *Planet. Space Sci.*, **10,** 195 (1963).
87. M. J. Seaton, Excitation processes in the aurora and airglow, III, Low-latitude aurorae, *In*: *The Airglow and the Aurorae*, E. B. Armstrong and A. Dalgarno, eds., 225 (Pergamon Press, 1956).
88. N. N. Shefov, On the nature of helium emission 10830 Å in aurorae, *In*: *Aurorae and Airglow No. 5*, 47 (Section IV of IGY Program, Acad. Sci. USSR, Moscow, 1961), *Also*: *Planet. Space Sci.*, **5,** 75 (1961).
89. N. N. Shefov, The helium emission in the upper atmosphere, *In*: *Aurorae and Airglow No. 8*, 50 (Section IV of IGY Program, Acad. Sci. USSR, Moscow, 1962).
90. N. N. Shefov, Helium in the upper atmosphere, *Planet. Space Sci.*, **10,** 73 (1963).
91. W. R. Steiger and S. Matsushita, Photographs of the high-altitude nuclear explosion 'Teak', *J. Geophys. Res.*, **65,** 545 (1960).
92. W. Stoffregen and H. Derblom, Auroral hydrogen emission related to charge separation in the magnetosphere, *Planet. Space Sci.*, **9,** 711 (1962).
93. T. Tohmatsu and F. E. Roach, The morphology of mid-latitude 6300 Å arcs, *J. Geophys. Res.*, **67,** 1817 (1962).

94. E. C. Turgeon and G. G. Shepherd, Upper atmospheric temperatures from Doppler line widths-II, *Planet Space Sci.*, **9,** 295 (1962).
95. D. Q. Wark, Doppler widths of the atomic oxygen lines in the airglow, *Astrophys. J.*, **131,** 491 (1960).

Section 8

96. K. A. Anderson, Soft radiation events at high altitude during the magnetic storm of August 29/30, 1957, *Phys. Rev.*, **111,** 1397 (1957).
97. K. A. Anderson and D. C. Enemark, Balloon observations of x-rays in the auroral zone II, *J. Geophys. Res.*, **65,** 3521 (1960).
98. K. A. Anderson, C. D. Anger, R. R. Brown, and D. S. Evans, Simultaneous electron precipitation in the northern and southern auroral zones, *J. Geophys. Res.*, **67,** 4076 (1962).
99. R. L. Arnoldy, R. A. Hoffman, and J. R. Winckler, Observations of the Van Allen radiation regions during August and September 1959, Part 1, *J. Geophys. Res.* **65,** 1361 (1960).
100. R. L. Arnoldy, R. A. Hoffman, J. R. Winckler, and S.-I. Akasofu, Observations of the Van Allen radiation region during August and September 1959, Part 5, Visual auroras, high-altitude x-ray bursts, and simultaneous satellite observations, *J. Geophys. Res.*, **67,** 3673 (1962).
101. R. R. Brown, Balloon observations of auroral-zone x-rays, *J. Geophys. Res.*, **66,** 1379 (1961).
102. R. R. Brown and W. H. Campbell, An auroral zone electron precipitation event and its relationship to a magnetic bay, *J. Geophys. Res.*, **67,** 1357 (1962).
103. W. H. Campbell and S. Matsushita, Auroral-zone geomagnetic micropulsations with periods of 5 to 30 seconds, *J. Geophys. Res.*, **67,** 555 (1962).
104. B. J. O'Brien, Life-times of outer-zone electrons and their precipitation into the atmosphere, *J. Geophys. Res.*, **67,** 3687 (1962). See also: B. J. O'Brien, C. D. Laughlin, J. A. Van Allen, and L. A. Frank, Measurements of the intensity and spectrum of electrons at 1000-kilometer altitude and high latitudes, *J. Geophys. Res.*, **67,** 1209 (1962).
105. J. R. Winckler, Balloon study of high altitude radiations during the International Geophysical Year, *J. Geophys. Res.*, **65,** 1331 (1960).
106. J. R. Winckler, Atmospheric phenomena, energetic electrons and the geomagnetic field, *J. Res. NBS*, **66D,** 127 (1962).
107. J. R. Winckler, L. Peterson, R. L. Arnoldy, and R. A. Hoffman, X-rays from visible aurorae at Minneapolis, *Phys. Rev.*, **110,** 1221 (1958).
108. J. R. Winckler, P. D. Bhavsar, and K. A. Anderson, A study of the precipitation of energetic electrons from the geomagnetic field during magnetic storms, *J. Geophys. Res.*, **67,** 3717 (1962).

Section 9

109. D. Baker, H. K. Sutcliffe and C. D. Watkins, Some radar observations of meteors and aurorae at 300 and 500 Mc/s using a large radio telescope, II, *J. Atmos. Terr. Phys.*, **24,** 599 (1962).
110. R. P. Basler, Radio wave absorption in the auroral ionosphere, *J. Geophys. Res.*, **68,** 4665 (1963).
111. H. G. Booker, Radar studies of the aurora, *In*: *Physics of the Upper Atmosphere*, J. A. Ratcliffe, ed., 355 (Academic Press, 1960).
112. S. Chapman, The geometry of radio echoes from aurora, *J. Atmos. Terr. Phys.*, **3,** 1 (1952).
113. S. Chapman and C. G. Little, The non-deviative absorption of high-frequency radio waves in auroral latitudes, *J. Atmos. Terr. Phys.*, **10,** 20 (1957).
114. P. A. Forsyth, On the geometry of radio reflections from aurora, *Can. J. Phys.*, 38, 385 (1960).
115. P. A. Forsyth, Reflection mechanisms for radio aurora, *Planet. Space Sci.*, **10,** 179 (1963).

116. M. Gadsden, Studies of the upper atmosphere from Invercargill, New Zealand, Part III, Radar echoes and visual aurorae, *Ann. Géophys.*, **15,** 403 (1959).
117. T. R. Kaiser, The geometry of auroral ionization, *J. Geophys. Res.*, **62,** 297 (1957).
118. R. L. Leadabrand, R. I. Presnell, M. R. Berg, and R. B. Dyce, Doppler investigations of the radar aurora at 400 Mc, *J. Geophys. Res.*, **64,** 1197 (1959).
119. R. S. Leonard, Distribution of radar auroras over Alaska, *J. Geophys. Res.*, **67,** 939 (1962).
120. C. G. Little, The measurement of ionospheric absorption using extra-terrestrial radio waves, *Ann. IGY, III*, Part II, 207 (1957).
121. C. G. Little and H. Leinbach, Some measurements of high-latitude ionospheric absorption using extra-terrestrial radio waves, *Proc. Inst. Radio Eng.*, **46,** 335 (1958).
122. G. F. Lyon and P. A. Forsyth, Radio-auroral reflection mechanisms, *Can. J. Phys.*, **40,** 749 (1962).
123. G. F. Lyon and A. Kavadas, Horizontal motions in radar echoes from aurora, *Can. J. Phys.*, **36,** 1661 (1958).
124. V. I. Pogorelov, A short review of the results of radar observations at Roschino Station, *In*: *Aurorae and Airglow*, Nos. 2–3, 32 (Section IV of IGY Program, Acad. Sci. USSR, Moscow, 1960).
125. T. J. Seed, VHF observations in the aurora australis, *J. Geophys. Res.*, **63,** 517 (1958).
126. R. S. Unwin, Studies of the upper atmosphere from Invercargill, New Zealand, I, *Ann. Géophys.*, **15,** 377 (1959).

Section 10

127. S.-I. Akasofu, Large-scale auroral motions and polar magnetic disturbances, I, A polar disturbance at about 1100 hours on 23 September 1957, *J. Atmos. Terr. Phys.*, **19,** 19 (1960).
128. S.-I. Akasofu and S. Chapman, A neutral line discharge theory of the aurora polaris, *Phil. Trans. Roy. Soc.*, **A253,** 339 (1961).
129. S.-I. Akasofu and S. Chapman, The development of the main phase of magnetic storms, *J. Geophys. Res.*, **68,** 125 (1963).
130. W. I. Axford and C. O. Hines, A unifying theory of high-latitude geophysical phenomena and geomagnetic storms, *Can. J. Phys.*, **39,** 1433 (1961).
131. J. W. Chamberlain, Theory of auroral bombardment, *Astrophys. J.*, **134,** 401 (1961).
132. K. D. Cole, On Chamberlain's theory of auroral bombardment, *Astrophys. J.*, **136,** 677 (1962).
133. K. D. Cole, Atmospheric blow-up at the auroral zone, *Nature*, **194,** 761 (1962).
134. J. W. Kern, A charge separation mechanism for the production of polar auroras and electrojets, *J. Geophys. Res.*, **67,** 2649 (1962).
135. J. H. Piddington, A hydromagnetic theory of geomagnetic storms and auroras, *Planet. Space Sci.*, **9,** 947 (1962).
136. E. M. Wescott, R. N. DeWitt, and S.-I. Akasofu, The *Sq* variation at geomagnetically conjugate areas, *J. Geophys. Res.*, **68,** 6377 (1963).

CHAPTER 16

AIRGLOW

D. Barbier

1. Introduction

The program established for the IGY included: (*a*) coordinated synoptic study of the most intense upper atmosphere night sky radiations from a large number of stations; and (*b*) encouragement to individual investigators to carry on studies of their own on other subjects. Twenty-eight stations took part in the measurements required by the first point of this program. They may be broken down by latitude as follows: 3 in auroral zones, 18 between 56°N and 32°N, 6 between 25°N and 13°S, and 1 at 34°S. The number of stations in the equatorial zone was rather less than adequate while coverage in the Southern Hemisphere was very inadequate. The observations were published in the *Annals of the International Geophysical Year* [89]. They represent an abundant mass of data, of great use to researchers; however, these data must be used carefully, owing to various difficulties now reviewed.

The absolute calibration of a photometer designed for measuring the intensity of monochromatic lines is delicate and may not last very long; this makes it necessary to know the transmission curve (as a function of wavelength) of the interference filter or other device used to isolate the radiation under study. The more selective the filter or other device, the more difficult it is to obtain this curve. It is equally possible that this curve may also be temperature-dependent.

Contamination of the radiation under study by other kinds of radiation may cause difficulties, which become greater as the selectivity of the filter used is decreased. The OH-bands and the continuous emission spectrum of the upper atmosphere are thus very troublesome when the green line at 5577 Å or the sodium doublet is being measured. Combinations of measurements made through two or even three filters can reduce this inconvenience. Unfortunately, authors reporting the measurements have not always indicated whether the attempt was made to decontaminate them.

It has recently been discovered that in regions within 15° of the true magnetic equator, the 5577 Å line is emitted not only at the usual altitude of 100 km, but also from another much higher layer, where its intensity is proportional to that of the 6300 Å red line. The published observations of the IGY show no correction for this high-altitude emission, and this very important correction cannot have been made in any case except for those stations where the intensities of the 5577 Å and 6300 Å lines were measured simultaneously.

Individual studies have perhaps a greater importance than was foreseen in setting up the program of the IGY. The use of rockets and the development of infrared spectroscopic measurement methods have contributed in particular to new and important results.

The present review will not try to give a complete bibliography of everything published during the IGY and the International Geophysical Cooperation, but will consider the results obtained on certain important subjects, including studies originating during the IGY which have developed further since then. (In what follows, we will use the rayleigh as the unit of intensity. Its value for the radiation being considered is 10^6 transitions/sec for a column 1 cm² in cross section.)

2. Discovery of New Types of Radiation

Hydrogen Lines. The presence of the Lyman α line (1215.7 Å) in the night airglow was discovered in 1955 by Byram, Chubb, Friedman, and Kupperian [27] after rocket observations made through a filter isolating the spectral region from 1050–1225 Å. The same authors later obtained the intensity distribution over the celestial sphere of this radiation [55], which shows a minimum in the direction away from the sun. According to these observations, the line appears against the sky at an altitude of 75 km; at 85 km it also appears below (that is to say, against the ground); intensity measured toward the sky, like that measured toward the ground, increases up to 120 km, and then remains constant up to the maximum altitude attained by the rocket, i.e., 146 km. Another rocket, launched 14 January 1960, provided data for the interval from 350–1200 km [55]. The intensity of $L\ \alpha$ is of the order of 2500 rayleighs.

This radiation is manifestly diffused by the hydrogen atoms of the upper atmosphere (the albedo of the earth for $L\ \alpha$ is estimated at 40 per cent). It is caused by the solar $L\ \alpha$ line; the problem is to establish how this radiation reaches that hemisphere of the earth not directly illuminated by the sun. This may be due either to scattering or $L\ \alpha$ in interplanetary space or to scatter by an extended geocorona; both hypotheses have been argued.

The Balmer Hα line, long known in the aurora, was first observed in the night airglow in 1958 by Prokudina [68] and independently by Kvifte [56, 57]. This line is much narrower than the Hα line of the aurora. After its discovery, the line was observed by various investigators: L. M. Fishkova and G. M. Markova, V. I. Yarin, M. and J. Dufay, R. X. Haynoullina, and Z. V. Kariahma. At first, important variations in the intensity of this line were announced, but later on it was shown [36] that these variations are satisfactorily explained by the passage of diffuse nebulas through the field of the spectrograph. They further established that the radial velocity of Hα confirmed this point of view. Finally, the covariation with Hα of the [NII] 6583 Å line, characteristic of nebulas, which had already been noted by Kvifte, constitutes a new proof. From this it follows that the Hα line, corrected for contamination by nebulas, has an intensity of the order of 5 rayleighs, and that its *true* variations are still unknown. It seems extremely probable that the Hα line results from the absorption of the $L\,\alpha$ line in the upper atmosphere.

Helium 10830 Å Line. This line, discovered in the aurora, has there an intensity vastly greater than the other helium lines; it is only present when the aurora is illuminated by the sun. Divorced from association with auroral activity, it has been observed at twilight, by Shefov using a spectrograph [80] and by Shcheglov using an interferometer [78]. Its intensity was then of the order of 1000 rayleighs.

Shefov [80] explains the emission of the twilight 10830 Å line in the following manner (Fig. 1): Helium atoms in the ground state absorb solar (helium) lines at 537.1 Å and 584.4 Å (resonance line), which populates the ^1P-levels; some of these excited atoms return to the metastable 2 ^1S-level; electron collisions may bring them to the 2 ^3S-level, also metastable; and these atoms are then able to emit the 10830 Å line by resonance. These processes take place between 500 and 1500 km. The resultant helium density is quite comparable to the global atmospheric density at the same altitudes as deduced from the retardation of artificial satellites, and this agrees with the results obtained theoretically by Nicolet [65].

Metallic Lines. At the beginning of the IGY, both the twilight and the night sky sodium D doublet had long been known, and the twilight H, K doublet of Ca II had just been discovered by A. Vallance Jones.

The discovery of the lithium 6708 twilight doublet (nonseparated) was first announced by Delannoy and Weill [33], and independently by Gadsden and Salmon [41]. This discovery followed the thermonuclear explosions produced at Johnston Island in the Pacific (on 1 and 12 August 1958), so that Barber proposed an artificial origin for atmospheric lithium [4]. It is now certain that the exceptional values (more than 1000 rayleighs) of lithium intensity occur following thermonuclear explosions, as has been observed after the American [40] and Soviet [64] explosions of 1962.

Meanwhile, it is certain that besides this lithium artificially introduced into the atmosphere, natural lithium with an intensity of the order of 100

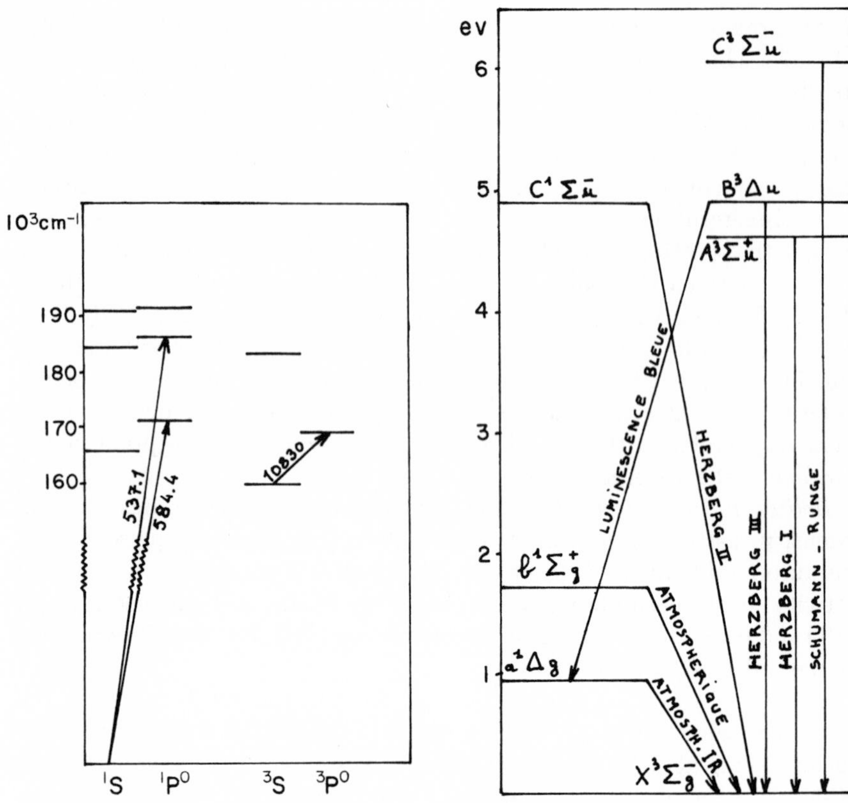

rayleighs is also sometimes observed. In particular, the spectra obtained by Weill in August and September, 1957, before any *known* high-altitude explosion, show a rather intense lithium line. It has been observed fairly regularly since 1960 as well, by Sullivan and Hunten [83].

Since the discovery of twilight lithium, many authors have speculated on the attempt to deduce from observations the ratio between the amounts of sodium and lithium, and thereby to establish whether the metals of the upper atmosphere come from ocean spray or from meteors. Certain of these calculations, based on lithium introduced artificially into the atmosphere, are invalid on fundamental grounds. In any case, the estimate is delicate: absorption in the sodium layer, which is optically dense, must be taken into account, and the ratios of atoms which are ionized or (still more difficult) combined into molecules, must also be taken into account. At present, the most likely value of the Na/Li ratio would be 500 [83], indicating a largely oceanic origin for the metals.

[*NI*] *5199 Å Line.* This line, known both as an auroral and as a twilight line, was often observed during the IGY at the Observatory of Haute Provence by Dufay [37].

Atmospheric Infrared O_2 System. At the beginning of the IGY two systems of molecular oxygen lines had been identified with certainty in the airglow (Fig. 2); Herzberg's system $A\ ^3\Sigma_u^+ - X\ ^3\Sigma_g^-$ in the ultraviolet, and the atmospheric system $b\ ^1\Sigma_g^- - X\ ^3\Sigma_g^+$ in the near infrared; these two systems appear at night and are not reinforced at twilight. (Some slight doubt remains for the system $b\ ^1\Sigma_g^+ - X\ ^3\Sigma_g^-$). The system $a\ ^1\Delta_g^+ - X\ ^3\Sigma_g^-$, discovered in 1958 by Jones and Harrison, is itself purely twilight. The first band of this system to be identified [50] was the 0.1 band, with a wavelength of 1.58 μ and an intensity of the order of 15 kilorayleighs. A second band, the 0.0–1.27 μ band, was identified by Noxon and Jones [66] on spectra taken from an airplane at an altitude of 13,000 m; it could not be observed from the ground because of its reabsorption in the lower layers of the atmosphere. At high altitudes, it is detectable even in full daylight.

The possible modes of excitation proposed by Jones and Harrison are as follows:

$$O_2(^3\Sigma_g^-) + h\nu \rightarrow O_2'$$

$$O + O_3 \rightarrow 2\ O_2'$$

Other mechanisms have since been proposed by Jones and Gattinger [49]:

$$O_3 + h\nu(\lambda < 3100\ \text{Å}) = O('D) + O_2(^1\Delta g)$$

$$O('D) + O_2(^3\Sigma_g^-) = O(^3P) + O_2(^1\Delta g)$$

The first of these two mechanisms would be the most useful and would account for the strong annual variation observed.

Continuous Emission Spectrum. In 1951, Barbier, Dufay, and Williams [14] announced the presence of a continuous emission spectrum in the airglow, and showed that the intensity of its radiation in the 5200 Å region was in close correlation with that of the green line. Soviet observers have confirmed the existence of this continuum [53] and have shown that it possesses two maxima, one in the red and one in the blue.

3. Altitudes and Correlations

Determination of the altitude of an airglow emitting layer from variations of intensity with zenith distance (Van Rhyn's method) has led to many difficulties. Shortly before the beginning of the IGY the first direct measurements were made from rockets (cf. bibliography, p. 497 [29]).

Summarized, the results are as follows for the regions of maximum emission:

[OI]λ 5577 Å Herzberg O_2 Continuum in the green	100 km
Na D OH	85 km
[OI]λ 6300 Å	>160 km

This is in excellent agreement with a classification proposed in 1954 [5] of radiations by correlation of their intensities. Variation of these altitudes with latitude is still completely unknown.

The altitude of the [OI] 6300 Å red line was at first evaluated with the assumption that these intensity variations are essentially a phenomenon related to local time. Altitudes of 275 km at a latitude of +44° [8] and from 210–300 km at a latitude of +22° [17] were thus obtained. Subsequently, the discovery of intertropical arcs (see below) permitted triangulation between stations [20], which has yielded altitudes between 240 and 300 km in general, and attaining values between 340 and 400 km in exceptional cases. More recently measured altitudes have been between 235 and 280 km [1]. The variability of altitude in the low latitudes is quite real and in good correlation with the altitudes for the base of the *F*-layer.

Correlations between radiations have been the object of a detailed study [16], which has permitted the above to be made more exact. The most unexpected of these was the correlation between the Na D and OH emissions. Ballif and Venkateswaran [3] have explained this fact by admitting certain reactions leading to the emission of D lines and OH bands which give, in both cases, an emission that is essentially a function of the concentration of ozone molecules.

4. Interferometric and Spectroscopic Temperature Determination

The contours of the 5577 and 6300 Å lines are Doppler contours; study of them, or at least, determination of their half-widths, should thus give the temperatures prevailing in the regions where these radiations are emitted. The 5577 Å line emitted near 100 km yields temperatures of the order of 200°K; and the red line, emitted higher, gives higher temperatures as can be seen from Table 1.

The discrepancy between the last two figures may perhaps arise from a difference in the phase of the solar cycle. In the *F*-layer, temperatures are higher during periods of maximum activity.

In the main, these temperatures are in agreement with those obtained by rockets or satellites.

TABLE 1

Line	Author	Temperature °K
[01] 5577	E. B. Armstrong [2]	180–220
	D. Q. Wark [88]	180 ± 15
	M. Perrin [67]	175–235
[01] 6300	J. Cabannes and J. Dufay [28]	500
	D. Q. Wark [88]	980 ± 120

One method, as yet very uncertain, of determining the temperature in the case of the red line consists in determination of the scale height resulting from a comparison of its intensity with ionospheric data (see below). By this means temperatures of 920°K in November, 1960 and 520°K in October, 1962 have been obtained [13].

The contour of the sodium doublet is not purely thermal owing to phenomena of reabsorption in the atmosphere; this accounts for its seeming to have been little studied recently.

The determination of temperatures by the rotational structure of OH has become a routine operation performed at numerous stations. The conditions for its use have been exactly described:

(*a*) These rotation temperatures are kinetic atmospheric temperatures; McPherson and Jones [60] state, in fact, that the average life of the excited levels is 10^{-2} sec, and that at an altitude of 90 km the collision frequency is 1.9×10^4/sec, which assures an average of 200 collisions before the molecule radiates. This is sufficient to assure thermal equilibrium between rotation levels. Wallace [87] has calculated how, in the absence of collision redistribution, rotation levels of different vibration levels would be populated by several models. In any case, rotation temperatures would increase as vibration levels decrease. Observations show, on the contrary, that the rotation temperature is the same for all bands studied (see, e.g., [56]) so that redistribution by collisions surely intervenes. But Krassovsky [52] notes that the rotation temperatures increase in proportion to rise in the vibration level; this is in direct contradiction to Wallace's prediction.

(*b*) The intensity of a rotation line is given by

$$I = Ci(J') \exp [-F(J')/kT],$$

where J' is the rotation energy of the upper level, $i(J')$ the intensity factor (in the following expressions the branches considered are known), and C is a constant; $F(J')$ is the rotation energy of the upper level. Many researchers, following Meinel [61] have used the following expression for this value:

$$F(J') = B_v J'(J' + 1)$$

Wallace [86] has shown that this expression is insufficiently correct for the OH bands and that an 8 per cent overestimate of temperatures measured from $P1$ branches has resulted. The temperatures given below are corrected temperatures.

Shefov and Yarin [81] give a list of temperatures deduced from the rotational structure of the OH bands that includes this last correction. It is similar to, but a little more extensive than, the list given by Chamberlain [29]. There is no point in reproducing it here. We now turn to definitively established systematic effects or to those which are suspected.

Latitude Effect. This effect is now well established. Chamberlain and Oliver [31] discovered in 1953 that in northern Greenland, at a latitude +76°, the OH rotation temperature was of the order of 300°K, i.e., clearly greater than in the intermediate latitudes (220°K). Since then other comparisons have been published. Mironov *et al.* [62] obtained temperatures of 213°K and 282°K at latitudes of 55.7° and 68.6°, respectively. Prokudina [69] again obtained 222°K at 55.7°, and a temperature varying between 280°K and 460°K at 68.3°. Finally, McPherson and Jones [60] obtained temperatures of 216°K, 227°K, and 274°K from observations made at latitudes of 52.1°, 58.8°, and 74.7°.

The rotation temperature increases sharply with latitude; in fact, at latitude 59.7°, Kvifte [56] obtained $T = 215$°K, and it is thus at latitudes a little above 60° that the temperature begins to increase. In the whole region from 40° to 60°N latitude, the mean temperature is of the order of 220°K. Below 40°N latitude, only a single determination, made for a single spectrum [22], is known; this was at 16.3°S latitude and yielded a temperature of 294°K. It would be of the greatest importance to extend the range of latitudes for which the rotation temperature of OH has been studied.

A priori, two extreme possibilities may account for the variation of temperature with latitude. Either it is a question of a variation of temperature with latitude at constant altitude, or else the temperature is the same at a constant altitude for all latitudes and it is the altitude of OH emission that varies. From rocket measurements of temperature the choice appears to be in favor of the first case cited.

Annual Variation. If there does exist an annual variation of the OH rotation temperature, it is certainly weak at middle latitudes: at Yerkes Observatory, Wallace [87] has admitted the possibility of two maxima, one in February–March, and the other, less pronounced, in August–September; the amplitude would not exceed 20°. In higher latitudes the amplitude is greater, exceeding 60° according to observations made in Yakutsk ($\phi = 62°$, a latitude where observations are interrupted from April to September), which show a maximum in February [54]; the same authors do not note any appreciable annual variation at $\phi = 55.7°$. On the other hand, Fishkova [39] in Abastumani finds a variation of more than 50° between a summer minimum and a winter maximum.

Correlation between OH Intensity and Its Rotation Temperature. At a latitude below 60°, no such correlation exists [51, 79]. However, at 62° it appears clearly for temperatures in excess of 250°K [90]. This fact, like those noted in the preceding paragraphs, seems to show that there is something clearly different in OH band emissions in latitudes above 60°, perhaps even in the mechanism of this emission.

Random Temperature Variations. At a single station, the measured temperature can vary by considerable proportions: Krassovsky [52] gives 200°K and 400°K as the extreme values observed in Zvenigorod (ϕ = 55.7°) and notes variations of tens of degrees from one day to another. He is of the opinion that it must be a question of altitude variations, since temperature changes at a single altitude would represent impossibly large quantities of absorbed energy. (It is my opinion that changes in the nature of air masses might also be considered, polar air masses being warmer than the others.) Shefov and Yarin [82] have found good correlation between temperature variations measured simultaneously at the two stations of Zvenigorod and Yakutsk.

5. Structure of the Upper Night Layer

By upper layer we mean the layer that emits the 6300 Å line. Its study is particularly easy since, at least in the absence of auroras, when the variations are less important, its behavior is fairly regular. The emission of the red line results from several quite distinct phenomena, at least from the standpoint of morphology [10]. *Polar aurora*: we will examine this subject summarily in Section 8. *Twilight phenomenon*: long known; its existence, recently placed in doubt, has been confirmed [6]; it is due to the radiative dissociation of O_2; its intensity increases during periods of magnetic activity [8]. *Western "sheet"*: previously called posttwilight emission. *Subpolar "sheets"*: previously called pretwilight emission. *Intertropical arcs*: only very recently discovered [17]. Perhaps, but more doubtful, the *paratwilight phenomenon* observed at Tamanrasset (ϕ = 22.8°).

Of all these phenomena, the intertropical arcs are certainly the most interesting, for they permit thorough investigation of the emission conditions for the 6300 Å line. Their simple geometric structure permits precise altitude measurements by triangulation, and their rapid intensity variations at times permit the firm establishment of the correlation between optical phenomena and ionospheric data. Finally, these well-defined structures must help us to understand the mechanisms of red line emission, and no doubt also the equatorial anomaly of the F-layer (Fig. 3).

Following the discovery of the northern intertropical arc [17], observations made by airplane have made it possible to establish the existence of the southern arc [20]. These two arcs are generally situated twelve degrees from the true magnetic equator; in the course of the night, they tend to approach the equator. The northern arc disappears during the northern summer in Africa; this season is marked by sharp intensity jumps of 6300 emission, which may be tenfold and whose duration is of the order of two to three hours [6]; this behavior has especially been studied at the station of Maui (Hawaiian Islands) [19]. During periods near the solar activity minimum, the northern intertropical arc in Africa becomes weaker and approaches much more rapidly the equator during the course of the night [1]. It has been shown that ionospheric storms have a considerable effect on the behavior of the intertropical arcs [11].

Red line emission in the intertropical arcs is always accompanied by a green line emission whose intensity is about five times weaker. The importance of this green line emission will be brought out further on.

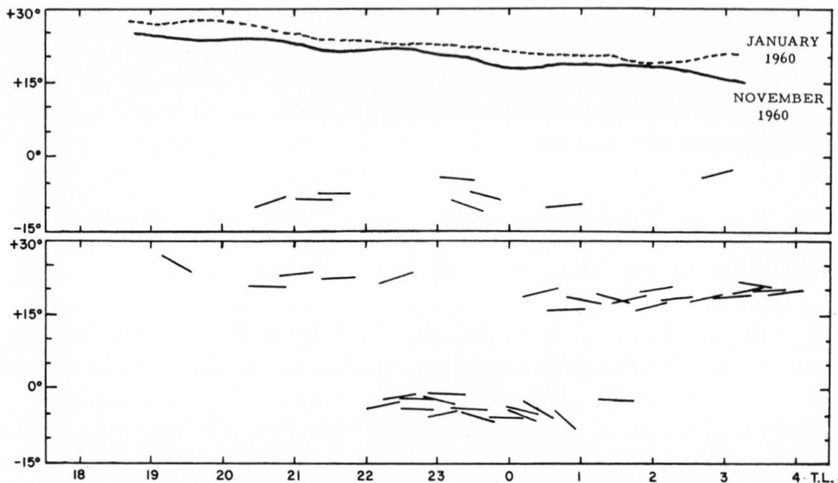

FIG. 3. Position of intertropical arcs. Above: the northern arc from ground observations, January and November, 1960; southern arc from airborne observations, November, 1960. Below: both arcs from airborne observations, March, 1961.

Observations conducted at low latitudes are easily interpreted in terms of the intertropical arcs. This refers particularly to the observations at Lwiro (Congo) [34] in the immediate vicinity of the southern arc, at Maruyama (Japan) [48] well to the north of the northern arc, but where the northern "wing" toward the southern horizon was occasionally observed, and at Poona (India) [32] in the neighborhood of the northern arc, where results of 25–26 January 1960 show the arc and its displacement in the course of the night clearly.

A semiempirical formula, justified by the hypothesis of Bates and Massey [21], according to which the red line is emitted by electron dissociative recombination of O_2^+, was proposed in 1959. With the addition of a constant additive factor, whose presence is apparently indispensable, this formula giving the intensity Q of the red line at the zenith in terms of the virtual altitude h' and critical frequency f_0 of the F-layer, may be written:

$$Q = Kf_0^2 e - \frac{h' - 200}{H} + C \qquad (1)$$

where K and C are constants and H is the scale height of molecular oxygen. With the above formula, taking $C = 0$, it has been possible to represent observations conducted at midlatitude sites [8, 48]; but the simultaneous determination of the two constants K and H was very uncertain, since in these regions variations of f_0 and h' are in very close correlation.

A. and D. Delsemme [34] were able to determine a very plausible H-value using data from Lwiro; then Barbier and Glaume [18] analyzed the Tamanrasset observations; and Barbier, Roach, and Steiger [19] published a preliminary analysis of the Maui results (Fig. 4). Using the above formula, which accommodates measurements made at different stations well, it has been possible to predict the behavior of the red line at other stations [12, 18]. This must be very different in South America from what it is in Africa; the southern arc above South America must behave in a manner recalling the behavior of the northern arc over Africa. The zones of appearance of the arcs are zones of f_0 maximum and their location is almost uniquely a function of the true magnetic latitude. The intensity of the arcs, primarily a function of h', would be dependent simultaneously on this latitude and on the geographic latitude.

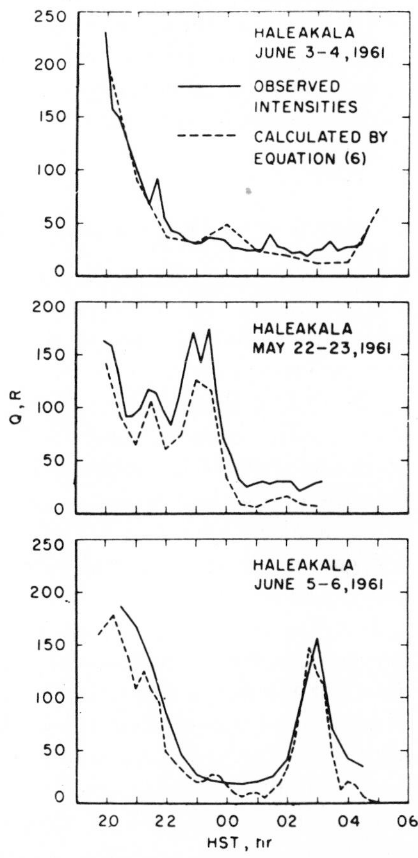

FIG. 4. Haleakala Station (Maui Island, Hawaii). Comparison of observed intensities (solid line) and intensities calculated from ionospheric data (from [19]).

The as yet unpublished discussion of the data obtained at Tamanrasset in October, 1962 has made it possible, through the cooperation of the CNET, to advance the problem: Equation 1, while it permits the establishment of a satisfactory connection between photometric and ionospheric observations, leads to mediocre results as regards determination of the scale height H. A formula which is much better justified theoretically follows:

$$Q = Kf_0^2(h' + H)e - \frac{h' - 200}{H} + C \tag{2}$$

Here f_0 no longer refers to the altitude of maximum electron concentration but to the altitude of the base of the F-layer plus a scale height. Calculation of the profile of electron distributions as a function of altitude has also been accomplished and permits the attainment of still better precision in the relationships between optical and ionospheric phenomena.

There is no doubt that the western "sheet" is also the result of electron dissociative recombination of O_2^+, and that it too can be interpreted by a formula similar to formula 1.

The subpolar "sheet," as observed at the Observatory of Haute Provence [8, 10], appears toward the middle of the night on the northern horizon and bit by bit covers the entire sky. This sheet does not show up in the measurements of all stations, but is fairly apparent in winter measurements made in Australia, at Camden (according to [89]). Its nature is completely unknown.

6. Structure of the Nocturnal Layer at an Altitude of 100 km

The 5577 Å green line is the best studied radiation emitted at this altitude. Roach, with various collaborators, has made particularly valuable contributions to the study of the structure of this layer [70–72, 74, 76] and has introduced two very useful procedures.

The first of these consists of examination of the ratio of intensities at equal zenith distances, generally 75° in the plane of the meridian, to the north and south of the station; this ratio is abbreviated N/S (Roach used the ratio of the number of cases when intensity was maximum in the north to the analogous number in the south) [70, 71]. This value, being independent of the absolute scale, lends itself especially well to comparisons between different stations.

The other procedure consists of establishing graphs which give the intensity observed in the plane of the meridian as a function of time. (The observed intensities are reduced to their zenithal values; in the case of observations conducted around the horizon, the intensities are the mean of intensities observed at pairs of points symmetrically located with respect to the meridian.) If the intensity of the emitting layer was only a function of local time at each latitude, these graphs will represent maps of the emissive layer [72, 76].

At lower latitudes it is essential, as noted and done by Christophe Glaume [44], to correct the intensities of line 5577 Å for the contribution due to the presence of the high-altitude layer. It has not so far been possible to do this except for the Tamanrasset observations (where the contributions of the two layers may be of the same order of magnitude), and for some other observations made by the research team of the Astrophysical Institute in the course of their work.

Observations conducted at midlatitude stations, say from 30° to 50° (i.e., at almost all stations), show that the emitting layer most often has a very complex structure, which generally changes completely from one night to the next. On the other hand, at lower latitudes, once the emission of the high-altitude layer has been eliminated, the structure of the 100-km layer is seen to be very regular as shown by Christophe Glaume using observations made at latitudes of 22.8° and 17.0° [45]. The emission is stronger in the north than in the south, where it attains an intensity minimum very probably situated at the equator or in its vicinity. Intensity in the north is especially strong a little after the middle of the night (Fig. 5).

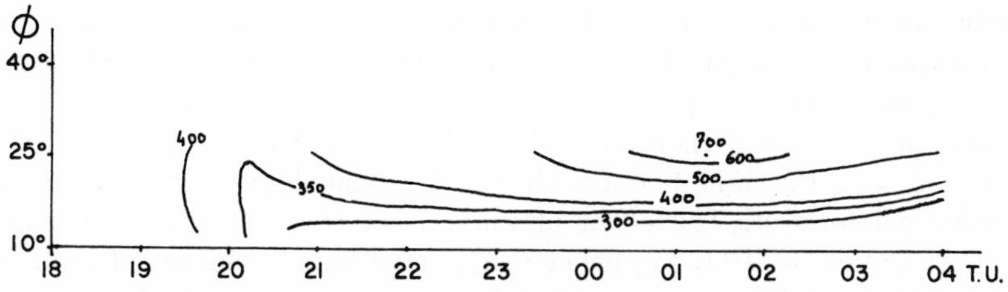

Fig. 5. Diagram of 5577 Å emission for the night of 26 October 1962, from observations made at Tamanrasset and Agadez.

At midlatitudes, if one wishes to obtain a general view of the emitting layer, it is desirable to eliminate all structures of a transitory character and consider the average ones. In this manner Christophe Glaume [45], perfecting the results of Roach, obtained the following table for the latitude of the line of the intensity maximum according to all available data (it should be noted that in America the data are not always comparable to those obtained in Europe or Japan):

Month	J	F	M	A	M	J	J	A	S	O	N	D
ϕ	45°5	37°	38°	37°	38°5	55°	50°	55°5	41°	42°	41°	52°

At the Observatory of Haute Provence, the mean layer is fairly regular and most often shows a maximum to the south, generally a little after midnight [45] (Fig. 6). At higher latitudes, auroral 5577 emission has complicated study of the structure of the airglow layer, so that it has not yet been possible to describe its behavior precisely.

As stated above, important irregularities are superimposed on the structure of the mean layer in the region of the midlatitudes and usually masks

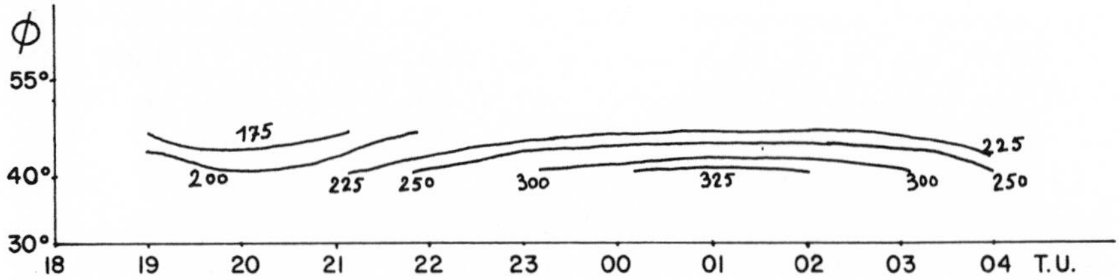

FIG. 6. Diagram of 5577 Å emission for the mean of six nights in February, 1961, from observations made at the Observatory of Haute Provence.

its more important characteristics. Roach *et al.* [74] have stated that these irregularities, called "cells," are circular and up to 2500 km in diameter. The same authors [75] have found their displacement velocity to be of the order of 100 m/sec and believe they have found evidence of their rotational motion. For Haug [46], the diameter of these cells is rarely over 1000 km. Barbier and Glaume [15] finally describe them as lines of maxima not very extensive in longitude. An important point, not yet examined, is the life of these cells.

Some investigation has been made to determine if the properties of the layer emitting the 5577 line are all directly related to other elements of geophysical interest. The effect of lunar time (tide) is still in dispute: while Nagata *et al.* [63, 85] believe they have found evidence of such an effect, Glaume [43] maintains that it is not detectable. At higher geomagnetic latitudes, the intensity of the 5577 Å band is clearly dependent on the planetary magnetic index K_p, and this dependency is a result, essentially, of the auroras that are superimposed on the nightglow emission itself. McCaulley *et al.* [59] have shown that a much better correlation of the intensity of the 5577 line with ΔH (instantaneous deviation of the horizontal magnetic component H from the normal), than with K_p, which represents the magnitude of fluctuations of H without reference to the normal value. Glaume has shown [42] that the intensity of the 5577 Å line begins to increase immediately after the sudden commencement (ssc) of a magnetic perturbation, passes through a weak first maximum 45 minutes later, and then, after a brief subsidence, begins again to increase over a period not yet precisely determined but in excess of four hours. Twenty-four hours after the sudden commencement, the intensity of the green line has returned to normal. McCaulley and Hough [58] have found a relation between the intensity of the 5577 Å line and a nocturnal ionospheric layer located in the region from 90 to 110 km in altitude.

7. Twilight and Diurnal Sodium

The layer emitting sodium D-lines during the night has been studied relatively little, which is no doubt due to the effects of a very serious contamination by OH-bands and by the continuous emission spectrum of the atmosphere, which makes the interpretation of observations made through interference filters very delicate, especially in summer when the Na D emission is weak. On the other hand, the twilight emission of this doublet is fairly strong, which has permitted its observation by means of improved filters, the most recent of which is Blamont's magnetic modulation filter [23]. A recent improvement in the observation method has permitted Blamont and Donahue [25] to measure the D-lines in full daylight.

The difficulty in interpreting measurements of twilight D-lines arises from the fact that the emitting layer also produces absorption phenomena; an analysis of this effect is found in Chamberlain [29]. Difficulties of physical order result from this because certain data are not reliably known and also because observations in a given place depend on the properties of the sodium layer at the point where it is first encountered by the rays of the sun, that is to say, at points fairly remote from the observer.

The intensity for a given declination of the sun is not proportional to the numerical density of sodium atoms in the layer, when this number is high. Perhaps the variable ratio of the intensities of the D1- and D2-lines of the doublet will furnish a procedure for obtaining a better determination of density in the latter case.

The study of the altitude distribution of sodium atoms has recently been resumed [77, 47]. The annual variation of twilight sodium was studied for the first time by means of an extended series of measurements in the Southern Hemisphere by Tinsley and Jones [84]: the variation of the D-lines, found by comparison of observations with a shift of six months, is in perfect agreement with that found in the Northern Hemisphere [24, 26, 30]. The result was a sinusoidal variation in D-line intensity, threefold, with a minimum in summer and a maximum in winter.

In reality the variation is not so simple, as shown by Donahue and Blamont [35]. They observed only weak intensity variations at Tamanrasset ($\phi = 22.8°$), and two major ones at the Observatory of Haute Provence ($\phi = 43.9°$), one approximately in November and the other approximately in March; while at Saskatoon ($\phi = 52°$) there was only one maximum in December. Their interpretation of the facts is that there exists on the globe an increased sodium emission belt, several thousand kilometers in width, which goes through an annual displacement in latitude. Its lowest latitude is higher than that of Tamanrasset; in its movement northward, it would pass above the Observatory of Haute Provence at the beginning of November, arrive at Saskatoon at the end of December, then move south again, passing over the Observatory of Haute Provence again in March.

Diurnal sodium is about four times more intense than twilight sodium [25].

8. Lower Latitude Auroras

This section in principle exceeds the scope of this article. However, during the IGY–IGC (a period of maximum solar activity) auroras made frequent incursions into the regions where photometers specifically intended for studying upper atmosphere airglow were installed. These devices were sufficiently sensitive to permit detection of subvisual auroras. At each station there is a threshold past which the green 5577 Å band is in correlation with planetary magnetic activity characterized by the index K_p. In the auroral zones, this threshold corresponds to a $K_p = 0$ or 1. In lower latitudes, the threshold increases rapidly as a function of McIlwain's parameter L; we have:

Station	Rapid City	Fritz Peak	Camden	Haute Provence
	+44°	+40°	−34°	+44°
L	2.91	2.35	1.91	1.75
K_p	4	5	6	7

For $L = 1.75$, i.e., in general for a geomagnetic latitude of 45°, the observation of auroras by 5577 Å radiation becomes quite exceptional. At the same time, it should be mentioned that subvisual auroras illuminated by the sun are somewhat more frequent and have proven detectable on several occasions at Tamanrasset ($L = 1.09$), but perhaps it is in that case simply a matter of glows located further north and scattered by the atmosphere.

The threshold for auroral observation is much lower for the light of the 6300 Å line; it begins, for example, at $K_p = 4$ at the Observatory of Haute Provence. Auroras, in general subvisual, may thus become very frequent for this type of radiation during periods of solar activity and may be detected during more than 25 per cent of the night hours [7] (e.g., observation periods from 19 June to 6 July 1957, or from 15 September to 3 October 1957 at the Observatory of Haute Provence).

Strong auroras, and occasionally weaker auroras, leave behind (when they withdraw toward the polar regions) an arc in the region of 50° geomagnetic latitude. This arc so far seems to be monochromatic, due solely to the 6300 Å radiation, and lasts quite long, in general until daybreak (Fig. 7), i.e., sometimes 7 hours or more. The discovery of these arcs, now called stable auroral arcs, was announced independently by Barbier [7] and Duncan [38]. (See review articles [9, 73].) One may remark with Roach that if the sensitivity of the eye were as great at 6300 Å as it is around 5200 Å, many of these arcs would be visible to the eye and would even be rather spectacular phenomena.

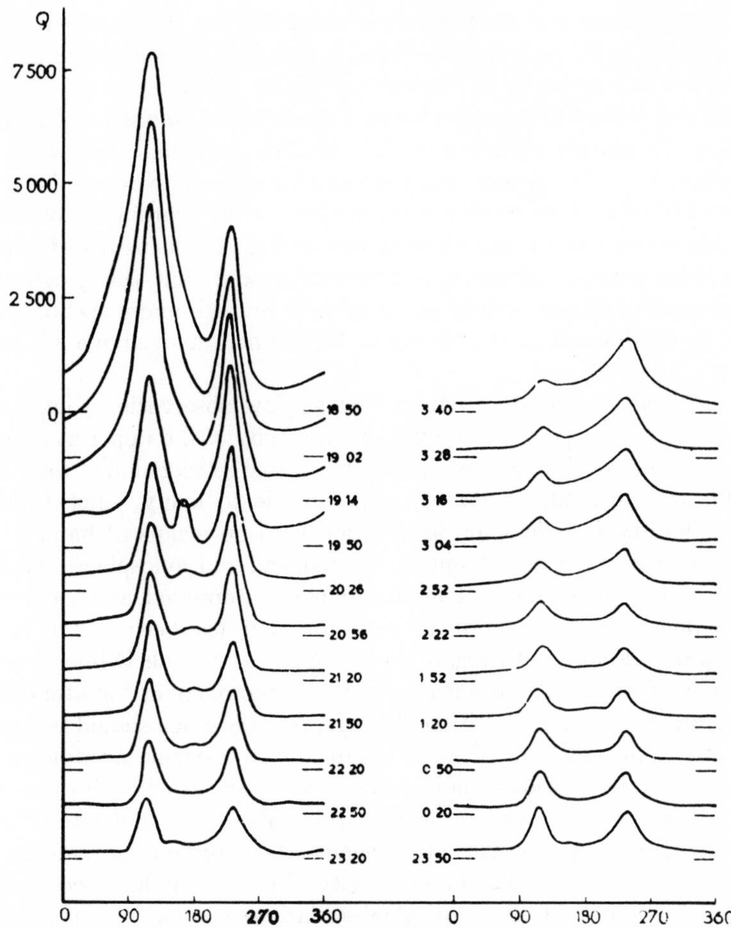

Fig. 7. Stable auroral arc observed at the Observatory of Haute Provence. Intensity of the 6300 Å line at a zenith distance of 75° as a function of azimuth. From 1950–2150 hr UT, a little auroral activity to the north. At the beginning and end of the night, twilight phenomenon was superimposed on the arc.

9. Conclusions

At the moment of finishing a first discussion of the data gathered during the IGY-IGC, and preparing for the observations for the IQSY, it is useful to draw some general conclusions from the foregoing analysis. To begin with, as concerns the precision of the observations, it would be desirable for the photometric measurements conducted at various stations to be more easily comparable to one another; i.e., it is necessary to improve absolute scales, which is, however, difficult; or, at the very least, to proceed by making comparisons between groups of stations. It is also important that the scale of the photometer not vary in the course of time at any given station. Ratios of intensities measured at a zenith distance of 75° to the north and south of a station, being in principle not subject to absolute scale errors, will prove to be of very appreciable service.

Much less than 10 years ago, we still spoke of the emission temperature of OH or the diurnal variation of the 6300 line as though these were constants or values to be determined once and for all time. Now we know that all elements concerning airglow are functions of the coordinates of the observation stations and many other factors as well, as for instance the phase of the solar cycle. The result is a second lesson: that the geographical distribution of stations should be completely revised, many stations needing to be established in the Southern Hemisphere and, above all, in the tropics.

Let us turn now to the usefulness of airglow observations, i.e., to the possibilities they open to us to advance the study of the upper atmosphere or of the sun. At the time when the IGY was getting under way, these possibilities appeared, no doubt, rather feeble to many, since these researches had been developing in isolation with no means at hand to find clear correlations between luminous phenomena and ionospheric, geomagnetic, or solar phenomena. The situation has improved as concerns the 6300 Å line in that a relation to the ionosphere has been found. It may also improve rapidly with regard to the 5577 Å line, the D-lines, and the OH-bands, if we have an exact idea of the meteorology of the atmospheric layers from 80–100 km in altitude. Finally, the 10830 line should be capable of serving as an indicator of solar activity in the extreme ultraviolet.

Numerous observations made from rockets or satellites furnish basic data on the upper atmosphere, which will enable us to understand better the properties of the upper atmosphere; then airglow phenomena will furnish us frequently and from a diversity of places the data necessary for a detailed synoptic study. Optical observations are made impossible by clouds and, in general, can be made only at night, but they have the advantage of yielding an analysis which is valid, not only for the observer's vicinity, but anywhere within a large circle, having a diameter of approximately 700 km for the 5577 Å line and 1500 km for the 6300 Å line; and this advantage is very important.

References

1. L. Argemi, D. Barbier, G. Camman, J. Marsan, S. Huille, and N. Morguleff, Observations de l'arc intertropical Nord en radiation 6 300 Å, *C. R. Acad. Sci.*, **256,** 2215 (1963).
2. E. B. Armstrong, The temperature in the atmospheric region emitting the nightglow OI 5577 line and in regions above faint auroral arcs, *J. Atmos. Sci.*, **13,** 205 (1959).
3. J. R. Ballif and S. V. Vankateswaran, An explanation of the observed correlation between the hydroxyl and sodium emissions of the night sky, *J. Atmos. Sci.*, **19,** 426 (1962).
4. D. R. Barber, Origin of the upper-atmosphere lithium, *Nature*, **183,** 384 (1959).

5. D. Barbier, Résultats d'observations photométriques de la lumière du ciel nocturne, *C. R. Acad. Sci.*, **238,** 770 (1954).
6. D. Barbier, La lumière du ciel nocturne en été à Tamanrasset, *C. R. Acad. Sci.*, **245,** 1559 (1957).
7. D. Barbier, Activité aurorale aux basses latitudes, *Ann. Géophys.*, **14,** 334 (1958).
8. D. Barbier, Recherches sur la raie 6 300 de la luminescence atmosphérique nocturne, *Ann. Géophys.*, **15,** 179 (1959).
9. D. Barbier, L'arc auroral stable, *Ann. Géophys.*, **16,** 544 (1960).
10. D. Barbier, Les variations d'intensité de la raie 6300 Å de la luminescence noturne, *Ann. Géophys.*, **17,** 3 (1961).
11. D. Barbier, Airglow and earth storm, *J. Phys. Soc. Japan*, **17,** Suppl. A-1, 255 (1962).
12. D. Barbier, Étude de la couche *F* d'après l'émission de la raie rouge du ciel nocturne, *Planet. Space Sci.*, **10,** 29 (1963).
13. D. Barbier; in press.
14. D. Barbier, J. Dufay, and D. R. Williams, Recherches sur l'émission de la raie verte de la lumière du ciel nocturne, *Ann. Astrophys.*, **14,** 399 (1951).
15. D. Barbier and J. Glaume, Contribution à l'étude de la couche qui émet la raie 5577 du ciel nocturne, *Ann. Géophys.*, **15,** 266 (1959).
16. D. Barbier and J. Glaume, Correlations entre les intensités de diverses radiations de la luminescence atmosphérique nocturne, *Ann. Géophys.*, **16,** 56 (1960).
17. D. Barbier and J. Glaume, Les radiations de l'oxygène 6 300 à 5 577 Å de la luminescence du ciel nocturne dans une station de basse latitude, *Ann. Géophys.*, **16,** 319 (1960).
18. D. Barbier and J. Glaume, La couche ionosphérique nocturne *F* dans la zone intertropicale et ses relations avec l'émission de la raie 6300 Å du ciel nocturne, *Planet. Space Sci.*, **9,** 133 (1962).
19. D. Barbier, F. E. Roach, and W. R. Steiger, The summer intensity variations of (OI) 6300 Å in the tropics, *J. Res.*, **66*D*,** 145 (1962).
20. D. Barbier, G. Weill, and J. Glaume, L'émission de la raie rouge du ciel nocturne en Afrique, *Ann. Géophys.*, **17,** 305 (1961).
21. D. R. Bates and H. S. W. Massey, The basic reactions in the upper atmosphere, I, *Proc. Roy. Soc. A*, **187,** 261 (1946).
22. D. E. Blackwell, M. F. Ingham, and H. Rundle, The night sky spectrum λ 5000–6500 A, *Astropys. J.*, **131,** 15 (1960).
23. J. E. Blamont, Observations de l'émission atmosphérique des raies D du sodium au moyen d'un appareil à balayage magnétique, *In*: *The Airglow and The Aurorae*, E. B. Armstrong and A. Dalgarno (eds.), 99 Pergamon Press, 1956).
24. J. E. Blamont, T. M. Donahue, and V. R. Stull, The sodium twilight airglow 1955–1957, II, *Ann. Géophys.*, **14,** 253 (1958).
25. J. E. Blamont and T. M. Donahue, The dayglow of the sodium D lines, *J. Geophys. Res.*, **66,** 1407 (1961).
26. W. R. Bullock and D. M. Hunten, Vertical distribution of sodium in the upper atmosphere, *Can. J. Phys.*, **39,** 976 (1961).
27. E. T. Byram, T. A. Chubb, H. Friedman, and J. E. Kupperian, Jr., Far ultraviolet radiation in the night sky, *In*: *The Threshold of Space*, M. Zelikoff (ed.), 203 (Pergamon Press, 1957).
28. J. Cabannes and J. Dufay, Étude interférentielle des raies rouges du ciel nocturne, *In*: *The Airglow and the Aurorae*, E. B. Armstrong and A. Dalgarno (eds.), 73 (Pergamon Press, 1956).
29. J. W. Chamberlain, *Physics of the Aurora and Airglow*, 497 (Academic Press, 1961).
30. J. W. Chamberlain, D. M. Hunten, and J. E. Mack, Resonance scattering by atmospheric sodium, Pt. 4, Abundance of sodium in twilight, *J. Atmos. Terr. Phys.*, **12,** 153 (1958).
31. J. W. Chamberlain and N. J. Oliver, OH in the airglow at high latitudes, *Phys. Rev.*, **90,** 1118 (1953).
32. M. W. Chiplonkar and V. V. Agashe, A simultaneous study of the λλ 5577, 5893 and 6300 emissions of the night airglow at Poona, *Ann. Géophys.*, **17,** 231 (1961).

33. J. Delannoy and G. Weill, Observation d'une nouvelle raie d'émission crépusculaire atmosphérique, *C. R. Acad. Sci.*, **247,** 808 (1958).
34. A. Delsemme and D. Delsemme, La raie rouge du ciel nocturne à l'équateur, *Ann. Géophys.*, **16,** 507 (1960).
35. T. M. Donahue and J. E. Blamont, Sodium in the upper atmosphere, *Ann. Géophys.*, **17,** 116 (1961).
36. J. Dufay, M. Dufay, and Nguyen-Huu-Doan, Sur les variations d'intensité des raies Hα et [N II] 6 863 Å dans le spectre du ciel nocturne, *C. R. Acad. Sci.*, **253,** 974 (1961).
37. M. Dufay, Présence de la raie interdite ^4S–^2D de l'atome d'azote dans le spectre du ciel nocturne, *C. R. Acad. Sci.*, **248,** 2505 (1959).
38. R. A. Duncan, Photometric observations of subvisual red auroral arcs at middle latitudes, *Austral. J. Phys.*, **12,** 197 (1959).
39. L. M. Fishkova, Seasonal and annual intensity variations of the airglow in Abastumani, *In*: *Aurorae and Airglow, No. 9*, 5 (Section IV of IGY Program, Acad. Sci. USSR, Moscow, 1962).
40. M. Gadsden, Observations of lithium in twilight after a high-altitude thermonuclear explosion, *Ann. Géophys.*, **18,** 392 (1962).
41. M. Gadsden and K. Salmon, Presence of 6707 A radiation in the twilight sky, *Nature*, **182,** 1598 (1958).
42. J. Christophe Glaume, Influence des marées lunaires sur l'émission de la raie verte 5 577 Å de l'oxygéne, *C. R. Acad. Sci.*, **254,** 3399 (1962).
43. J. Christophe Glaume, Renforcement d'intensité de la raie verte de l'oxygéne lié aux débuts brusques d'orages magnétiques, *C. R. Acad. Aci.*, **256,** 998 (1963).
44. J. Christophe Glaume, L'emission de la raie verte de l'oxygène le long d'un meridien en octobre 1962, *C. R. Acad. Sci.*, **257,** 210 (1963).
45. J. Christophe Glaume, Emission de la raie verte de l'oxygène en fonction de la latitude, *C. R. Acad. Sci.*, **257,** 486 (1963).
46. U. Haug, Zur Statistik der raumlichen Helligkeitsschwankungen der (OI) 5577 A in Nachthimmelsleuchten, *J. Atmos. Terr. Phys.*, **21,** 225 (1961).
47. D. M. Hunten, Resonance scattering by atmospheric sodium, Pt. 8, An improved method of deducing the vertical distribution, *J. Atmos. Terr. Phys.*, **17,** 295 (1960).
48. M. Huruhata, T. Nakamura, H. Tanabe, and T. Tohmatsu, Oxygen red line in the night airglow and ionospheric *F*2 region, *Rept. Ionos. Space Res. in Japan*, **13,** 283 (1959).
49. A. Vallance Jones and R. L. Gattinger, The seasonal variation and excitation mechanism of the 1.5 μ $^1\Delta_g$–$^3\Sigma_g$-twilight airglow band, *Planet. Space Sci.*, **11,** 961 (1963).
50. A. Vallance Jones and A. W. Harrison, $^1\Delta_g$–$^3\Sigma_g$–O_2 infrared emission band in the twilight airglow spectrum, *J. Atmos. Terr. Phys.*, **13,** 45 (1958).
51. V. I. Karyagina, The hydroxyl emission in the airglow spectrum according to observations in Alma-Ata, *In*: *Aurorae and Airglow, No. 8*, 6 (Section IV of IGY Program, Acad. Sci. USSR, Moscow, 1962).
52. V. I. Krassovsky, Some results of investigations of aurorae and night airglow during the IGY and IGC, *Planet. Space Sci.*, **8,** 125 (1961).
53. V. I. Krassovsky and G. I. Galperin, A brief report on research in the USSR [See bibliography], *Appendix to*: La luminescence cu ciel, *In*: *Trans. IAU, XIA*: *Repts. on Astronomy*, 211 (Academic Press, 1961).
54. V. I. Krassovsky, N. N. Shefov, and V. I. Yarin, On the OH airglow, *J. Atmos. Terr. Phys.*, **21,** 46 (1961).
55. J. E. Kupperian, Jr., E. T. Byram, T. A. Chubb, and H. Friedman, Far ultraviolet radiation in the night sky, *Planet. Space Sci.*, **1,** 3 (1959).
56. G. Kvifte, Auroral and nightglow observations at Ås, Norway, *J. Atmos. Terr. Phys.*, **16,** 252 (1959).
57. G. Kvifte, Nightglow observations at Ås during the IGY, *Geofysiske Publikasjoner*, **20,** 15 p. (1959).
58. J. W. McCaulley and W. S. Hough, A relationship between the lower ionosphere and the (OI) 5577 nightglow emission, *J. Geophys. Res.*, **64,** 2307 (1959).

59. J. W. McCaulley, F. E. Roach, and S. Matsushita, A study of local geomagnetic influence on the [OI] 5577 nightglow emission at Fritz Peak, *J. Geophys. Res.*, **65,** 1499 (1960).
60. D. H. McPherson and A. V. Jones, A study of the latitude dependence of OH rotational temperatures for Canadian stations, *J. Atmos. Terr. Phys.*, **17,** 302 (1960).
61. A. B. Meinel, OH emission bands in the spectrum of the night sky, II, *Astrophys. J.*, **112,** 120 (1950).
62. A. V. Mironov, V. S. Prokudina, and N. N. Shefov, Results from studies of the night airglow and aurorae in the USSR, III, Some results of investigations of night airglow and aurorae, *Ann. Géophys.*, **14,** 364 (1958).
63. T. Nagata, T. Tohmatsu and E. Kaneda, Lunar time variation of the oxygen green line in the airglow, *Rept. Ionos. Space Res. Japan*, **15,** 253 (1961).
64. Nguyen-Huu-Doan, Sur l'excitation crépusculaire de la raie de résonance du lithium (6 708 Å) observée á l'Observatoire de Haute Provence depuis novembre 1962, *C. R. Acad. Sci.*, **256,** 1141 (1963).
65. M. Nicolet, Helium, an important constituent in the lower exosphere, *J. Geophys. Res.*, **66,** 2263 (1961).
66. J. F. Noxon and A. V. Jones, Observations of the (O, O) band of the ($^1\Delta_g$–$^{3-}\Sigma_g$) system of oxygen in the day and twilight airglow, *Nature*, **196,** 157 (1962).
67. M. Perrin, Mesures interférometriques sur la raie verte de la lueur nocturne, *C. R. Acad. Sci.*, **250,** 2406 (1960).
68. V. S. Prokudina, Observations of the line λ 6562 A in the night airglow spectrum, *In*: *Spectral, Electrophotometrical and Radar Researches of Aurorae and Airglow, No. 1*, 43 (Section IV of IGY Program, Acad. Sci. USSR, Moscow, 1959).
69. V. S. Prokudina, Determination of the rotation temperature of hydroxyl in the upper atmosphere, *Izv. Akad. Nauk. SSR, Ser. Geofiz.*, **125,** 629 (1959).
70. F. E. Roach, A review of observational results in airglow photometry, *Ann. Géophys.*, **11,** 214 (1955).
71. F. E. Roach, Variations of [OI] 5577 Å emission in the upper atmosphere, *Ann. Géophys.*, **17,** 172 (1961).
72. F. E. Roach and H. B. Pettit, Excitation patterns in the nightglow, *Mem. Soc. Roy. Sci. Liège*, **12,** 13 (1952).
73. F. E. Roach and J. R. Roach, Stable 6300 Å arcs in mid-latitudes, *Planet. Space Sci.*, **11,** 523 (1963).
74. F. E. Roach, E. Tandberg-Hanssen, and L. R. Megill, The characteristic size of airglow cells, *J. Atmos. Terr. Phys.*, **13,** 113 (1958).
75. F. E. Roach, E. Tandberg-Hanssen, and L. R. Megill, Movements of airglow cells, *J. Atmos. Terr. Phys.*, **13,** 122 (1958).
76. F. E. Roach, D. R. Williams, and H. B. Pettit, The diurnal variation of [OI] 5577 in the nightglow: Geographical studies, *J. Geophys. Res.*, **58,** 73 (1953).
77. H. N. Rundle, D. M. Hunten, and J. W. Chamberlain, Resonance scattering by atmospheric sodium, VII: Measurement of the vertical distribution in twilight, *J. Atmos. Terr. Phys.*, **17,** 205 (1960).
78. P. V. Shcheglov, Observations of the twilight helium emission λ 10830 Å, *Astron. Zh.*, **39,** 158 (1962).
79. N. N. Shefov, Observations of the OH emission in Zvenigorod, *In*: *Aurorae and Airglow, No. 5*, 18 (Section IV of IGY Program, Acad. Sci. USSR, Moscow, 1961).
80. N. N. Shefov, Emission de l'hélium dans la haute atmosphere, *Ann. Géophys.* **17,** 395 (1961).
81. N. N. Shefov and V. I. Yarin, On the latitudinal dependence of the OH rotational temperature, *In*: *Aurorae and Airglow, No. 5*, 25 (Section IV of IGY Program, Acad. Sci. USSR, Moscow, 1961).
82. N. N. Shefov and V. I. Yarin, Latitudinal and planetary variations of the OH airglow, *In*: *Aurorae and Airglow, No. 9*, 19 (Sections IV of IGY Program, Acad. Sci. USSR, Moscow, 1962).
83. H. M. Sullivan and D. M. Hunten, Relative abundance of lithium, sodium, and potassium in the upper atmosphere, *Nature*, **195,** 589 (1962).

84. V. A. Tinsley and A. V. Jones, The seasonal variation of the twilight sodium airglow in the southern atmosphere, *J. Atmos. Terr. Phys.*, **24,** 345 (1962).
85. T. Tohmatsu and T. Nagata, Dynamical studies of the oxygen green line in the airglow, *Planet. Space Sci.*, **10,** 103 (1963).
86. L. Wallace, Note on airglow temperature determinations from OH spectra, *J. Geophys. Res.*, **65,** 921 (1960).
87. L. Wallace, Seasonal variation and interpretation of the OH rotational temperature of the airglow, *J. Atmos. Terr. Phys.*, **20,** 85 (1961).
88. D. Q. Wark, Doppler widths of the atomic oxygen lines in the airglow, *Astrophys. J.*, **131,** 491 (1960).
89. I. G. Yao (ed.), Observations of the night airglow: 1 July 1957–31 December 1959, *Annals of the International Geophysical Year*, **24,** 322 p. (1962).
90. V. I. Yarin, The OH emission according to observations in Yakutsk, *In*: *Aurorae and Airglow*, *No. 5*, 10 (Section IV of IGY Program, Acad. Sci. USSR, Moscow, 1961).

CHAPTER 17

MAGNETIC FIELD AT THE POLES

Takesi Nagata

1. The Field over the Polar Regions

The World Magnetic Survey (WMS) now under way, using airborne three-component magnetometers and shipborne magnetometers as well as ordinary surface magnetometers, is collecting detailed data on the distribution of geomagnetic field over the whole earth's surface. The proposed surveys by satelliteborne magnetometers will provide us with knowledge of the spatial distribution of the geomagnetic field in the vicinity of the earth.

During the IGY, geomagnetic measurements were undertaken in the Antarctic, where extremely few measurements had been made in the past, and this work has been carried on to the present. Based on the geomagnetic data obtained in Antarctica, the British Admiralty World Magnetic Charts and the U. S. Hydrographic Charts and similar ones for the epoch of 1960 have achieved a much higher degree of accuracy than before for the south polar region. For example, Figure 1 illustrates a map of the isodynamic lines of geomagnetic total force in 1960 over this region, which was recompiled by adding new data [5, 32, 45] to the provisional chart for the epoch of 1957 [22] based on the IGY observations at southern stations and results of several magnetic traverse surveys in Antarctica.

In the antarctic area, the magnetic dip pole, at which the horizontal force H is zero and the dip angle is $-90°$, coincides almost exactly with the location of the maximum of total force F as well as that of vertical force Z. However, the intensity of Z and consequently that of F at the south magnetic dip pole amounts to 0.7 gauss, which exceeds the field intensity caused by the earth's centered magnetic dipole by about 0.07 gauss. In other words, the dipole field is regionally intensified by about 10 per cent in the antarctic area.

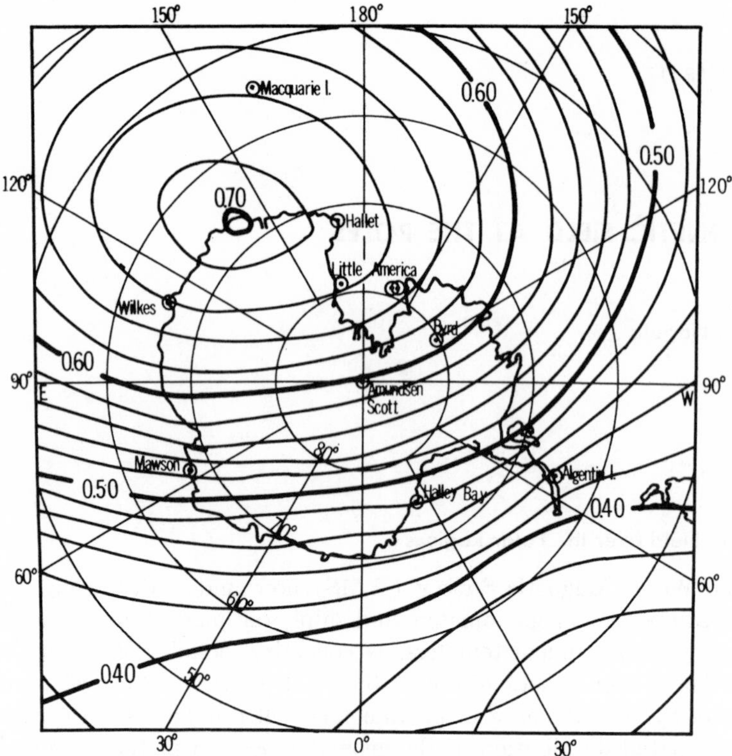

FIG. 1. Isodynamic chart for total magnetic force (F) around the South Pole for the epoch of 1960 (unit = gauss).

It had been known before the IGY, on the other hand, that there are two maxima of the total force F and vertical force Z in the Northern Hemisphere, one in northern Canada and another in Siberia, and contours of isodynamic lines of horizontal force H become very elongated, approximately parallel to the direction from 90°E to 90°W in longitude, as the H-values approach zero in the Arctic area [14, 15]. This unique pattern of geomagnetic isodynamic lines has been called the great arctic anomaly [15]. Orlov [35] and Alldredge and Van Voorhis [1] have recently again considered this problem. Contours of isodynamic lines of F and Z form the saddle-point shape in the neighborhood of the north dip pole. The values of F and Z at the North Pole amount only to 0.57 gauss, which is about 0.06 gauss less than the centered dipole field value. Thus, the dipole field is reduced by about 10 per cent in the arctic area and is instead regionally strengthened in Siberia and in North America.

Hope [14, 15] has ascribed the arctic magnetic anomaly to an anomalous geological structure which results in deep parts of the earth's crust of this area being below the rock's Curie temperature. It seems, however, that this interpretation is hardly acceptable from the viewpoint of rock magnetism. Alternatively, Alldredge and Van Voorhis [1] have demonstrated that all aspects of the arctic magnetic anomaly can be interpreted as due to electric current vortices located on the core-mantle intersurface. These vortices are approximately represented by radial magnetic dipoles on the intersurface. According to their results, clockwise current vortices beneath Siberia and North America and a counterclockwise vortex nearby the north dip pole, viewed from the outside, can explain the geometric anomaly in northern high latitudes. It thus seems likely that geomagnetic regional anomalies in the north and south polar regions are attributable to the localized poloidal magnetic fields caused by electric current vortices flowing just beneath the core-mantle intersurface. This interpretation is acceptable, in principle, from the standpoint of the core-dynamo theory of the geomagnetic field (for example, Nagata and Rikitake [30], Nagata [23]. However, why they are there is still unsolved and may well deserve future studies.

2. Secular Variation during and after the IGY

Enough time has passed since the beginning of the IGY so that sufficiently reliable data of recent secular variation in the geomagnetic field have become available at a number of stations established for the IGY. Provisional data obtained in the first half of the period permitted the study of a remarkably intense anomaly of geomagnetic secular variation in East Antarctica [22, 30, 33]. In a further study of the distribution of secular variation [23] the features of the secular variation were summarized as consisting of (*a*) a decrease in the intensity of the geomagnetic centered dipole, (*b*) a westward drift of 0.2 degree/year in the angular velocity of the nondipole field, (*c*) a northward shift of the centered dipole, and (*d*) residual regional variations. A nearly complete table of annual mean values of geomagnetic elements for the period of 1955–1962, recently compiled by Nagata and Sawada [32], covers data obtained at 149 magnetic observatories, 112 in the Northern and 37 in the Southern Hemisphere. The annual rates of secular variation of the three geomagnetic field elements can be estimated with a certain accuracy at 99 stations in the Northern and 30 stations in the Southern Hemisphere. The general aspects of the revised secular variation as based on the newly compiled data are basically the same as those obtained from the provisional data: the three regular factors of secular variation characteristics — (*a*), (*b*), and (*c*) — are also conspicuous in the new isoporic chart. Here, therefore, only those several aspects of the secular variation specifically remarkable in the polar regions will be considered.

Figures 2 and 3 illustrate the distribution of the recent annual rate of change of geomagnetic total force F in the Northern and Southern Hemi-

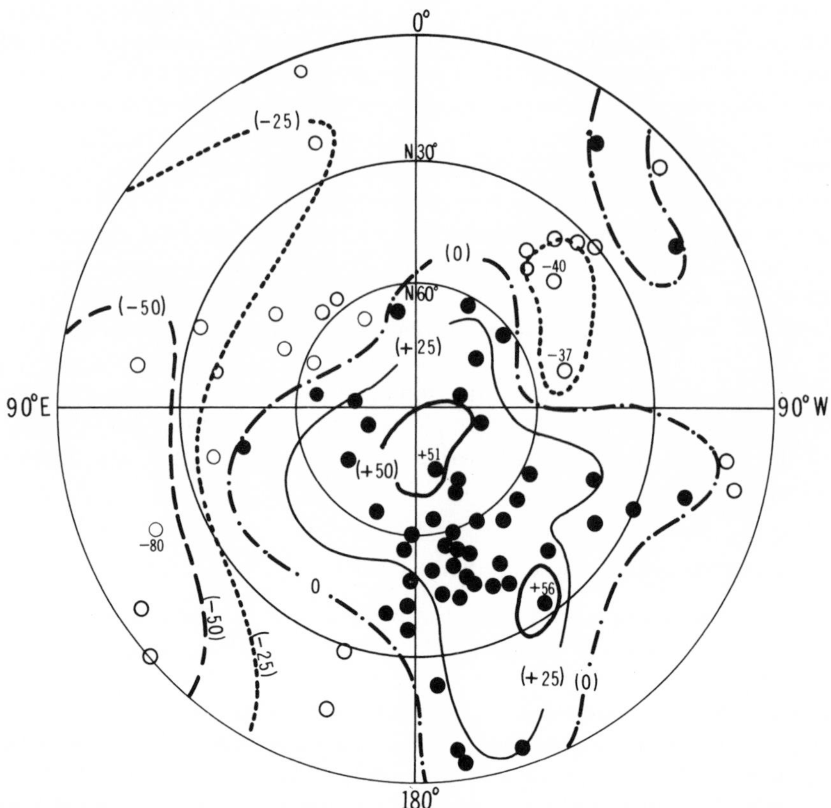

Fig. 2. Isopric chart for total magnetic force in the Northern Hemisphere for the epoch of 1960 (unit = gamma/year.) Full circle, $\dot{F} > 0$. Hollow circle, $\dot{F} < 0$.

spheres. In Figure 3, isoporic contours of F in a pentagon area are derived from magnetic survey data obtained by shipborne proton-precision magnetometers during 1957–1960 [17]. The isoporic contours seem to harmonize well with the data observed at surrounding stations. The most remarkable contrast between the two polar regions is that the geomagnetic total force F is increasing around the North Pole while it is decreasing around the South Pole. Although the geomagnetic field as a whole is decreasing continuously, as represented by the decrease in the centered dipole moment and as indicated by the general tendency of decrease in F by 10–20γ over temperate and low-latitude zones in Figures 2 and 3, it looks as if the field is being intensified in the north while it is being reduced abnormally rapidly in the south. These opposite tendencies in the two polar regions may be interpreted hypothetically as due to a northward shift of the earth's magnetic dipole. If the dipole is assumed to be shifting northwards with the speed of 2.25 km/year, the vertical force at the North

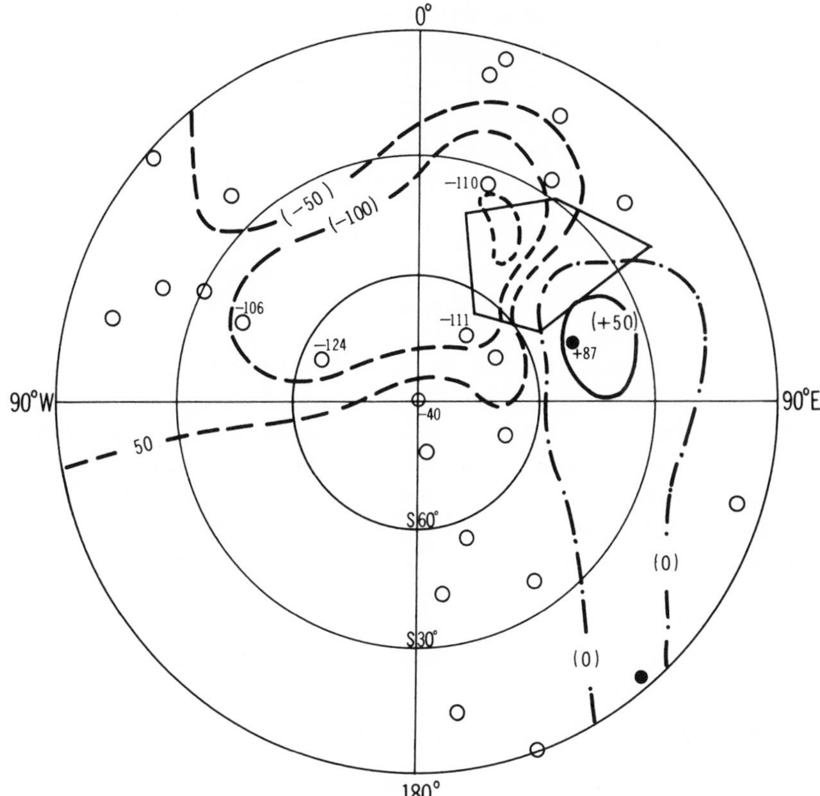

FIG. 3. Isoporic chart for total magnetic force in the Southern Hemisphere for the epoch of 1960 (unit = gamma/year.) Full circle, $\dot{F} > 0$. Hollow circle, $\dot{F} < 0$.

Pole increases by 65γ/year and decreases at the South Pole by the same amount. By taking into account the effect of a decrease of the dipole moment, which results in a decrease in Z by 27γ/year at the poles, the annual rates of change of F at the North and South Poles become $\dot{F} = +65 - 27 = +38$ (γ/year) and $\dot{F} = -65 - 27 = -92$ (γ/year), respectively. This result of hypothetical northward shifting of the dipole is in rough accord with the polar anomalies of $\dot{F}$ shown in Figures 2 and 3.

The possibility of such a northward shifting of the dipole has been theoretically examined by Nagata and Rikitake [31] as a problem of North-South oscillation of the poloidal S_1-field of Bullard's geomagnetic dynamo. The problem is expressed mathematically as an examination of the stability of hydromagnetic oscillation of an axial quadrupole field within the dynamo system. Calculation, based on the assumption that the electric conductivity within the core is infinitely large, has shown that the quadrupole field can perform a stable, simple harmonic oscillation of small amplitude with a period of about 10^2 years. If we assume that the northward shifting of the dipole is a phase of the theoretical North-South oscillation, the theoretical period of 10^2 years is too short, because it seems likely that the northward shifting has continued nearly a hundred years in the past. No satisfactory interpretation has been given to explain the northward shifting of the dipole, and this problem deserves further theoretical studies.

After eliminating the three regular factors from the observed distribution of secular variation, several unusual local anomalies of variation remain at various localities over the earth's surface. The most remarkable anomaly is that located between East Antarctica and South Africa. The conspicuous positive anomaly of $\dot{F}$, which was originally found in the early data (1952–1954) at Heard Island (S53°.0, E73°.4) has been confirmed by the new data (for 1959–1961) obtained at Port-aux-Français (S49°.3 E70°.2). Such local anomalies may be attributable to local anomalous convectional motions of core material near the core's surface. For example, a local upwelling of core material can generate a localized poloidal field by distorting the intense toroidal field which must be within the core to maintain the geomagnetic dynamo. Nagata and Rikitake [30] showed that a local convectional motion of 10^{-2}–10^{-1} cm/sec in velocity within the core can generate the secular variation anomaly of observed magnitude.

3. Morphology of Geomagnetic Daily Variation on Quiet Days

Based on magnetograph data in the northern polar region in the winter season of the Second International Polar Year, 1932–1933, when the sunspot activity was nearly at its minimum, Nagata and Mizuno [29] suggested that the pattern of geomagnetic daily variation in the polar regions on geomagnetically very quiet days, which may be defined as the days of $\Sigma K_p = 0_0$, may be represented by an extension into the polar areas of the S_q-field pattern which is well established in low and temperate latitudes. Such a S_q-field pattern on the absolutely quiet day has been called the $S_q{}^0$-field pattern.

It has been pointed out (by Witham and Loomer [48], Lassen [18], Bobrov [6], and others) that the geomagnetic variation in the polar region is more or less disturbed on most geomagnetically quiet days. It seems, therefore, that the $S_q{}^0$-field can take place only in the dark polar region on exceptionally quiet days.

Using the K-indices for the IGY period, Fukushima [11, 12] has shown: (*a*) Some geomagnetic agitation takes place almost always in the polar regions when the geomagnetic field as a whole is extremely quiet ($K_p = 0_0$), the disturbances in the sunlit polar cap being definitely larger than those in the dark polar cap. (*b*) The polar cap area only is disturbed, without auroral zone enhancement when K_p is zero or very small, but auroral zone

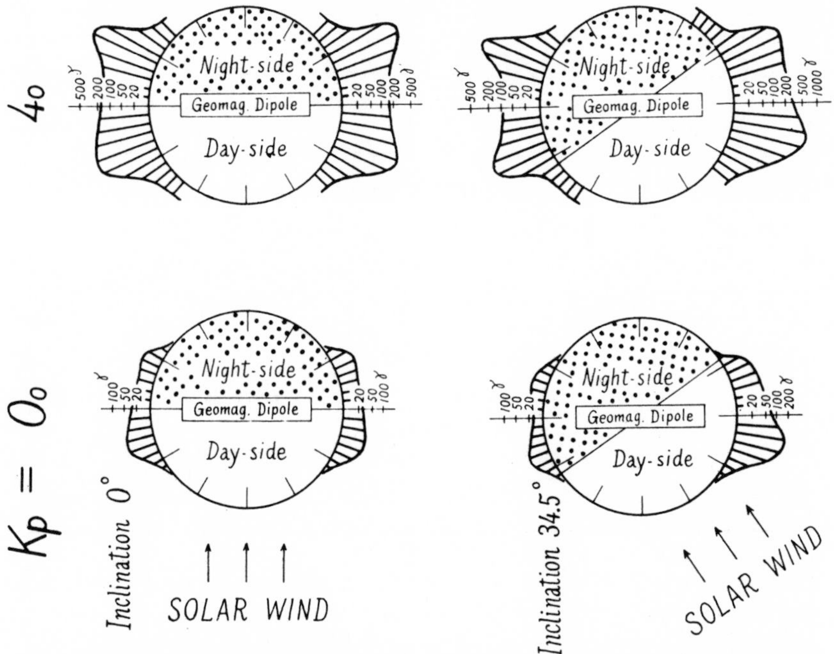

FIG. 4. Polar magnetic disturbances near the noon and midnight meridian plane for the extremely quiet period ($K_p = 0_0$) and for moderately disturbed period ($K_p = 4_0$) (after Fukushima).

disturbances increase and become larger than the simultaneous polar cap disturbances with increase in the K_p-value. These characteristics are illustrated in Figure 4. Fukushima [12] has further shown that rapid changes in the quarter-hourly Q-indices observed during the IGY period in the polar regions are localized around only a single station in most cases (80 per cent) when the worldwide geomagnetic activity is rather low ($K_p \leqq 3$).

Nagata [21] and Nagata and Kokubun [25, 26] have studied in some detail the quiet-day variation in the polar regions. Figure 5 illustrates examples of magnetograms at Resolute Bay (+82.9° in geomagnetic latitude) and at Mirny (−77.0° in geomagnetic latitude) on extremely quiet days during the IGY. As shown in the figure, considerable geomagnetic agitation takes place in the sunlit polar area even in case of $K_p = 0$, while magnetogram traces in the dark polar region are much less disturbed, being rather flat. Using magnetogram data at 13 stations in high northern latitudes and 7 stations in southern ones, the average pattern of geomagnetic variation over the polar region on the quietest days of every month during the IGY was constructed. As indicated in Figure 5, special interest of this study has been in the quiet-day variation in the solstitial seasons, that is, the June solstice season consisting of May, June, and July, and the

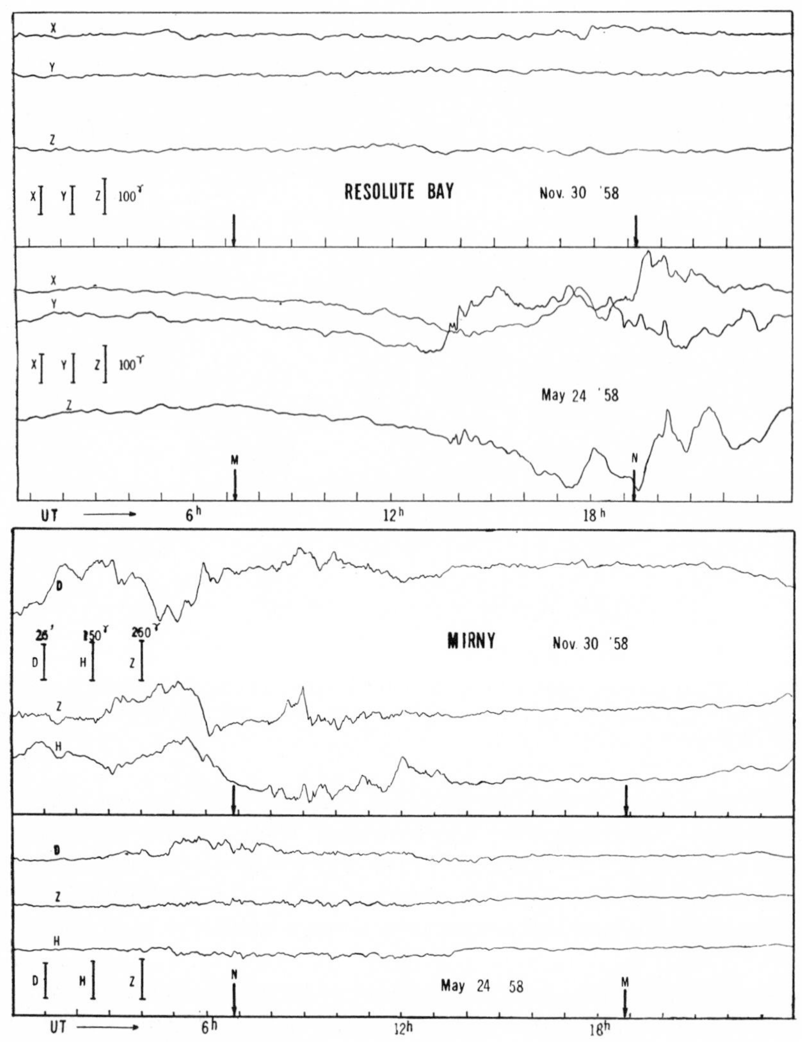

Fig. 5. Examples of magnetograms on extremely quiet days during the IGY at Resolute Bay and Mirny (May 24 and November 30, 1958). K_p-indices during these periods were as follows:

GMT		0–3	3–6	6–9	9–12	12–15	15–18	18–21	21–24h	Sum
K_p	May 24	0_0	0_+	0_+	1_0	1_+	1_-	0_+	0_+	4_+
	Nov. 30	0_0	1_-	0_+	1_0	1_0	0_0	0_+	0_0	3_+

(After Nagata and Kokubun.)

December solstice season of November, December, and January. The average values of the daily sum of K_p-indices ($\bar{\Sigma}K_p$) are 10.3 and 8.8, respectively, for the June and December solstices. These values of the average daily sum of K_p are a little larger than the corresponding value during the Second Polar Year when $\bar{\Sigma}K_p = 5.1$. However, the patterns of daily variation between 55°N and 55°S in geomagnetic latitude for the solstitial seasons are the same as the typical pattern of $S_q{}^0$-field. It may therefore be considered that the geomagnetic field concerned was substantially quiet on these days.

Figures 6(*a*) and (*b*) illustrate the equivalent ionospheric current systems of the polar S_q-field for the north polar region in the June solstice and for

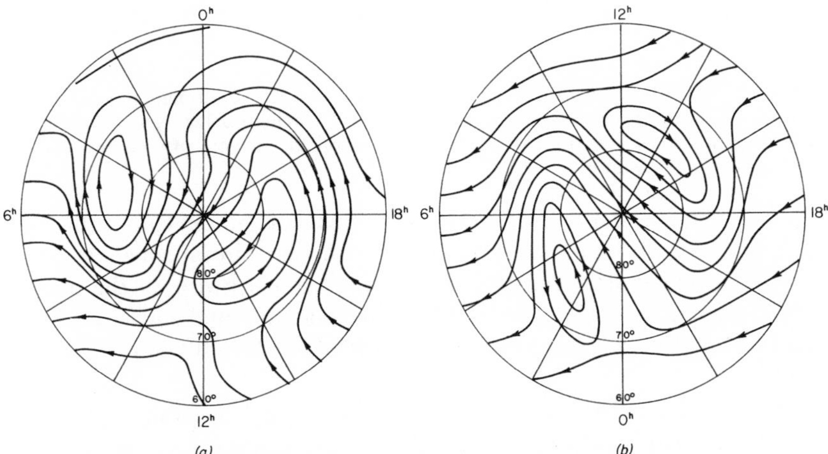

FIG. 6. Equivalent ionospheric current patterns of the S_q-field over the sunlit polar regions. Electric current between adjacent current lines is 2×10^4 amp. (*a*) Northern polar region for May, June, and July. (*b*) Southern polar region for November, December, and January. (After Nagata and Kokubun.)

the south polar region in the December solstice, respectively. It seems likely that the polar S_q-field consists of an extension of the $S_q{}^0$-field and an additional particular field which may be called the $S_q{}^p$ field, namely,

$$S_q = S_q{}^0 + S_q{}^p$$

The $S_q{}^0$-field was determined from the distribution of the S_q-field between two latitude circles of $\pm 55°$ in geomagnetic latitude and its extrapolation into both the polar regions. The patterns of $S_q{}^p = S_q - S_q{}^0$ for various seasons are obtained for both polar regions. The equivalent ionospheric current systems of the $S_q{}^p$-field in the sunlit and dark polar regions are illustrated in Figures 7 and 8. The patterns for the dark polar region are much less accurate compared with those for the sunlit polar region because of the former's much smaller intensity. In any case, the $S_q{}^p$-

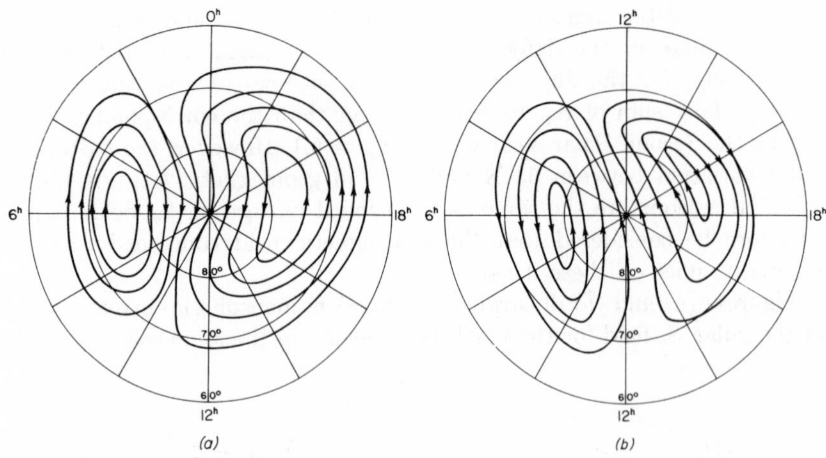

Fig. 7. Equivalent ionospheric current patterns of the additional quiet-day daily variation field ($S_q{}^p$) for the sunlit polar regions. (*a*) Northern polar region. (*b*) Southern polar region. (After Nagata and Kokubun.) Equivalent current between adjacent current lines is 2×10^4 amp.

current system is limited within the polar cap area and the current intensity does not seem to be particularly enhanced in the auroral zone.

The current system consists of two vortices, clockwise on the morning side and counterclockwise on the afternoon side, the total currents amounting to 17×10^4 amp (sunlit polar cap) and about 5×10^4 amp (dark polar cap).

It seems thus that the morphology of the daily variation in the polar region $S_q{}^p$-field has been established at least qualitatively based on the

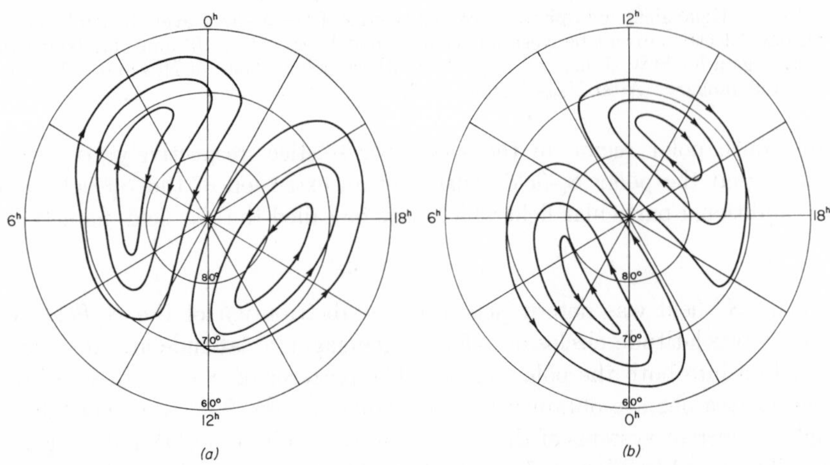

Fig. 8. Equivalent ionospheric current patterns of the additional quiet-day daily variation field ($S_q{}^p$) for the dark polar regions. (*a*) Northern polar region. (*b*) Southern polar region. Electric current between adjacent current lines is 10^4 amp.

IGY data. There is very little room for doubt that the $S_q{}^0$-field is generated by the ionospheric dynamo which is controlled mostly by the solar radiation resulting in ionospheric ionization and the ionospheric wind. On the contrary, the $S_q{}^p$-field, which is confined within the polar regions, may be caused by the energy agency transferred from the earth's outer space to the polar ionosphere by charged corpuscles along the lines of magnetic force.

The observed fact that the $S_q{}^p$-field intensity in the dark polar cap is about one-third of that in the sunlit polar cap may be ascribed to the effect of reduction of ionospheric conductivity in the dark polar region. Because the ratios of the height-integrated values of Pedersen (Σ_1) and Hall (Σ_2) conductivities of the sunlit ionosphere to those of the dark ionosphere have been estimated to be 5 and 9, respectively [20], whence the ratios of the average values of Σ_1 and Σ_2 for the summer solstitial three months to those for the winter solstitial three months become 2.8 and 3.4.

Extensive studies on the $S_q{}^p$-field during the IQSY period while the solar activity is at a minimum will be extremely interesting from both observational and theoretical viewpoints. Judging from Fukushima's work [12] on the polar magnetic disturbances on quiet days during the Second Polar Year, it seems almost certain that the $S_q{}^p$-field will survive during the IQSY period.

4. Conjugate Relationship of Geomagnetic Bay Disturbances

The patterns of polar magnetic disturbances, such as the *Ds*-field, are approximately symmetric with respect to the magnetic equatorial plane, and simultaneity and similarity of individual geomagnetic variations at magnetically conjugate areas was noted even in the pre-IGY data [3]. It does not seem, however, that the concept of geomagnetic conjugacy had been explicitly established before the IGY. Since the concept of trapped particles forming the radiation belts was established, the magnetically conjugate relationship between various disturbance phenomena in the northern and southern polar upper atmospheres has been studied in its light. (And one of the great merits of the IGY was its initiation of extensive controlled studies on the magnetic conjugacy using not only geomagnetic data but also direct measurements of precipitating particles, bremsstrahlung X-rays, auroral displays, ionospheric disturbances, cosmic noise absorption, etc.)

Table 1 shows the best five magnetically conjugate pairs among the IGY high-latitude magnetic stations. The locations of the geomagnetically conjugate points were calculated by Vestine [40] from Finch-Leaton's analysis of the geomagnetic field for 1955. The actual location of the stations in both the North and South are also given. The figure in the last column indicates the distance between the station and the conjugate point

TABLE 1

THE BEST FIVE CONJUGATE PAIRS AMONG THE IGY HIGH-LATITUDE MAGNETIC STATIONS

Names of Pair Stations	Geographic		Geomagnetic		Conjugate Point Geographic		Distance of Conjugate Point from Pair Station
	Lat.	Long.	Lat.	Long.	Lat.	Long.	
(N) Reykjavik	N64°–11′	W21°–42′	70.2	71.0			
(S) Syowa Base	S69°–02′,	E39°–36′	−69.7	77.4	N63°–44′,	W21°–17′	54 km
(N) Kotzebue	N66°–40′,	W162°–30	63.4	242.4	S54°–03′,	E160°–22	101
(S) Macquarie Is.	S54°–30′,	E158°–57	−61.1	243.1			
(N) Anchorage	N61°–10′,	W149°–55	60.9	258.1	S53°–19′,	E172°–04	≃270
(S) Campbell Is.	S52°–33′,	E169°–09	−57.4	253.4	N61°–59′	W154°–38	
(N) Baker Lake	N64°–18′	W96°–05′	73.7	315.1	S75°–33′	W173°–47	≃420
(S) Little America	S78°–18′,	W162°–10	−74.0	312.0			
(N) Healy	N63°–51′	W149°–00	63.6	256.5	S55°–03′	E169°–15	≃670
(S) Macquarie Is.	S53°–30′,	E158°–57	−61.1	243.1			

TABLE 2

APPROXIMATELY CONJUGATE PAIR GROUPS IN HIGH LATITUDES

Northern Stations			Southern Stations		
	Geomagnetic			Geomagnetic	
Name	Lat.	Long.	Name	Lat.	Long.
Reykjavik	70.2	71.0	Syowa Base	−69.7	77.4
Anchorage	60.9	258.1	Campbell Is.	−57.4	253.4
Cape Wellen	61.8	237.0	Macquarie Is.	−61.1	243.1
Kotzebue	63.4	242.4			
Healy	63.6	256.5			
Big Delta	64.4	259.0			
College	64.7	256.5			
Churchill	68.7	322.7	Byrd Station	−70.6	336.0
Baker Lake	73.7	315.1	Little America	−74.0	312.0
Bjørnøya	71.1	124.0	Mirny	−73.6	136.3
Tikhaya Bay	71.1	155.5			
Leningrad	56.3	117.3	Port-aux-Français	−57.2	128.0
Nurmijarvi	57.9	112.6			

of the corresponding pair station. As seen in Table 1, the conjugate relationship holds especially good for Reykjavik-Syowa Base and Kotzebue-Macquarie Island pairs. Table 2 shows a list of approximate conjugate pair groups in high latitudes among the IGY–IGC magnetic stations. Conjugate relations in Tables 1 and 2 are expressed with regard to the undisturbed geomagnetic field of internal origin and the geomagnetic-centered dipole field, respectively, regardless of a possible distortion of the field by the solar wind or the magnetic field originating in the electric current in the radiation belts.

In their first work on magnetic conjugacy of geomagnetic disturbances in high latitudes, Nagata and Kokubun [24] examined the correlation of horizontal disturbance vector $\mathbf{\Delta H} = (\Delta H, H\Delta D)$ of simultaneous individual bay-type variations during the IGY between Baker Lake (BL) and Little America (LA) with reference to Fort Churchill (Ch) and Byrd Station (BS). The average correlation coefficients $\bar{r}$ for night geomagnetic bays between these stations are

$$\bar{r}(\text{BL, LA}) = 0.76,\ r(\text{BL, Ch}) = 0.53,\ r(\text{LA, Ch}) = 0.55$$

for instantaneous values

$$\bar{r}(\text{BL, LA}) = 0.85,\ r(\text{BL, Ch}) = 0.50,\ r(\text{LA, Ch}) = 0.64$$

for 10-min average values

The correlation coefficient between Baker Lake and Little America is definitely greater than that between Baker Lake and Churchill or that between Little America and Churchill. Compared with the case of night bays, the correlation of **ΔH** for daytime bays become appreciably lower, $\bar{r}$(BL, LA) being 0.40 for instantaneous values, 0.51 for 15-min average values and 0.37 for 30-min average values.

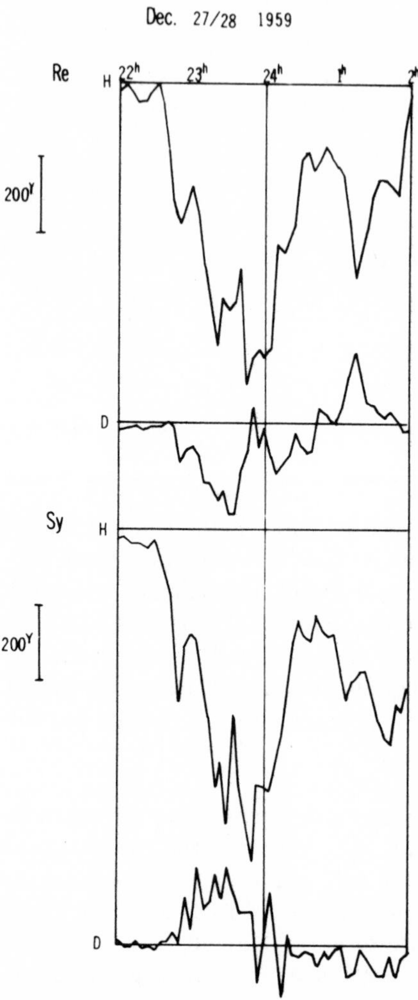

FIG. 9. An example of a bay-type variation observed at geomagnetically conjugate stations, Reykjavik (Re) and Syowa Base (Sy).

In their further study, Nagata, Kokubun, and Iijima examined the correlation between **ΔH**-values of isolated night and daytime bays observed during IGC-1959 at the best conjugate pair stations, Reykjavik (Re) and Syowa Base (Sy). Figure 9 illustrates an example of simultaneous magnetograms at these two stations in the case of a geomagnetic bay. The correlation coefficients for individual bays r(Re, Sy) are ranged between 0.62 and 0.96 for instantaneous values, the average coefficient $\bar{r}$(Re, Sy) amounting to 0.86. The simultaneity and similarity between **ΔH**-values at these stations is extremely good. For instance, the ratio of the $\Delta H(t)$-value at Syowa Base to the simultaneous value at Reykjavik is ranged from 0.63 to 1.65 for individual plots, the average value of ratios amounting to 1.05. As for the conjugacy between the second best pair stations, Kotzebue and Macquarie Island, Wescott [43, 44] pointed out that magnetograms at these stations resemble each other even with regard to their details, and suggested that the conjugate point of Macquarie Island may be located somewhere between Kotzebue and Healy.

Nagata *et al.* [27] using Q-indices and Ondoh and Maeda [34] using K-indices and hourly values of ΔH examined statistically the spatial extension of conjugate areas and the dependency of the conjugacy on local time, season, and storm time.

Figure 10 illustrates four typical examples of correlation between Q-index values at two different stations during the rather disturbed period of September 2–6, 1957, where $X(t)$ denotes the Q-index value at time t at Station X and $Y\ (t + \Delta t)$ the Q-value at time $t + \Delta t$ at station Y. All eight stations picked as examples are located within or near the auroral maximal zones. However, each of the four selected pairs has its own geo-

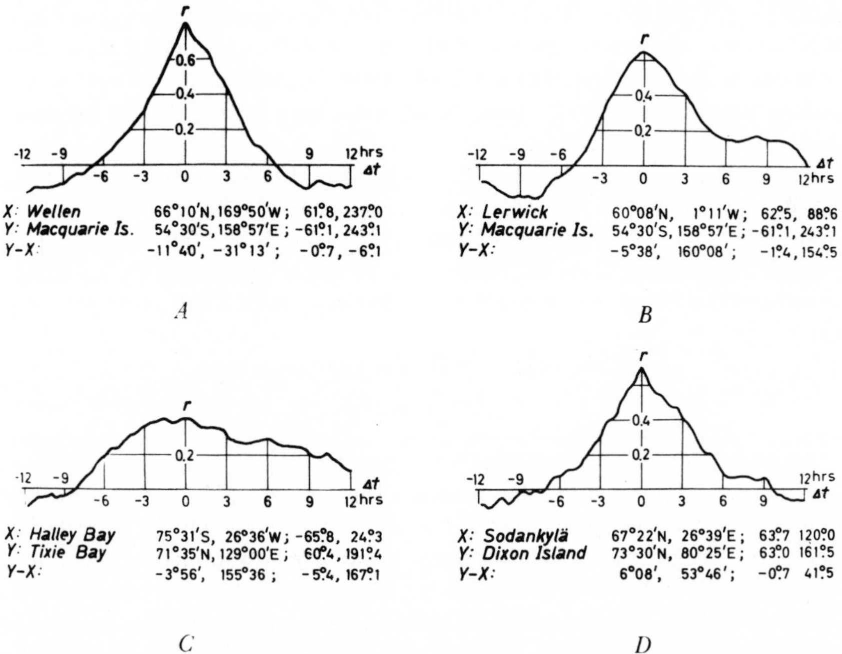

FIG. 10. Correlation coefficient, $r[X(t), Y(t + \Delta t)]$, of Q-indices between two magnetic stations for the period of September 2–6, 1957. (After Nagata, Kokubun, and Fukushima.)

metrical characteristic; namely (A) the pair of Cape Wellen and Macquarie Island composes an approximately conjugate relation; (B) the pair of Lerwick and Macquarie Island represents a case for which X and Y Stations are nearly conjugate in their geomagnetic latitudes but are different by nearly 180° in geomagnetic longitude; (C) the pair of Tixie Bay and Halley Bay is a case for which two stations are apart by nearly 180° in geomagnetic longitude and further are different from the conjugate relationship with respect to their geomagnetic latitude by about 5°; and (D) the pair of Sodankylä and Dixon Island is a case for which both X

and Y stations are located nearly on the same geomagnetic latitude circle but are about 40° apart from each other in longitude. Throughout all examples, the correlation coefficient between X and Y is the largest for their simultaneous values, namely for the case of $\Delta t = 0$. Among cases (A), (B), and (C), the correlation coefficient as a whole as well as that for $\Delta t = 0$ is the largest for case (A) and the smallest for case (C). As shown in this result and also in the cases of r(BL, LA), r(BL, Ch), and r(LA, Ch) described before, the correlation is very sensitive to a comparatively small departure from the conjugate relationship with respect to geomagnetic latitude. A further notable fact will be that the correlation between Cape Wellen and Macquarie Island (Case A) is definitely better than that between Sodankylä and Dixon Island (Case D), which are almost on the same geomagnetic latitude circle, being apart only by about 1600 km from each other along the circle.

Throughout the whole period of the IGY, the correlation coefficient r(CW, MI) between the Q-indices of geomagnetic bays between Cape Wellen (CW) and Macquarie Island (MI), which are both located just outside the auroral maximal zones, was between 0.60 and 0.85 for nighttime bays and between 0.60 and 0.82 for daytime bays. Their average values are

$$r(\mathrm{CW, MI}) = 0.75, \text{ for nighttime bays}$$
$$= 0.73, \text{ for daytime bays}$$

As for a similar correlation for magnetic storm variations Nagata, Kokubun, and Fukushima have shown that r(CW, MI) is between 0.59 and 0.83 almost independently of the storm time. The similar correlation between College (Co) and Macquarie Island (MI) obtained by them and independently by Ondoh and Maeda [34] shows the same characteristic. The correlation of geomagnetic disturbances at approximately conjugate stations located within the auroral zones (such as Re-Sy), and on the equatorial side of the auroral zones (such as CW–MI or Co–MI), is kept at a high value ($\bar{r} > 0.7$) regardless of storminess of the geomagnetic field and almost independently of storm time and local time. For conjugate stations located within the polar cap areas (such as BL–LA), the correlation becomes much worse during magnetic storm period compared with that in quiet time. For example,

$$r(\mathrm{BL, LA}) = 0.32$$

for a 30-min average during a storm period. It seems likely, in general, that the conjugate relationship between polar cap stations, which are linked by lines of magnetic force passing near the intersurface of the solar wind, is greatly disturbed upon the onset of a magnetic storm. On the other hand, the lines of force which link conjugate pairs within the auroral zones or on their equatorial side seem to be much less disturbed by a magnetic storm. The conjugate areas in these lower latitudes are apt to be rather broadened when an intense magnetic storm takes place. Figure 11 illustrates examples of the dependence of the average correlation coefficients for individual magnetic storm disturbances between College (Co) and Macquarie Island (MI) and between Lerwick (Le, 62.5° in geomagnetic latitude, 88.6° in geomagnetic longitude) and Halley Bay (HB, −65.6° in

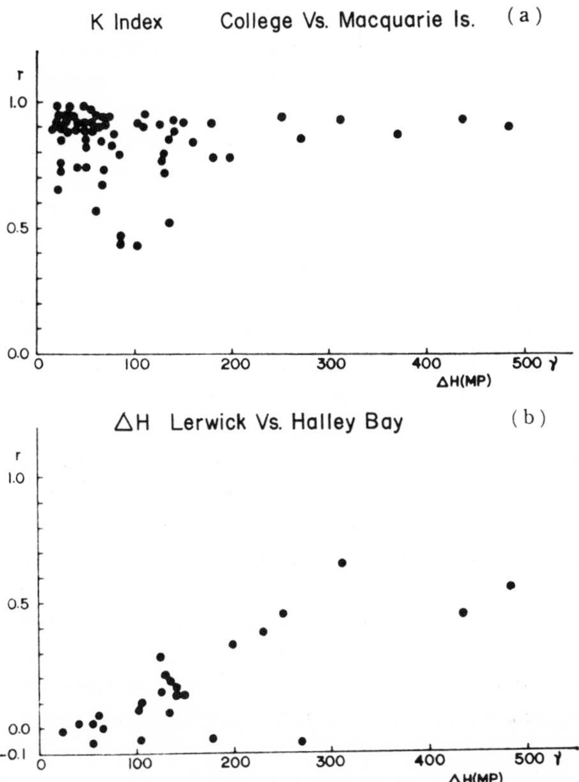

FIG. 11. Dependence of the correlation coefficient of geomagnetic disturbances between two stations upon the magnitude of main phase of magnetic storms. (After Ondoh and Maeda.)

geomagnetic latitude, 24.2° in geomagnetic longitude) on the magnitudes of the main phase of magnetic storms. The $\bar{r}$(Co, MI) values for individual magnetic storms are kept at high values almost regardless of the magnitude of the storm's main phase, because Co and MI are in approximately conjugate relation. Magnetic disturbances at Le and HB have no correlation when the storminess is small, but $\bar{r}$(Le, HB) increases with increase in the storminess and attains to 0.5 for large magnetic storms during the IGY. This result may indicate that the geomagnetically conjugate areas expand along the auroral zone with increasing magnitude of the storm, becoming nearly 3000 km long in cases of large magnetic storms.

Based mostly on Alaskan data of geomagnetic and auroral observations during the IGY, Nagata [21] concluded that the activated area of an isolated auroral electrojet accompanied by aurora is elongated along the auroral maximal zone. The dimensions of the activated area for a well-developed isolated electrojet are about 500 km in the magnetically N–S direction and more than 2000 km in the magnetically E–W direction. In a recent special experiment on the geomagnetic conjugacy between Eights Station (S 75°.15′, W 77°.15′) and three closely spaced stations bracketing the calculated conjugate point along a meridian line in Canada [7], the result of observation has shown a high degree of conjugacy of bay-type variations over an area hundreds of kilometers in extent in the N–S direction. The highest correlation coefficient is 0.95 between the best conjugate pair.

From the geomagnetic observations at conjugate areas already described, it may be derived that, in the case of a polar storm, a beam of charged particles having a cross section of the activated area is precipitating into the ionosphere level over the conjugate area in both polar regions, particularly in the auroral zones. Direct balloon measurements of simultaneous precipitation of electrons at a conjugate pair of stations were carried out by Anderson *et al.* [2], using balloonborne counters for bremsstrahlung X-rays at College (Co) and Macquarie Island (MI). At the two stations, a remarkable peak of bremsstrahlung X-rays associated with a negative geomagnetic bay took place simultaneously. Judged from the flight routes of the balloons during the observation period, it was concluded by the authors that the zone of electron precipitation in this case is at least 2° wide in latitude and 14° long in longitude. This estimate of dimensions of the activated area is in rough accord with that obtained by Nagata indirectly from the extension of auroral displays and that of the auroral electrojet. Simultaneity and similarity of the ionospheric absorption [13] and aurora [9] observed at the approximately conjugate pair of Farewell and Campbell Island (see Table 1) can be considered as indirect evidence of simultaneous precipitation of corpuscular streams at the conjugate areas.

It will be concluded that charged particles in the earth's outer space are apt to precipitate simultaneously along the lines of geomagnetic force toward both northern and southern polar regions, causing simultaneous polar magnetic storms of a similar form and associated aurora and ionospheric phenomena. However, it has not yet been ascertained whether the precipitating particles are the dumped particles released from the radiation belt of trapped particle, as Vestine and Sibley [41, 42] have suggested, or the particles having appropriately small initial pitch angle, which are generated by a certain acceleration mechanism near the equatorial plane, as Akasofu and Chapman have suggested.

Conjugate areas are broadened and conjugacy becomes complicated in the case of magnetic storms. This result will be easy to understand in view of the following theoretical facts of a magnetic storm: The geomagnetic cavity is greatly compressed by the strong solar wind, the geomagnetic field is greatly distorted by the ring current as well as by the compression, and particles themselves can be severely agitated in the geomagnetic cavity. Therefore, possible systematic studies on the conjugacy of isolated polar magnetic storms associated with auroral and ionospheric disturbances

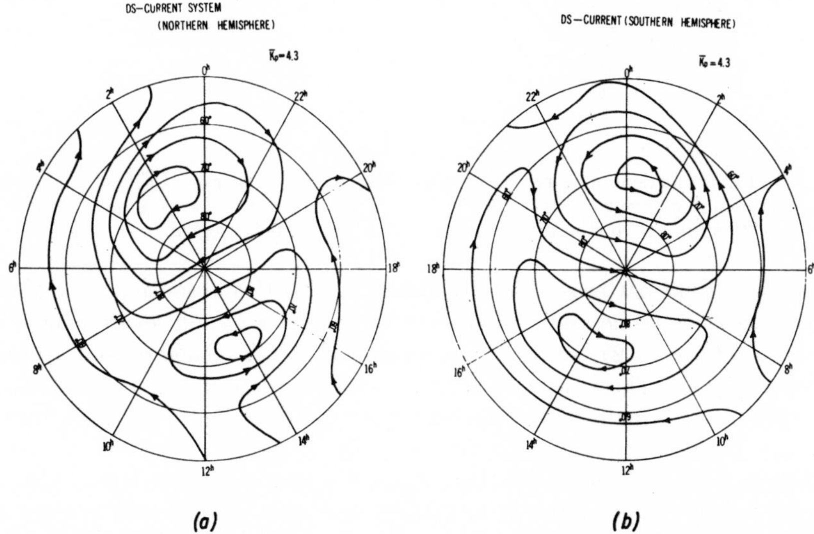

FIG. 12. Equivalent ionospheric current pattern of the average *DS*-field for moderate magnetic storms during the IGY ($\overline{K_p} = 4.3$). Electric current between adjacent current lines is 10^5 amp. (*a*) Northern polar region. (*b*) Southern polar region.

during the IQSY period may give us a great opportunity to deal with the basic points of the geomagnetic conjugacy of precipitating charged particles.

As individual bays and auroral electrojets which occur during magnetic disturbances have the conjugate relationship between conjugate areas, the average patterns of polar magnetic storms (the *DS*-fields) must also have a similar conjugacy between the northern and southern polar regions. The approximate conjugacy for the *DS*-field has been roughly sketched [22, 27].

The IGY network of magnetic stations has made it possible to compare the southern *DS*-pattern with the simultaneous northern *DS*-pattern in fair detail. Figures 12 and 13 represent the simultaneous equivalent iono-

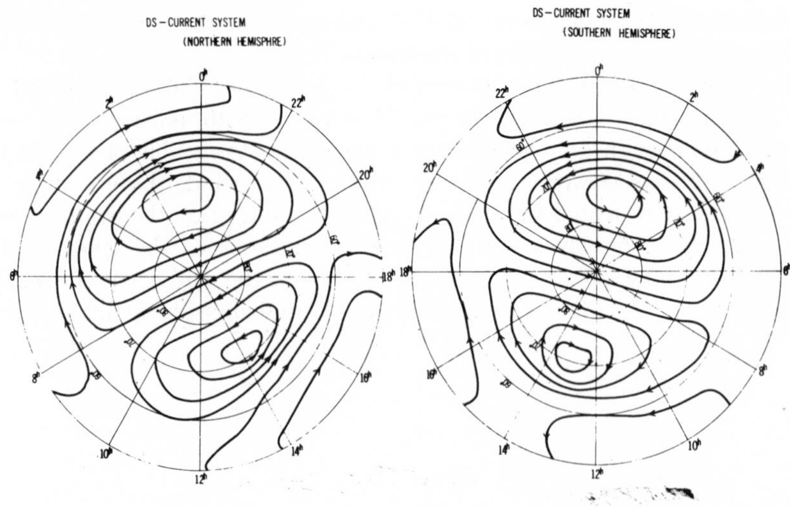

FIG. 13. Equivalent ionospheric current pattern of the average *DS*-field for severe magnetic storms during the IGY ($\overline{K}_p = 7.2$). Electric current between adjacent current lines is 10^5 amp. (*a*) Northern polar region. (*b*) Southern polar region.

spheric current patterns of the *DS*-field in the north and south polar regions in the cases of moderate magnetic storms ($\bar{K}_p = 4.3$) and severe magnetic storms ($\bar{K}_p = 7.2$), respectively, during the IGY (Nagata and Iijima, unpublished). These patterns are constructed based on simultaneous hourly mean value data for the main part (from 6^h to 12^h in storm time) of individual magnetic storms. As shown in the figures, the conjugate relationship holds satisfactorily in both cases. The southern pattern is an almost exact mirror image of the simultaneous northern pattern with respect to the geomagnetic equatorial plane. These figures also show that the auroral zone currents in both polar regions are more enhanced as compared with the polar cap currents when the magnetic storms become more intense. In the S_q^p-current patterns, in the cases of $\bar{K}_p = 1.3$ for the June solstitial season and $\bar{K}_p = 1.1$ for the December solstitial season, practically no enhancement of the auroral zone current can be identified (Fig. 6). It is suggested that the main part of the polar cap current of the *DS*-field can be ascribed to an intensified stage of the S_q^p-current system, and that the electric current in the auroral zones, enhanced by their increased electric conductivity accounts for an appreciable part of the auroral electrojet.

5. Conjugacy of Large-Amplitude Pulsative Variations

The simultaneous occurrence of pulsative variations of large amplitude in the geomagnetic field at conjugate areas was discovered by Sugiura [39] from the IGY magnetograms obtained at College and Kotzebue in the

North and Macquarie Island in the South. From characteristics of the polarization of the giant pulsations (i.e., geomagnetic damped waves, according to the author's own expression) having a period of several minutes with amplitude of several hundred gammas, Sugiura has suggested that the pulsative variations may be interpreted as low-frequency hydromagnetic waves generated in the magnetosphere at an altitude of several earth's radii and transmitted to both polar regions along lines of geomagnetic force. The same problem of the conjugate relationship of low-frequency hydromagnetic waves has also been studied by Nagata, Kokubun, and Iijima [28] using the IGY–IGC rapid-run magnetograms at Syowa Base,

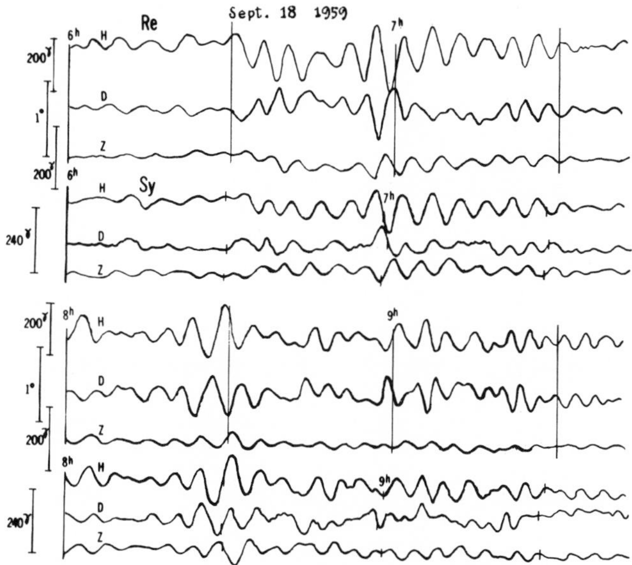

Fig. 14. Examples of rapid-run magnetograms of the large-amplitude magnetic pulsations observed at Reykjavik (Re) and Syowa Base (Sy) [28].

Reykjavik, and several Alaskan stations, i.e., Point Barrow, College, Big Delta, Healy, and Sitka. With regard to this point, the problem of the conjugate relationship for the pulsative variation may be distinguished from that of precipitating charged particles resulting in geomagnetic polar storms, auroral displays, and the ionospheric ionization.

Examples of simultaneous traces of three component magnetograms at Reykjavik (Re) and Syowa Base (Sy) are shown in Figure 14, where pulsations of $100 \sim 200\gamma$ in amplitude and $3.5 \sim 8$ minutes in period are represented. Wave forms of H-variation are almost parallel to each other at the stations while those of D-variation are nearly antiparallel. All events of the large-amplitude pulsations selected from the Syowa Base magnetograms during the IGC period correspond, without exception, to simultaneous events of similar pulsations at Reykjavik having the above-mentioned characteristics. As a natural consequence, the correlation between H-components of pulsations at these two stations is extremely high,

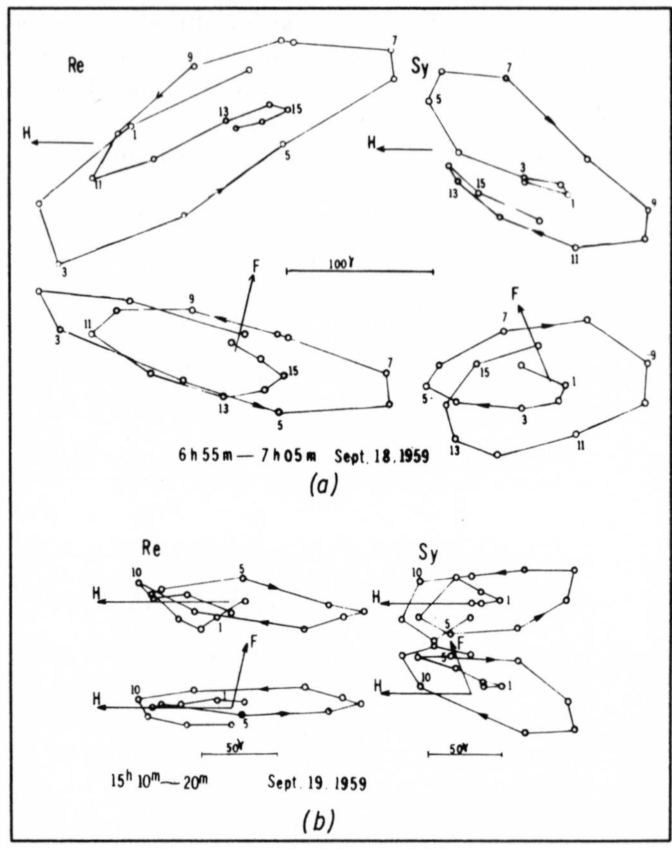

FIG. 15. Examples of simultaneous change in disturbance vectors of the large amplitude magnetic pulsation at Reykjavik (Re) and Syowa Base (Sy). Upper diagram; horizontal projection. Lower diagram; vertical projection onto the magnetic meridian plane. (*a*) Pulsation in the local morning. (*b*) Pulsation in the local afternoon. (After Nagata, Kokubun, and Iijima.)

the correlation coefficient amounting to 0.83 on average and 0.95 at maximum.

As will be noted from the characteristics of parallelism of H- and D-traces between these stations, the horizontal vector $\Delta\mathbf{H} = (\Delta H, H\Delta D)$ of the simultaneous pulsation rotates in the opposite sense between these two stations. Figure 15 illustrates examples of loci of the $\Delta\mathbf{H}$ vector on the horizontal plane and those of the projection of the polarization vector onto the magnetic meridian plane (ΔH, ΔZ) at Reykjavik and Syowa Base for the local morning and local afternoon. The loci of the $\Delta \mathbf{H}$ vector are approximately elliptic and the sense of rotation of the vectors are opposite to each other between these two stations, namely, counterclockwise at Reykjavik and clockwise at Syowa Base in the morning and vice versa in the afternoon. The above characteristics of the horizontal polarization vector hold for 28 cases among 30 analyzed events. The characteristics of local time dependence of the rotation of horizontal polarization vector of the pulsation was first pointed out by Nagata *et al.* [28] for the case of Alaskan stations, and since then they have been ascertained to hold as a general rule at stations within the auroral zones and at high latitudes on their equatorial side. Figures 16(*a*) and (*b*) represent examples of the horizontal

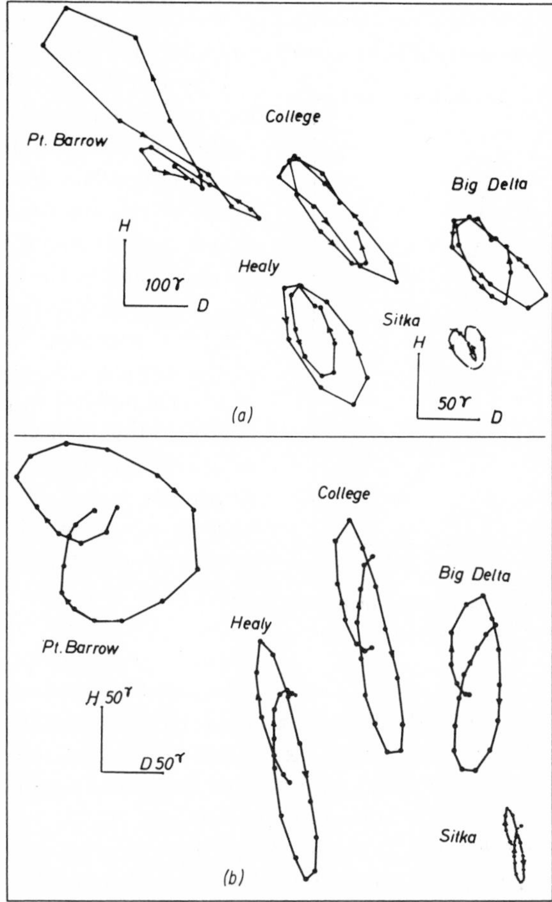

FIG. 16. Horizontal projection of disturbance vectors of the large-amplitude magnetic pulsation observed at Alaskan stations. (*a*) An example of pulsation in the local morning. (*b*) An example of pulsation in the local afternoon.

polarization vectors of pulsation at Point Barrow, College, Big Delta, Healy, and Sitka for the local morning and the local afternoon, respectively. As shown in these examples and in other events also, the polarization vector rotates counterclockwise in the morning and clockwise in the afternoon at College, Healy, Big Delta, and Sitka. The reversal of sense of rotation takes place around 11^h and 23^h in local geomagnetic time.

The loci of horizontal vectors are of an elliptic shape and are almost conformal to one another at College, Big Delta, Healy, and Sitka in both morning and afternoon. At Point Barrow which is located on the poleward side of the auroral zone, however, the locus of the vector is not regular for morning pulsations, and it becomes more nearly circular rather than strongly elliptic in the afternoon though the sense of rotation of $\Delta\mathbf{H}$ vector is the same as that at other lower latitude stations. Here again, a notable difference of geomagnetic variations in the polar cap area from those in the auroral zone and its equatorward neighborhood can be pointed out.

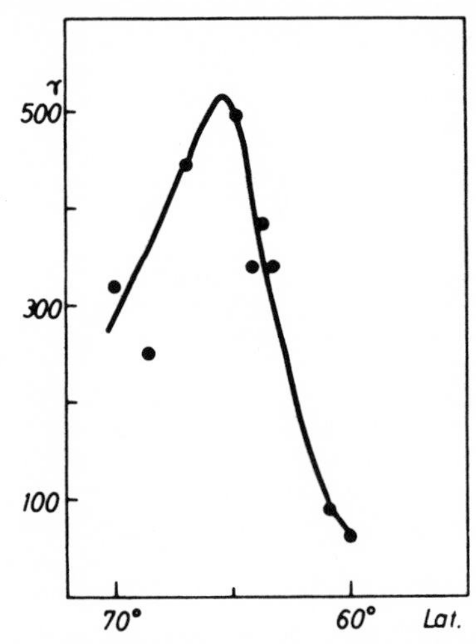

FIG. 17. Latitude dependence of average amplitude of the large-amplitude magnetic pulsation.

It is also shown in Figure 15 that the projection of the polarization vector of the pulsation onto the vertical meridian plane has also a locus of an approximately elliptic shape, and its major axis is nearly perpendicular to the direction of the line of geomagnetic force. As Sugiura [39] first suggested, the major parts of the geomagnetic giant pulsations of several minutes in period may be considered as transverse hydromagnetic waves which are polarized elliptically within the auroral zone and its equatorward vicinity. The mean amplitude of geomagnetic giant pulsation takes the maximum value in the auroral zone, decreasing toward both equatorial and polar sides, as illustrated in Figure 17.

As for the horizontal polarization of the pulsation observed simultaneously at Reykjavik and Syowa Base, both within the respective auroral zones, it has been concluded with a large statistical significance that the sense of rotation of the horizontal polarization vector, viewed from the above toward the earth, is reciprocal at these conjugate points for both morning and afternoon types of the pulsation which are mutually opposite in their sense of rotation. If we consider the pulsations as elliptically polarized transverse hydromagnetic waves propagating along the lines of force and view the rotation of transverse elliptic polarization vector of the waves along the direction of lines of force from the South to the North, the sense of rotation is counterclockwise on the morning side and clockwise on the afternoon side as illustrated in Figure 18. A recent result of measurements on Explorer VI (Judge and Coleman, 1962 [16]) seems to support the argument that the above-mentioned rule for rotation of the polarization vector also holds in outer space. According to Judge and Coleman, the observed magnetic data at a distance of about 4×10^4 km from the earth's center on the side of approximately 19^h in local time indicate that the transverse hydromagnetic wave of damped, quasi-sinusoidal oscillation form had a period of 200 seconds, was elliptically polarized, and was marked by a rotation of the polarization that would be clockwise to an observer looking along the unperturbed field line toward the North Geomagnetic Pole. This result is indeed in accordance with the above-mentioned conclusion of transverse hydromagnetic waves in the afternoon side space

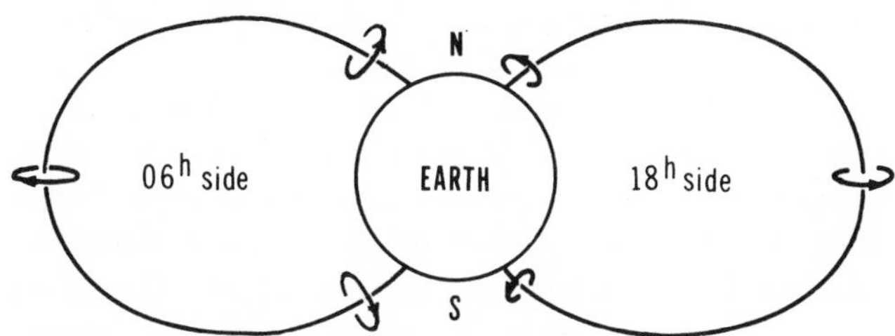

Fig. 18. Schematic illustration of the rotation characteristics of polarization vector of the large-amplitude magnetic pulsation, viewed from the 12^h side. (After Nagata, Kokubun, and Iijima.)

which was derived from ground-based observations at the conjugate pair stations. The characteristics of rotation of polarization vector of the geomagnetic pulsation and their local time dependence are in exact agreement with those of the transient sudden commencement field pointed out by Wilson and Sugiura [46, 47].

The amplitudes of simultaneous pulsations observed at the conjugate pair stations are nearly the same, the ratio of the amplitude at Syowa Base to that at Reykjavik, for example, ranging from 0.5 to 2.0, the average of which is 1.04. However, the amplitudes of morning pulsations are, in general, appreciably larger than those of afternoon pulsations. At College, for example, the average amplitudes of the horizontal component of counterclockwise rotating waves in the morning is 190^γ while that of clockwise rotating waves in the afternoon is 75^γ. The similar tendency of difference in amplitude between morning-type and afternoon-type pulsations has been found at Reykjavik, Syowa Base, and Byrd Station. In a schematic illustration in Figure 18, therefore, the range of elliptically polarized wave near the earth is shown to be larger in the morning side than in the afternoon side.

Piddington [37] has theoretically shown that Alfvén wave and modified Alfvén wave are coupled with each other in an anisotropic conducting gas in a uniform magnetic field, resulting in two different modes of elliptically polarized waves, i.e., ordinary (anisotropic) and extraordinary (isotropic) modes. This is true provided that the Alfvén wave velocity V_A is much larger than the sound wave velocity in the gas medium. The anisotropic mode, whose polarization vector rotates counterclockwise to an observer looking along the direction of line of magnetic force, propagates with a speed of $V_A \cos \Psi$ for the direction which makes an angle Ψ with the wave normal. On the other hand, the isotropic mode, whose polarization vector rotates clockwise viewed along the direction of line of force, propagates isotropically with the Alfvén's velocity V_A. Hence, the energy of the anisotropic mode wave is confined to a narrow cone along the line of force, while the energy of the isotropic wave is transmitted isotropically in all directions. In the present case of hydromagnetic waves in the earth's outer space, the involved magnetic field is far from a uniform field, and consequently the gradient in the field ought to seriously modify the above-mentioned result. If we assume, however, that Piddington's result can be applied qualitatively to the present problem, the morning and evening types of pulsation can be attributed, respectively, to the anisotropic and isotropic modes of the hydromagnetic wave. Then, the amplitude of the morning-type pulsation becomes larger than that of the afternoon type when observed on the earth's surface, even if these waves have the same magnitude at their origin in the magnetosphere. Thus, the conjugate relationship for the large-amplitude magnetic pulsation of several minutes in period may be interpreted consistently as due to low-frequency transverse hydromagnetic waves generated in the magnetosphere and transmitted toward both polar regions of the earth along the lines of geomagnetic force, so far as data observed and analyzed up to present are concerned. It will be necessary in the future to carry out simultaneous observations of magnetic pulsations and low-frequency electromagnetic waves at well-planned networks in the conjugate areas in order to obtain more quantitative features of propagation of hydromagnetic waves and electromagnetic waves along lines of magnetic force in the earth's outer space.

Actually, a special conjugate point experiment was carried out in 1961 at Great Whale River (N 55°.17′, W 77°.46′) and Byrd Station (S 79°.59′, W 120°.01′) to study the possible conjugacy for natural electromagnetic noises of the frequency range of 0.003 $\sim$ 15,000 [19, 49]. The results have shown that the correlation of the electromagnetic noises between the conjugate stations is fairly high for frequencies larger than 3 cps, suggesting their extra-atmospheric origin, but the pulsations of period larger than

0.3 sec have much less conjugate relationship. According to Yanagihara [49], it seems likely that micropulsation bursts are closely related to precipitation of charged particles into the auroral zone, causing auroral electrojets, and the so-called pearl, i.e., beating pulsation of 1–2 sec in period, may be caused by the bouncing of proton clouds with a 2-min period. It is hardly possible at present to deal with detailed physical structures of these complicated electromagnetic noises of low frequencies, but it should be stated that electromagnetic waves of low frequencies, which are generated secondarily in the ionospheric level by precipitation of charged particles, are also observable at high latitudes. In future studies of conjugacy this phenomenon will have also to be considered, in addition to hydromagnetic wave propagation (dealt with in this section) and the motion of charged particles trapped by lines of force (described in Section 4).

6. The Field around the Poles and the Magnetosphere

It is shown in Section 3 that the $S_q{}^p$-field is confined within the polar regions. The $S_q{}^p$-field seems to be generated by a certain kind of plasma stream coming from the earth's outer space to the polar ionosphere along the lines of geomagnetic force. This is because only streams of charged particles or plasma tied to the lines of magnetic force linking the two polar cap areas through the magnetosphere can account for the northern and southern $S_q{}^p$-fields, the extension of which is limited to the polar cap area, and which have a geomagnetically conjugate relationship.

As reported by many workers, based on observational and theoretical studies, it is now believed with certainty that the geomagnetic field is confined within the geomagnetic cavity, which is surrounded by the intersurface of the extremely conductive solar wind even on geomagnetically quiet days. The interior space of the geomagnetic cavity is also filled with highly ionized gas except in a spherical space around the earth bounded by the bottom surface of the ionosphere, as direct measurements on artificial satellites and space probes have proved. The energy of particles in the larger part of the geomagnetic cavity plasma is KeV or less (to an order of magnitude) so that those low-energy parts of the plasma are tied by the lines of geomagnetic force.

Since the low-energy magnetospheric plasma in the outer part of the cavity ought to be dragged continuously by the solar wind through the hydromagnetic viscous interaction [38] between two plasmas, the magnetospheric plasma of low energy will be forced to make such convective motions as schematically illustrated in Figure 19, as suggested by Axford and Hines [4]. The coupling is caused by the turbulent instability as theoretically derived by Dungey [10] and Parker [36] and as observed on space probes many times.

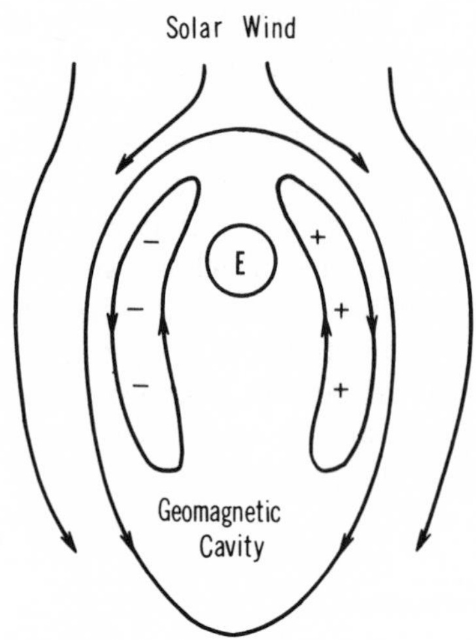

FIG. 19. Schematic illustration of the circulation of the low-energy magnetospheric plasma on the magnetic equatorial plane. (After Axford and Hines.)

As shown in Figure 19, the convective motion on the morning side is clockwise viewed from the north and counterclockwise on the afternoon side. Since the lines of geomagnetic force are almost frozen in the magnetospheric plasma, the two circulations of the plasma may cause twisting of the lines of force in the magnetosphere on and near the geomagnetic equatorial plane. The twist of the lines of force is projected to the polar ionosphere, at the lower boundary of which the lines of force partly frozen in the ionospheric plasma can slip horizontally against the free lines of force in the lower neutral atmosphere. Thus, the lines of force in the ionosphere in the north polar cap make a counterclockwise circulation on the morning side and a clockwise circulation on the afternoon side. In the lower ionosphere, electrons only are tightly held by the lines of force while ions are subject largely to the frictional force caused by their collision with neutral particles. Therefore, the electric current caused by the circulation of the lines of force will have the current pattern consisting of two vortices whose directions are opposite to those of the horizontal circulations of the lines of force. The current pattern thus derived is in agreement with the observed pattern of the $S_q{}^p$-field illustrated in Figures 7 and 8.

In this case, the average speed of horizontal motion of electrons in the lower ionosphere is roughly the same as the speed of horizontal circulation of the lines of force. Then, the electric current intensity shown in Figure 7 indicates that the speed of circulative motion of the lines of force in the ionosphere is roughly 10^4 cm/sec. If we assume that the angular velocity of circulation is conserved in the geomagnetic cavity, the speed of circulation of the lines of force on the equatorial plane in the magnetosphere is estimated to be about 3×10^5 cm/sec. As the observed speed and density of the solar wind on quiet days are about 3×10^7 cm/sec. and $10/\text{cm}^3$, respectively [8], it would be reasonable to assume that the outer part of the magnetospheric plasma is forced to make circular motions of 3 km/sec in speed by its hydromagnetically viscous interaction with the solar wind.

The model structure of the magnetospheric motion, illustrated by Figure 19, seems to be favorable also to an interpretation of the rotation characteristics of the polarization vector of the large-amplitude geomagnetic pulsations and the sudden commencements observed at high latitudes (discussed in Section 5). As the magnetospheric plasma is rotating clockwise on the morning side and counterclockwise on the afternoon side when viewed from the north, a magnetic disturbance taking place accidentally in the magnetosphere may generate the anisotropic mode transverse hydromagnetic wave on the morning side, and the isotropic mode on the afternoon side. This mechanism may account for the observed local time dependence of rotation characteristics of the polarization vector of geomagnetic pulsations, summarized in Figure 18.

References

1. L. R. Alldredge and G. Van Voorhis, Source of the great Arctic anomaly, *J. Geophys. Res.*, **67,** 1573–1578 (1962).
2. K. A. Anderson, C. D. Anger, R. R. Brown, and D. S. Evans, Simultaneous electron precipitation in the northern and southern auroral zones, *J. Geophys. Res.*, **67,** 4076–4077 (1962).
3. S. M. Ahmed and W. E. Scott, Time relationship of small magnetic disturbances in Arctic and Antarctic, *J. Geophys. Res.*, **60,** 147–159 (1955).
4. W. I. Axford and C. O. Hines, A unifying theory of high latitude geophysical phenomena and geomagnetic storms, *Can. J. Phys.* **39,** 1433–1464 (1961).
5. J. C. Behrendt and R. J. Wold, Aeromagnetic survey in West Antarctica, 1963, *Univ. Wisconsin Geophys. and Polar Res. Center Res. Rep., No. 63-1.* 1–49 (1963).
6. M. S. Bobrov, All planetary representation of geomagnetic disturbances of corpuscular origin, Results Res. IGY Program, Section VI, No. 1, 36–97 (1961).
7. G. M. Boyd, The conjugacy of magnetic disturbance variations, *J. Geophys. Res.*, **68,** 1011–1013 (1963).
8. H. S. Bridge, C. Dilworth, A. J. Lazarus, E. F. Lyon, B. Rossi, and F. Scherb, Direct observation of the interplanetary plasma, *J. Phys. Soc. Japan, 17,* Suppl. A-I, 553–560 (1962).
9. R. N. DeWitt, The occurrence of aurora in geomagnetically conjugate areas, *J. Geophys. Res.*, **67,** 1347–1352 (1962).
10. J. W. Dungey, *The Physics of the Ionosphere,* Phys. Soc. London, 229–236 (1954).
11. N. Fukushima, Morphology of magnetic storms, *J. Phys. Soc. Japan,* **17,** Suppl. A-I, 70–78 (1962).
12. N. Fukushima, Gross character of geomagnetic disturbance during the International Geophysical Year and the Second Polar Year, *Rep. Ionos. Space Res. Japan,* **16,** 37–56 (1962). N. Fukushima and T. Hirasawa, Frequent occurrence of local geomagnetic disturbance in high latitudes, *J. Geomag. Geoelectr.*, **15,** 161–171 (1964).
13. J. L. Hook, Some observations of ionospheric absorption at geomagnetic conjugate stations in the auroral zone, *J. Geophys. Res.* **67,** 115–122 (1962).
14. E. R. Hope, Linear oscillation of the northern magnetic pole, *J. Geophys. Res.*, **62,** 19–27 (1957).
15. E. R. Hope, Geotectonics of the Arctic Ocean and the great Arctic magnetic anomaly, *J. Geophys. Res.*, **64,** 407–427 (1959).
16. D. L. Judge and P. L. Coleman, Jr., Observation of low frequency hydromagnetic waves in the distant geomagnetic field: Explorer 6, *J. Geophys. Res.*, **67,** 5071–5090 (1962).
17. S. Kakinuma and Y. Muraishi, Report on geomagnetic total force observation in the fourth Japanese Antarctic expedition, *Antarctic Record,* No. 11, 200–203 (1961).

18. K. Lassen, On the variation of magnetic activity at Godhavn, *Pull. Danske Meteor. Inst. Comm. Mag.*, No. 23 (1958).
19. J. E. Lokken, J. A. Shand, C. S. Wright, L. H. Martin, N. M. Brice, and R. A. Helliwell, Stanford-Pacific Naval Laboratory Conjugate Point Experiment, *Nature*, **192,** 319–321 (1961).
20. N. Matuura and T. Nagata, Turbulent condition in the upper atmosphere, *Rep, Ionos. Space Res. Japan* **16,** 185–255 (1962).
21. T. Nagata, Polar magnetic storms, especially in the southern polar region, *J. Phys. Soc. Japan*, **17,** Suppl. A-I, 157–164 (1962).
22. T. Nagata, Morphology and some interpretation of geomagnetic variation in Antarctica, *Antarctic Research, Geophys. Monograph No. 7 A.G.U.*, 89–110 (1962).
23. T. Nagata, Two main aspects of geomagnetic secular variation—westward drift and non-drifting components, *Proc. Benedum Symp. Earth Magnetism, 1962*, 39–56 (1962).
24. T. Nagata and S. Kokubun, Polar magnetic storms, with special reference to relation between geomagnetic disturbances in the northern and southern auroral zones, *Rep. Ionos. Space Res. Japan*, **14,** 273–290 (1960).
25. T. Nagata and S. Kokubun, A particular geomagnetic daily variation ($S_q{}^p$) in the polar regions on geomagnetically quiet days, *Nature*, **195,** 555–557 (1962).
26. T. Nagata and S. Kokubun, An additional geomagnetic daily variation field ($S_q{}^p$-field) in the polar region on geomagnetically quiet days, *Rep. Ionos. Space Res. Japan*, **16,** 256–274 (1962).
27. T. Nagata, S. Kokubun, and N. Fukushima, Similarity and simultaneity of magnetic disturbances in the Northern and Southern Hemisphere, *J. Phys. Soc. Japan*, **17,** Suppl. A-I, 35–39 (1962).
28. T. Nagata, S. Kokubun, and T. Iijima, Geomagnetically conjugate relationship of giant pulsations at Syowa Base in Antarctica and Reykjavik in Iceland, *J. Geophy. Res.*, **68,** 4621–4625 (1963).
29. T. Nagata and H. Mizuno, S_q-field in the polar region on absolutely quiet days, *J. Geomag. Geoelect.*, **7,** 69–74 (1955).
30. T. Nagata and T. Rikitake, Geomagnetic secular variation and poloidal magnetic field produced by convectional motions in the earth's core, *J. Geomag. Geoelect.*, **13,** 42–53 (1961).
31. T. Nagata and T. Rikitake, The northward shifting of the geomagnetic dipole and stability of the axial magnetic quadruple of the earth, *J. Geomag. Geoelect.*, **14,** 213–220 (1962).
32. T. Nagata and M. Sawada, Annual mean values of geomagnetic elements since 1955, *Rep. Comm. Secular Variation and Paleomagnetism IAGA*, (1963).
33. T. Nagata and Y. Syono, Geomagnetic secular variation during the period from 1955 to 1960, *J. Geomag. Geoelect.*, **12,** 84–98 (1960).
34. T. Ondoh and H. Maeda, Geomagnetic-storm correlation between the Northern and Southern Hemispheres, *J. Geomag. Geoelect.*, **14,** 22–32 (1962).
35. V. P. Orlov, World chart of magnetic meridian for the epoch of 1955, *Izvestia, Acad. Sci. USSR Geophys. Ser.*, 104–106, 1961 (English translation by AGU. 63, May, 1961).
36. E. N. Parker, Interaction of the solar wind with the geomagnetic field, *Physics of Fluid*, **1,** 171–187 (1958).
37. J. H. Piddington, Hydromagnetic waves in ionized gas, *Mon. Not. Roy. Astr. Soc.*, **115,** 671–683 (1955).
38. J. H. Piddington, A theory of polar geomagnetic storms, *Geophys. J.*, **3,** 314–332 (1960).
39. M. Sugiura, Evidence for low-frequency hydromagnetic waves in the exosphere, *J. Geophys. Res.*, **66,** 4087–4095 (1961).
40. E. H. Vestine, Note on conjugate point of geomagnetic field line for some selected auroral station of the IGY, *J. Geophys. Res.*, **64,** 1411–1414 (1959).
41. E. H. Vestine and W. L. Sibley, Remarks on auroral isochasms, *J. Geophys. Res.*, **64,** 1338–1339 (1959).

42. E. H. VESTINE AND W. L. SIBLEY, The conjugate field in space, ring currents, and auroral isochasms, *J. Geophys. Res.*, **65**, 1967–1979 (1960).
43. E. M. WESCOTT, Magnetic variations at conjugate points, *J. Geophys. Res.*, **66**, 1789–1792 (1961).
44. E. M. WESCOTT, Magnetic activity during periods of aurora at geomagnetically conjugate points, *J. Geophys. Res.*, **67**, 1353–1355 (1962).
45. P. J. WASILEWSKI, *Geomagnetic Report, Antarctic Peninsula Traverse 1961–62* (U.S. Coast and Geodetic Survey, 1963).
46. C. R. WILSON AND M. SUGIURA, Hydromagnetic interpretation of sudden commencement of magnetic storms, *J. Geophys. Res.*, **66**, 4097–4111 (1961).
47. C. R. Wilson and M. Sugiura, Discussion of our earlier paper Hydromagnetic interpretation of sudden commencement of magnetic storms, *J. Geophys. Res.*, **68**, 3314–3320 (1963).
48. K. WITHAM AND E. I. LOOMER, Characteristics of magnetic disturbances at the Canadian Arctic Observatories, *Publ. Dominion Obs.*, (Ottawa, 1956).
49. K. YANAGIHARA, Geomagnetic micropulsation with periods from 0.03 to 10 seconds in the auroral zone with special reference to conjugate point study, *J. Geophys. Res.*, **68**, 3383–3397 (1963).

CHAPTER 18

GEOMAGNETIC STORMS AND RELATED PHENOMENA

S. Matsushita

1. Introduction

In the early history of geomagnetic storms, Birkeland [14] studied polar storms very extensively; he analyzed individual events in detail, and called severe, but rather localized and fairly short-lasting disturbances, "polar elementary storms." Later, Chapman [22, 24] investigated the average behavior of storms and showed that a typical storm has initial, main, and recovery phases according to the storm time which is reckoned from the beginning of the storm, and found that it has universal-time and local-time components; the former component is called storm-time variation and is indicated by *Dst,* and the latter is called disturbance-daily variation. He also showed idealized current systems responsible for these components.

The notation of the disturbance-daily variation was originally S_D, and the combination of S_D and daily variation on quiet-day Sq was shown by Sd. However, Sugiura and Chapman [109] found that both the amplitude and the time of the maximum amplitude of the disturbance-daily variation change during the course of the storm. Thus the disturbance-daily variation at a certain period during the storm was later called Ds or DS, and S_D or SD was considered as an average of Ds or DS. In order to avoid confusion, DS and average-DS for S_D or SD are used in the present article.

Using the data obtained during the Second Polar Year, 1932–1933, several workers [44, 48, 49, 80, 101, 112, 114] studied the DS, average-DS, and bay current systems; some of the results are shown in Figure 1 and are compared with Chapman's idealized average-DS current system. Silsbee and Vestine [101] found that the bay current system was similar to the DS-system, and Fukushima [44] investigated the bay and DS very extensively. As is shown in the top diagram of Figure 2, Fukushima suggested

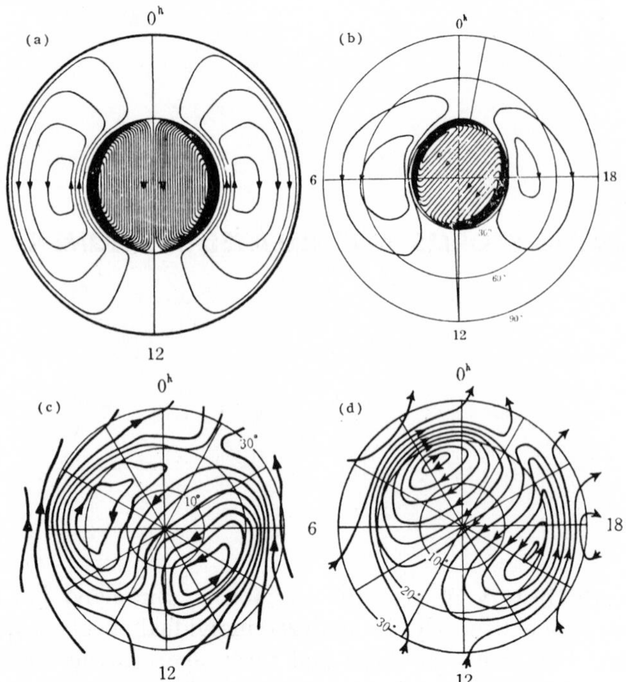

FIG. 1. Idealized average-*DS* current system shown by Chapman [22, 24] (*a*), *DS*-current at 1600 GMT, 1 May 1933, obtained by Vestine [112] (*b*), and the average-*DS* currents in the northern high latitudes obtained from the data during the Second Polar Year by Hasegawa [49] (*c*), and by Nagata [80] (*d*). These are viewed from over the North Pole.

a patchy structure of the bay and *DS*. A study of current systems during storms was also made by Benkova [13].

A very extensive study of the morphology of *Dst* and *DS* was conducted by Sugiura and Chapman [109], using the data obtained at 26 stations for 346 storms during 44 years, 1902–1945. One of their results is shown in Figure 3; the amplitude of *DS*(*H*) varies during the course of a storm. The time of the maximum amplitude also shifts, and the range of *Dst*(*H*) is larger at lower latitudes.

Morphologies of sudden commencements (SC), such as different types of SC and their dependence on local time and latitude, were studied by Newton [82] and Ferraro *et al.* [40]; a further study of morphology and responsible current systems was made by several workers [57, 68, 78, 88]. The bottom diagram of Figure 2 represents the current systems suggested by Obayashi and Jacobs [57]. It must be noted that the *DS*(SC) changes very rapidly. An interesting behavior of SC was the daytime enhancement of its size at Huancayo [41, 108].

After a detailed study of geomagnetic data obtained at Terre Adélie,

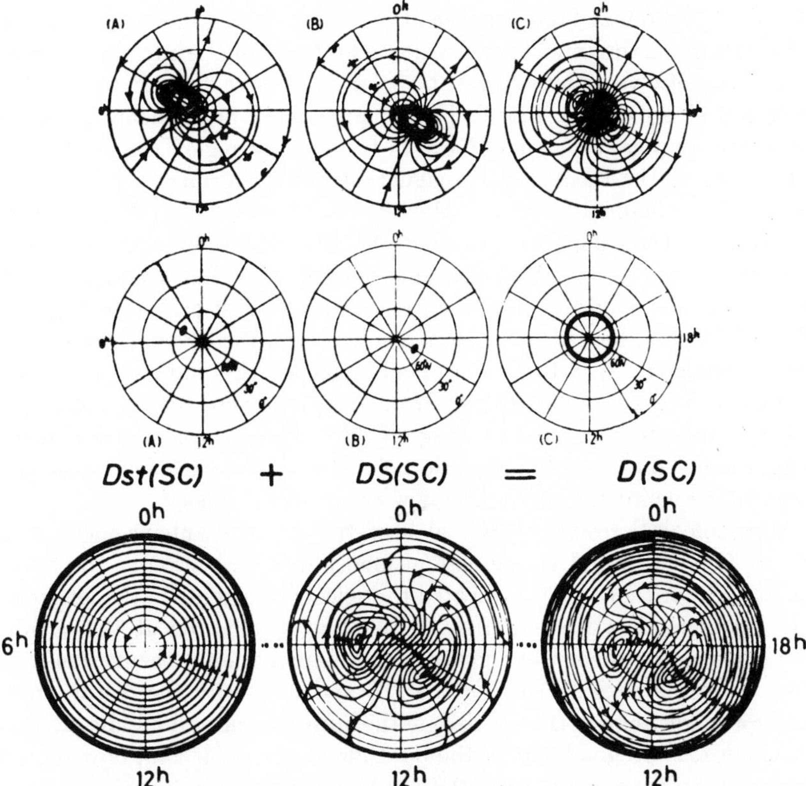

FIG. 2. Distribution of the activated area along the auroral zone (upper part of the top diagram) and the resulting electric currents in the ionosphere (lower part of the top diagram), shown by Fukushima [44]. Electric current systems for sudden commencements obtained by Obayashi and Jacobs (bottom diagram) [57].

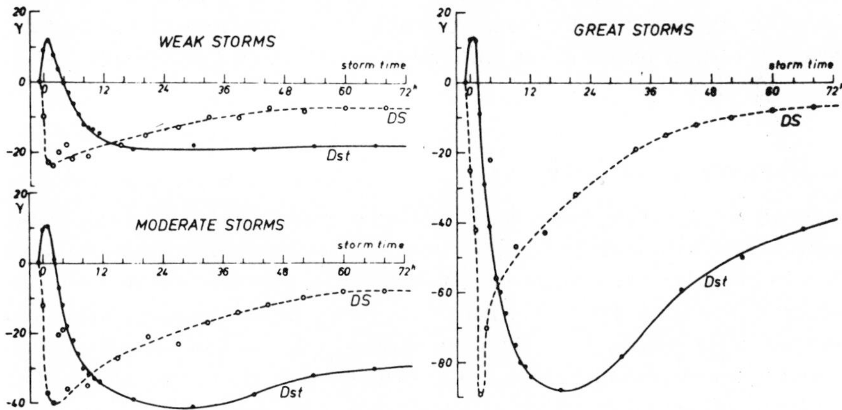

FIG. 3. Average *Dst* and the range of *DS* of *H* in middle latitudes obtained by Sugiura and Chapman [109].

Mayaud [75] found "the permanent presence, during daytime, of a magnetic agitation, the intensity of which increased from winter to summer."

Geomagnetic variations caused by solar flares were discussed by McNish [62] and Nagata [77]. Bartels [24] studied solar phenomena responsible for storms and gave a name *M*-region to the solar region responsible.

Concerning the theory of geomagnetic storms, Störmer [106], Hulburt-Maris [55], Chapman–Ferraro–Martyn [25], and Alfvén [9] gave different ideas. Several Japanese workers [44, 67, 80, 86, 96] tried to explain the *DS*-current system by a dynamo action. A similar attempt [57, 78, 86, 88] was also made for the SC-current systems. Just before the beginning of the IGY, two new ideas of geomagnetic storm theory were presented: a heat expansion effect to the *Dst*-field suggested by Parker [90], and a shock wave effect to the SC and Störmer–Alfvén type of trapped particle effect to the *Dst* suggested by Singer [102]. These theories and Dungey's suggestion [36] of hydromagnetic behavior in the exosphere played an important role for the succeeding new era of storm theory.

Morphological results of SC, such as the daytime enhancement of the size at Huancayo and an increase of ionospheric ionization at the time of SC at high latitudes [68], indicated that electric currents in the ionosphere and impinging particles at high latitudes were required at the event of SC; however, no theory was a satisfactory explanation. Other serious questions were the ones concerning the *DS* and bay: why the disturbance is larger at night than in the daytime in the auroral zone and middle latitudes, although it is predominant in the daytime at the polar cap; how particles responsible for the cause of the *DS* and bay current obtain sufficient energy to penetrate into the ionosphere; and, also, what the original cause of the bay is. Current systems similar to the *DS* and average-*DS* were obtained by a dynamo action [44, 67, 80, 86, 96]. However, a certain assumption was always needed, such as a change of wind system, double dynamo layers in which the wind system was reversed, or a formation of electrostatic fields at certain places in certain directions. All these assumptions needed to be checked.

2. Observations and Morphology

Since the IGY extensive studies of solar phenomena have been made, particularly with solar radio observations. As mentioned in other chapters, important solar phenomena closely related to magnetic storm were discovered: so-called Type IV solar radio burst, polar cap absorption, and intense solar cosmic ray. Detailed studies [64, 117] of the correlation between these phenomena and the occurrence of storm provide a much better picture of solar-terrestrial relationship (see Chapter 14 by Obayashi).

Several interesting phenomena were also discovered concerning solar flare effects on the earth's atmosphere: for example, exospheric heating by satellite-drag observations, $foF2$ increase by ionosondes, ionospheric oscillations corresponding to geomagnetic pulsations [74] by a Doppler frequency shift technique. The ionospheric current system responsible for the geomagnetic solar-flare effect (sfe) or crochet was studied by several workers [110, 111, 116, 122]; one example is shown in Figure 4, which shows that the sfe-current system is generally an augmentation of the

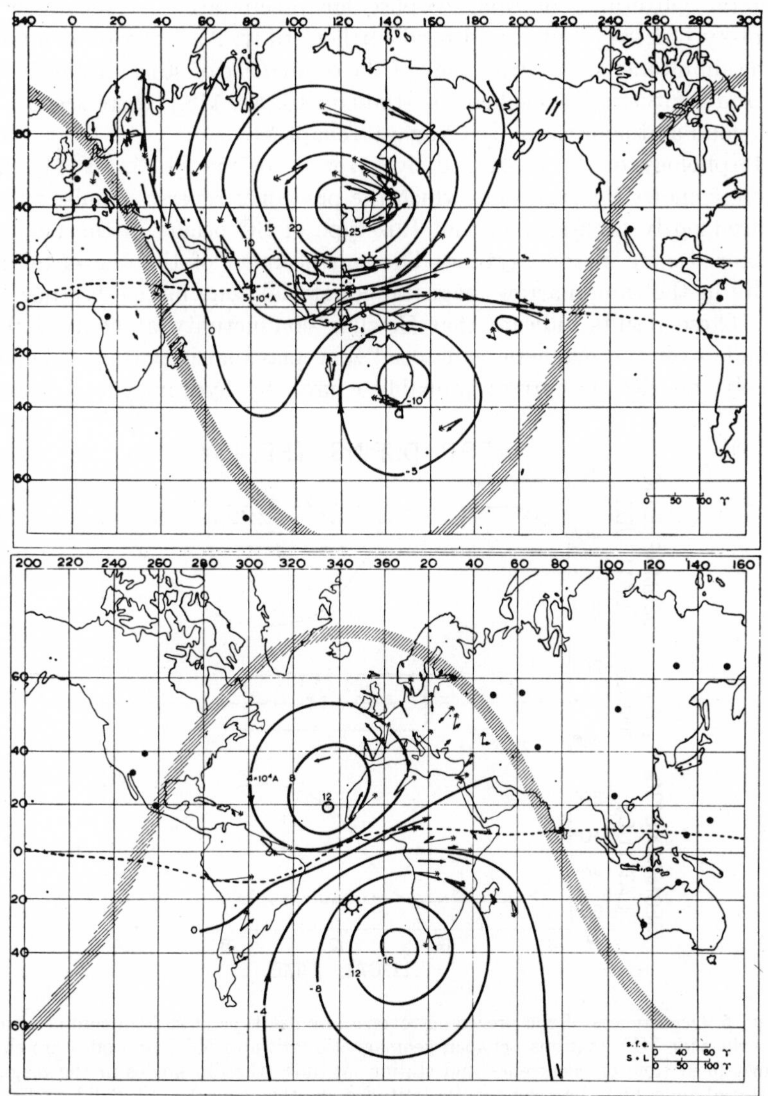

FIG. 4. Current systems caused by the solar flare at 0311 GMT, 29 July 1958 (top) and at 1301 GMT, 12 December 1958 (bottom) obtained by van Sabben [110]. Dotted line shows magnetic equator; shaded curve outlines sunlit zone.

Sq-current system in the sunlit hemisphere, where the *Sq* is somewhat like the one suggested by Matsushita [71, 72], rather than the well-known one by Chapman and Bartels [24]. These sfe current systems were theoretically discussed by Rikitake and Yukutake [98].

Geomagnetic activities in the polar cap are studied [39, 43] using *Q*-indices, and Mayaud's suggestion [75] of the daytime activity is confirmed. A spiral patterning of solar corpuscular precipitation is suggested by Nikolsky [54, 84], but it will need further study. An important question of the simultaneity and conjugacy of the occurrence of storm in the Northern and Southern Hemispheres is studied [16, 81, 118]; there seem to be both good and poor cases (see Nagata's chapter).

Morphology of SC is studied by several workers [1, 5, 70, 74, 100]. Figure 5 shows the regions in which the preceding reverse impulse type of SC frequently occurs; note that this type of SC occurs in the magnetic equatorial zone in the daytime. The enhancement of the size of SC also occurs in the same narrow magnetic equatorial zone in the daytime [66, 74]. These results indicate that Cowling conductivity at about 100-km altitude over the magnetic equatorial zone plays an important role [58]; namely, an electric current probably caused by hydromagnetic pressure

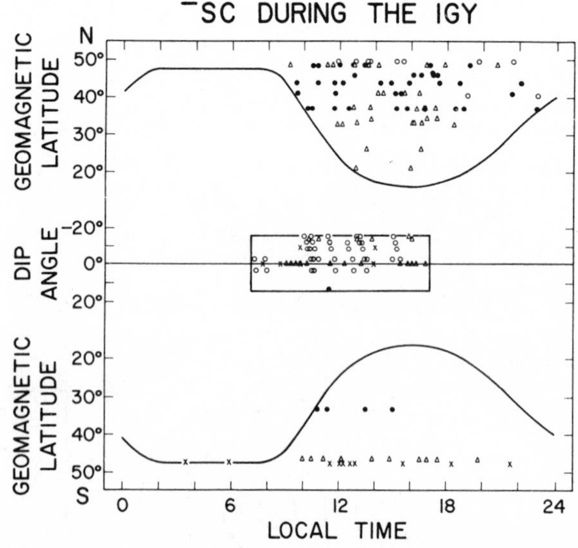

Fig. 5. Occurrences of the preceding reverse impulse type of sudden commencement at world-wide IGY stations between geomagnetic latitudes 50°N and 50°S are shown against local time of occurrence and station latitude (the dip angles in the magnetic equatorial zone, and the geomagnetic latitudes at other zones) [74]. Solid circles, triangles, crosses, and open circles indicate, respectively, the following four longitude zones: Europe and Africa (geomagnetic 50°E–140°E); Asia and Australia (geomagnetic 140°E–230°E); northwest America and New Zealand (geomagnetic 230°E–320°E); and northeast and south America (geomagnetic 320°E–50°E).

flows in the ionospheric *E*-region at the time of SC [72, 74]. A cause of preliminary reverse impulse type of SC in high latitudes is discussed by Vestine and Kern [115] based on the current system responsible [78]. Also, an earth-induction effect on the vertical component of SC is found at a net of U.S. IGY stations [70].

Another interesting discovery of SC is its accompanying phenomena, such as sudden increases of cosmic noise absorption in riometer records [74, 89] (see Fig. 6), bursts of bremsstrahlung X-rays at balloon altitudes [17, 18, 74] (see Fig. 7), and commencements of geomagnetic micropulsations and ionospheric oscillations [74]. All these phenomena indicate much more clearly than conjectured before the IGY that at the time of SC charged particles, probably electrons, hit the ionospheric region at high latitudes, and the ionosphere in middle and low latitudes shows a certain variation. In other words, the geomagnetic SC variation is not simply due to the mere distortion of the earth's field caused by the incoming plasma front.

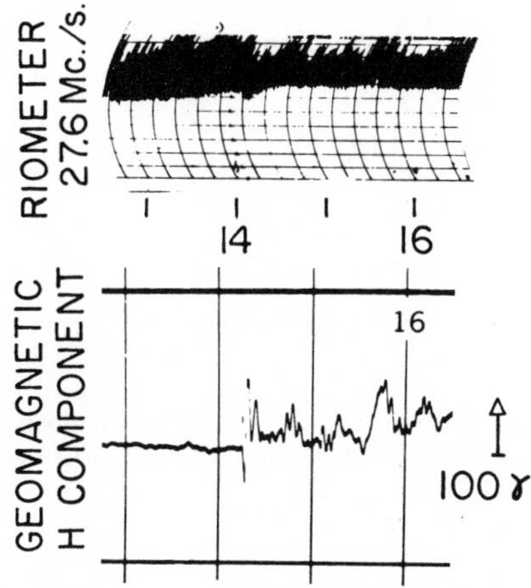

Fig. 6. An example of the increase of absorption in the 27.6 Mc/sec riometer record at the time of the sudden commencement 14 16, 150° WMT, 28 September 1957 [74]; records obtained at College, Alaska.

As shown in Figure 8, Wilson and Sugiura [120] suggest that in the Northern Hemisphere the rotation of the SC vector diagram frequently is counterclockwise in the meridian zone from 2200 to 1000 local time and clockwise from 1000 to 2200; they interpret that these are due to hydromagnetic waves.

Sudden impulses (SI) [74] and similar world-wide changes [85] were found to have a very similar behavior to SC, except a negative type, such as is shown in Figure 9. The negative type of SI occurs all over the world, while the same type of SC occurs only at high latitudes; the former seems to be due to a magnetospheric expansion. Based on the study of SC, SI, and other storm behavior observed during the IGY, Matsushita [74] suggested an idea of a family of storms.

The simultaneity of SC and SI, studied by several workers [45, 85], needs a further detailed investigation because conclusions differ. The investigation should be done in the near future because the hydromagnetic propagation can be estimated by this study.

Concerning the main phase of geomagnetic storms, *Dst* and *DS* are often separated statistically, and *DS* is studied by harmonic analysis. Sugiura

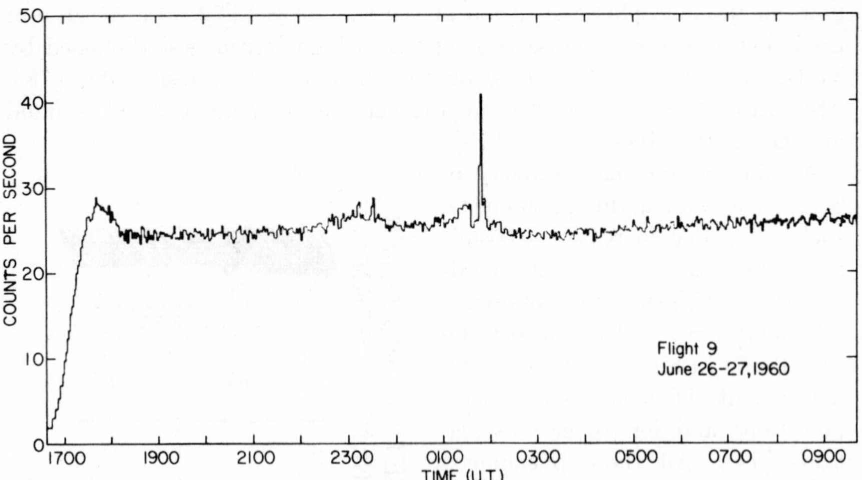

FIG. 7. Intense X-ray bursts at a balloon altitude near College, Alaska, coincident with the sudden commencement at 0145 GMT, 27 June 1960 [17].

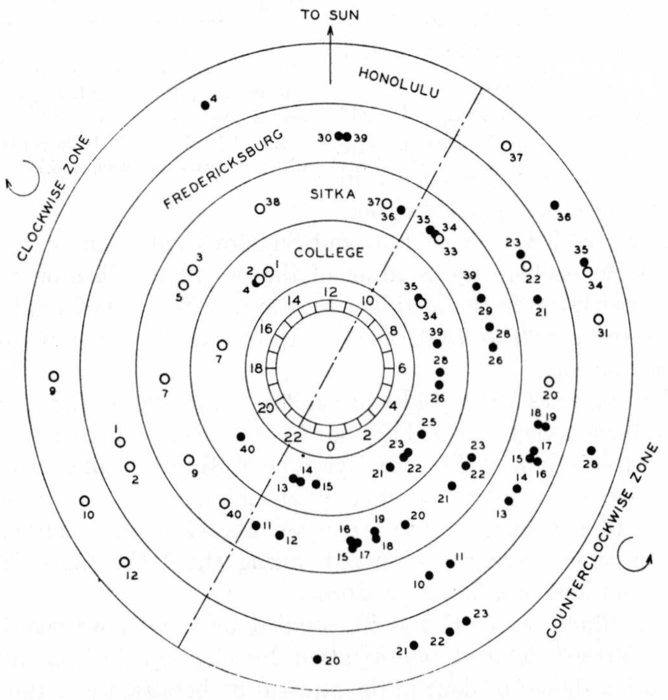

FIG. 8. Local time distribution of sudden commencements with counterclockwise rotation (black circles) and with clockwise rotation (open circles) of the magnetic vector for stations in the Northern Hemisphere. The zones of opposite directions of rotation are separated by the meridian plane through 1000 and 2200 hours local time [120].

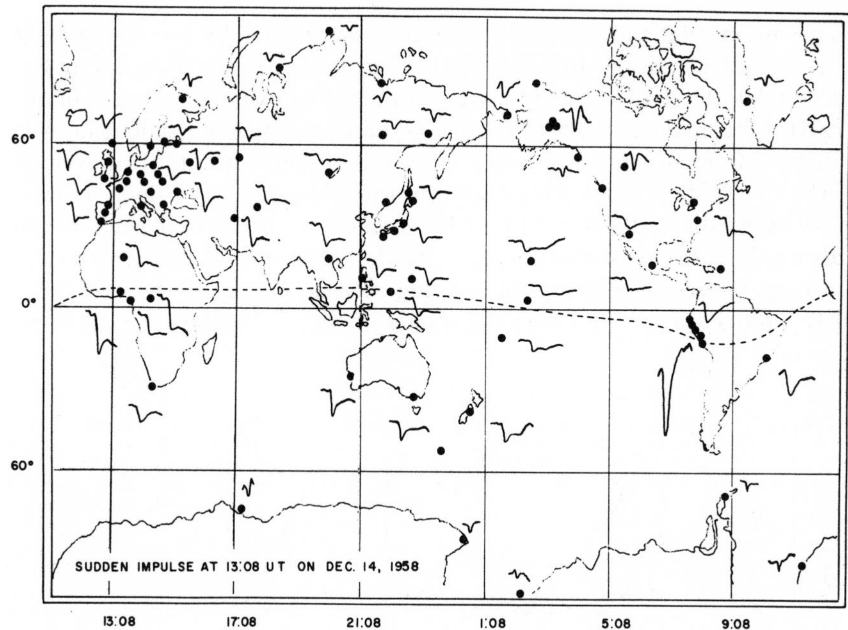

FIG. 9. Example of negative sudden impulse, which has no positive change on the horizontal field, at the world-wide geomagnetic stations. The broken line shows the magnetic equator, and the enhancement of the decrease can be seen at the stations in the magnetic equatorial zone during the daytime.

[107] warns of a certain misleading result of the DS-analysis which may be derived from the statistical process. Chapman and Akasofu [7, 23] recently gave the names DCF, DR, and DP for the three systems of storm currents, where CF, R, and P denote corpuscular flux, ring current, and polar substorm, respectively; roughly speaking they correspond to the initial phase, *Dst*, and DS. These workers emphasize [7] that at high latitudes *Dst* and DS should be studied case by case instead of on an average, and suggest [8] that the *Dst* of severe storms is formed by two ring currents, DR_1 and DR_2. Matsushita [74] studied the duration of *Dst*, comparing the result with the theoretical conclusion of the decay process of the ring current obtained by Dessler *et al.* [33].

Many workers [2, 15, 72, 79, 83, 99], examining DS, bay, and related auroral motions, find that the behavior of these is generally the same in both Northern and Southern Hemispheres; Cole [28] has an extensive review of these studies.

Bremsstrahlung X-ray and cosmic-ray observations during storms by balloons were carried out by several workers [10, 17, 18, 121]. These results and observations by rockets (for example, the work by Cahill [19] over Greenland) provide valuable information on storm mechanism, particularly of the energy flux of particles and ionospheric currents. The most interesting and exciting observations were made by several satellites [11, 20, 29, 35, 47, 51, 103, 104, 105]. Magnetometer data obtained by Explorer VI and Lunik I and II are shown in Figure 10. A decrease of the earth's magnetic-field intensity at a certain geocentric altitude, shown in Figure 10, seems to indicate the existence of ring currents. However, as Smith [103] points out after studying other observations made by Pioneer I, Vanguard III, Pioneer V, and Explorer X, all observed results do not always indicate consistent evidence for the existence of ring currents.

Very interesting observations during storms were made by Pioneer V [47] and Explorer VI [103]. As shown in Figure 11, the correlation be-

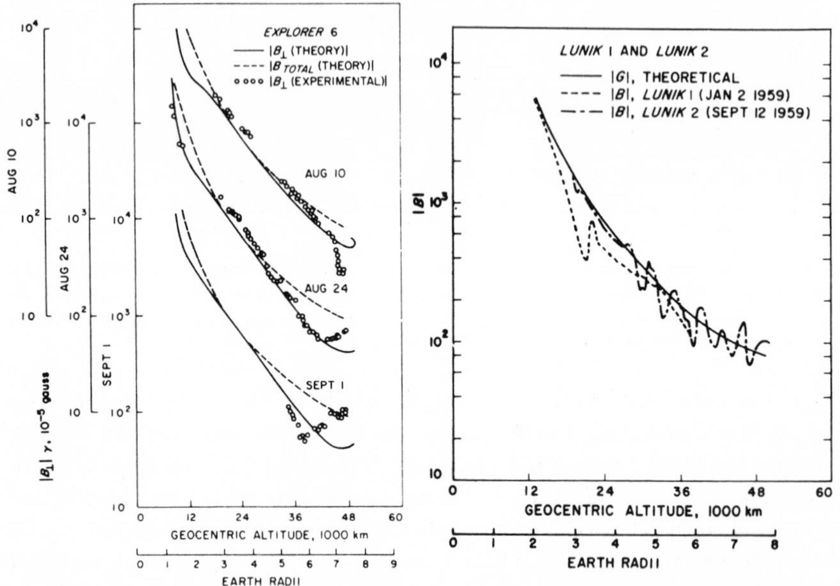

FIG. 10. Magnetometer data obtained by Explorer VI and Lunik I and II [103].

tween the magnetic index a_p and the magnetic-field intensity observed by Pioneer V (left diagram), and the correlation between the horizontal component at Huancayo or average *Dst* and the field intensity obtained by Explorer VI (right diagram), are remarkable. Recently, Mariner II observed a good correlation between the magnetic index and the speed of the plasma particles in the interplanetary space (private communication). Dessler and Fejer [31] interpret that the K_p-index is "a measure of the time rate of change of the sum of plasma plus magnetic pressure acting on the magnetosphere." They also propose "*M*-region geomagnetic storms are due to sheets of turbulence or irregularities that are generated by the collision of a region of high solar-wind velocity with a low velocity region."

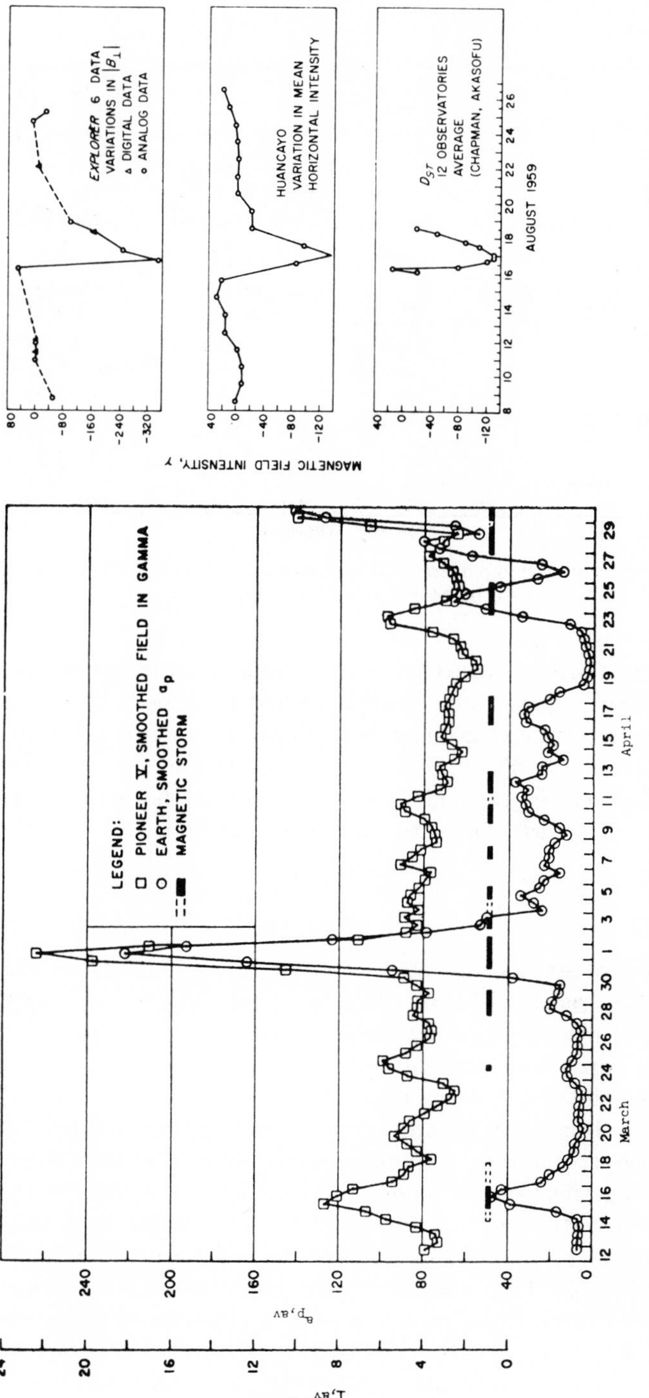

FIG. 11. Comparison of the observations of the earth-surface magnetic variations and the interplanetary magnetic fields obtained by Pioneer V [47] and Explorer VI [103].

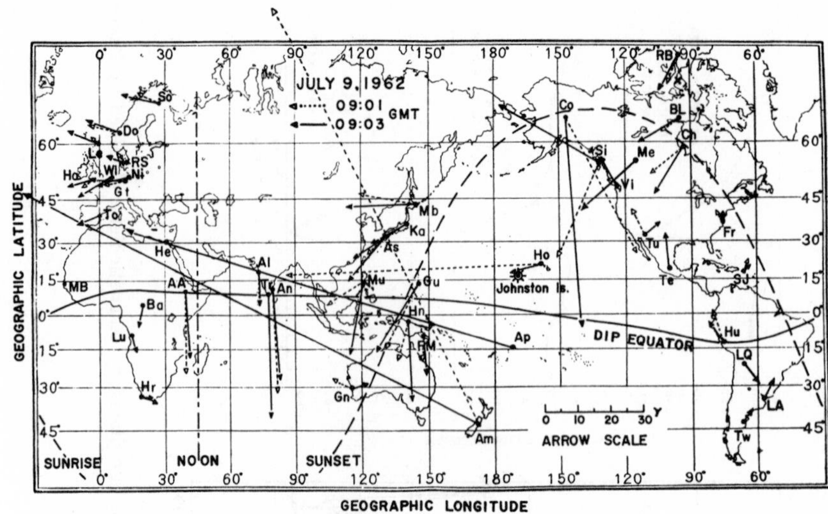

Fig. 12. Observed world-wide pattern of the horizontal vectors of geomagnetic changes caused by Starfish on 9 July 1962 [65].

Geomagnetic effects caused by high-altitude nuclear explosions, such as Teak, Orange, Argus, and Starfish, should be added. In addition to micropulsations, artificial geomagnetic storms are associated with these explosions [21, 61, 63, 65, 69, 87]. One example of the Starfish is shown in Figure 12. This can be explained to some extent by the combination of a diamagnetic effect, drift currents, and an augmentation of *Sq* [65].

3. Theories

New models of storms suggested by Parker [90] and Singer [102] just before the IGY lead to the succeeding era of new theories of storms. The introduction of plasma theories to storm models, in which Alfvén [9] has played many important roles, and various discoveries of storm phenomena obtained from the observations made at the earth's surface and in space since the IGY, bring new light to previous explanations and provide new models of magnetic storms. A question of the delay that may elapse, due to the shielding effect of the conducting medium in the outer ionosphere, between the formation of the ring current and the occurrence of the resulting geomagnetic storm at the earth's surface, which was raised by Parker [53], has been solved by introducing the propagation of hydromagnetic waves; the effect of the ring current should be transmitted to the earth by hydromagnetic waves. Dessler and Parker [34] and Piddington [93] present a hydromagnetic theory of magnetic storms (see reference [123] for a review of hydromagnetic theory of storms).

Concerning SC, the first part of their model is the same as Chapman and Ferraro's; the storm plasma is stopped by the earth's magnetic field and forms a forbidden region or cavity at the place where the magnetic pressure $B^2/(2\mu_0)$ balances the impact pressure of the solar plasma ρV^2; here B is the magnetic-field strength, μ_0 is the permeability of a vacuum, ρ is the mass density of the plasma, and V is the plasma speed at the front. The difference is a formation of hydromagnetic waves by this impact. These hydromagnetic waves propagate toward the earth and cause SC. Dessler [30] and Francis *et al.* [42] calculate the speed v of the longitudinal hydromagnetic wave at various altitudes, using Alfvén's equation

$$v = B'/\sqrt{4\pi\rho'}$$

where B' and ρ' are the magnetic-field strength and the mass density, respectively, at each height. They conclude that this hydromagnetic wave is stable until an altitude of about 400 km with an average speed of about 10^7 cm/sec.

Using the ray path theory, Francis *et al.* [42] and Dessler *et al.* [32] discuss SC rise times and the time lag of the occurrence of SC among different stations; the time lag between the stations at the noon meridian and at the midnight meridian, in the equatorial plane, for waves generated at six earth radii is found to be approximately 11 sec. However, the actual mode of propagation should be much more complicated than their model. As is mentioned in the previous section, the time lag of SC is not yet established from observations. A further study of this problem is essential for both statistics and theory.

The main cause of both the enhancement of the size of SC and the frequent occurrence of the reverse impulse SC in the magnetic equatorial zone in the daytime may be due not to the convergence of hydromagnetic waves from the magnetosphere to the magnetic equator, but to the combined effect of high Cowling conductivity of the ionosphere in the magnetic equatorial zone and of hydromagnetic waves.

Piddington [92] discussed hydromagnetic twist waves concerning the DS part of SC. As shown at the top of Figure 13, the electric space-charge field Ep which opposes the induction field $E_i(= V \times B)$ and the bend or drag of geomagnetic lines of force may be formed by solar wind of velocity V. This drag will cause a hydromagnetic twist wave, and, as shown at the bottom of Figure 13, the twist wave may propagate along the magnetic field H_z, having total radial current J_r and Hall current J_θ; this causes the DS of SC in high altitudes. Wilson and Sugiura's interpretation [120] of vector diagrams of SC is based on this idea of the bend of field lines.

The storm-time variation *Dst* during the main phase which is characterized by a large decrease of the horizontal component can be explained by the main-phase ring current. However, different ideas of the formation of the ring current have been presented. Based on the suggestion made by

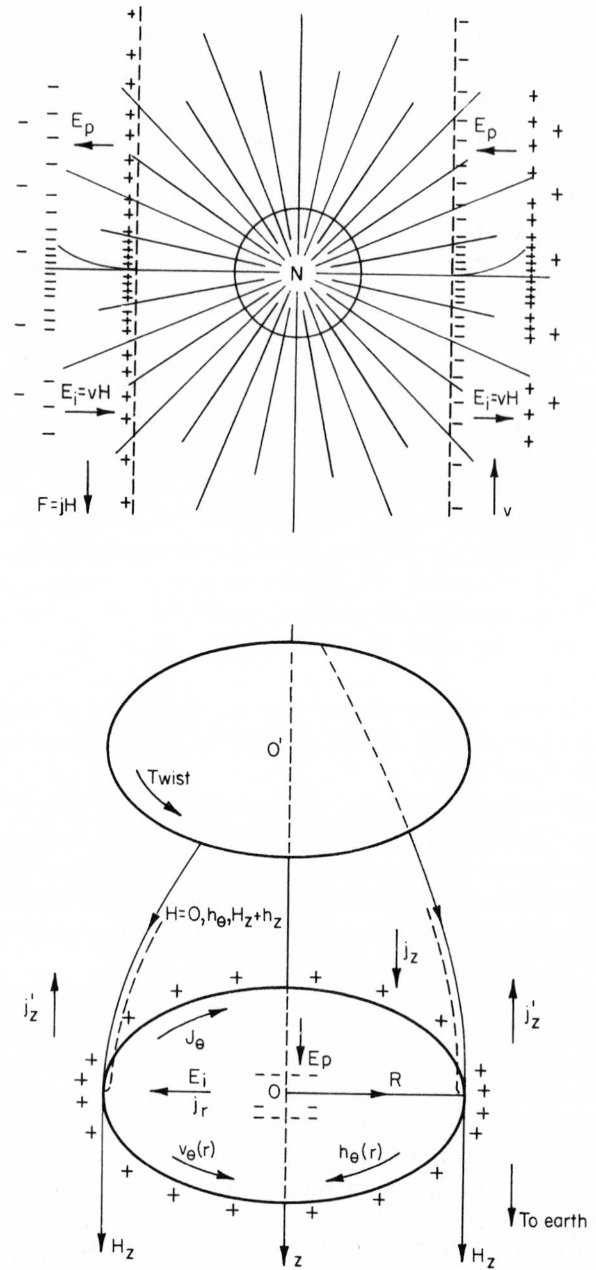

FIG. 13. Electric space-charge field *Ep* and the bend of geomagnetic lines of force due to the solar wind of velocity *V* (top), and an idealized hydromagnetic twist propagating down the magnetic field H_z, which is responsible for the *DS* (bottom), suggested by Piddington [92].

Alfvén [9] and Singer [102] before the IGY and the observed results of the newly discovered Van Allen radiation belts, Akasofu and Chapman [3, 6] showed that the drift motion of trapped particles of solar storm plasma may form a westward main-phase ring current, after the calculation of circulating, drift, and polarization currents. As an example under a simplified model, in order to get 100γ decrease of the horizontal component, 136 protons per cm^3 at 20 kev or 27 electrons per cm^3 at 100 kev at five earth radii are required. They [3] and their colleagues [4] also calculated current intensity and magnetic field distributions of a model ring current

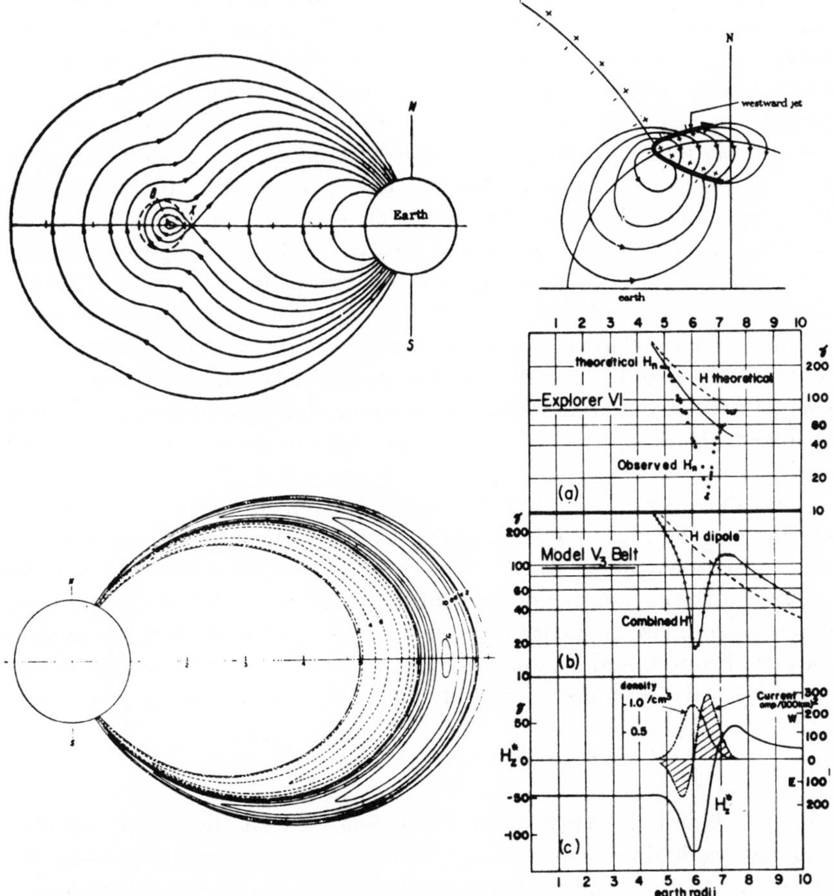

FIG. 14. The X- and O-type neutral lines due to a toroidal ring current whose cross section is shown by the broken line (top left) [6] and a formation of electrostatic field toward low latitudes for the westward polar electrojet in the ionosphere (top right) [6]. Current intensity distribution in an idealized ring current belt (bottom left) [3] and magnetic field intensity distribution due to the idealized belt, which is compared with the observation by the Explorer VI (bottom right) [3].

or radiation belt. Their current intensity distribution is shown at the bottom left of Figure 14, and the magnetic field intensity distribution compared with the observation by Explorer VI is shown at the bottom right.

Instead of the above-mentioned idea that the trapped particles originating directly from the solar storm plasma form the main-phase ring current, Dessler, Hanson, and Parker [33] suggested that the ambient protons which already constitute the protonosphere may be accelerated or heated during storms in the vicinity of four earth radii geocentric distance and beyond, and that these protons form a diamagnetic main-phase ring current. Since the proton density at four earth radii geocentric distance is of the order of 10^2 protons/cm^3 and about 10^{15} joules of trapped particle energy are needed to give 100γ decrease of the horizontal component, the protons must be accelerated or heated to 1 kev energy during the main phase; comparing this to Akasofu and Chapman's model, protons of less energy may form the ring current. A solar-wind density of 50 protons/cm^3 moving with a velocity of 10^3 km/sec delivers about 4×10^{-2} watt/m^2 to the geomagnetic field, so that over a cross section of radius four earth radii the energy incident is 8×10^{13} joules/sec. By assuming that a significant fraction of this energy goes into hydromagnetic-wave generation, Dessler, Hanson, and Parker concluded that there is ample wave energy during the main phase of the storm to generate the required energy of 10^{15} joules. They also discussed the bombardment of the upper atmosphere by energetic hydrogen atoms from the decaying ring current and the possible change in the decay time constant of the ring current through the sunspot cycle.

The above-mentioned hydromagnetic heating of trapped particles is effective in the nightside hemisphere. However, Kern [59] proposed that strong hydromagnetic shock waves give a required energy to trapped protons in the dayside hemisphere, although his basic idea of the formation of the main-phase ring current by already existing protons is the same as Dessler, Hanson, and Parker's. According to Kern, the transverse kinetic energy density E_n following n hydromagnetic shock events is given by

$$E_n = E_0 2^{-2n}\left[\left(\frac{V}{v}\right)^{1/3} + \left(\frac{v}{V}\right)^{1/3}\right]^{2n}$$

where E_0 is initial energy density, V is solar stream (or piston) velocity, and v is local hydromagnetic wave (Alfvén) velocity. Thus the geomagnetic effect due to this type of ring current depends on the number of hydromagnetic shock events n.

Vestine [113] discussed a transient equatorial ring current at a height within the outer reaches of the inner radiation belt, attributing its height variation to the higher main-phase ring current.

Several theories have also been presented for the DS-field in the last few years. Akasofu and Chapman [6] proposed a neutral line discharge theory. As shown at the top left of Figure 14, the X- and O-shape of neutral lines of the earth's magnetic field may be formed by the magnetic field which is caused by the main-phase ring current already mentioned. These neutral lines will not be formed in the dayside hemisphere because of the earth's strong field caused by the incoming solar plasma. Akasofu and Chapman suggested that particles at the X-shape neutral line may come down toward the ionosphere, to cause thin auroras which spread widely toward the East-West direction at night. When these particles form an electrostatic field toward low latitudes as shown at the top right of Figure 14, a strong westward polar electrojet may flow in the ionosphere and its return currents flow in the middle latitudes and the polar cap. When the direction of the electrostatic field is reversed, the polar electrojet flows toward the east as can be seen from the simplified relations among the current intensity I, electric field E, and electric conductivity σ,

$$
\begin{aligned}
I_y &= \sigma_{yx}E_x + \sigma_{yy}E_y \\
&\simeq -\frac{\sigma_2 E_x}{\sin\phi} + \sigma_1 E_y \\
&\simeq -\sigma_2 E_q
\end{aligned}
$$

where subscripts x, y, and q stand for the southward, eastward, and equatorward directions, ϕ is the magnetic dip angle, σ_{ij} is a tensor component of the conductivity, and σ_1 and σ_2 are Pedersen and Hall conductivities ($\sigma_2 \gg \sigma_1$ in high latitudes). Thus the DS-current by this process may flow in the ionosphere and cause the DS-field.

The same type of electrostatic field for the DS but due to a different process was suggested by Kern [60]. If an eastward geomagnetic field gradient $\nabla_\phi B$ can be assumed to arise at the equatorial cross section of trapped neutral plasma, a drift separation of trapped protons and electrons occurs (Fig. 15, top); protons are at the inner surface and electrons are at the outer surface. An electric field E_2 which is parallel to the earth's magnetic field B is assumed to arise from excess charge resulting from this charge separation. Then the acceleration of a particle $\ddot{z}$ parallel to B will be given by

$$
\ddot{z} = \frac{1}{m}(-\mu\nabla_2 B + eE_2)
$$

where m, μ, and e are the mass, magnetic moment, and charge of the particle, and $\nabla_2 B$ is the component of the gradient of B parallel to B. Here z is taken as a displacement from the equatorial plane along B, and the electric force eE_2 is taken as being in the same direction. By this acceleration, positive and negative particles may come down toward the ionosphere along the field lines, forming the proton and electron sheets (bottom of

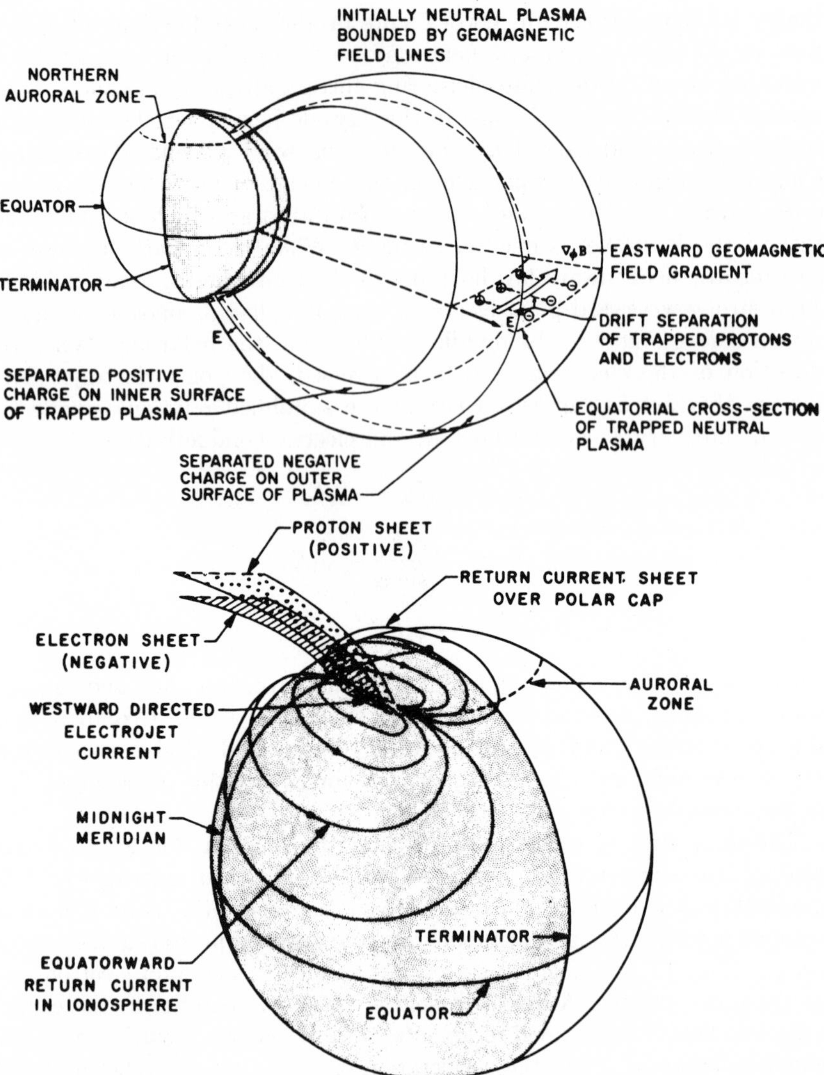

Fig. 15. Charge separation in geomagnetically trapped radiation due to eastward geomagnetic field gradient (top) and polar electrojet currents caused by polarization of radiation incident in the auroral zone and the Hall conductivity (bottom) [60].

Fig. 15). When the required electrostatic field arises in the ionosphere by this process, this field and Hall conductivity may cause the polar jet current; in the case of the bottom diagram the electrostatic field is equatorward, hence the polar jet is westward. In the case of the top diagram, however, the static field will be poleward; hence the jet will be eastward. In other words, if the assumed geomagnetic field gradient in a shell of trapped particles is eastward (top diagram), the eastward jet will flow; if the field gradient is westward, the jet also will be westward (bottom diagram). Accordingly, for average-*DS* field, the eastward and westward field gradients should be assumed to occur before and after the magnetic midnight, respectively. Kern also discussed acceleration of charged particles by hydromagnetic shock waves.

Matsushita [72] emphasized the longitudinal electrostatic-field effect for the bay from the point of view of ionospheric density variations. Cole [27] discussed the *DS* and bay from the viewpoint of auroral motions and also suggested that Joule heating caused by the *DS* and bay currents may cause ionospheric height variation during storms.

A completely new idea of the explanation of the *DS* and bay fields was proposed by Axford and Hines [12]: namely, that magnetospheric motion causes these fields. First, viscous-like interaction of the magnetosphere with the solar wind causes tubes of force, which lie near the surface of the magnetosphere, to be pulled around into the geomagnetic tail, and then a return flow is assumed to take place in the interior of the magnetosphere; circulations will be formed in the magnetosphere. In the presence of rotation, a proposed pattern of streamlines or of the equipotentials of the electric field caused by these circulations in the equatorial plane of the magnetosphere is shown in the top right of Figure 16. The effect of this proposed pattern on energetic trapped particles is that the electrons drift on lower latitude field lines during the morning hours and the protons drift during the afternoon hours (Fig. 16, top left). The pattern of motion at ionospheric level, which is obtained by mapping the streamline (top right diagram, Fig. 16) down onto the Northern Hemisphere along the geomagnetic field lines, is shown at the bottom of Figure 16. Axford and Hines suggested that this motion is the cause of the *DS* and bay currents.

Another picture of the magnetospheric motion as the cause of the *DS* and bay currents was proposed by Fejer [37]. An excess ring current i_R on the dayside, caused by a temporary distortion of a previously stable belt of energetic charged particles, flows along a half-circle R in the equatorial plane (Fig. 17, top). In the sunset-sunrise meridian i_R flows along field lines and becomes $i_R/2$ ionospheric currents in the polar regions. Here the ring current is taken to be caused entirely by particle drift, and for simplicity it is assumed to be a line current in the equatorial plane. The ionospheric currents are driven by a quasi-static electric field which has polarization charges. This electric field and strong Hall conductivity cause the Hall current i_H as is shown in the top of Figure 17; the loops of the Hall current around the points A, B, C, and D are similar to the *DS* and bay current pattern.

A more recent model suggested by Fejer [38] is shown by the diagram of a meridional cross section of the proton belt (bottom of Fig. 17). The magnetosphere is assumed to convect outward over a considerable range

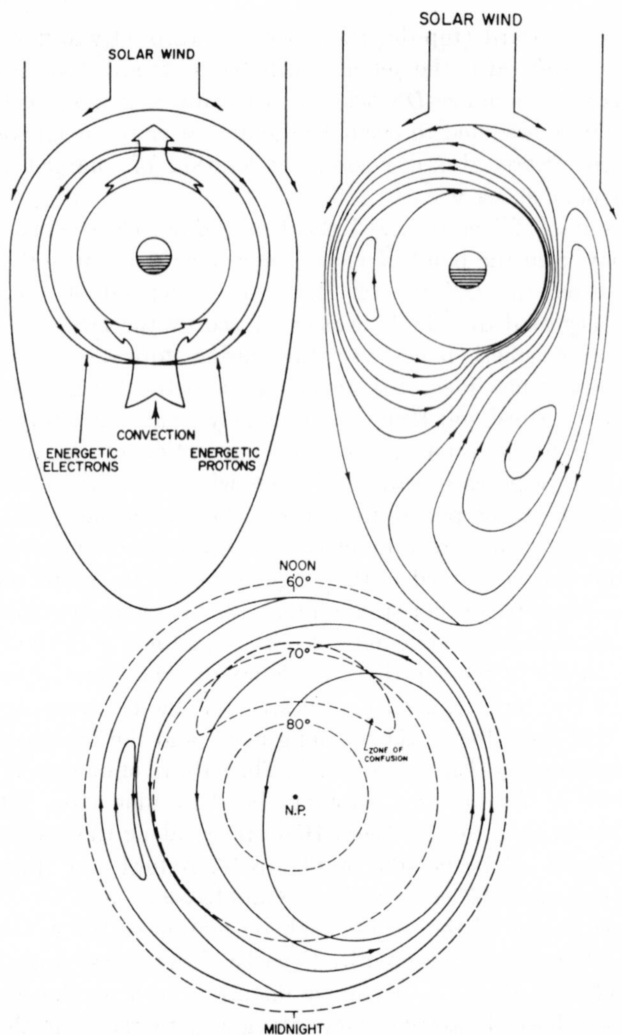

FIG. 16. Magnetospheric motions responsible for *DS* and bay (top diagrams), and ionospheric motions in the northern high latitudes (bottom) caused by the magnetospheric motion shown in the top right diagram [12].

of longitudes. The convection only affects the low-energy particles whose outward moving excess negative space charge causes an accumulation of negative charge on the outside and positive charge on the inside of the belt. Electric fields are soon established by the accumulating space charge, and a discharge occurs along the field lines and through a short ionospheric path across the auroral zone. The electric fields which drive these ionospheric currents cause the simultaneous flow of much larger Hall currents; in the case of the bottom of Figure 17, the electric field is poleward, and

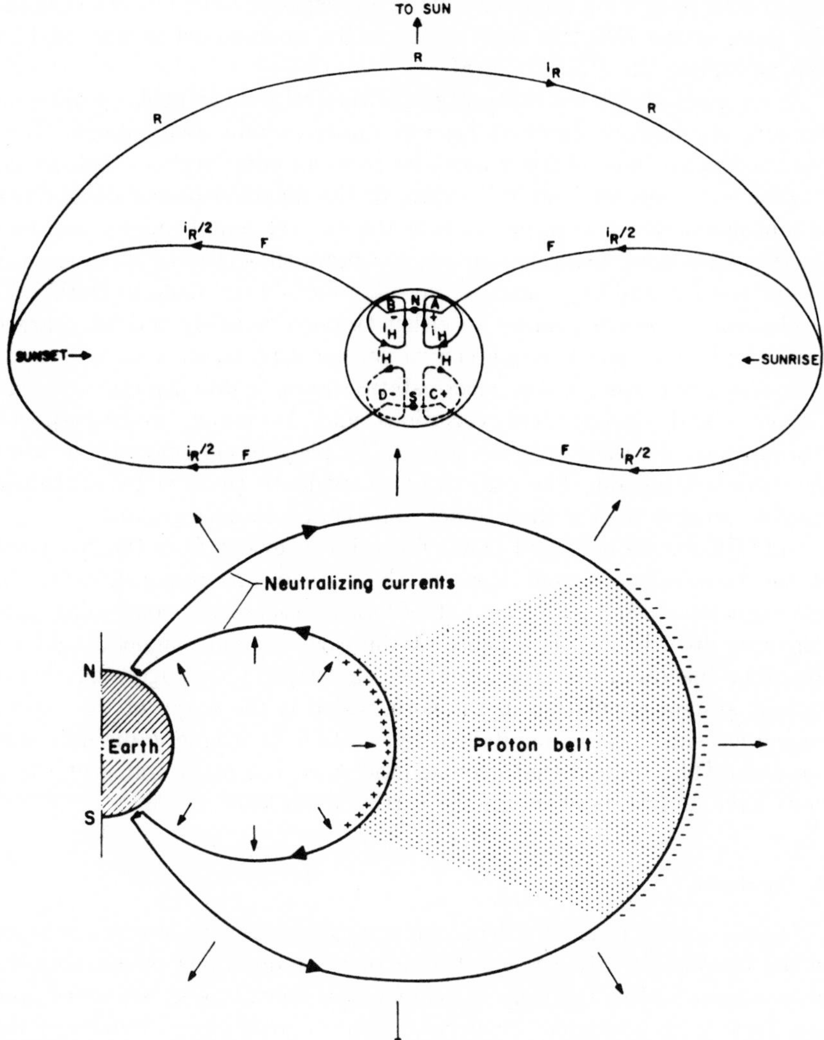

FIG. 17. Magnetospheric and ionospheric currents associated with an excess ring current i_R on the day side (top) [37], and neutralizing currents caused by the outward convection of the magnetosphere (bottom) [38].

hence the Hall current is eastward. If this Hall current should be the *DS* or bay current, an outward drift of the magnetosphere would create the eastward auroral jet current and an inward drift would cause the westward jet. Accordingly, in order to explain the average-*DS* field, the outward and inward drifts of the magnetosphere should occur before and after the magnetic midnight, respectively.

Piddington [94] also discussed magnetospheric motions with small vortex cells combining them with his hydromagnetic twist model to explain the cause of the DS; this twist model is the same model as was used by him to explain the DS part of SC.

As reviewed above, the explanations of the DS and bay fields by different workers emphasized different aspects under certain assumptions. They tried to explain how charged particles from an outer region (such as the ring-current zone, the trapped region, or the magnetosphere) come down to ionospheric level, particularly into the auroral zone at night, and how electric fields arise in the ionosphere to obtain the observed direction and size of the DS and bay currents. Special efforts were made to clarify the mechanism of energy transfer to either trapped or newly arrived charged particles; here emphasis was given to various aspects, such as hydromagnetic shock and twist waves, electrostatic waves, hydromagnetic heatings, magnetic and electric field variations and formation, magnetospheric motions, etc. All these theories seem to be plausible in general, but some uncertainties remain. The only way to evaluate them is by continued satellite observations of the magnetospheric and trapped regions.

Gold [46] and Parker [91] have fine critical reviews from the viewpoint of the theorist on current ideas of the mechanisms responsible for the geomagnetic storm. Also, some theoretical discussions concerning geomagnetic disturbances as a cause of the earth's main magnetic field are found in the literature: for example, Chatterjee [26] suggested that a current system circulating in the core, which is the origin of the earth's magnetic field, may be maintained by world-wide magnetic disturbances, but Price [95] showed that geomagnetic storms or other transient variations have no lasting effect on the earth's main field.

4. Conclusion

Several questions and problems concerning geomagnetic storms are noted in the introduction. In Section 2 some of these questions (concerning the observations and morphology of geomagnetic storms) were answered, and new facts were presented. However, further morphological studies of the simultaneity of SC and SI and that of storms and daytime activities in the polar cap are needed.

Many workers have traditionally studied the overhead current system responsible for geomagnetic variations. Except for the ring current, they often postulated the overhead current system as an ionospheric system in a thin shell. However, while it appears that the DS and bay polar-jet current, the equatorial electrojet and part of SC and SI are probably ionospheric currents, other current systems need to be examined by rocket observations. Moreover, quiet-time geomagnetic variations, such as the solar quiet daily variation S_q and lunar daily variation L, should be reexamined. In fact, since the IGY several workers [50, 52, 56, 71, 73, 76,

97, 119] have been studying these S_q- and L-fields. But further investigation of the overhead current system of these basic geomagnetic fields will be needed during the IQSY. The question of whether this overhead current system is entirely an ionospheric current in the so-called dynamo region, or is partly due to certain magnetospheric motions, should be examined. The underground induction current effect also needs more study. Furthermore, based on these results some disturbance phenomena, such as sfe and *Sd*, and storm mechanism can be discussed.

Valuable observations were made by artificial satellites, and various interesting theories have been proposed based on these observations. These explanations have served to answer some questions, and the introduction of the idea of the solar wind and magnetosphere, using plasma theories and with the discovery of radiation belts, has led to the treatment of storm phenomena on a larger, three-dimensional scale than in the past. Further satellite observations of the magnetospheric region and solar winds, on both quiet and stormy days, are essential to evaluate these various ideas and to provide better theories.

References

1. S. Abe, Morphology of ssc and ssc*, *J. Geomag. Geoele.*, **10,** 153 (1959).
2. S.-I. Akasofu, Large-scale auroral motions and polar magnetic disturbances — "I," *J. Atmos. Terr. Phys.*, **19,** 10 (1960); "II," *ibid.*, **24,** 723 (1962); S.-I. Akasofu and S. Chapman, "III," *ibid.*, **24,** 785 (1962); S.-I. Akasofu and S. Chapman, Magnetic storms: The simultaneous development of the main phase (*DR*) and of polar magnetic substorms (*DP*), *J. Geophys. Res.*, **68,** 3155 (1963).
3. S.-I. Akasofu, The ring current and the outer atmosphere, *J. Geophys. Res.*, **65,** 535 (1960); S.-I. Akasofu and S. Chapman, The ring current, geomagnetic disturbances, and the Van Allen radiation belts, *J. Geophys. Res.*, **66,** 1321 (1961).
4. S.-I. Akasofu, J. C. Cain, and S. Chapman, The magnetic field of a model radiation belt, numerically computed, *J. Geophys. Res.*, **66,** 4013 (1961); S.-I. Akasofu, J. C. Cain, and S. Chapman, The magnetic field of the quiet-time proton belt, *J. Geophys. Res.*, **67,** 2645 (1962); S.-I. Akasofu, On a self-consistent calculation of the ring current field, *J. Geophys. Res.*, **67,** 3617 (1962); S.-I. Akasofu and J. C. Cain, The magnetic field of the radiation belts, *J. Geophys. Res.*, **67,** 4078 (1962); S.-I. Akasofu and W. C. Lin, The magnetic moment of model ring current belts and the cutoff rigidity of solar protons, *J. Geophys. Res.*, **68,** 973 (1963).
5. S.-I. Akasofu and S. Chapman, The sudden commencement of geomagnetic storms, *Vrania*, No. 250 (1960).
6. S.-I. Akasofu and S. Chapman, A neutral line discharge theory of the aurora polaris, *Phil. Trans. Roy. Soc. London, A*, **253,** 359 (1961); The ring current and a neutral line discharge theory of the aurora polaris, *J. Phys. Soc. Japan*, **17,** Suppl. A-1, 169 (1962).
7. S.-I. Akasofu and S. Chapman, The development of the main phase of magnetic storms, *J. Geophys. Res.*, **68,** 125 (1963).
8. S.-I. Akasofu, S. Chapman, and D. Venkatesan, The main phase of great magnetic storms, *J. Geophys. Res.*, **68,** 3345 (1963).
9. H. Alfvén, On the electric field theory of magnetic storms and aurorae, *Tellus*, **7,** 50 (1955); *Cosmical Electrodynamics* (Oxford Univ. Press, 1950).
10. K. A. Anderson, Balloon observations of X rays in the auroral zone, "I," *J. Geophys. Res.*, **65,** 551 (1960); K. A. Anderson and D. C. Enemark, "II,"

J. Geophys. Res., **65**, 3521 (1960); K. A. ANDERSON, R. R. BROWN, AND D. S. EVANS, Simultaneous electron precipitation in the northern and southern auroral zone, *J. Geophys. Res.*, **67**, 4076 (1962).

11. M. G. ANTSILEVICH AND A. D. SHEVNIN, On the geomagnetic observations performed using the equipment on board the first Soviet cosmic rocket, *Dok. Akad. Nauk*, **135**, 298 (1960; translation in *Physics Express*, 26, Feb. 1961); A. D. SHEVNIN, The extra-ionospheric current system, *Geomag. i. Aeronomiya*, translated in *Geomag. and Aeronomy*, AGU, **1**, 160 (1961).
12. W. I. AXFORD AND C. O. HINES, A unifying theory of high-latitude geophysical phenomena and geomagnetic storms, *Can. J. Phys.*, **39**, 1433 (1961); C. O. HINES, The energization of plasma in the magnetosphere: hydromagnetic and particle-drift approaches, *Planet. Space Sci.*, **10**, 239 (1963).
13. N. P. BENKOVA, Magnetic storms and systems of electric currents, *Works, Sci.-Res. Inst. Terr. Mag. Leningrad, No. 10(20)* (1953).
14. K. BIRKELAND, *The Norwegian Aurora Polaris Expedition, 1902–1903* (H. Aschehoug and Co., 1908, 1913).
15. F. R. BOND, Motion of the aurora and magnetic bays, *Austral. J. Phys.*, **13**, 477 (1960).
16. G. M. BOYD, The conjugacy of magnetic disturbance variations, *J. Geophys. Res.*, **68**, 1011 (1963).
17. R. R. BROWN, Balloon observations of auroral-zone X rays, *J. Geophys. Res.*, **66**, 1379 (1961).
18. R. R. BROWN, T. R. HARTZ, B. LANDMARK, H. LEINBACH, AND J. ORTNER, Large-scale electron bombardment of the atmosphere at the sudden commencement of a geomagnetic storm, *J. Geophys. Res.*, **66**, 1035 (1961).
19. L. J. CAHILL, JR., Detection of an electric current in the ionosphere above Greenland, *J. Geophys. Res.*, **64**, 1377 (1959).
20. L. J. CAHILL AND P. G. AMAZEEN, The boundary of the geomagnetic field, *J. Geophys. Res.*, **68**, 1835 (1963).
21. M. CASAVERDE, A. GIESECKE, AND R. COHEN, Effects of the nuclear explosion over Johnston Island observed in Peru on July 9, 1962, *J. Geophys. Res.*, **68**, 2603 (1963).
22. S. CHAPMAN, The electric current-systems of magnetic storms, *Terr. Mag. Atmos. Elec.*, **40**, 349 (1935).
23. S. CHAPMAN, Magnetic storms: Their geometrical and physical analysis, and their classification, *Studia Geophys. Geod.*, **5**, 30 (1961); Earth storms: Retrospect and prospect, *J. Phys. Soc. Japan*, **17**, Suppl. A-1, 6 (1962).
24. S. CHAPMAN AND J. BARTELS, *Geomagnetism* (Clarendon Press, 1940).
25. S. CHAPMAN AND V. C. A. FERRARO, A new theory of magnetic storms, *Terr. Mag. Atmos. Elec.*, **36**, 77, 171 (1931); **37**, 147, 269, 421 (1932); **38**, 79 (1933); The theory of the first phase of a geomagnetic storm, *Terr. Mag. Atmos. Elec.*, **45**, 245 (1940); V. C. A. FERRARO, On the theory of the first phase of a geomagnetic storm, *J. Geophys. Res.*, **57**, 15 (1952); D. F. MARTYN, The theory of magnetic storms and aurora, *Nature*, **167**, 92 (1951).
26. J. S. CHATTERJEE, Magnetic disturbances and the earth's magnetic field, *J. Geophys. Res.*, **66**, 1535 (1961).
27. K. D. COLE, A dynamo theory of the aurora and magnetic disturbance, *Austral. J. Phys.*, **13**, 484 (1960); Damping of magnetospheric motions by the ionosphere, *J. Geophys. Res.*, **68**, 3231 (1963).
28. K. D. COLE, Motions of the aurora and radio-aurora and their relationships to ionospheric currents, *Planet. Space Sci.*, **10**, 129 (1963).
29. P. J. COLEMAN, JR., C. P. SONETT, D. L. JUDGE, AND E. J. SMITH, Some preliminary results of the Pioneer V magnetometer experiment, *J. Geophys. Res.*, **65**, 1856 (1960).
30. A. J. DESSLER, The propagation velocity of worldwide sudden commencements of magnetic storms, *J. Geophys. Res.*, **63**, 405 (1958).
31. A. J. DESSLER AND J. A. FEJER, Interpretation of *Kp* index and *M*-region geomagnetic storms, *Planet Space Sci.*, **11**, 505 (1963).

32. A. J. Dessler, W. E. Francis, and E. N. Parker, Geomagnetic storm sudden-commencement rise times, *J. Geophys. Res.*, **65,** 2715 (1960).
33. A. J. Dessler, W. B. Hanson, and E. N. Parker, Formation of the geomagnetic storm main-phase ring current, *J. Geophys. Res.*, **66,** 3631 (1961).
34. A. J. Dessler and E. N. Parker, Hydromagnetic theory of geomagnetic storms, *J. Geophys. Res.*, **64,** 2239 (1959).
35. S. Sh. Dolginov and N. V. Pushkov, The results of measuring the earth's magnetic field by the instruments on board a cosmic rocket, *Dok. Akad. Nauk*, **129,** 77 (1959; translated in *Physics Express*, 8, April 1960).
36. J. W. Dungey, Electrodynamics of the outer atmosphere, *Proc. Phys. Soc. Conf. Phys. Ionosph.*, 229 (1955).
37. J. A. Fejer, The effects of energetic trapped particles on magnetospheric motions and ionospheric currents, *Can. J. Phys.*, **39,** 1409 (1961).
38. J. A. Fejer, Theory of auroral electrojets, *J. Geophys. Res.*, **68,** 2147 (1963).
39. Ya. I. Feldshtein, The Dickson Island and Cape Chelinskin *Q*-indices of magnetic activity, *Vozmushcheniya Elektromagnitnogo Polia Zemli, Moscow* (1960; translated by E. R. Hope, DRB Canada, T 347 R 1961).
40. V. C. A. Ferraro, W. C. Parkinson, and H. W. Unthank, Sudden commencements and sudden impulses in geomagnetism: their hourly frequency at Cheltenham (Md.), Tucson, San Juan, Honolulu, Huancayo and Watheroo, *J. Geophys. Res.*, **56,** 177 (1951); V. C. A. Ferraro and H. W. Unthank, Sudden commencements and sudden impulses in geomagnetism: their diurnal variation in amplitude, *Geofis. Pura e Appl.*, **20,** 3 (1951).
41. S. E. Forbush and E. H. Vestine, Daytime enhancement of size of sudden commencements and initial phase of magnetic storms at Huancayo, *J. Geophys. Res.*, **60,** 299 (1955).
42. W. E. Francis, M. I. Green, and A. J. Dessler, Hydromagnetic propagation of sudden commencements of magnetic storms, *J. Geophys. Res.*, **64,** 1643 (1959).
43. N. Fukushima, Morphology of magnetic storms, *J. Phys. Soc. Japan*, **17,** Suppl. A-1, 70 (1962).
44. N. Fukushima, Polar magnetic storms and geomagnetic bays, *J. Fac. Sci. Univ. Tokyo*, **8,** Sec. II, Part 5 (1953).
45. V. B. Gerard, The propagation of world-wide sudden commencements of magnetic storms, *J. Geophys. Res.*, **64,** 593 (1959); V. L. Williams, The simultaneity of sudden commencements of magnetic storms, *J. Geophys. Res.*, **65,** 85 (1960); M. Yamamoto and H. Maeda, The simultaneity of geomagnetic sudden impulses, *J. Atmos. Terr. Phys.*, **20,** 212 (1961); S. Matsushita, On the simultaneity of geomagnetic sudden commencements and sudden impulses, *J. Geophys. Res.*, **67,** 3579 (1962).
46. T. Gold, Magnetic storms, *Space Sci. Rev.*, **1,** 100 (1962).
47. E. W. Greenstadt, Magnetic storms in interplanetary space as observed by Pioneer V, *Nature*, **191,** 329 (1961).
48. L. Harang, The mean field of disturbance of polar geomagnetic storms, *Terr. Mag. Atmos. Elec.*, **51,** 353 (1946).
49. M. Hasegawa, Provisional report of the statistical study on the diurnal variations of terrestrial magnetism in the north polar regions, *Trans. Washington Meeting IATME-IUGG*, 311 (1940).
50. M. Hasegawa, On the position of the focus of the geomagnetic *Sq* current system, *J. Geophys. Res.*, **65,** 1437 (1960).
51. J. P. Heppner, N. F. Ness, T. L. Skillman, and C. S. Scearce, Magnetic field measurements with the Explorer 10 satellite, *J. Phys. Soc. Japan*, **17,** Suppl. A-II, 546 (1962); Explorer 10 magnetic field measurements, *J. Geophys. Res.*, **68,** 1 (1963).
52. C. O. Hines, Geomagnetism and the ionosphere, *Proc. Int. Conf. The Ionosphere*, 103 (Inst. Phys. and Phys. Soc., London, 1963).
53. C. O. Hines and L. R. O. Storey, Time constants in the geomagnetic storm effect, *J. Geophys. Res.*, **63,** 671 (1958); E. N. Parker, Inadequacy of ring-current theory for the main phase of a geomagnetic storm, *J. Geophys. Res.*, **63,** 683

(1958); C. O. Hines and E. N. Parker, Statement of differences regarding the ring-current effect, *J. Geophys. Res.*, **63,** 691 (1958).

54. E. R. Hope, Spiral patterning of solar corpuscular precipitation, *Nature,* **177,** 571 (1956); Low-latitude and high-latitude geomagnetic agitation, *J. Geophys. Res.*, **66,** 747 (1961).
55. E. O. Hulburt and H. B. Maris, A theory of aurora and magnetic storms, *Phys. Rev.*, **36,** 1560 (1930).
56. International Symposium on Equatorial Aeronomy, *J. Geophys. Res.*, **68,** 2359 (1963).
57. J. A. Jacobs and T. Obayashi, Average electric current-systems for the sudden commencement of magnetic storms, *Geofis. Pura e Appl.*, **34,** 21 (1956); T. Obayashi and J. A. Jacobs, Sudden commencement of magnetic storms and atmospheric dynamo action, *J. Geophys. Res.*, **62,** 589 (1957).
58. J. A. Jacobs and T. Watanabe, The equatorial enhancement of sudden commencements of geomagnetic storms, *J. Atmos. Terr. Phys.*, **25,** 267 (1963).
59. J. W. Kern, A note on the generation of the main-phase ring current of a geomagnetic storm, *J. Geophys. Res.*, **67,** 3737 (1962).
60. J. W. Kern, Solar stream distortion of the geomagnetic field and polar electrojets, *J. Geophys. Res.*, **66,** 1290 (1961); A charge separation mechanism for the production of polar auroras and electrojets, *J. Geophys. Res.*, **67,** 2649 (1962); Acceleration of charged particles by hydromagnetic shock waves, *RAND Memo. RM-3527-NASA* (1963).
61. J. A. Lawrie, V. B. Gerard, and P. J. Gill, Magnetic effects resulting from the Johnston Island high altitude nuclear explosions, *N. Z. J. Geol. Geophys.*, **4,** 109 (1961).
62. A. G. McNish, Terrestrial magnetic and ionospheric effect associated with bright chromospheric eruptions, *Terr. Mag. Atmos. Elec.*, **42,** 109 (1937).
63. A. G. McNish, Geomagnetic effects of high-altitude nuclear explosions, *J. Geophys. Res.*, **64,** 2253 (1959).
64. H. Maeda, K. Sakurai, U. Ondoh, and M. Yamamoto, Solar-terrestrial relationships during the IGY and IGC, *J. Phys. Soc. Japan*, **17,** Suppl. A-1, 45 (1962); A study of solar-terrestrial relationships during the IGY and IGC, *Ann. Géophys.*, **18,** 305 (1962).
65. H. Maeda, A. J. Shirgaokar, M. Yasuhara, and S. Matsushita, On the geomagnetic effect of the Starfish high-altitude nuclear explosion, *J. Geophys. Res.*, **69,** 917 (1964).
66. H. Maeda and M. Yamamoto, A note on daytime enhancement of the amplitude of geomagnetic-storm sudden commencements in the equatorial region, *J. Geophys. Res.*, **65,** 2538 (1960).
67. S. Matsushita, Ionospheric variations associated with geomagnetic disturbances, *J. Geomag. Geoelect.*, **5,** 109 (1953).
68. S. Matsushita, On sudden commencements of magnetic storms at high latitudes, *J. Geophys. Res.*, **62,** 162 (1957).
69. S. Matsushita, On artificial geomagnetic and ionospheric storms associated with high-altitude explosions, *J. Geophys. Res.*, **64,** 1149 (1959).
70. S. Matsushita, Studies on sudden commencements of geomagnetic storms using IGY data from United States stations, *J. Geophys. Res.*, **65,** 1423 (1960).
71. S. Matsushita, Seasonal and day-to-day changes of the central position of the *Sq* overhead current system, *J. Geophys. Res.*, **65,** 3835 (1960).
72. S. Matsushita, Interrelations of sporadic *E* and ionospheric currents, *Ionospheric Sporadic-E*, E. K. Smith and S. Matsushita (eds.), 344 (Pergamon Press, 1962).
73. S. Matsushita, Lunar variations of geomagnetic fields, *Geomagnetica, Lisboa,* 209 (1962); Lunar tides in the ionosphere, *Handbuch der Physik,* **49A** (in press).
74. S. Matsushita, On geomagnetic sudden commencements, sudden impulses, and storm durations, *J. Geophys. Res.*, **67,** 3753 (1962).
75. P.-N. Mayaud, Activité magnétique dans les régions polaires, *Terre Adélie 1951–1952, Magnétisme Terrestre* (Expéditions Polaires Françaises, Paris, 1955).
76. F. Molina and O. Battelli, Variazione stagionale del sistema di correnti *Sq*, *Annali di Geofisica,* **14,** 443 (1961).

77. T. Nagata, The solar-flare type variation in geomagnetic field and the integrated electrical conductivity of the ionosphere, "I," *Rept. Ionos. Res. Japan*, **4**, 155 (1950); T. Nagata and T. Suzuki, "II," *Rept. Ionos. Res. Japan*, **4**, 201 (1950); T. Nagata and M. Tazima, "III," *Rept. Ionos. Res. Japan*, **5**, 113 (1951); T. Nagata, "IV," *Rept. Ionos. Res. Japan*, **5**, 123 (1951); T. Nagata, Solar flare effect on geomagnetic field, *J. Geophys. Res.*, **57**, 1 (1952).
78. T. Nagata, Distribution of SC* of magnetic storms, *Rept. Ionos. Res. Japan*, **6**, 13 (1952); T. Nagata and S. Abe, Notes on the distribution of SC* in high latitudes, *Rept. Ionos. Res. Japan*, **9**, 39 (1955).
79. T. Nagata, Polar magnetic storms, especially in the southern polar region, *J. Phys. Soc. Japan*, **17**, Suppl. A-I, 157 (1962).
80. T. Nagata and N. Fukushima, Constitution of polar magnetic storms, *Rept. Ionos. Res. Japan*, **6**, 85 (1952).
81. T. Nagata and S. Kokubun, Polar magnetic storms, with special reference to relation between geomagnetic disturbances in the northern and southern auroral zone, *Rept. Ionos. Space Res. Japan*, **14**, 273 (1960); T. Nagata, S. Kokubun, and N. Fukushima, Similarity and simultaneity of magnetic disturbance in the northern and southern hemispheres, *J. Phys. Soc. Japan*, **17**, Suppl. A-I, 35 (1962).
82. H. W. Newton, Sudden commencements in the Greenwich magnetic records (1879–1944) and related sunspot data, *Mon. Not. Roy. Astron. Soc., Geophys. Suppl.*, **5**, 159 (1948).
83. A. P. Nikolsky, Diurnal variation of the magnetic disturbance at the geomagnetic pole in the Antarctic, *Geomag. i Aeronomiya*, translated in *Geomag. and Aeronomy*, AGU, **1**, 688 (1961).
84. A. P. Nikolsky, Geographic distribution of magnetic disturbance in the circum-polar region of the Arctic, *Dok. Akad. Nauk*, **109**, 939 (1956; translated by E. R. Hope, DRB Canada, T232R, 1957); The geographic distribution of magnetic activity in the Antarctic, *Dok. Akad. Nauk*, **112**, 846 (1957; translated by E. R. Hope, DRB Canada, T244R, 1957); The world-wide distribution of magneto-ionospheric disturbance and aurora, *Dok. Akad. Nauk*, **115**, 84 (1957; translated by E. R. Hope, DRB Canada, T266R, 1957); *Magnetic and Ionospheric Disturbances*, Yu. D. Kalinin (ed.), Academy of Sciences USSR (1959; translated *NASA-TT*, *F-49*, 1961); On the geographical distribution of the areas of the solar corpuscular impingements in the Arctic, *J. Phys. Soc. Japan*, **17**, Suppl. A-I, 187 (1962).
85. A. Nishida and J. A. Jacobs, World-wide changes in the geomagnetic field, *J. Geophys. Res.*, **67**, 525 (1962).
86. T. Obayashi, Geomagnetic storms and the earth's outer atmosphere, *Rept. Ionos. Res. Japan*, **12**, 301 (1958); Geomagnetic storms and ionospheric disturbances, *J. Radio Res. Lab. Japan*, **6**, 375 (1959).
87. T. Obayashi, Upper atmospheric disturbances due to high altitude nuclear explosions, *Planet. Space Sci.*, **10**, 47 (1963).
88. T. Oguti, Notes on the morphology of SC, *Rept. Ionos. Res. Japan*, **10**, 81 (1956).
89. J. Ortner, B. Hultqvist, R. R. Brown, T. R. Hartz, O. Holt, B. Landmark, J. L. Hook, and H. Leinbach, Cosmic noise absorption accompanying geomagnetic storm sudden commencements, *J. Geophys. Res.*, **67**, 4169 (1962).
90. E. N. Parker, On the geomagnetic storm effect, *J. Geophys. Res.*, **61**, 625 (1956).
91. E. N. Parker, Dynamics of the geomagnetic storm, *Space Sci. Rev.*, **1**, 62 (1962).
92. J. H. Piddington, A theory of polar geomagnetic storms, *Geophys. J.*, **3**, 314 (1960).
93. J. H. Piddington, The transmission of geomagnetic disturbances through the atmosphere and interplanetary space, *Geophys. J.*, **2**, 173 (1959); Geomagnetic storm theory, *J. Geophys. Res.*, **65**, 93 (1960).
94. J. H. Piddington, A hydromagnetic theory of geomagnetic storms, *Geophys. J.*, **7**, 183 (1962); A hydromagnetic theory of geomagnetic storms and auroras, *Planet. Space Sci.*, **9**, 947 (1962); Connexions between geomagnetic and auroral activity and trapped ions, *Planet. Space Sci.*, **11**, 451 (1963).
95. A. T. Price, Magnetic disturbance and the earth's main field, *J. Geophys. Res.*, **67**, 4309 (1962).

96. T. Rikitake, Dynamo theoretical studies on solar daily disturbances variations, *Rept. Ions. Res. Japan*, **2,** 57 (1948).
97. T. Rikitake, Electromagnetic induction in a hemispherical ocean by *Sq*, *J. Geomag. Geoelect.* **11,** 65 (1960); *Sq* and ocean, *J. Geophys. Res.*, **66,** 3245 (1961); Supplement to paper: *Sq* and ocean, *J. Geophys. Res.*, **67,** 2588 (1962).
98. T. Rikitake and T. Yukutake, A theory of s.f.e. current systems, *J. Atmos. Terr. Phys.*, **24,** 93 (1962).
99. C. S. Robertson, Magnetic bays at Macquarie Island, *Austral. J. Phys.*, **13,** 470 (1960).
100. T. Sato, Sudden commencements of geomagnetic storms in high latitudes, *Rept. Ionos. Space Res. Japan*, **15,** 215 (1961); Structures of sudden commencements of geomagnetic storms and giant pulsations in high latitudes, *Rept. Ions. Space Res. Japan*, **16,** 295 (1962).
101. H. C. Silsbee and E. H. Vestine, Geomagnetic bays, their frequency and current systems, *Terr. Mag. Atmos. Elec.*, **47,** 195 (1942).
102. S. F. Singer, A new model of magnetic storms and aurorae, *Trans. Amer. Geophys. Un.*, **38,** 175 (1957).
103. E. J. Smith, Theoretical and experimental aspects of ring currents, *Space Science*, D. P. LeGalley (ed.), 316 (Wiley, 1963); A comparison of Explorer VI and Explorer X magnetometer data, *J. Geophys. Res.*, **67,** 2045 (1962).
104. E. J. Smith, P. J. Coleman, D. L. Judge, and C. P. Sonett, Characteristics of the extraterrestrial current system: Explorer VI and Pioneer V, *J. Geophys. Res.*, **65,** 1858 (1960).
105. C. P. Sonett, E. J. Smith, D. L. Judge, and P. J. Coleman, Jr., Current systems in the vestigial geomagnetic field: Explorer VI, *Phys. Rev. Letters*, **4,** 161 (1960).
106. C. Störmer, *The Polar Aurora* (Clarendon Press, 1955).
107. M. Sugiura, A note on harmonic analysis of geophysical data with special reference to the analysis of geomagnetic storms, *J. Geophys. Res.*, **65,** 2721 (1960).
108. M. Sugiura, The solar diurnal variation in the amplitude of sudden commencements of magnetic storms at the geomagnetic equator, *J. Geophys. Res.*, **58,** 558 (1953).
109. M. Sugiura and S. Chapman, A study of the morphology of magnetic storms, *Geophys. Inst., Univ. Alaska, Final Report* (*AFCRC-TR-56-450*, 1956), (*AFCRC-TR-57-295*, 1957), (*AFCRC-TR-58-266*, 1958); The average morphology of geomagnetic storms with sudden commencement, *Abhandl. Akad. Wiss. Göttingen, Math.-Phys. Kl., Sonderheft 4* (1960).
110. D. van Sabben, Ionospheric current systems of ten IGY-solar flare effects, *J. Atmos. Terr. Phys.*, **22,** 32 (1961).
111. J. Veldkamp and D. van Sabben, On the current system of solar-flare effects, *J. Atmos. Terr. Phys.*, **18,** 192 (1960).
112. E. H. Vestine, The disturbance field of magnetic storms, *Trans. Washington Meeting IATME-IUGG*, 360 (1940); E. H. Vestine, L. Laporte, I. Lange, and W. E. Scott, The geomagnetic field, its description and analysis, *Carnegie Inst. Wash. Publ. 580* (1947).
113. E. H. Vestine, Note on low-level geomagnetic ring-current effects, *RAND Memo., RM-3674-NASA* (1963).
114. E. H. Vestine and S. Chapman, The electric current system of geomagnetic disturbances, *Terr. Mag. Atmos. Elec.*, **43,** 351 (1948).
115. E. H. Vestine and J. W. Kern, Cause of the preliminary reverse impulse of storms, *J. Geophys. Res.*, **67,** 2181 (1962).
116. H. Volland and J. Taubenheim, On the ionospheric current system of the geomagnetic solar flare effect (s.f.e.), *J. Atmos. Terr. Phys.*, **12,** 258 (1958).
117. C. S. Warwick and M. W. Haurwitz, A study of solar activity associated with polar-cap absorption, *J. Geophys. Res.*, **67,** 1317 (1962).
118. E. M. Wescott, Magnetic variations at conjugate points, *J. Geophys. Res.*, **66,** 1789 (1961); E. M. Wescott and K. B. Mather, Diurnal effects in magnetic conjugacy at very high latitude, *Nature*, **197,** 1259 (1963).

119. M. V. Wilkes, The solar and luni-solar harmonic components of geomagnetic variations at San Fernando, *J. Atmos. Terr. Phys.*, **24,** 73 (1962).
120. C. R. Wilson and M. Sugiura, Hydromagnetic interpretation of sudden commencements of magnetic storms, *J. Geophys. Res.*, **66,** 4097 (1961); Discussion, *J. Geophys. Res.*, **68,** 3314 (1963); C. R. Wilson, Hydromagnetic interpretation of sudden commencements of geomagnetic storms, *Geophys. Inst., Univ. of Alaska, Sci. Rept. AFCRL-63-605* (1963).
121. J. R. Winckler, Balloon study of high altitude radiations during the International Geophysical Year, *J. Geophys. Res.*, **65,** 1331 (1960).
122. M. Yasuhara and H. Maeda, Geomagnetic crochet of 15 November 1960, *J. Atmos. Terr. Phys.*, **21,** 289 (1961).
123. I. A. Zhulin, The magnetohydrodynamic theory of geomagnetic storms: a review, *Geomag. i Aeronomiya*, translated in *Geomag. and Aeronomy*, AGU, **1,** 123 (1961).

CHAPTER 19

RAPID VARIATIONS OF THE ELECTROMAGNETIC FIELD OF THE EARTH

V. A. Troitskaya

Introduction

The study of the rapid variations of the electromagnetic field of the earth was one of the major tasks of the IGY research program. Interest in these small and rapid pulsations of the field had greatly increased before the beginning of the IGY, for experimental and theoretical research during 1953–1956 revealed that short-period pulsations can be used as one of the sensitive indirect criteria characterizing the changes in the state of the upper atmosphere.

Storey found that the space between the outer boundary of the magnetic field and the ionosphere is filled with plasma: thus, any disturbances reaching the outer limit of that space can be transmitted to the earth in the form of hydromagnetic waves. Major theoretical concepts about the character of magnetohydrodynamic waves in the exosphere were presented by Dungey and further developed by Japanese, Canadian, and other researchers (Kato, Jacobs, Watanabe, Tamao, Obayashi, etc.).

By the beginning of the IGY the necessity of international coordination of experimental studies of pulsations was strongly felt. Though the first references to rapid pulsations of the field are found in the works of the second half of the nineteenth century (B. Stuart), the systematic research in this range of the electromagnetic field spectrum of the earth actually did not begin before the IGY. The analysis of papers on pulsations published before the IGY was difficult due to the absence of a unified classification scheme. Before the beginning of the IGY, Committee 10 of the International Association of Geomagnetism and Aeronomy dedicated much of its activity to the international classification of pulsations, and a scheme was adopted in March, 1957 at Copenhagen. The new classification covered the spectral range from 10 to 150 seconds. Within this range the two main types of pulsations were introduced: pulsation trains and continuous pulsations. Classifications which dealt with the short-period changes of the field with greater duration remained unaltered (sfe, b, sse, Si, etc.).

IGY studies revealed the deficiency of this classification, led to the widening of the spectral range for pulsations, and introduced new principles for the basis of this classification. The spectral range of pulsations now studied on an international scale covers the range of periods from several tenths of seconds to values of 7–10 minutes. As to small periods, this range is expressed by the pulsations of the pearl type (PP) (or by hydromagnetic emissions) and, as to long-period pulsations, by the so called long-period continuous pulsations (Lpc), actually representing the widened class of giant pulsations. (Because of the new classification of pulsations adopted at Berkeley, 1963, PP = Pc 1 and Lpc = Pc 5.)

The IGY and following years constituted the period of active development of the studies of short-period pulsations. For the first time, these rapid changes of the field were systematically investigated in both polar regions. For the first time, too, pulsations with periods less than 15 sec were studied with detail on a world-wide scale. And, for the first time, due to extremely favorable conditions for complex geophysical research during the IGY, analysis was made of the connections between different types of pulsations and the whole complex of electromagnetic phenomena in the upper atmosphere.

During these studies the unknown correlations between these phenomena were revealed: the results of the studies of pulsations became interesting and important not only to geomagneticians but to a large group of scientists studying the whole complex of the upper atmosphere and solar-terrestrial problems. Moreover, the data about pulsations became essential for practical work concerned with crustal structure and prospecting for minerals.

According to modern concepts, the nature and mechanism of excitation of pulsations are caused by magnetohydrodynamic waves which can be generated on the boundary of the magnetosphere and within it (for instance, during injection of plasma). These waves propagate in the magnetosphere along (toroidal pulsations) and across (poloidal pulsations) the lines of force. They travel at these velocities to the lower limit of the ionosphere. There they are transformed into electromagnetic waves which are observed on the surface as pulsations of the magnetic field and earth currents.

Theoretical research has shown that, for magnetohydrodynamic waves, the magnetosphere is a layered inhomogeneous medium, whose coefficient of refraction changes with altitude (Dessler, Fidger, Francis, and Karplus). At about 2000–3000 km altitude the vertical gradient of the refraction index reaches a large value, in other words the coefficient undergoes a sudden change. The existence of this layer causes the formation of cavities that divide the magnetosphere into two parts. In each of them, under the influence of a disturbing agent, resonance oscillations can originate, manifested in pulsations observed on the surface. The periods of these pulsations characterize the dimensions of cavities; their intensity and modulation depend on the activity of the primary source and on its structure.

The sunlit ionosphere is practically opaque to the pulsations with periods less than 1 sec. Probably, therefore, we experimentally observe the cutoff for the pulsation spectrum at frequencies of 3–5 cps. Besides this type of excitation, short-period pulsations can originate during injection of plasma into the ionosphere. In this case the region of the generation of pulsations is located in the immediate vicinity of the earth, and the properties of these pulsations are to a great extent connected with the properties and structure of plasma clouds. Moreover, there exists a possibility that part of the observed pulsations is caused by oscillating bunches of charged particles trapped in the magnetosphere along the lines of forces (Tepley, Wentworth, Gendrin). Their influence can be exercised either directly or by excitation of resonance pulsations in the lower part of the exosphere (Jacobs, Watanabe).

Finally, it is also probable that the highest frequency part of the short-period pulsation spectrum (0.5–5 cps) is caused by processes similar to those which are held responsible for the generation of the VLF emissions ($\sim$5 kc/sec). In this case the frequency of the short-period pulsations is directly connected to the intensity of the magnetic field in the region where the generation of pulsations takes place. It should be noted that the pulsation frequencies 0.5–5 cps correspond to the cyclotron frequency of protons for a 33–330 gamma magnetic field, and the ratio of frequencies typical for VLF emissions (about 5 kc/sec) to the preceding frequency (0.5–5 cps) has the order of the ratio of the mass of the proton to the mass of the electron. For the dipole field the indicated values (33–330 gammas) correspond to distances of 5–11 earth radii. Within these distances, according to modern concepts, the outer boundary of the magnetosphere is located on the sunlit side of the earth.

Basing on theoretical models we can suppose that all the regular pulsations of the electromagnetic field of the earth covering the whole spectral range of pulsations may be caused by resonance excitation in the cavities of the magnetosphere. The whole family of continuous pulsations (Section 1) can be considered as such pulsations, including perhaps the pulsations of the pearl type (Section 2). At the same time we should bear in mind that the frequency characteristics of the system (the outer boundary of the magnetosphere — the lower limit of the ionosphere) is changing and is considerably influenced by many factors (pressure of solar streams which squeeze the magnetosphere and determine its dimensions, distribution of plasma within the magnetosphere, presence of additional sources of disturbances in the magnetosphere, etc.). Therefore, even with one type of input disturbance of the system, on the earth's surface various phenomena can be observed connected with the changes of transient characteristics of the system. It should be directly acknowledged, therefore, that the pulsations are probably the only indicator of the state of the magnetosphere in the sense mentioned above.

All the phenomena in the magnetosphere occurring during the injection of the plasma into the magnetosphere, and also the events which appear during possible dumping of the radiation belts, find expression in a family of pulsations — namely, in the family of genetically connected disturbances of the electromagnetic field of the earth (Section 2). In this case the origin of certain members of this family (SIP) are attributed to the electric currents appearing during these injections in the lower ionosphere (Campbell).

In connection with the researches planned for the International Quiet Sun Year, when corpuscular streams from the disturbed regions of the sun are more easily separated from streams which actually represent solar wind, studies of the regular pulsations, attributed to the resonance oscillations within the magnetosphere, acquire special importance. On the other hand the results of the study during the IQSY of the characteristics of genetically connected family of disturbances and pulsations can, evidently, be applied for the building of concepts about the fine structure of the corpuscular streams in the period of the maximum and minimum solar activity.

The present review has two sections. The first deals with the results of the studies of continuous pulsations, pulsation trains, and application of rapid variations for the solution of geological problems. The second section gives results of researches on pearls (PP), rapid irregular pulsations (SIP), and of the fine structure of magnetic storms.

Section 1

1.1. Continuous Pulsations (Pc)

Due to results of recent years, continuous pulsations may be divided into three main groups [all designations of pulsations are in the old terminology]:

1. Pc (or Pc-1) [42], regular continuous pulsations with periods 10–40 sec. Their properties were intensively investigated during the IGY and IGC.
2. Pc^0 or Pc-II [42, 51], continuous pulsations with periods 60–(100–150) sec.
3. Lpc or Pc-III [8, 20, 42], continuous pulsations with periods from 2 to 7 minutes.

This threefold division of Pc is based on investigations in a wide spectral range, conducted in different regions and by different investigators [1, 4,

5, 7, 9, 11–14, 16, 17, 19, 27, 28, 33, 35, 43, 52, 53]. Each group differs in geographical distribution, and consequently in latitude dependence of their periods, in relation to magnetic field activity, and in occurrences during the solar cycle. Their nature is also revealed in type of polarization and the character of its changes, which are linked to hydromagnetic waves that are thought to be responsible for the observed pulsations. The differences are also shown in other properties described below.

The common feature of all three groups is the continuity of their regimen, and an important property of all is the absence of the fine structure and of any connection with phenomena in the high atmosphere, which may be due to injections of charged particles during Pc-occurrence. Diurnal variation with maximum around noon is observed for the first and second groups of Pc. Although Lpc were recently introduced as an independent type, a number of their properties show that they are the same pulsations which have long been known as giant pulsations (Pg). In the past, standard magnetograms used for studying of Pg revealed only the most intensive pulsations; nowadays sensitive installations widely distributed in polar regions record pulsations with significantly smaller amplitude. The several cases of Pg reported on standard magnetograms were traced on the records of high sensitivity stations as a burst of amplitude of a long Lpc-series. Diurnal variations of Lpc and Pg are similar.

A feature of all Pc relates to their excitation possibility in different combinations: (1) All three groups may be excited simultaneously at the stations located at different latitudes. (2) Pulsations of different types and periods may occur simultaneously at high- and middle-latitude stations. (3) Pulsations of one type and period may occur simultaneously at different stations.

Because the latitude dependence of amplitude differs for different Pc-groups, observation of all types is possible only on highly sensitive records. These peculiarities of Pc-excitation and lack of coordinate equipment at different stations probably account for present discrepancies in opinions on latitude dependence of Pc-periods.

For the studying of Pc-period diurnal changes, it is necessary to take into account the dependence of Pc-properties on magnetic activity (namely, the dependence of their period on Kp). It seems that in these investigations it is more correct to measure periods for hours of the day with the same value of Kp, even for different days, than to determine their periods without account of Kp. The discrepancies now in the literature are perhaps due to the above dependence.

All data gathered for the Pc-family indicate that they are the effect of hydromagnetic poloidal (Pc-1) and toroidal (Pc-II and Pc-III) waves, which are generated by the interactions of solar corpuscular streams with the magnetosphere [15, 24, 29, 34, 55, 56]. The periods of observed pulsations characterize the dimensions of the magnetosphere and of its resonant cavities. The dependence of their periods on latitude for toroidal oscillations determines the distance in the equatorial plane at which the interaction of corpuscular stream with magnetosphere takes place. The intensity of Pc-amplitude and its modulation may be used for judging the degree of irregularity of the corpuscular stream structure. Thus, the properties of Pc and their variations probably represent a unique criterion of magnetospheric structure and of the composition of corpuscular streams and their

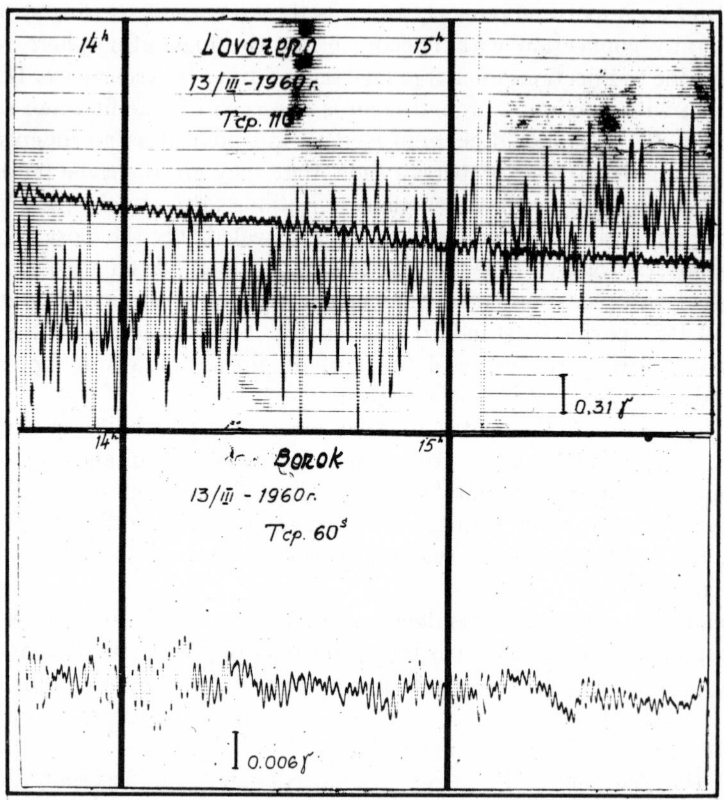

FIG. 1. Simultaneous Pc of different periods at Lovozero (T, 110 sec) and Borok (T, 60 sec).

changes. It is worth stressing that some of these changes cannot be traced in any macroscopic, slow-field variations.

a. General Morphological Characteristics. The records of Pc appear many times in papers already mentioned. Distinct examples of simultaneous records of Lpc and Pc^0 having different periods are more rare: hence Figure 1, which shows such a case for Borok ($T \sim 60$ sec) and Lovozero ($T \sim 110$ sec). Most thoroughly studied are the classical Pc-1. They present the usual picture for the state of the electromagnetic field of the earth in the middle latitudes, often occupying around 80 per cent of all recording hours at high-sensitivity installations [53]. There exist days, however, when their duration is significantly less and even cases when they are completely absent. For instance, the world-wide net of stations showed that Pc-1 were absent 5 days in 1958 and 4 days in 1959. Seven of these days were magnetically quiet, 2 of them were weakly disturbed days. So the days without Pc during the IGY-IGC amounted to 1 per cent [53].

Analysis of Pc-1 polarization shows that its form and direction change with time. Besides, Pc-polarization has a diurnal variation. When Pc-amplitudes are rising, the rotation of the vector is mainly counterclockwise, and vice versa. The study of Lpc- and Pc^0-polarization [42] showed that three-dimensional hodographs of corresponding vectors for both types of pulsations are normal to the field line in high latitudes and become parallel to it in middle and low latitudes.

The elliptical polarization of Lpc was obtained at magnetically conjugate points [36, 46]. The state of knowledge about the polarization of Pc in general is not satisfactory. To investigate this question, systematic studies of simultaneous pulsations at adequately sensitive stations homogeneously distributed in longitude and latitude are necessary; and geological structure of the region of observation must also be taken into account. Contrary to Pc-1, the geographical distribution of Pc^0 and Lpc has its characteristic peculiarities. It seems that the frequency of Pc^0 has its maximum near 50° geomagnetic latitude and in the auroral zone. The frequency of Lpc undoubtedly has its maximum in the auroral zone. As already noted, the excitation character of all Pc-groups may change from case to case, but in low latitudes the most characteristic group of Pc is Pc-1. Some papers mentioned earlier indicate regularities of Pc-amplitude changes with latitude; most of these refer to Pc-1 and Lpc. The common feature of these distributions for all groups of Pc is the tendency of Pc-amplitude to rise with latitude. But for some cases of Pc-1 a significantly smoother character of amplitude dependence on latitude than for other forms of Pc was discovered. This dependence is illustrated in Figure 2. However, the regularities of Pc amplitudes distributions (on θ and λ) have not been investigated sufficiently and must be studied using records of a small net of reasonably distributed stations. An interesting feature of Pc-regimen was discovered [8]: with diminishing of latitude the property of continuity gradually shifts to pulsations of smaller periods.

There exist no widely adopted opinions about the borders in the spectral distribution of all three groups of Pc. For instance in [42] the border of the group Pc^0 from the side of long periods is given equal to 150 sec. On the other hand, the results of systematic observations in Borok having approximately the same latitude (52°) are 90–100 sec. The records of Borok station show also that pulsations with periods 50 sec are significantly

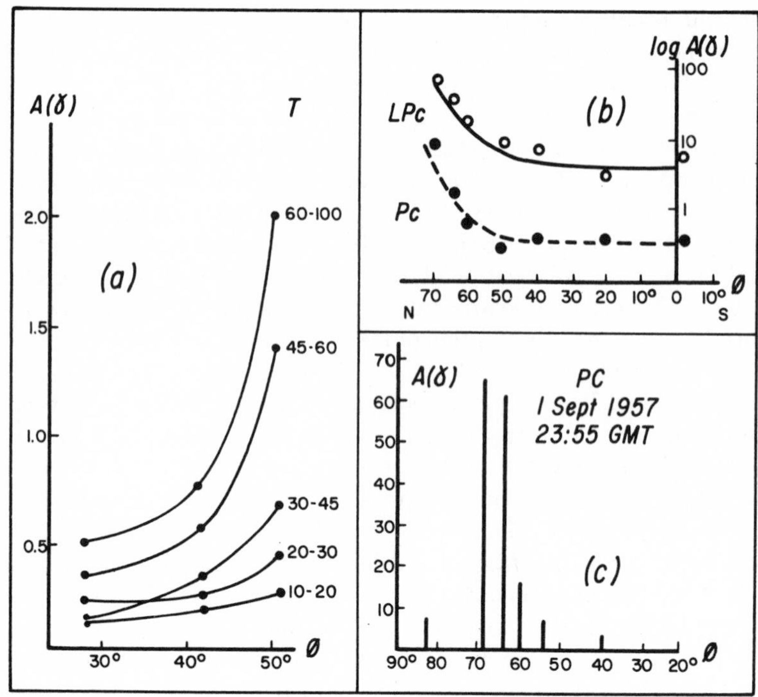

FIG. 2. Dependence of Pc-amplitude on latitude. (*a*) Results of Ellis for simultaneous Pc at 3 stations in Australia. (*b*) Results of Jacobs and Sinno for Pc and Lpc on 12 February 1958. (*c*) Results of Y. Kato.

more rare than pulsations of all other periods. Therefore it is natural to adopt for the border of Pc-1 the value 40–50 sec.

Figure 3 shows the distribution of all three groups of Pc on periods [42]. Of course, these data need checking on much more numerous experimental material.

An interesting morphological feature of Pc-1 is the frequently observed simultaneous modulation of their amplitude over great longitude and latitude intervals (Borok–Kerguelen, Borok–Petropavlovsk, etc.). This modulation is expressed most strongly in simultaneous beginnings and endings of Pc at the stations, for which a shift in the beginning of Pc-series due to local time control is usually observed. Cases were found when sudden endings of Pc-series took place at all Soviet stations simultaneously.

Pc are observed simultaneously at the magnetically conjugate stations. Detailed comparison of Pc-1 features at conjugate points was impossible because of the slow time scale of the records. The comparison was thus done for hourly intervals. The records at Mirny and Heiss showed that the best correlation is observed for equinoxes. In the months of solstices Pc-1 are much more intensive in the sunlit hemisphere. In the other hemi-

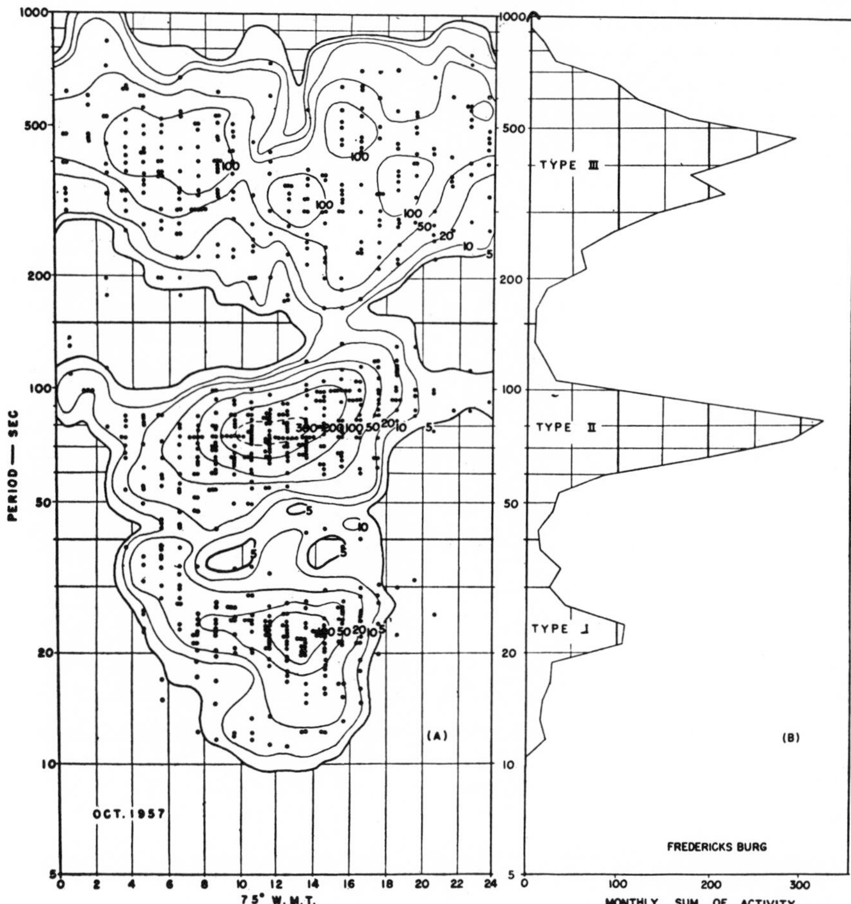

FIG. 3. Distribution of Pc in periods (results of T. Saito).

sphere at the same time, these pulsations show either weak traces or cannot be detected at all [51].

b. Diurnal Variations of Pc. Pc-1 and Pc^0 have similar diurnal variations with maximum near noon. Maxima of Pc-1 show significant scattering between the hours 8–10, 10–12, and 12–14 LMT. (Diurnal variation of Pc^0 has not yet been thoroughly investigated, but undoubtedly scattering also takes place.) In [42] it is stressed that observed scattering of Pc diurnal variation maxima repeat the characteristic features of f_0F2. Pc diurnal variation in the equatorial regions has quite specific peculiarities [18, 41]; it has three maxima with main maximum at evening (18–20^h), a peculiarity which does not yet have any explanation.

Diurnal variation of Lpc has two maxima at some stations, one in the early morning and the other in the afternoon. Depending on the geographical site of the station, sometimes only the first and sometimes only the second maximum is observed [36].

c. Pc Seasonal Variation. Pc-1 seasonal variation was studied in many regions. All these investigations yield the general opinion that the minimum of Pc falls in winter months. The maximum of the variation is shifted, year to year, from summer to equinoxes (and vice versa) or is presented by a curve with a flat maximum during summer and both equinoxes [1, 4, 5, 7–9, 11–14, 16, 17, 19, 20, 27, 28, 33, 35, 42, 43, 51–53]. Differences in equipment and different methods of data processing at each station probably account for different shapes of Pc-1 seasonal variations obtained even

TABLE 1

Pc-1 SEASONAL VARIATIONS FOR DIFFERENT STATIONS (SAITO [42])

Station	Geomagnetic Latitude	Type of the Seasonal Variation for Different Years*							
		53	54	55	56	57	58	59	60
Oasis	−77°					|	S	|	
Alaska	+65°				|	M	|		
Lovozero	+63°					|	S |		
Fredericksburg	+50°						| E	|	
California	+44°						| M	|	E |
Dusheti	+38°					|	S		|
Ashkhabad	+30°				|	S		|	
Onagava	+28°	|	E	| M	|		S		|

* S — summer maximum; E — equinox maximum; M — mixed maximum.

for the same year. The results at Irkutsk [53] over 12 years (1944–1955) show that the most stable maximum occurs at the spring equinox. Most of the Soviet earth current stations show a maximum of Pc-1 seasonal variation in summer for the period of IGY-IGC. Table 1 shows the character of Pc-1 seasonal variation for different stations during the IGY-IGC and adjacent years [42].

It has been suggested [42] that shifting of seasonal maxima is due to *F*-2 control of Pc. A clear seasonal effect was observed in polar regions. Immediately after simultaneous observations of pulsations in the Arctic and the Antarctic were set up, it was discovered that they have inverted seasonal variations. This effect was called polar night effect for Pc-1 [51].

Seasonal variation of Pc^0, as well as other properties of this group, have not yet been thoroughly studied. Preliminary results show that their seasonal variations are either weak or do not even exist. For 1958 [42] the minimal activity for Pc^0 and Pc-III was observed during the autumn equinox.

Published data about seasonal variations of giant pulsations (Pg) show that maxima of their occurrence shift from morning hours in winter to afternoon hours in summer. The period of Pg changes over the solar cycle: it becomes 1.5 times greater during years of maximum solar activity. An interesting feature of Pc seasonal variations is the change of their period. Pc^0- and Lpc-periods are shorter in summer (Pc^0, 40 sec; Lpc, 400 sec) than in winter (Pc^0, 70 sec; Lpc, 450 sec) [42]. There is no generally adopted opinion about the seasonal changes of Pc-1 periods; in [42] it is stated they do not show seasonal variations. Investigations in the Soviet Union showed that Pc-1 periods in summer are about 15–20 sec and in winter 25–30 sec. This question requires special investigations at a number of stations, in which special attention must be given to the state of magnetic activity.

d. 27-Day Recurrence for Pc. The 27-day recurrence is confirmed by many investigations [25, 26, 31, 38, 53]. Above all, this regularity characterizes Pc of shortest periods, i.e., 10–20 sec, which occur mainly during the first phase of the magnetic storms. This property of Pc-1 may be traced even during the complicated conditions at solar activity maximum, but it is completely evident in the years close to solar activity minimum. It is especially evident during the series of recurrent storms in which Pc form one of the main elements of their fine structure. For Pc^0 the 27-day recurrency was not observed; for Lpc this tendency apparently exists.

e. Changes Over the Solar Cycle. Because the Pc-period depends on Kp, the relation between the number of observed cases of Pc and Pc^0 varies with changes of planetary activity. When the activity diminishes, the number of Pc of small periods (Pc-1) becomes less, and the number of Pc with large periods (Pc^0) becomes greater. Pulsations of Pc^0 type dominate in the years close to solar activity minimum. The number of Lpc is also greatest during these years. But the general number of the hours with Pc on the records does not change significantly. An appreciable change is observed for the amplitude of Pc-1, which diminishes by two times (Fig. 4).

f. Pc-Regimen and Magnetic Activity. A clear dependence of Pc-periods on planetary magnetic activity was discovered. There exists a range of Kp-values for which the excitation of all Pc-types may take place. But there also exist some values of Kp for which excitation of some types is practically prohibited. Figure 5 shows that Pc^0 are observed for the smallest values of Kp ($\sim$0–2.5). Most cases of Pc-1 occur in the interval of Kp values 1–3.5, and the number falls sharply for Kp equal to 5 or more. Finally, for very disturbed magnetic fields, only Pc with small periods ($T \sim$ 8–15 sec) are observed.

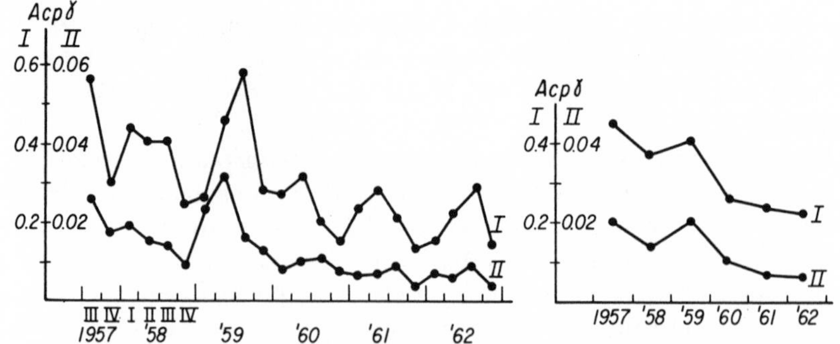

FIG. 4. Amplitude Pc-changes during solar cycle (I, Petropavlovsk; II, Borok; *Z*-component).

Besides this dependence of periods on magnetic activity, Pc-amplitudes rise during disturbed days in contrast to their level on quiet ones.

Both these regularities were traced during the last series of recurrent storms. Figure 5*b* shows how the character of Pc-period (averaged for one day) changes with respect to Kp for one of these storms. A similar picture is also obtained by more detailed comparisons. Figure 5*c* shows the general dependence of Pc-periods on Kp.

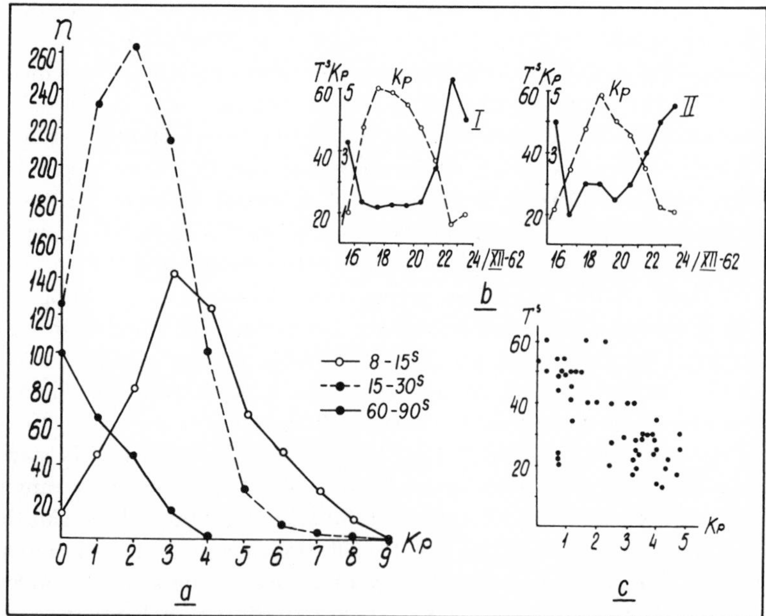

FIG. 5. Pc and magnetic activity. (*a*) Dependence of occurrence frequency of Pc of different periods on Kp (Borok 1957–1962). (*b*) Dependence of Pc periods on Kp for the recurrent storm (I, Borok; II, Petropavlovsk). (*c*) Dependence of Pc periods on Kp for recurrent storms from November, 1962 to May, 1963.

g. Pc and Other Geophysical Phenomena. Changes in Pc associated with changes of the ionospheric layer *F*-2 have been noticed by several authors [1, 42, 53]. The similarity in geographical distribution of diurnal variations of f_0F2 and diurnal Pc variations was noted [42]. But the character of this connection with ionospheric changes requires further study.

Most investigations show no connections of Pc^0 and Lpc with phenomena in the high atmosphere, but the occurrence of Lpc coincident with intensification of long-period X-ray bursts was reported [39]. In [42] a correlation between Pc^0 and Lpc and the degree of whistler dispersion was traced. The results of investigation of all three groups of Pc are given in detail in [42]. Tables 2 and 3 from this paper summarize Pc-properties.

h. Theoretical Consideration. Modern conceptions of the Pc excitation mechanism are based on the assumption that the interaction between the corpuscular stream and the magnetosphere is transferred to the lower ionosphere by hydromagnetic waves. When the magnetic energy density of the gas becomes less than its kinetic energy, all hydromagnetic movements are expressed in hydromagnetic waves. Then, any disturbance at the border of the magnetosphere (e.g., pressure caused by a corpuscular stream) is transferred further by hydromagnetic waves which can propagate along and across the magnetic lines [15, 24, 29, 34, 55, 56]. In their general form the equations of the hydromagnetic waves in the magnetosphere have not yet been solved. To simplify the problem, toroidal and po-

TABLE 2

Relationship Between Solar Events and Pc-1 Micropulsations (Saito [42])

Phenomena	Effects on Pc-1
Solar cycle	11-year cycle
Solar rotation	27-day recurrence
Unipolar region (Calcium plages, 1000 Mc/sec emission)	Regular Pc
Disturbances	Irregular Pc
Extended solar magnetic field	Shifting of the diurnal variation maximum on hours before noon
Position of internal border of cavities	Period
f_0F2	Seasonal Pc-variations with maxima at equinoxes; shifting of the diurnal variation maximum on morning or evening hours
E-layer	Blunting of latitudinal dependence of amplitude
Earth's rotation	Diurnal variation both in activity and period
Seasonal variation in inclination of dipole axis to the sun	Seasonal variation of the periods

TABLE 3

RELATIONSHIP BETWEEN SOLAR EVENTS AND Pc^0 AND Lpc MICROPULSATIONS (SAITO [42])

Phenomena	Effects of Pc^0 and Lpc
Solar rotation	27-day recurrence
Extended solar magnetic field	Shifting of hour of shortest period to morning side
Distortion of field-line by solar wind; non-axial symmetric distribution of ion density	Diurnal variation of the periods
Distortion of field-line by ring current	Separation of Pc^0 from Lpc
Ionosphere layer	Blunting of latitudinal dependence of amplitude
Earth's rotation	Diurnal variation both in activity and period
Seasonal variation in inclination of dipole axis to the sun	Seasonal variation of the periods

loidal oscillations are usually treated separately. Continuous pulsations of Lpc-type are usually described as toroidal oscillations propagating on field lines.

The periods of hydromagnetic waves propagating along field lines depend on their length and on particle density in the magnetosphere. Using the results of observations on the latitude dependence of periods and adopting some law of the ion density distribution in the magnetosphere, we can select a calculated theoretical curve of period dependence on geomagnetic latitude which is most suitable for the experimental results. Such calculations were conducted for different assumptions about the density distribution in the magnetosphere and for different forms of the magnetosphere [20].

Pc-1 are usually explained as standing oscillations in a cavity between the ionosphere and the layer of maximal Alfvén velocity. These oscillations must be poloidal. Because part of the hydromagnetic wave energy is spent on the generation of electric currents in the ionosphere, the occurrence of Pc-1 in a wide latitude range may be explained by the existence of these current systems [42].

If the magnetic field is presented as a dipole field, then the distribution of Pc^0 and Lpc will not have sharp borders, because the length of magnetic field lines (S) changes gradually. However, between geomagnetic latitude 50° and the auroral zone, a sudden increase of the length of S may take place [45]. If this is really so, then a minimum must exist between the distribution of Pc^0 and Pc-1, dividing these oscillations. This minimum is experimentally observed.

The change of the type of polarization in the frames of one group of pulsations, which is observed at different latitudes (e.g., the transition from elliptical to linear polarization), may probably be explained by the transformation in certain conditions of the poloidal wave into the toroidal one due to the coupling of these oscillations, which is not yet taken into account. If the changes of periods and polarization with latitude are known, it is possible to determine the distance in the equatorial plane at which this transformation of hydromagnetic waves takes place [42]. Therefore observations of pulsation polarization are very important for working out a method to determine the origin of the primary hydromagnetic waves and to fix the regions of the magnetosphere where different types arise.

Recently an attempt was made to solve the question of the dynamics of the magnetosphere from the point of view of its impedance [54]. It was suggested that all variations in the solar wind structure consist of step-shaped impulses. These impulses exercise a stress on the outer border of the magnetosphere, and all signals observed at the earth's surface are the result of oscillations excited by these impulses in the resonant cavities of the magnetosphere. These resonant cavities are due to the existence of the gradient of the Alfvén velocity and of a layer with maximal value of this velocity. The reflecting power of the borders of these cavities, the changes of their relative positions, the additional sources of disturbances inside the magnetosphere — all these properties of magnetosphere may determine the character, periods, and the degree of regularity of the observed pulsations.

For Pc-1 we have to assume a significantly greater value of Q for the resonant cavity during the day than at night because only in this case can one explain continuous resonance oscillations. The modulation of Pc is then explained by the random distribution of irregularities of density and velocity of particles in the corpuscular stream.

The irregular form of Pc often observed during disturbed periods is explained by the penetration of randomly distributed, dense, plasma clouds inside the magnetosphere. If we know the character of the disturbance at the outer boundary of the magnetosphere (which, it seems, may be described as a step function) and know the variations of the field at the earth's surface, this theory suggests that we can obtain the characteristics of the state of the magnetosphere. This point of view, however, supposes that the properties of the magnetosphere itself remain unchanged.

1.2. Pulsation Trains (Pt)

Pulsation trains consist of series of damped oscillations lasting usually less than one hour. Maximum of the spectral distribution of Pt falls at 50–90 sec. Such pulsations have been investigated for many years [22, 30] and were called bps [3, 47], i.e., pulsations connected with bays, night pulsations [44], etc., yet many questions connected with their morphology and theory remain unanswered.

a. Morphological Characteristics. Pt may occur against a quiet background as one or several series of oscillations, or they may coincide with the beginning of a bay. Pt are observed in all regions, and sometimes the longitudinal interval in which they can be traced exceeds 100 degrees. The most characteristic feature of Pt (distinguishing them, for instance, from Pc^0) is their short duration, and the existence of the microstructure consisting of short irregular variations (SIP), which sometimes are followed by PP (Section 2.2). Surface distribution [52] of Pt is different for Pt occurring before a negative bay in the auroral zone (Pt) and for Pt occurring either before a positive bay or against a quiet field (Pt^+). Maximum of the amplitude is observed in the auroral zone for the first case and near geomagnetic latitude 50° for the second (Fig. 6). (The same regularity is found for Pc^0.) In this connection note that Pt always begin with augmenting of the north component; i.e., ΔH or dH/dt is always positive.

The diurnal variation of Pt polarization ellipses is peculiar. The latter oscillate regularly about the N-S direction. Before midnight their azimuth lies N-E, after midnight, N-W. The rotation of the vectors is counterclockwise before and clockwise after midnight [42, 5]. Neither the number of Pt nor their period is latitude-dependent. It seems that their period depends on local time.

b. Diurnal Variation. Diurnal variation of Pt has been confirmed in many investigations. Its maximum falls at the midnight hours. But simi-

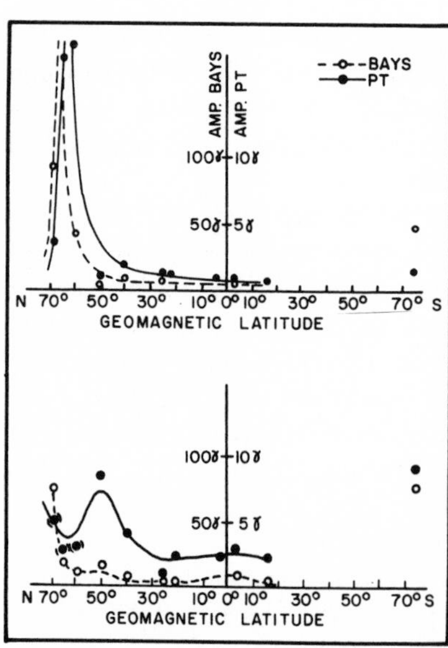

FIG. 6. Amplitude dependence on latitude for Pt^- (upper) and Pt^+ (lower) (after Jacobs and Sinno).

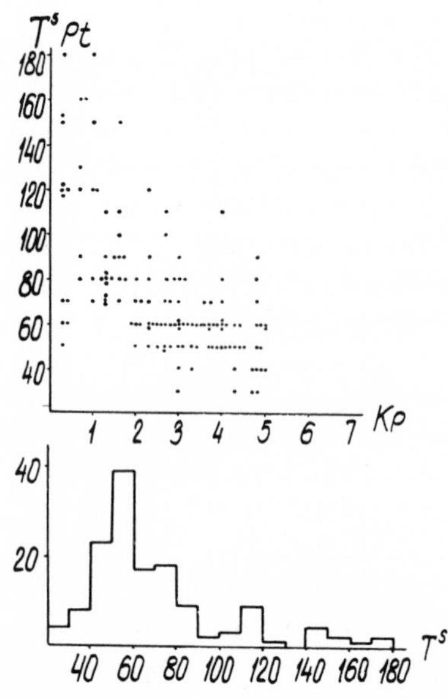

FIG. 7. Dependence of Pt-periods on level of magnetic activity for Borok (November, 1962–May, 1963) for series of recurrent storms (upper). In the lower part of the figure is given the distribution of processed Pt on periods (lower).

larly to Pc, the maxima of diurnal variations at different stations show some longitudinal scattering. The best coincidence of Pt maxima is observed in geomagnetic time (0–2 hr). The maximum of this variation is shifted to earlier hours on disturbed days.

c. Seasonal Variation. Numerous investigations show that the maxima of this variation fall mainly on equinoxes, and sometimes on winter months. In any case, this question is not yet finally solved because some results [53] show absence of any definite seasonal variation. These discrepancies apparently stem from records with great time scale and sensitivity now available and, of course, these records show many more cases of Pt than the standard slow records which were used in early investigations. Undoubtedly the latter showed only the most intensive cases, for which it seems distinct maxima at equinoxes were obtained.

d. Connection with Magnetic Activity. The greatest number of Pt is observed on moderately disturbed days. For instance, for the period 1958–1959 at Irkutsk [53] 25 per cent were observed on quiet days, 20 per cent on disturbed days, and 55 per cent on moderately disturbed days. Pt periods depend on Kp, and diminish with increasing magnetic activity (Figs. 7 and 8).

e. Variations with the Solar Cycle. The number of observed Pt changes inversely with solar activity [30, 47, 53]. A characteristic feature, during the cycle, is the increase of Pt occurring on a background of a quiet field, and of sequences of Pt-series. Another important morphological property is the change of their character in polar regions, where they became similar to Pt in middle latitudes in the phase of solar activity minimum. The amplitude of Pt, as well as of Pc, gradually diminishes in the course of the solar cycle (Fig. 9).

f. Geographical Distribution. In spite of their strong dependence on

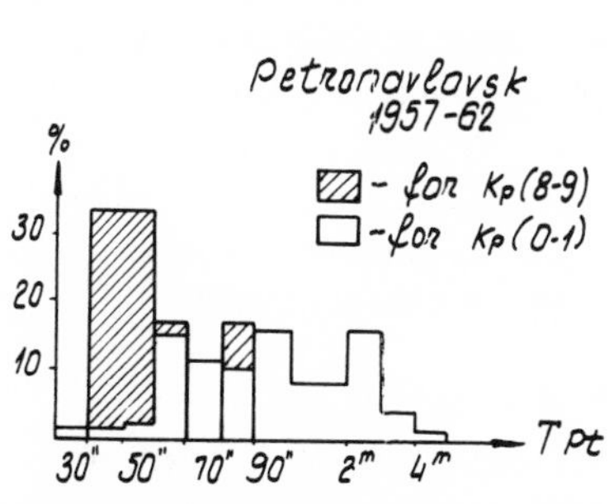

FIG. 8. Pt-distribution on periods for Kp = 0–1 and Kp = 8–9 [Petropavlovsk (Z-component) 1957–1962].

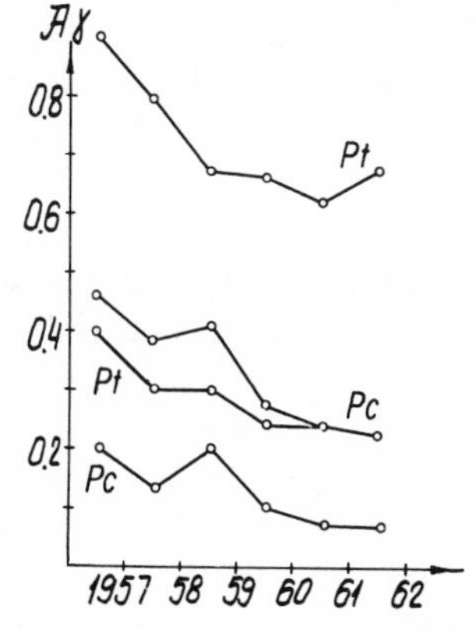

FIG. 9. Pt and Pc amplitude changes during the solar cycle (Borok, lower two curves; Petropavlovsk, upper two).

local time, many Pt are observed over a broad longitudinal interval ($\lambda \sim 100°$).

Magnetic conjugacy for Pt and for pulsations constituting their fine structure (Section 2.3) have been studied. These investigations showed that almost simultaneous excitation of Pt and SIP is observed in most cases for magnetically conjugate regions. The precision which can be obtained in determining the time of the first oscillation of SIP series is limited by the insufficient front steepness of the first movement on rapid run records. This property of conjugacy (or at least the symmetry of the intensity of the SIP or Pt bursts) can be sometimes violated, even during as short an interval as one hour: i.e., after occurrence of Pt at both conjugate stations with almost equal amplitude, the next Pt may be observed with significantly different amplitude at the two stations [23, 51].

g. Theoretical Considerations. In recent theories the origin of Pt (and of Pc) is attributed to hydromagnetic waves originating in the high atmosphere [20]. The practically constant period of Pt for different latitudes, their predominant occurrence at night, and their close connection with phenomena in the high atmosphere are evidence for the mechanism of their excitation by hydromagnetic processes developing in the equatorial plane of the night magnetosphere. They may be due to interactions between the magnetic field and the radial electric field in the equatorial plane [37], while Pt-excitation has also been discussed in connection with their correlation with VLF emissions [48].

From an experimental point of view Pt may be identified with poloidal hydromagnetic waves developing in the inner cavity of the magnetosphere. Their great period is then explained by greater dimensions of this cavity on the night side [54]. Pt-excitation is also attributed to injections of dense plasma clouds into the atmosphere. The observed particles may be either particles of solar plasma or particles trapped in the magnetosphere and drifting around the earth. In the last case, their injection into atmosphere is more probable at the night side due to possible transition of the particles on shorter field lines. But the properties of Pt-excitation in magnetically conjugate regions show that the mechanism of solar particle trapping, drift, and periodical injection is apparently less probable than direct injection into the atmosphere of rapid charged particles trapped into dense clouds of solar plasma, and released near the earth.

1.3. Application to Crustal and Upper Mantle Studies

Theoretical and experimental studies show [2, 6, 10, 32, 40, 48, 50] that quantitative relations between earth currents and magnetic field variations, observed at the earth's surface, can be used for determining its structure (more precisely its geoelectric section) down to very great depths. The comparatively high frequency part of the spectrum (from 10 to 0.01 cps and less) finds application in studying the upper layers of the earth's crust and in solving structural problems of prospecting (mainly oil and gas). Thus these variations are used in investigations down to 5–8 km. Variations with periods of the order of minutes and more are useful down to tens of kilometers, permitting studies of the crust and upper mantle. Besides their geophysical interest, these investigations also have practical value in prospecting. Finally, disturbances of the magnetic field lasting an hour and more and diurnal variations permit the study of conductivity distribution down to depths of a hundred kilometers.

These methods, based on the investigations of the earth's electromagnetic field, are now actively developed in many countries. Significant results have been obtained in working out the theoretical background of these methods. Corresponding programs for electronic computers are compiled, and calculations of amplitude and phase characteristics of complex, apparent electric resistivity are carried out for three layers [49] and in some cases of four and five layer models of the crust. These theoretical curves are used not only for interpreting experimental results but also for studying the resolving power of the magnetotelluric method in different geological and geophysical regions. The experience obtained in different countries shows that this method may be of great importance in studies of the earth's interior. But further development of this method requires overcoming some serious difficulties.

The theoretical outlines of magnetotelluric method are based nowadays on the well-known Tichonov–Cagniard model (plane wave falling normally on the horizontal layered half-space). Simultaneous observations of the five components of the electromagnetic field (Ex, Ey, Hx, Hy, Hz) in a wide spectral range show a very complicated field structure. These observations show, as already mentioned (J. R. Wait, A. T. Price, and others), that the adopted model is in many respects too primitive. Therefore, in practical work it is important to choose those cases which are sufficiently close to the adopted model [(Ex; 0; 0; Hy, 0) and (0; Ey; 0; Hx; 0; 0)]. A very important question is the investigation of the influence of the sphericity and azimuthal inhomogeneity of the earth. Even in the model of the half-space, the effects of the horizontal inhomogeneities, of the inclined layers and of tectonic formations of great scale are not yet known. The interpretation of the experimental results is often based on the materials obtained over large territories, in different geological regions, etc. Current data are not sufficient to say whether the magnetotelluric method allows tracing of the borders which are revealed by seismic methods (e.g. and above all, the Mohorovicic level). Undoubtedly, there is a probability that methods using electromagnetic fields may give other surfaces of discontinuities, which are not yet detected by other methods. In this connection, the importance of conductivity distribution investigations inside the earth is quite clear.

Studies of models may be of great significance both for studying the sources of field variations and the influence of geological structure. At the same time these investigations will be useful for working out of more precise methods of quantitative interpretation.

Section 2

2.1. Rapid Irregular Pulsations (SIP)

Intensive investigations of rapid variations of magnetic field, together with the analysis of slow disturbances of electromagnetic field, made it possible to reveal oscillations which are most typical for the disturbed periods. These oscillations have irregular form, and their most characteristic periods are from 6 to 10 sec. Their connection with auroral intensity variations, bursts of X-rays, and absorption of cosmic noise has been established.

They have different names in different papers: rapid irregular oscillations [105], noise bursts [112], *C*-type oscillations [58], Spt [91], oscillations bursts [85], and etc. [In the new classification they have the symbol Pi 1 (pulsations irregular — 1).] These oscillations form, as a rule, the microstructure of slow electromagnetic field disturbances, observed at the main phase of magnetic storms. They are a part of microstructure of isolated bays and Pt. Moreover, they may be observed in the absence of any visible slow magnetic disturbances in the auroral zone [105]. The connection of these oscillations to definite slow magnetic field disturbances, and the peculiarities and sequence of their development, define a family of genetically connected disturbances of the electromagnetic field (Fig. 10).

The scheme implies independent development, in the electromagnetic field, of oscillations to the right of the family mentioned. Thus, PP may be observed on the records without analogs in slower variations; on the other hand they may be the final phase of the microstructure of a very intensive

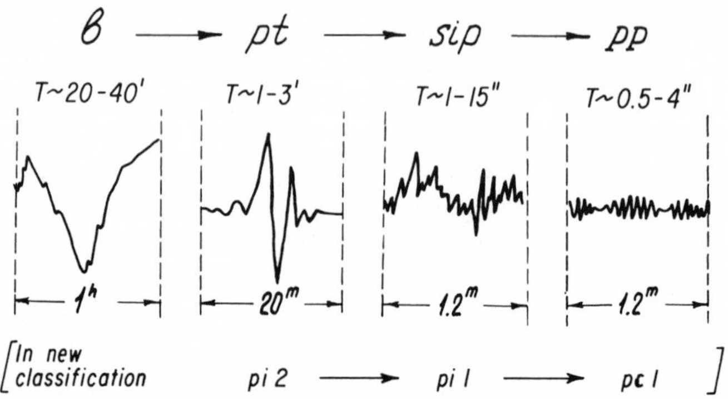

Fig. 10. Family of genetically connected disturbances (IPDP, with $T \sim 10''$–$1''$, not sketched).

bay during a magnetic storm. (For example, the second phase of the interval of pulsations diminishing on periods (IPDP) for the storms on 11 February 1958 and 15 July 1959 [107].) In years of solar activity decay, PP of the same or slightly varying period are often observed as an element of fine structure of separate Pt.

SIP may also appear on a background of almost quiet field, even in auroral zones. While these two kinds of micropulsations are sometimes recorded simultaneously with slow disturbances, and sometimes as independent field disturbances, Pt-type pulsations are always accompanied by disturbances of either SIP or of both SIP + PP. The most complete development of the disturbed field microstructure is expressed in the IPDP. These facts show that the occurrence of all these disturbances is a complex phenomenon, which is due to the same primary source. These phenomena differ from case to case only by their intensity, and degree of development of each element of the family.

a. General Morphological Characteristics. SIP have irregular form; their periods, as a rule, are less than 15 sec (mainly 6–10 sec); their amplitudes have maximum values in auroral zones. SIP intensity decreases sharply with latitude. For example, their intensity averages 10 times greater in College (Alaska) than in California [65]. However, on very sensitive records (10^{-3}–$10^{-2}\gamma$/mm) they may be traced at middle-latitude stations. Their spectrum differs greatly from the spectrum of PP which shows few frequency maxima corresponding to the main periods of observed PP [111].

b. Diurnal Variation. SIP are observed mainly early in the morning and late at night. According to [105] there are two maxima in SIP distribution. The first is connected with SIP which form the fine structure of the slow disturbances; the second reflects SIP excitation mainly on the background of comparatively quiet field (Fig. 11). Maxima of diurnal variations for SIP probably show spiral or elliptical regularities of geographic distribution according to [84].

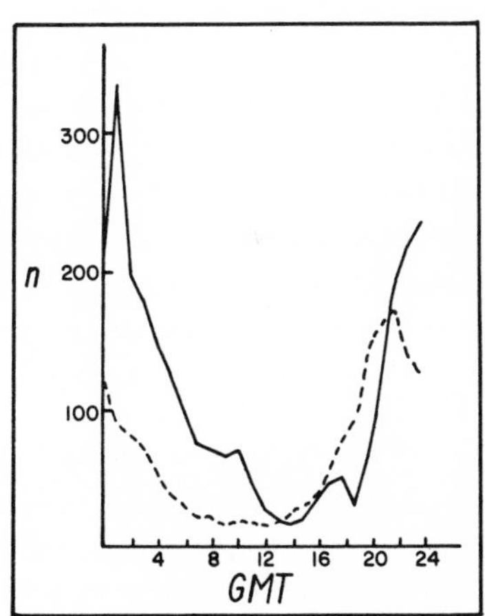

FIG. 11. Diurnal variation of SIP (Pi 1) at Lovozero (1957–1959); disturbed periods (broken line), quiet periods (solid line).

c. Seasonal Variation. No distinct results have been obtained for SIP seasonal variations (or for Pt). SIP connected mainly with disturbances show seasonal variation with equinox maxima. However, if all cases are included, SIP seasonal distribution is variable from year to year, having only a tendency to the equinox maxima [65].

d. Variation during the Solar Cycle. The most characteristic variation during the solar cycle is the decrease in SIP duration from years of maximum solar activity to years of decay. For example, analysis of the storms of 1957–1959 and of 1962–1963 shows a decrease in duration by 8–10 times in the period close to minimum activity. Besides, SIP duration shows a distinct dependence on Kp-index: it increases with increasing Kp [108].

e. Connection with High Atmosphere Phenomena. SIP are closely connected to auroral intensity variations [64, 65, 84, 85, 104, 105]. A comparative investigation of auroral intensity variations in the line $\lambda = 3914$ Å and of the short period oscillations was conducted for the years 1959–1960 in [66]. Detailed coincidences of every consecutive intensity variation in these two phenomena were often observed. The best correspondence between oscillations of $\lambda = 3914$ Å intensity and short-period oscillations is discovered for early morning hours. The absence of oscillations in aurora intensity during rather high micropulsations activity level was observed before midnight. An empirical correlation between micropulsations amplitude in gamma (M) and auroral pulsations (C), $\lambda = 3914$ Å (in kilorayleigh), gives:

$$M^2 = 0.29C^2 + 1.23C$$

In two cases of red aurora (unaccompanied by a simultaneous intensity increase of the green line), pulsations were not observed in either auroral intensity or in the magnetic field. On the other hand red aurora during very severe storms in low latitudes are accompanied by intensive SIP [107].

Pulsating auroral forms are seldom observed at the northern border of the auroral zone. Therefore it is possible to assume that SIP amplitudes would also decrease in the polar cap direction. Thus SIP are often recorded at College but do not occur so often at Barrow [85]. In the Soviet Union SIP are most intensive at Lovozero station (southern border of aurora zone) where they are revealed not only at the high sensitive rapid-run records (time scale, 30 mm/min), but at much less sensitive records (time scale, 90 mm/hr). It is difficult to determine periods of SIP according to these records, but it is easy to measure their amplitude: at Lovozero station their amplitude reaches units of gammas in the magnetic field (Z-component) and 50–100 mv/km in earth currents.

Study of the connection between aurora and micropulsations at this station showed that correlation for all the auroral forms is equal to 86 per cent, and the maximum correlation percentage is discovered for the rayed aurora [105]. A quiet (as regards SIP) electromagnetic field always corresponded to an undisturbed state of a night sky. Earth currents flow along the direction of auroral arcs [86]: no case was observed when arcs and earth currents were not parallel. Similar relationships were recorded at Tixie [96]. A connection between micropulsations having periods from 5–30 sec with the absorption of cosmic noise was observed [64]; for night hours, a correlation coefficient of 0.8 was obtained. However, for PCA absorption, some decrease of micropulsation activity was observed. The comparison of SIP activity with the critical frequency variation of F-2 layer shows that during the days of great SIP activity some decrease in f_0F-2 takes place. This connection is very distinctly seen during the main phase of strong magnetic storms at the moments of IPDP-occurrence, which always begins with the intensive SIP and coincides, as a rule, with a sharp decrease of critical frequency F-2 or with a complete absorption [107].

One of the most interesting results of recent years was the discovery of the connection between SIP-excitation and X-ray bursts [57, 61]. Not only are comparable oscillation periods observed, but the beginnings of these two phenomena practically coincide (sometimes with a one-minute delay). The interval of periods for which this correlation is observed is very wide. However, the main period of 7–9 sec in X-ray bursts coincides with the most frequent, characteristic SIP-period [57, 61, 64, 86]. For simultaneous micropulsations and auroral intensity variations in lines $\lambda = 3914$ Å and $\lambda = 5577$ Å, the height of emissions and the energy, which is necessary for the observed ionization, was determined [64, 86]. The height coincided with the E-layer; the energy, determined according to micropulsations, was much less than that which is necessary for the observed phenomena. This fact was a base for an idea that both phenomena are due to the same cause namely, to fluctuations in the primary corpuscular stream structure.

f. State of Theoretical Ideas. In working out a mechanism to explain the nature of short irregular pulsations, it is necessary to have in mind that these pulsations are genetically connected with a number of other field disturbances. Therefore, a theory should first of all explain this connection.

Morphological features of SIP and their connection with aurora and X-ray bursts confirm the idea that SIP-excitation is caused by the injections of charged particles (probably of electrons with energy of tens of kev) into the high atmosphere. These injections result in auroral excitation, X-ray occurrence, and in development of current systems in the ionosphere, which are responsible for the observed bays. Simultaneously with SIP-development, train pulsations are recorded in the magnetic field ($T \sim$ 60–90 sec). The primary reason for all these disturbances is probably the interaction of the corpuscular stream with the magnetic field in the equatorial plane at a great distance from the earth. It is thought that due to this interaction the pitch angles of trapped particles are redistributed and symmetrical dumping of particles into the ionosphere of both polar caps takes place [66]. These ideas are confirmed by the simultaneity of auroral excitation and their development at conjugate points [71]. They are also confirmed by the excitation character of the family of connected disturbances (Fig. 10). The conjugacy property of bay disturbances is well known [94, 103]; for SIP it is expressed even better because their almost simultaneous excitation is confirmed up to several seconds. The precision of determining simultaneity of their onset depends only on the front steepness of SIP first movement. Conjugacy also marks PP; however, simultaneity and similarity of their series development is not, as a rule, distinctly shown [106]. Pulsation periods are more stable for PP series than for SIP series; this, together with some difference in their development in magnetoconjugate regions, can be regarded as a confirmation of their origin as an effect of oscillations of particle bunches along lines of force. Therefore, it is necessary to bear in mind that the processes, developing in the equatorial plane under the influence of corpuscular streams, lead on the one hand to symmetrical dumping of charged particles into both hemispheres and on the other hand to the development of pulsating currents in the lower ionosphere (E-layer). These pulsations are observed as SIPS. When PP are observed simultaneously with SIP, two kinds of phenomena may take place: (*a*) resonant pulsations are selectively amplified [88] in a cavity formed by the ionosphere and the Alfvén velocity maximum level; or (*b*) conditions should develop which allow the formation of particle bunches, oscillating along the lines of force [112]. The last two processes may be responsible for PP-origin. In both cases it must be considered that hydromagnetic waves propagating in the ionosphere carry the effect of disturbance into the lower ionosphere.

2.2. Pearl-Type Pulsations (PP)

Pearl-type pulsations are the regular sinusoidal oscillations with periods mainly from 0.3 to 4 sec. These pulsations may occur in the form of separate bursts (individual pearls), gradually developing into a series of pulsations lasting from tens of minutes to tens of hours. They may also occur in the form of characteristic consecutive groups of pulsations with sharply varying frequency (intervals IPDP, solar whistles) [72, 104].

The first data about, apparently, these pulsations were mentioned in 1936 [81, 104]. Observations for a long period of time at a single rapid-run station were obtained at Alma-Ata (Middle Asia) from 1952 and in California from 1955 [58]. But systematic study of PP on a net of stations, with an extensive longitudinal and latitudinal range, began with the IGY. Detailed investigations of PP by American, Canadian, and French scientists [75–77, 82, 83, 87, 92, 112] showed that the character of PP-development, and of the variation of adjacent groups of pulsations, has some interesting regularities, which make it possible to suggest the existence and movement of bunches of charged particles in the earth's magnetosphere.

a. General Morphological Features. Pulsations of PP-type are observed in all regions, but diurnal distribution, periods and amplitudes, fine structure inside the series, and other properties vary in different zones. One of the most interesting properties of the fine structure is the short, repetitive bursts of PP, inside of which frequency increases. The product of the main frequency of PP and the interval between bursts is approximately constant:

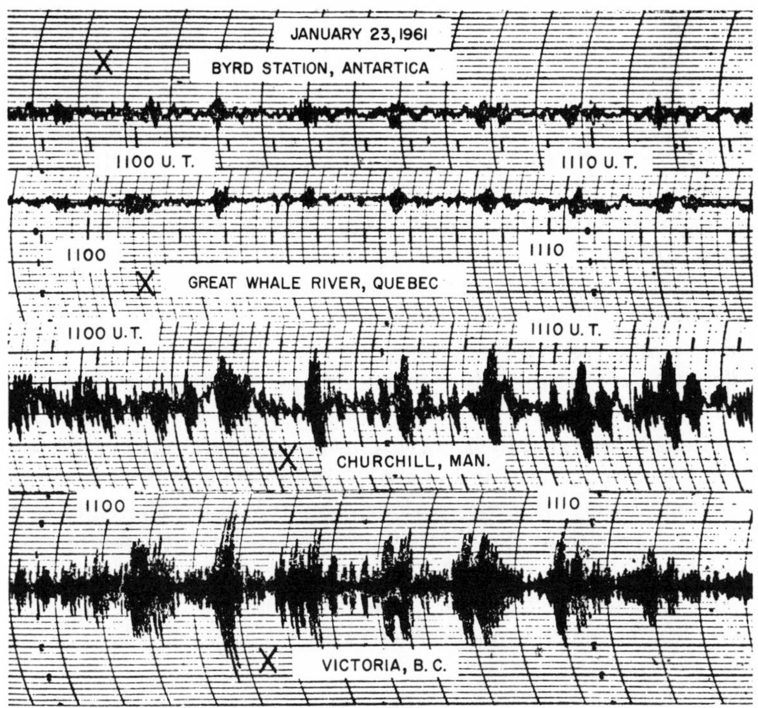

FIG. 12. Simultaneous record of PP-series from four stations (from Y. E. Lokken *et al.* [92], Section II).

about 140^s. According to [76, 82, 83, 112], PP-periods in most cases are 1–2 sec and the spacing between bursts is 1–5 min, with the most characteristic spacing about 2 min (Fig. 12).

PP have been recorded at middle latitudes, in auroral zones, inside of them (Barentzburg, Heiss, Mirny) and at drifting ice-floe stations [82]. Little has been recorded on PP in the equatorial zone. Data for the equatorial zone are mentioned in some work in Peru [87]; here single PP-bursts of about 1-min duration and main frequency of about 2 sec were observed. These bursts were not traced in higher latitudes. A summary of PP-recording in equatorial zone by Tepley was obtained after the manuscript was completed: it seems that PP are also common in equatorial regions.

Amplitudes of PP in middle latitudes average 10^{-2}–10^{-3} gamma for the magnetic field and 0.1–1 mv/km for earth currents. In auroral zones and polar caps their amplitude reaches 0.1 gamma and tens of mv/km; the most intensive PP recorded had amplitudes of several gamma in magnetic field and about 70 mv/km in earth current at high latitudes [85]; but typical amplitudes (in gamma) are, for example: Kerguelen, ~0.25; French antarctic station, ~0.48; Novolazarevskaja (Antarctic), ~0.5–1.

For middle latitudes the mean PP-amplitudes are the following: Chambon-la-Forêt, $\sim 0.4 \times 10^{-3}$ gamma; Budkov (Czechoslovakia) $\sim 10^{-3}$ gamma; a number of sites in middle latitudes of the Soviet Union, from 0.01 to 0.06 gamma. Earth current amplitudes are (in mv/km) as follows: Borok, 0.1–0.2; Irkutsk, 0.5–0.6; Lovozero, 15.6; Mirny, 4.0; Heiss, 2.0; Alma–Ata, 1.95; Petropavlovsk, 0.64.

Analysis of PP-periods in middle- and high-latitude stations shows that pulsations with periods less than 2 sec are most common at all the stations [104], but pulsations having greater periods are obviously more characteristic of high-latitude stations. (Variations in apparatus complicate comparisons and make results uncertain.)

Distribution of PP according to periods for middle-latitude and polar stations is given in Figure 13. The sharp decrease in observed PP with small periods (confirmed by observations at many stations) raises a question about spectrum cutoff and about critical frequency of PP for different geomagnetic latitudes. PP with periods about 0.3 sec for all middle-latitude stations are practically the limit cases. Pulsations with shorter periods occurred only a few times for the whole period of observation.

Table 4 gives some data on maximum frequency of PP at different latitudes. Similar data were obtained at Soviet stations. These data were

TABLE 4

MAXIMUM FREQUENCIES (TEPLEY AND WENTWORTH [112])

Station	Geomagnetic Latitude	Maximum Frequency of PP Observed at the Station	Maximum Calculated Frequency cps	Maximum Calculated Frequency cps 500 miles to the South
Palo Alto	45°	5	5.25	7.8
Victoria	55°	3	3.18	4.6
Uppsala	60°	3	2.46	3.6
Reykjavik	70°	2	1.34	2.1

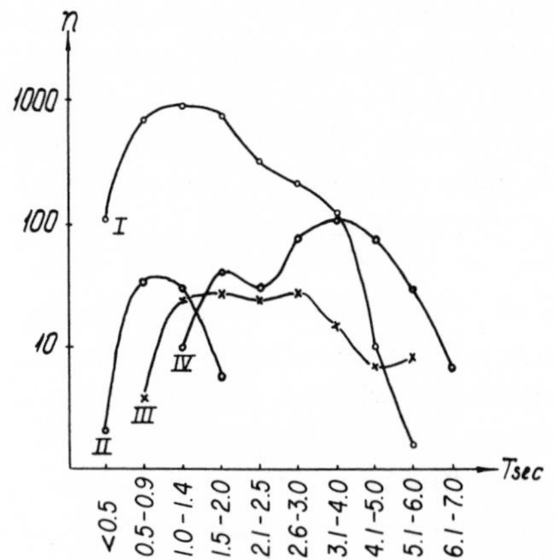

Fig. 13. Distribution of PP according to periods. I, Borok (1957–1962); II, Alushta; III, Mirny; IV, Heiss (1958–1961). The data for cases II, III, IV are given for different intervals of time.

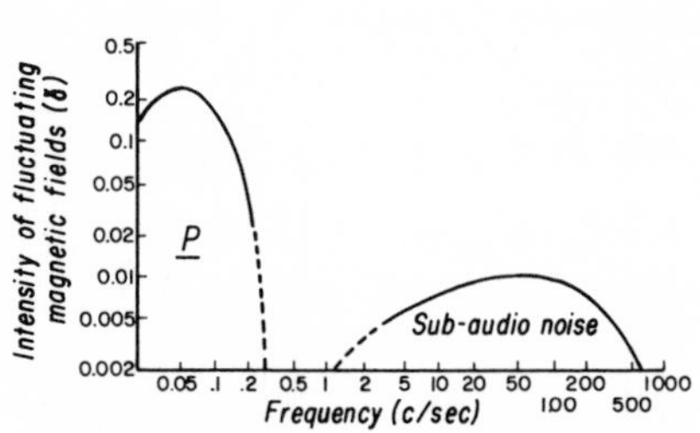

Fig. 14. The character of micropulsations spectral cutoff and of a low-frequency part of atmospherics (from W. Campbell).

assumed as a basis in the determination of the boundary between micropulsations of the earth's field and the main low-frequency resonant-oscillations in the earth-ionosphere cavity (7–8 cps, 14 cps, 25 cps). The first diagram in which this property is reflected is given in Figure 14.

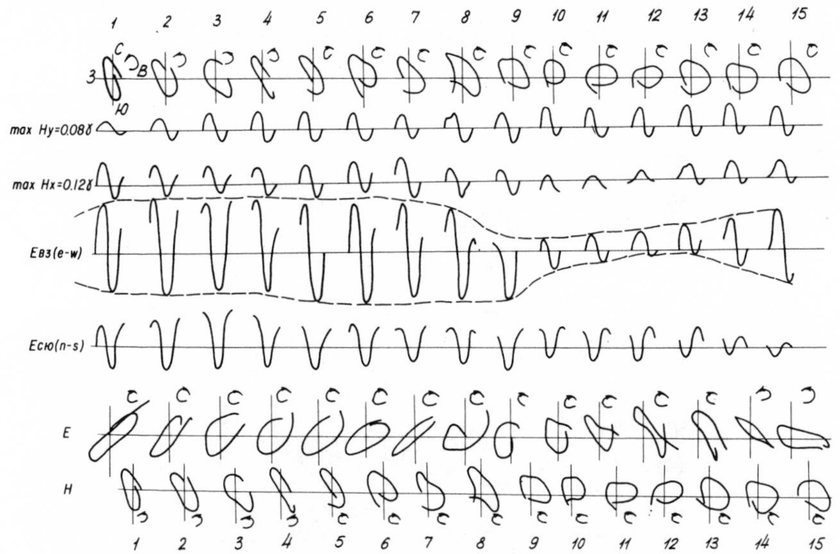

Fig. 15. Character of individual oscillations of pulsations PP = Pc 1 and the corresponding ellipses of polarization.

PP polarization is complicated and variable. Figure 15 presents 15 pulsations from a long series (period ~2.5 sec) at Lovozero with polarization ellipses at the bottom. A curve characterizing the variation of ellipse eccentricities is given in Figure 16. The eccentricity shows that PP-polarization may change sharply (10–20 sec) from elliptical to circular. Different polarization was observed in field expeditions for the same direction of the main polarization axis, showing that change of polarization depends on the source of PP, and not only on local geoelectric structure.

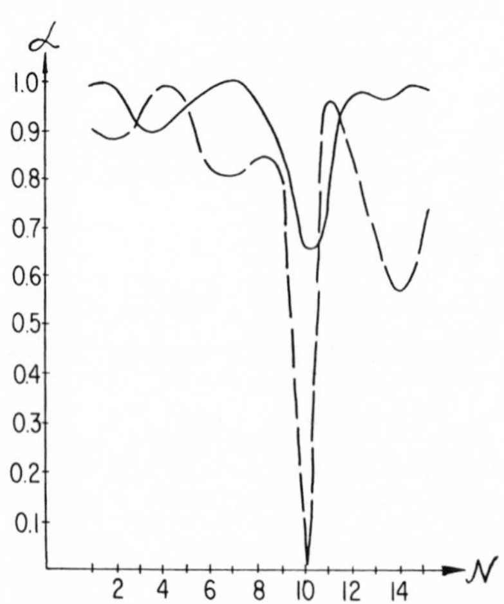

FIG. 16. Changes in the eccentricity (α) of ellipses of polarization for interval of Fig. 15; magnetic field (solid line), earth currents (broken line). N = the number of oscillations presented in Figure 15.

b. Diurnal Variation. Variation in middle latitudes has a distinct maximum after midnight and in early morning hours. There is a characteristic shift of hours with a maximum number of PP during the year. PP-variation for two middle-latitude stations is given in Figure 17.

Even early investigations of PP in polar regions showed that diurnal variation for high latitudes differs from middle-latitude stations. The maximum moves toward the day hours or is smoothed away [93] and then

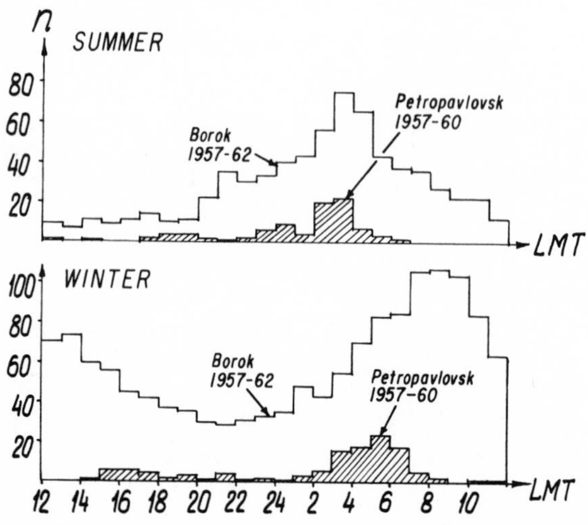

FIG. 17. Diurnal variations of PP for two middle-latitude stations (n, number of cases).

the excitation probability is distributed more or less uniformly (with some indistinct maximums) during 24 hours. Diurnal variation of PP for several stations situated in and outside the auroral zone is given in Figure 18. Similar variation occurs in Alaska [85].

c. Seasonal Variation. Seasonal influence on PP-excitation shifts the curve of PP diurnal variation. Analysis of data from Borok (the most complete data for PP) shows that maximum PP-occurrence falls mainly in autumn and winter months. However, it is difficult to give a final characteristic of these changes because of the sharp changes in PP-occurrence during the solar cycle. For example, maximum amplitudes, longest duration of series, and maximum PP-occurrence were observed in autumn and winter

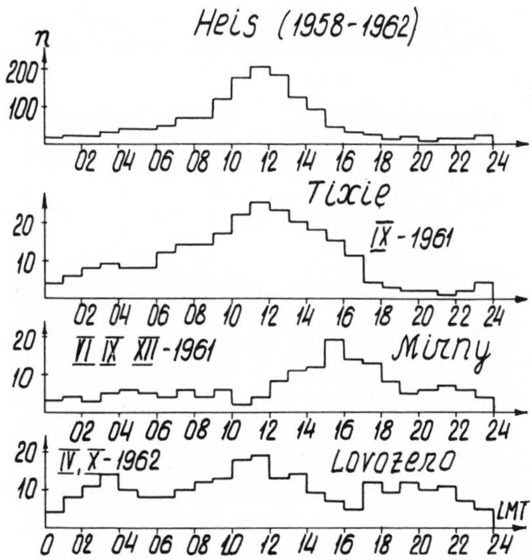

FIG. 18. Diurnal variations of PP at four polar stations (n, number of cases).

of 1960, 1961, and 1962 while autumn months of 1957 were practically empty. There were practically no pearls on the records; if they did occur, the series duration was very short. PP-development for the period from 1957 to 1962 for Borok is presented in Figure 19.

d. Variation during Solar Cycle. PP undergo large changes during the solar cycle — in duration, average amplitude, and number.

There are very few PP in quiet and moderately disturbed days during the years of solar maximum. Thus even very sensitive installations failed to record a single PP for the whole month (e.g., December, 1957) (see Fig. 19). On the other hand, intensive series of pearls diminishing on their period in the main phase of magnetic storms (IPDP) are characteristic of the years of maximum. Curves of mean annual amplitude and mean dura-

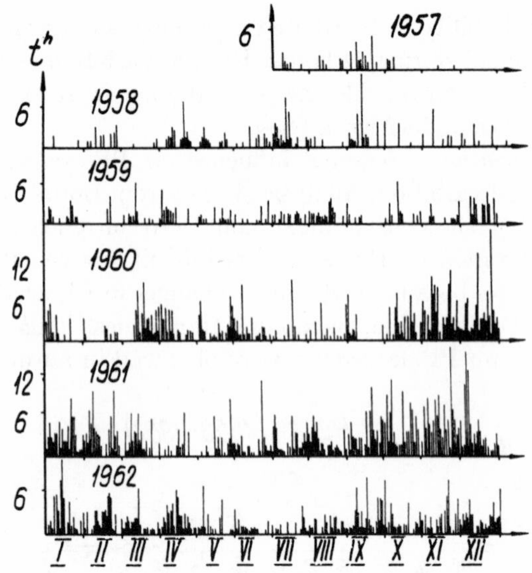

FIG. 19. Number and duration of all PP series at Borok, 1957–1962; t, time in hours occupied by PP-series each day.

tion in different years of solar cycle are given in Figure 20, which shows that mean duration increases about 2 times (1957–1961) and mean-annual amplitude by almost 1.5 times (1957–1960). Figure 21 averages a great number of cases: to find out more about PP-series development during the last 6 years see Figure 19.

The most complete data on the character of the change of PP-occurrence for 1952–1962 are presented in Figure 21. California data (1955–1959)

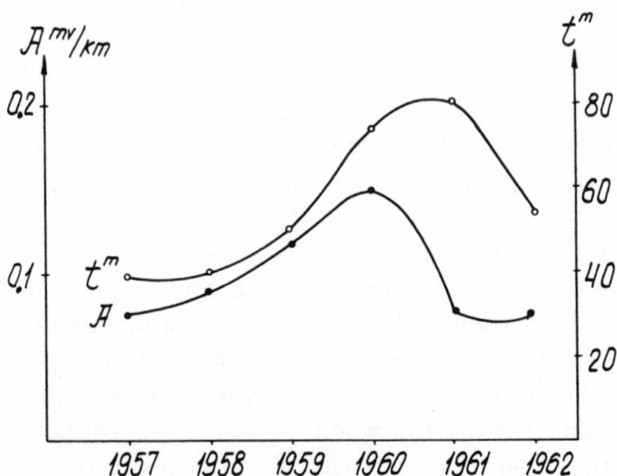

FIG. 20. Changes of average PP-amplitude (A) and average duration of PP series (t^m) during the solar cycle.

[58] are like the Alma-Ata data. Similar regularity during the solar cycle characterized Irkutsk [110], Heiss, etc. Therefore, the main features of the change of PP-regime during the solar cycle may probably be considered as established. Figure 21 shows an important regularity: maximum activity is observed during solar activity decrease. During the current cycle maximum occurrence was observed in 1961, which exceeded PP-occurrence in 1958 by ~7 times. In 1962 there was a sharp decrease of PP-occurrence (about 30 per cent less than 1961). Only 314 cases of PP-occurrence were recorded at Borok for the first half of 1963: arbitrary extrapolation would bring all of 1963 to the level of 1959.

e. PP and Magnetic Field Disturbances. All available data show that PP-series develop in conditions of a quiet field, at K-indexes which do not

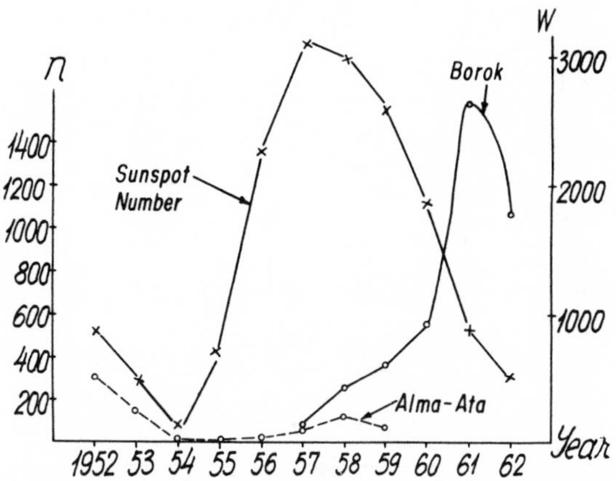

FIG. 21. Variation of PP-occurrence during the solar cycle (Alma-Ata, 1952–1959; Borok, 1957–1962).

exceed 1–2 (e.g., [85] shows that more than 50 per cent of PP-occurrence falls on Kp less than 2). Therefore, slowly developing PP-series should not be considered as a fine structure of some other macroscopic slow-field variations but as a sign of a special undisturbed magnetospheric state which is necessary for the development of these pulsations. On the other hand, some separate short bursts of PP as well as PP-series decreasing on their period, are the characteristic features of the most intensive disturbances during magnetic storms and disturbances of a sudden commencement type [85, 104, 112].

f. Planetary Distribution. All available data show complicated and variable character of the planetary distribution of PP. Cases of local PP-excitation are observed as well as cases when PP are traced in both polar caps and in aurora zones, cases when PP with same periods take place at all stations, and cases when PP periods at high-latitude stations are greater than at middle-latitude ones. To study the character of simultaneous PP-occurrence at high and middle latitudes, records for three months of 1961 (June, December, and September — months of equinoxes and solstices) were processed for Mirny, Borok, and Heiss; and, to study differences in PP in auroral zones and polar caps, records for January and February, 1962 were compared with records at Kerguelen and Lovozero, which are situated almost in the conjugate zones. The results are presented in Figure 22. This diagram shows that simultaneous PP-occurrences have small periods (less than 2 sec), while simultaneous occurrences with periods

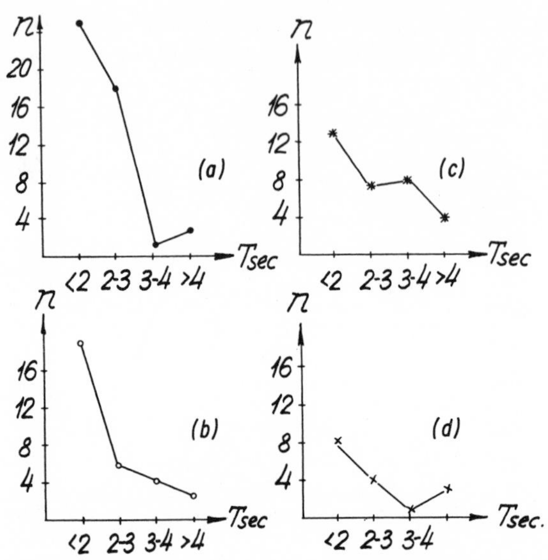

FIG. 22. Distribution according to periods of PP simultaneously registered at (*a*) Mirny — Borok, (*b*) Heiss — Borok, (*c*) Mirny — Heiss, and (*d*) Mirny — Heiss — Borok (*n*, number of PP; *T*, period).

greater than 2 sec are rather rare. All recorded simultaneous PP-occurrences, including cases with different periods for several pairs of stations, are presented in Figure 23. Scattering for periods less than 2 sec is small, i e. coincidence of periods takes place; for periods more than 2 sec, scattering is much greater.

For Borok and Heiss [Fig. 23(*a*)] all the dots are above the bisector, i e., periods either coincide or are bigger in Heiss. Figure 23(*b*) : for Heiss and Mirny, at $T > 2$ sec, scattering is more or less symmetrical against the bisector; i e., at simultaneous excitation, periods are bigger either at Heiss or at Mirny. Figure 23(*c*) : for Mirny–Borok stations a small number of occurrences (when PP-periods, in spite of all the expectations, were less in

Mirny than in Borok) were observed. Figure 23(*d*) : a striking coincidence of periods for Borok–Kerguelen and Kerguelen–Lovozero stations was discovered. It is necessary to note that all the PP-cases given in [100] were observed at Lovozero and Borok stations, and all the periods have coincided with precision of 0.1 sec.

Two typical examples of the character of PP-occurrence are given in Figure 24. In (*a*), PP periods are the same at all the stations; in (*b*), for simultaneous excitations of PP, having small periods of 1–2 sec on middle latitudes and auroral zones, we observe an excitation of pulsations having a

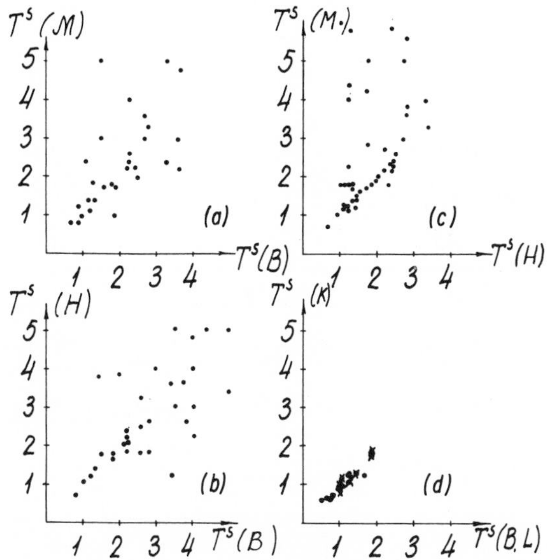

FIG. 23. Distribution of simultaneous PP according to periods in seconds (both axes) for PP at different stations: (*a*) Mirny — Borok, (*b*) Mirny — Heiss, (*c*) Heiss — Borok, and (*d*) Borok — Kerguelen (dots), Kerguelen — Lovozero (crosses).

period of 6 sec in polar caps. From the figures it is possible to get an idea about the character of the time distribution of series of simultaneous PP: coincidence takes place only for some separate intervals of the series, which have significant local peculiarities. The results are in good agreement with [92], which is concerned with conjugate point experiments and which concludes that, though conjugacy exists for PP-series, the peculiarities of their development may differ significantly. A very important result of [92] concerns that type of PP-series which consists of separate beatings of pulsations, spaced approximately at the same distance from each other. These bursts are shifted 180° against each other (Fig. 12) in magnetically conjugate regions. This fact is of great importance because it can be used for working out a theory of PP-occurrence as a parameter which determines the energy of particles exciting PP [57]. Study of longitudinal PP-distribution also reveals a very complicated picture [115].

g. PP and Other Geophysical Phenomena. The first attempt to compare PP-excitation with other geophysical phenomena was made for PP-series observed before storms and for PP composing the second phase of IPDP [104]. Intensive bursts of solar protons, registered in stratosphere before the storm of 15 July, and of 11 July 1959, coincided in time with the excitation of PP-series [104]. Similar coincidence was obtained for some other storms (e.g., 30 September 1961). Short PP, superimposed on the field changes, corresponding to the SSC, coincide in time with the intensive X-ray bursts, caused by electron bombardment at the moment of SSC [59, 108, 112].

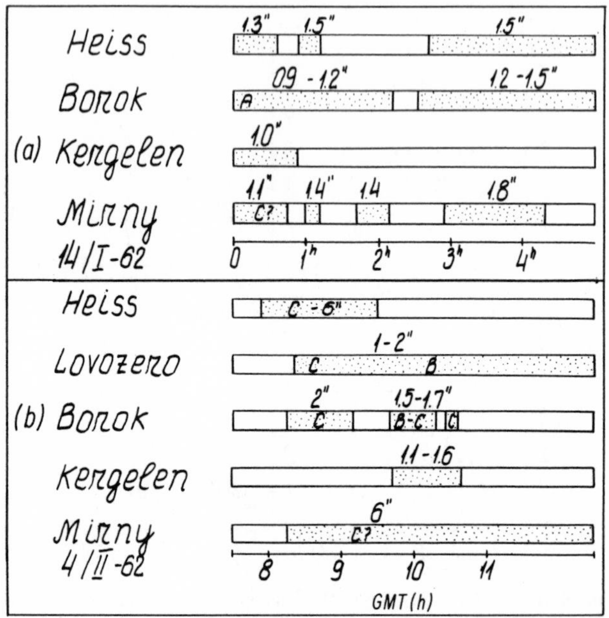

FIG. 24. Simultaneous PP occurrence in middle and high latitudes: (*a*) with almost the same periods, (*b*) with different periods. (*A*, *B*, *C* — qualitative characteristics of PP intensity in decreasing order; periods in seconds are given by numbers.)

The largest storms during IGY contained in their main phase a typical complex of micropulsation disturbances composing the fine structure of very intensive bays. The first phase of this complex consists of typical intensive irregular pulsations (noise bursts) after which PP-series develop, changing distinctly their period (IPDP), and usually an increase of oscillation frequency is observed.

During a storm one to three IPDP may occur (sometimes even more, e.g., 11 February 1958). In all cases the appearance of this complex of micropulsations is connected with red aurora at low latitudes and with the beginning of strong disturbances in ionosphere (decreasing of critical frequencies of the F-2 layer, its diffusion or full absorption). Red aurora appearance at low latitudes coincides (within a minute) with onset of irregular micropulsations (the first phase of fine structures of an intensive bay). After these pulsations, lasting some 10–20 min, the PP-series begins. As a rule, by this time the red aurora is over and green luminosity appears. This auroral transformation coincides with the moment of the regular PP-appearance in the IPDP.

This picture of the development is confirmed by the observations made in Alaska [86]: PP appear not at the moments of active auroral forms but after their decaying; strong pulsating aurora preceded PP-appearance; it was observed, that gradually developing PP-series do not correlate with the cosmic noise absorption, but if PP-bursts appear suddenly and with large amplitude, they may be accompanied by increased absorption. It is pointed out [112] that PP-series usually develop after cosmic noise absorption intervals, which as a rule coincide better with short irregular pulsations. All these facts give approximately the same picture of the developments, which are reflected best of all in IPDP fine structure. (On 7 November 1957 the second Soviet Sputnik registered sharp fluctuations of radiation intensity in the outer belt [109]. Analysis of rapid earth current records showed that it was just at these hours (2–3^h GMT) that IPDP took place.)

Spectral analysis of the counting rate variation in scintillation counters [112] aboard balloons during PP-observations showed that there are maxima at periods of 0.8 and 1.6 sec. This result was explained as corresponding to the oscillating of electron bunches with 60-kev energy and less along the magnetic lines. This was used as a base for the hypothesis which explains PP as a result of the movement of particle bunches along the lines of force.

It is of interest to note the following fact: Magnetic field measurements by Explorer X showed that the character of the field and its fluctuations changed sharply approximately at 6 o'clock (GMT) on 26 March, 4 hours before the solar flare. The only characteristic feature of the surface observations at this time was the excitation of the PP-series at a number of stations, also in [93], the shift in the spectrum of micropulsations is pointed out.

PP diurnal variation and changes in their excitation during the solar cycle suggest that the possibility of PP-observations must be connected with characteristic, regular changes in the ionosphere. Maximum of PP diurnal variation, in middle latitudes, occurs in night hours, i.e., hours when the absorption of waves with the periods of 1 sec sharply decreases (in day hours, the ionosphere is practically opaque for oscillations of such periods). Thus, the probability of PP is closely connected with electron concentration in the ionosphere. PP has also been found to depend sharply on ionospheric diffusive spread [96].

h. Theoretical Ideas. There are two main points of view concerning the nature of PP. Some [66, 88, 104, 108] suppose that these pulsations are a result of the oscillations of bunches of monochromatic particles trapped by the earth's magnetosphere. In this case PP-period equals the

TABLE 5

DATA FOR PP-OSCILLATIONS (TEPLEY AND WENTWORTH [112])

Station	Palo Alto	Victoria	Uppsala	Reykjavik
Geomagnetic latitude	45°	55°	60°	70°
Full length of arc ($\times 10^{-9}$ cm)	5.71	9.42	12.2	22.4
Energy of electrons for 1-cps oscillations (kev)	9.25	25.2	48.6	260
Electron drift velocity for 1-cps oscillations ($\times 10^{-5}$ rad/sec)	3.32	12.0	27.0	142
Maximum frequency of oscillations ($V = C$) (cps)	5.25	3.18	2.46	1.34
Maximum frequency of oscillations for a point 500 km distant (cps)	7.8	4.6	3.6	2.1
Maximum observed frequency of hydromagnetic emissions (cps)	5	3	3	2

period of the oscillations of the groups from one conjugate point to the other, and PP-amplitude is defined by the density and energy of the charged particles in the group, by the height of the mirror points, and by the absorption of hydromagnetic waves in the ionosphere. The basis for such a point of view is the morphologic features of the PP-series and their connection with phenomena in the high atmosphere. Until recently it was thought that the period of oscillations equaled the PP-period and the spacing between successive pearls was the drift time of the particles around the earth. Calculations of the corresponding periods, ranges of amplitudes, amount of particles and their energies gave results in keeping with modern ideas about the structure of the radiation belts and energies of their particles [66].

Table 5 shows calculated and observed data for PP-oscillations. The mirror points of particle bunches are thought to be situated above the F-2 layer of ionosphere. As the ionosphere has high conductivity, the arrival of a diamagnetic bunch of particles at the mirror point cannot be recorded directly on the surface of the earth. The disturbance must reach the E-layer as a hydromagnetic wave. Propagation through the ionosphere reduces the disturbance because of the absorption due to joule heating of the medium (viscosity may be neglected). Calculation of the absorption of hydromagnetic waves in ionosphere shows [72] that in the daytime, especially in years of maximum solar activity, the ionosphere is practically opaque even for the 1-cps waves. Absorption of PP is not very large at night. The character of PP diurnal variation in middle latitudes may be explained by these facts.

The other experimental consequence of the proposed theory must be the dependence of the period of the observed oscillations on latitude. An average PP-period must increase monotonically with the latitude. As shown above, this fact is not confirmed with certainty, though PP-excitation of larger periods tends to take place at high latitudes. Besides as noted [57] oscillations with 1–2 sec period occur more often in the auroral zones, and it was oscillations of these periods that marked most of the simultaneous cases of PP discovered in wide latitudinal range.

Another point of view on the nature of PP is based on the following fact: a few cases of single PP beads appearing in antiphase at the ends of conjugate lines were observed. These beads are spaced by dozens of seconds from each other [92]. This fact was explained as caused by slow oscillations of protons, whose velocities are of the order of 10^8 cm/sec. These oscillations occur with periods of dozens of seconds and cause resonant oscillations in the lower exosphere [88].

One more explanation of PP-nature involves the concept of selective properties of the lower exosphere. In the cavity between the earth and the layer of maximal Alfvén velocity, selective standing waves may occur. Their period is within the range of values characteristic for PP. The source of the standing waves is the Alfvén waves coming from the outer exosphere into the auroral zones (although the possible dissipation of the Alfvén wave in the exosphere has not been taken into consideration [80]). In the outer exosphere, disturbances have a wide spectrum, but because of the development of the standing waves, only narrow bands are selected from the spectrum.

2.3. Fine Structure of Magnetic Storms

a. Period before a Storm. Analysis of micropulsations records ($T < 15''$) on a wide net of stations showed that in many cases pulsation series of PP-type occur before storms. PP may occur some hours before or, more often, during the first minutes of a storm, when they are superimposed on the main pulsations, which make up SSC fine structure (Fig. 25). The diagram is obtained by analysis of the electromagnetic field state at 11 earth current stations before 29 storms [108]. The comparison of separate PP-series before storms (e.g., 15 and 11 July 1959) showed that their excitation coincided with bursts in the stratosphere of solar cosmic rays. A case interesting in this respect was observed on 30 September 1961 (observed and discussed by Tepley, paper not yet available). PP-series with about the same period were observed at a number of stations before the storm (Tixie, Petropavlovsk, Mirny). Then at a much greater number of stations SIP bursts occurred simultaneously with PP superimposed on them. This case is of interest because there are satellite observations for this period [68], which show that an increase of protons intensity, with energy in the range of 3–33 Mev, did take place at the time of PP-occurrence.

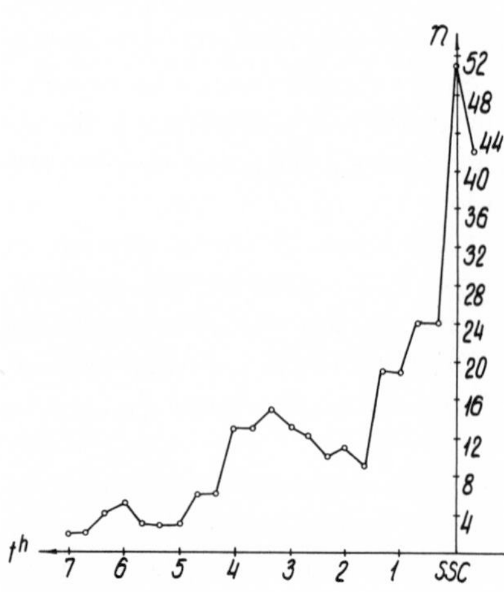

FIG. 25. Distribution of PP-series before storms (n, number of cases; t, time in hours before the beginning of the storm).

b. Magnetic Storm Sudden Commencements (SSC). There are many papers on SSC-properties based on rapid-run records. The following questions have been studied: SSC fine structure in different spectrum ranges, polarization of pulsations which occur in SSC-moment, simultaneous occurrence of SSC onsets and their front steepness. A number of papers consider phenomena in the high atmosphere accompanying sudden commencements, and theoretical ideas on SSC nature [60, 62, 71, 79, 90, 95, 98, 99, 112–113].

SSC fine structure at high latitudes contains, together with long-period oscillations ($T \sim 4$ min), a wide set of frequencies. In moderate latitudes SSC fine structure resembles in the daytime a series of damped pulsations of Pc-type with periods from 8 to 20 sec, and duration from 2 to 4 min. At night this characteristic oscillation regime disappears and SSC-phenomenon becomes some aperiodic field fluctuation, on which pulsations with periods less than 8 sec are superimposed. Spectral analysis of some SSC cases, conducted for a number of U.S.S.R. earth current stations (in the period range from 5 to 60 seconds), shows the tendency of the main spectrum peaks shifting to shorter periods when the latitude decreases [93].

Investigations [84, 108, 112] showed that PP are often superimposed [66, 71] on the main SSC-pulsations as well as on field fluctuation during the first minutes of a storm. This fact was interpreted as evidence of disturbances, caused by particle bunches oscillating along the lines of force. These particles were discovered on balloons and also due to their influence on the cosmic noise absorption [60, 98].

The investigation of distribution of the SSC-onsets at the earth's surface have not yet yielded generally agreed-upon results. For one thing, precision of determining of SSC-onset on rapid records is limited by the very smooth steepness of their first movement. The most reliable data suggest that the propagation time of SSC along the surface has an order of 10–40 sec [78]. It appears that a disturbance occurs first of all at stations situated in sunlit high latitudes, but this tendency is not generally accepted.

Magnetic field records, with higher sensitivity and time scale than standard ones but not enough for revealing SSC fine structure, were used for determining the rate of increase of H during sudden commencements. This time appeared to be 5–6 min [62, 99]. These data were used for working out the SSC theoretical model [69, 70, 100]. However, many details known of the SSC fine structure were not used.

Polarization of long-period oscillations, which accompany SSC in high latitudes ($\sim$4 min), and its variation in time were studied [113, 114]. For high and moderate latitudes, elliptic and mixed elliptic and linear polarizations, respectively, are observed. Polarization for equatorial zone is mainly linear. Sites where vectors are rotating clockwise are separated from ones which rotate counterclockwise by a meridional plane, which goes along the meridians of 10 and 22 hours of the local time (Fig. 26). With the knowledge that polarization will be circular for an ideal transversal hydromagnetic wave and linear for a longitudinal one, the following mechanism of SSC occurrence was proposed. As a result of an interaction of corpuscular stream front with the magnetosphere, a longitudinal hydromagnetic shock wave is formed. Propagating toward the earth, perpendicular to the magnetic field, the longitudinal wave generates a transverse wave, which propagates along the lines of force into high latitudes. This generation takes place at great distances (where coupling between toroidal and poloidal oscillations is effective). Rotation direction is connected with the character of a hydromagnetic wave mode.

In addition to these morphological characteristics of SSC, recent data show that in many cases SSC coincide with a brief absorption of cosmic noise, observed in auroral zone and near it (not more than 500 km south) [59].

c. Magnetic Storms: Initial and Main Phases. The fine structure of magnetic storms has been studied recently by many authors. Some methods have been based on classical concepts about storm phases and have presented an attempt to study the characteristic features of these phases according to micropulsations [63, 71, 104, 108]. On the other hand, investigations were conducted irrespective of storm divisions [65, 89].

The initial phase. For a long-lasting, clearly developed initial phase of a storm, the main pulsations are the continuous pulsations Pc of small periods (10–15 sec). Pc periods during storms show inverse dependence on Kp-index. This feature of storm microstructure was, for instance, clearly expressed for the storm of 29 September 1957, and this characteristic is especially apparent for recurrent storms. Analysis of the last series of such storms (1962–1963) showed that Pc are typical for the first phase

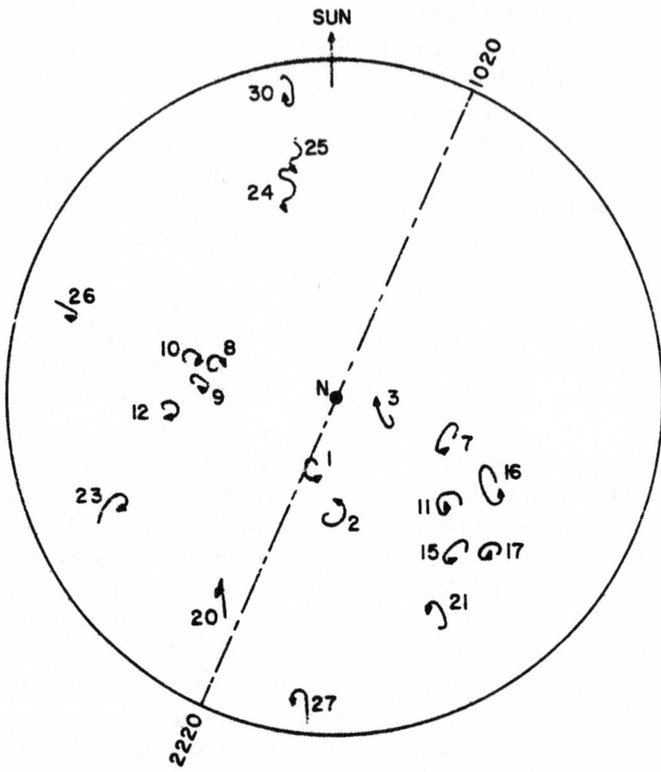

FIG. 26. Direction of rotation of SSG-oscillations with respect to meridional plane 10–22 LMT (from C. R. Wilson).

of a storm and that their periods undoubtedly depend on Kp-index (Fig. 5*b*).

Pc are also very typical for storms of floccular origin, for which the main phase is practically absent. The degree of Pc frequency of occurrence during storms of different types is also expressed in different duration of their series in these storms. For example, during the solar activity maximum, the mean Pc-duration for two flare storms (17 August 1958 and 28–29 March 1959) was about 50 minutes, while for two floccular storms (5–8 October 1958 and 14–16 October 1959) this value was about 400 minutes. With the fall of solar activity a small decrease of Pc-series duration (15–20 per cent) for floccular storms is observed.

Main phase. As mentioned, the main phase of magnetic storms is characterized by the development of intensive irregular pulsations and of IPDP. The more intensive are the planetary disturbances, the longer are the SIP-series (II). It is necessary to point out that the most expressive variation of magnetic storm fine structure with the solar cycle is the variation of SIP-series duration. SIP mean duration during the years close to minimum of solar activity is about 9–10 times less than that during maximum ones. Preliminary analysis of characteristic IPDP shows that they

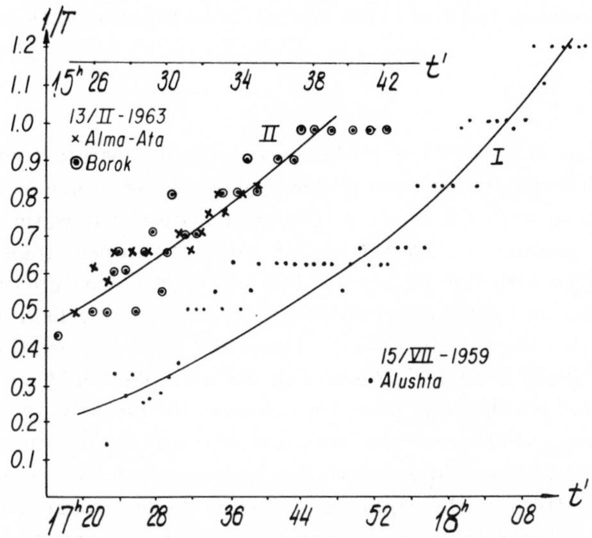

FIG. 27. Examples of IPDP development for epochs of solar activity: I, maximum (15 July 1959) and, II, minimum (13 February 1963) t'—time in minutes from the beginning of IPDP (upper time scale for Alma-Ata and Borok, lower scale for Alushta).

are (*a*) always observed for very intensive flare storms, (*b*) are not observed at all for floccular storms, and (*c*) may occur in recurrent storms. In the last case, their difference from the cases observed during intensive flare storms, is a smaller frequency range "swept" by pulsations inside IPDP. It was also observed that during years of decreasing solar activity a phenomenon similar to IPDP may occur in a number of cases for an isolated bay. Typical structure of PP-series in IPDP for the period of solar activity maximum (July, 1959) and of solar activity decrease (February, 1963) is presented in Figure 27. IPDP is detected without any change in periods in the Arctic, the Antarctic, and in longitudinal range of some 70–80° in middle latitudes. At greater longitudinal ranges, IPDP are usually not traced, probably due to ionosphere screening.

As mentioned, appearance of pulsations characteristic of the first phase of IPDP (SIP-type) correspond to the beginning of sharp disturbances in the ionosphere, to auroral propagation at low latitudes, and also to X-ray bursts. The second phase, PP-development diminishing on their period, takes place usually after the end of active auroral forms. Moreover, when IPDP's are observed microbarographs show, with a corresponding delay, pressure increase [67]. Thus, this phenomenon, typical only for the main phase of a storm, shows that great irregular formations exist in a corpuscular stream. These irregularities generate intensive hydromagnetic waves. They favor either pitch-angle redistribution and corresponding "dumping" of the charged particles into the high atmosphere, or a direct propagation of rapid particles, trapped along lines of force, into the earth's atmosphere.

Conclusions

A number of interesting problems deserving separate treatment have not been included in the above review. Some of these problems, for instance, are connected with the study of the peculiarities of pulsations caused by artificial injections of charged particles into the upper atmosphere; some are connected with the influence of local geological structure on amplitude, polarization, and ratio of components of the magnetic field and of earth currents (e.g., the so-called coast effect), and some concern the correlation between pulsations and phenomena in the ionosphere and magnetosphere. Among these problems we note, for instance, the recently revealed correlation between variations of the frequency of transmitted radiowaves (in the range 18–20 Mc/sec) and pulsations. These variations of frequency have the same pattern as the rapid variations of the electromagnetic field.

Among the questions of interest in this subject, and to which IQSY studies may be able to contribute, are the following:

1. Whether there is a connection (and its nature) between different types of pulsations and phenomena in the high atmosphere. It would be desirable to conduct simultaneous observations of short-period pulsations and of the phenomena in the high atmosphere with time scale sufficient for the determination of their simultaneity or of their relative lagging.
2. Whether the property of conjugacy is observed for different types of pulsations and, if so, its peculiarities; in other words, whether these pulsations are observed at magnetically conjugate points and what is the detailed character of variations of the conjugacy property with time during the year, with magnetic activity, etc.
3. To what extent do the data obtained as the result of the study of pulsations supplement data obtained about the high atmosphere with other more direct methods.

4. The dependence of the amplitude of pulsations of different types on latitude. It will probably be necessary to consider the influence of local geological structure and the possible influence of ionospheric blunting of this dependence.

5. What is the polarization of pulsations of all types, the character of its changes, and the limitations on current interpretations which do not take into consideration the peculiarities of local geological structure and the anisotropy of the ionosphere. To solve this problem it might perhaps be useful to organize observations of the electromagnetic field on drifting ice floes and on oceans in places of great depths for in these cases at least the influence of geology would be a minimum.

6. What are the maximum frequencies of pulsations of the electromagnetic field at different latitudes and longitudes, the detailed character of the cutoff spectrum, and whether this cutoff changes with latitude.

7. Correlations between pulsations observed on the earth's surface and the variations of the field in the upper atmosphere registered on satellites and rockets.

8. Special attention should be paid to classification because accidental mixing of pulsations of different properties and nature make the determination of any definite regularities hopeless, while these regularities can be basic for theoretical concepts. The most dangerous in this respect are the bordering regions which divide pulsations of different classes (e.g., when dividing short-period pulsations according to frequency).

References—Section 1

1. V. I. Afanasieva, Short-period pulsations of the earth's magnetic field, *Short-Period Pulsations of the Earth's Electromagnetic Field: Geomagnetism No. 3,* 5–10 (Soviet IGY Committee, Acad. Sci. USSR, 1961).
2. V. A. An, N. P. Vladiminov, Y. A. Yermolenko, and G. I. Rassomakhin, Equipment for registration of the earth's electromagnetic variations in the spectral range 0.5–1000 c/sec, *Proceedings, Questions of Theory and Practice of Electrometry* (Acad. Sci. USSR, 1961).
3. G. Angenheister, Uber die Fortpflanzungs-Geschwindigkeit Magnetisher Störungen und Pulsationen, *Göttingen, Nachr. Ges. Wiss.*, 565–581 (1912).
4. G. Angenheister and C. Consbrush, Pulsationen der Erdmagnetischen Feldes in Göttingen von 1953–1958, II. *Z. Geophys.*, **28**(3), 103–111 (1961).
5. H. Benioff, Observations of geomagnetic fluctuations in the period range 0.3 to 120 seconds, *J. Geophys. Res.*, **65**(5), 1413–1422 (1960).
6. M. N. Berdichevsky, *Electric Surveying by the Telluric Current Method* (Gostoptekhizdat, Moscow, 1960).
7. O. V. Bolshakova, Some features in the appearance of regular geomagnetic pulsations with 3–7 minute period at the polar station "Lovozero," *Izv. Acad. Nauk SSSR, Geophys. Ser. No. 12,* 1176–1177 (1961).
8. O. V. Bolshakova and K. Y. Zubin, On the frequency of occurrence and amplitude spectrum of the geomagnetic field pulsations, *Ann. Géophys.*, **17**(4), 345–350 (1961).
9. J. Bouska, Research into short-periodic variations of the earth's electromagnetic field at the Observatory of Budkov, *Studia Geophys. Geod.*, **4**, 280–284 (1960).

10. L. Cagniard, Basic theory of the magneto-telluric method of the geophysic prospecting, *Geophysics*, **18**(3), 605–635 (1953). J. R. Wait, Mutual coupling of the loops lying on the ground, *Geophysics*, **19**(2) 290–296 (1954).
11. W. H. Campbell, Studies of magnetic field micro-pulsations with period of 5 to 30 seconds, *J. Geophys. Res.*, **64**(11), 1819–1826 (1959).
12. S. J. de Moidrey, Pulsations magnétiques à Zi-Ka-Wei et à Lu-Kiapang, *Terr. Mag. Atmos. Elect.*, **22,** 113–120 (1917).
13. V. G. Doubrovskiy, Rapid geoelectric and geomagnetic variations and their regularities according to observations in Ashkhabad, *Short-Period Pulsations of the Earth's Electromagnetic Field: Geomagnetism No. 3*, 35–40 (Soviet IGY Committee, Acad. Sci. USSR, 1961).
14. R. A. Duncan, Some studies of geomagnetic micropulsations, *J. Geophys. Res.*, **66**(7), 2087–2094 (1961).
15. J. W. Dungey, Electrodynamics of the outer atmosphere, *Pennsylvania State Univ. Ionos. Res. Lab. Sci. Rept. 69* (1954).
16. G. R. A. Ellis, Geomagnetic micropulsations, *Austral. J. Phys.* **13**(4), 625–632 (1960).
17. E. R. R. Holmberg, Rapid periodic fluctuations of the geomagnetic field, *Mon. Not. Roy. Astron. Soc., Geophys. Suppl. 6*, 467–481 (1953).
18. V. R. Hutton, Equatorial micropulsations, *J. Phys. Soc. Japan* **17,** Suppl. A-II, 20–23 (1962).
19. IGY Committee, Soviet, *Short-Period Pulsations of the Earth's Electromagnetic Field, Collected Articles: Geomagnetism No. 3* (Acad. Sci. USSR, Moscow 114 p., 1961).
20. J. A. Jacobs and K. Sinno, World-wide characteristics of geomagnetic micropulsations, *Geophys. J. Roy. Astron. Soc.*, **3**(3), 333–353 (1960).
21. H. Jungul Sulhi, Magneto-telluric sounding three-layer interpretation curves, *Geophysics*, **26**(4) (1961).
22. Y. Kato, Investigation on the geomagnetic rapid pulsation, *Sci. Repts. Tohoku Univ., Ser. 5: Geophys.*, **11** (1959).
23. Y. Kato, Geomagnetic micropulsations, *Austral. J. Phys.*, **15**(1) (1962).
24. Y. Kato, Geomagnetic pulsations and hydromagnetic oscillations of exosphere, *J. Phys. Soc. Japan*, **17,** Suppl. A-II, 71–73 (1962).
25. Y. Kato and S. Akasofu, Relationships between the geomagnetic micropulsation and the solar UV region, *J. Atmos. Terr. Phys.*, **9**(5/6), 352–353 (1956).
26. Y. Kato, J. Ossaka, M. Okuda, T. Watanabe, and T. Tamao, Investigation of the magnetic disturbance by the induction magnetograph, 6: On the daily variation and the 27-day recurrence tendency in the geomagnetic pulsations, *Sci. Repts. Tohoku Univ.*, **8,** 19–23 (1956).
27. Y. Kato and T. Saito, Morphological study of geomagnetic pulsations, (*Preprint, Intn'l Conf. on Earth Storm, Kyoto*, 1–10, 1961).
28. Y. Kato and T. Saito, Morphological study of geomagnetic pulsations, *J. Phys. Soc. Japan*, **17,** Suppl. A–II, 34–39 (1962).
29. Y. Kato and T. Tamao, Hydromagnetic waves in the earth's exosphere and geomagnetic pulsations, *J. Phys. Soc. Japan*, **17,** Suppl. A-II, 39–43 (1962).
30. Y. Kato and T. Watanabe, A survey of observational knowledge of the geomagnetic pulsation, *Sci. Repts. Tohoku Univ., Ser. 5: Geophys.*, **8**(3) (1957).
31. V. V. Kebouladze and L. V. Kiziriya, On the steady short-period variations of earth currents, *Izv. Acad. Nauk SSSR, Geophys. Ser. No. 1*, 59–61 (1962).
32. N. V. Lipskaya, N. A. Deniskin, and Yu. M. Yegoroz, Plotting of the magneto-telluric curves based on observations of the variations of the earth's electromagnetic field, *Proceedings Questions on the Theory and Practice of Electrometry* (Acad. Sci. USSR, 1961).
33. E. Maple, Geomagnetic oscillations at middle latitudes, part I, The observational data, *J. Geophys. Res.*, **64**(10), 1395–1404 (1959).
34. T. Obayashi and J. A. Jacobs, Geomagnetic pulsation and the earth's outer atmosphere, *Geophys. J. Roy. Astron. Soc.*, **1**(1), 53–63 (1958).

35. A. I. OHL, Pulsations during sudden commencements of magnetic storms and long-period pulsations in high latitudes, *J. Phys. Soc. Japan*, **17**, Suppl. A-II, 24–26 (1962).
36. A. OHL, Giant pulsations (Report presented to the XIII Assembly of IUGG, Berkeley, 1963).
37. T. ONDOH, VLF emissions and geomagnetic disturbances of the auroral zone, part II: Chorus increases and geomagnetic pulsations at the auroral zone, IGY, *Rept. Ionos. Space Res. Japan*. **14**(2), 86–98 (1960).
38. H. OSHIMA, An attempt to give an index to the activity of Pc-type pulsations and its applications to the analysis of geomagnetic storms, *Mem. Kak. Mag. Obs.*, **10**(1), 1–5 (1961).
39. G. PFOTZER, A. EHMERT, H. ERBE, E. KEPPLER, B. HULTQVIST, AND J. ORTNER, A contribution to the morphology of X-ray bursts in the auroral zone, *J. Geophys. Res.*, **67**(2), 575–585 (1962).
40. G. PORTZENDORFER, *Freiberger Forschungshefte C 107*, *Geophysik* (Akademie-Verlag, Berlin, 1961).
41. A. ROMANA AND J. CARDUS, Sobre algunas singularidades de las curvas de horas con pe en las observatories de la zone ecutorial (Lisbon, 1962).
42. T. SAITO, Statistical studies of three types of geomagnetic continuous pulsations, *Sci. Repts. Tohoku Univ., Ser. 5: Geophys.*, **14**(3) (1962).
43. T. SATO, A morphology of geomagnetic giant pulsation [Abstract], *J. Geomag. Geoelect.*, **12**(2), 112 (1961).
44. J. G. SCHOLTE AND J. VELDKAMP, Geomagnetic and geoelectric variations, *J. Atmos. Terr. Phys.*, **6**(1) (1955).
45. R. J. SPREITER AND B. R. BRIGGS, Analysis of the effect of a ring current on whistlers, J. Geophys. Res., **67**(10), 3779–3790 (1962).
46. M. SUGIURA, Some evidence of hydromagnetic waves in the earth's magnetic field, *Phys. Rev. Letters* **6**, 255–257 (1961).
47. T. TERADA, On rapid periodic variations of terrestrial magnetism, *J. Univ. Tokyo Fac. Sci.*, Sect. II, **27** (1917).
48. A. N. TIKHONOV, The determination of electrical characteristics of the deep layers of the earth's crust, *Dok. Akad. Nauk*, **73**(2) (1950).
49. A. N. TIKHONOV, Z. D. LOMAKINA, AND D. N. SHAKHSUVAROV, *Tables of Impedances for Layered Space in the Field of a Plane Electromagnetic Wave* (Moscow Univ. Press, 1962).
50. A. N. TIKHONOV AND D. N. SHAKHSUVAROV, About the possibility of use of the earth's electromagnetic field impedance for investigation of the upper layers of the earth's crust, *Izv. Akad. Nauk SSSR, Geophys. Ser., No. 4* (1956).
51. V. A. TROITSKAYA, Continuous pulsations and pulsation trains in the Arctic and Antarctic, *Short-Period Pulsations of the Earth's Electromagnetic Field: Geomagnetism No. 3*, 41–61 (Soviet IGY Committee, Acad. Sci. USSR, 1961).
52. J. VERÖ, Ein Versuch zur Trennung der einzelnen Frequenzbander der Erdstromvariationen, *Geofis. Pura Appl.*, **49**, II, 83–118 (1961).
53. P. A. VINOGRADOV, Investigations of general regularities of earth currents, *Dissertation* (Moscow, 1962).
54. S. H. WARD, Dynamics of magnetosphere, *J. Geophys. Res.*, **68**(3), 781–788 (1963).
55. T. WATANABE, Hydromagnetic oscillation of the outer ionosphere and geomagnetic pulsation, *J. Geomag. Geoelect.*, **10**(4) 195–202 (1959).
56. T. WATANABE, On the origins of geomagnetic pulsations, *Sci. Repts. Tohoku Univ., Ser.* **5**: *Geophys.*, **13**(3), 127–140 (1961).

REFERENCES—SECTION 2

57. C. D. ANGER, J. R. BARCUS, R. R. Brown, znd D. S. EVANS, Auroral zone X-ray pulsations in the 1–15 sec period range, *J. Geophys. Res.*, **68**(4), 1023–1030 (1963).
58. H. BENIOFF, Observations of geomagnetic fluctuations in the period range 0.3–120 sec, *J. Geophys. Res.*, **65**(5), 1413–1422 (1960).

59. R. R. BROWN, Balloon observations of auroral-zone X-rays, *J. Geophys. Res.*, **66**(5), 1379–1388 (1961).
60. R. R. BROWN, X-rays accompanying the magnetic storm of June 27, 1960, *Arkiv Geofysik*, **3,** 435–439 (1961).
61. R. R. BROWN AND W. H. CAMPBELL, An auroral zone electron precipitation event and its relationship to a magnetic bay, *J. Geophys. Res.*, **67**(4), 1357–1365 (1962).
62. J. BOUŠKA, The microstructure of IS_c of geomagnetic storms, *J. Phys. Soc. Japan*, **17,** Suppl. A-II, 45–47 (1962).
63. J. BOUŠKA, A contribution to research into the pulsation characteristics of the different phases of geomagnetic storms (Report presented to the XIII Assembly of IUGG, Berkeley, 1963).
64. W. H. CAMPBELL AND H. LEINBACH, Ionospheric absorption at times of auroral and magnetic pulsations, *J. Geophys. Res.*, **66**(1), 25–34 (1961).
65. W. H. CAMPBELL AND S. MATSUSHITA, Auroral zone geomagnetic micropulsations with periods of 5 to 30 seconds, *J. Geophys. Res.*, **67**(2), 555–573 (1962).
66. W. H. CAMPBELL AND M. H. REES, A study of auroral coruscations, *J. Geophys. Res.*, **66**(1), 41–55 (1961).
67. P. CHRZANOWSKI, G. GREENE, K. T. LEMMON, AND J. M. YOUNG, Traveling pressure waves associated with geomagnetic activity, *J. Geophysics. Res.* **66**(11), 3727–3734 (1961).
68. L. R. DAVIS AND J. M. WILLIAMSON, Low energy trapped protons, *Space Research III*, 367–375 (North-Holland Publishing Co., 1963).
69. A. J. DESSLER, The propagation velocity of world wide SSC, *J. Geophys. Res.* **63**(2), 405–408 (1958).
70. A. J. DESSLER AND E. N. PARKER, Hydromagnetic theory of geomagnetic storms, *J. Geophys. Res.*, **64**(12), 2239–2252 (1959).
71. R. N. DEWITT, The occurrence of aurora in geomagnetically conjugate areas, *J. Geophys. Res.*, **67**(4), 1347–1355 (1962).
72. N. Y. DUFFUS, P. W. NASMYTH, J. A. SHAUD, AND CH. WRIGHT, Subaudible geomagnetic fluctuations, *Nature*, **181,** 1258–1259 (1958).
73. W. E. FRANCIS AND R. E. KARPLUS, Hydromagnetic waves in the ionosphere, *J. Geophys. Res.*, **65**(11), 3593–3600 (1960).
74. N. FUKUSHIMA, Some remarks on the morphology of geomagnetic bays, *J. Geomag. Geoelect.*, **10**(4), 164–71 (1959).
75. R. GENDRIN AND R. STEFANT, Magnetic records between 0.2 and 30 cycles per second (*Communication to AGARD Conference, Munich,* 1962).
76. R. GENDRIN, Pulsations structurées, *C.R. Acad. Sci.*, **255** (1963).
77. R. GENDRIN AND R. STEFANT, L' analyse de fréquence des oscillations en perles, *C.R. Acad. Sci.*, **255**(4) (1963).
78. V. B. GERARD, The propagation of world-wide sudden commencements of magnetic storms, *J. Geophys. Res.*, **64**(6), 593–596 (1959).
79. A. GRAFE, *Der SC in der Zeitlichen Gradientregiestrierung* (Akademie-Verlag, Berlin, 1962).
80. A. V. GUILJELMI, On the influence of the disintegration of the Alfvén wave in the exosphere upon the character of short-period pulsations of the earth's electromagnetic field (Report presented at the XIII Assembly of IUGG, Berkeley, 1963).
81. L. HARANG, Oscillations and vibrations in magnetic records at high latitude stations, *Terr. Mag. Atmos Elect.*, **41,** 329–336 (1936).
82. R. R. HEACOCK, Auroral-zone telluric current micropulsations, $T < 20$ seconds, *J. Geophys. Res.*, **68**(7), 1871–1884 (1963).
83. R. R. HEACOCK, Notes on pearl-type micropulsations, *J. Geophys. Res.*, **68**(2), 589–591 (1963).
84. R. R. HEACOCK AND V. P. HESSLER, Pearl-type telluric current micropulsations at College, *J. Geophys. Res.*, **67**(10), 3985–3996 (1962).
85. R. R. HEACOCK AND V. P. HESSLER, Telluric current micropulsation bursts, *J. Geophys. Res.*, **68**(3), 953–954 (1963).

86. V. P. HESSLER, Characteristics of telluric current at land and sea based stations, *J. Phys. Soc. Japan*, **17**, Suppl. A-I, 32–34 (1962).
87. J. A. JACOBS AND E. J. JOLLEY, Geomagnetic micropulsations with periods 0.3–3 sec. ('Pearls'), *Nature*, **194**(4829), 641–643 (1962).
88. J. A. JACOBS AND T. WATANABE, Propagation of hydromagnetic waves in the lower exosphere and origin of short period geomagnetic pulsations, *J. Atmos. Terr. Phys.* **24**, 413 (1962).
89. J. KATO, Investigation of the geomagnetic rapid pulsations, *Sci. Repts. Tohoku Univ., Ser. 9: Geophys.*, **11** (1959).
90. Y. KATO AND T. SAITO, On the damped type rapid pulsation accompanying sudden commencements, *Sci. Repts. Tohoku Univ., Ser. 5: Geophys.*, **9**(3) (1958).
91. Y. KATO AND T. WATANABE, A survey of observational knowledge of the geomagnetic pulsation, *Sci. Repts. Tohoku Univ., Ser. 5: Geophys.*, **8**(3), 157–189 (1957).
92. J. E. LOKKEN, J. A. SHAND, AND C. S. WRIGHT, Some characteristics of electromagnetic background signals in the vicinity of one cycle per second, *J. Geophys. Res.*, **68**(3), 789–794 (1963).
93. N. F. MALTSEVA, Some preliminary results of analysis of the frequency spectra of micropulsations accompanying SSC (Report presented at the XIII Assembly of IUGG, Berkeley, 1963).
94. K. B. MATHER AND M. WESCOTT, Telluric currents at geomagnetically conjugate stations in the Aleutian Islands and New Zealand, *J. Geophys. Res.*, **67**(12), 4825–4832 (1962).
95. S. MATSUSHITA, Studies on sudden commencements of geomagnetic storms using IGY data from United States stations, *J. Geophys. Res.*, **65**(5), 1423–1435 (1960).
96. YU. A. NADUBOVICH, Influence of the shore effect on geographic distribution of auroral arcs and bands according to observations of the Russian Polar Expedition of 1900–1902, *Geomag. Aeron.*, **3**(3), 502–513 (1963).
97. N. F. NESS, T. L. SKILLMAN, C. S. SCEARCE, AND J. P. HEPPNER, Correlation of magnetic field fluctuations at the earth and in interplanetary space, *IGY Bulletin No. 55*, 9–11 (1962), and *Trans. Amer. Geophys. Un.*, **43**(1), 93–95 (1962).
98. J. ORTNER, B. HULTQVIST, R. R. BROWN, T. R. HARTZ, O. HOLT, B. LANDMARK, J. L. HOOK, AND H. LEINBACH, Cosmic noise absorption accompanying SSC, *J. Geophys. Res.*, **67**(11), 4169–4186 (1962).
99. P. R. PISHAROTY AND B. J. SRIVASATAVA, Rise times versus magnitudes of sudden commencements of geomagnetic storms, *J. Geophys. Res.*, **67**(6), 2189–2193 (1962).
100. R. SCHLICH, Premier aperçu sur les travaux scientifiques de la campagne de l'été 1961–62 aux îles Kerguelen, *Magnétisme Bulletin T.A.A.F.* (1962).
101. S. F. SINGER, A new model of magnetic storms and aurora, *Trans. Amer. Geophys. Un.*, **38**, 175–190 (1957).
102. E. SUCKSDORFF, Occurrences of rapid micropulsations at Sodanklyä during 1932–1935, *Terr. Mag. Atmos. Elect.*, **41**, 337–344 (1936).
103. V. A. TROITSKAYA, Continuous pulsations and pulsation trains in the Arctic and Antarctic, *Short Period Pulsations of the Earth's Electromagnetic Field: Geomagnetism No. 3*, 41–61 (Soviet IGY Committee, Acad. Sci. USSR, 1961).
104. V. A. TROITSKAYA, Pulsations of earth's electromagnetic field ($T < 15$ sec) and their connection with phenomena in high atmosphere, *J. Geophys. Res.*, **66**(1), 5–18 (1961).
105. V. A. TROITSKAYA, L. V. ALPEROVICH, AND N. V. GIORGIO, On the relation between short-period pulsations of the electromagnetic field of the earth and aurora, *Izv. Akad. Nauk SSSR, Geophys. Ser., No. 2*, 262–270 (1962).
106. V. A. TROITSKAYA AND E. T. MATVEYEVA, Pulsations of type PP (Report presented at the XIII Assembly of IUGG, Berkeley, 1963).
107. V. A. TROITSKAYA AND M. V. MELNIKOVA, On the characteristic intervals of pulsations diminishing by periods (10–1 sec) in the electromagnetic field of the earth and their relation to phenomena in the upper atmosphere, *Dok. Akad. Nauk*, **128**(5) (1959).

108. V. A. Troitskaya, M. V. Melnikova, D. A. Rakityanskaya, O. V. Bolshakova, and G. A. Bulatova, Fine structure of magnetic storms (Report presented at the XIII Assembly of IUGG, Berkeley, 1963).
109. S. N. Vernov, G. L. Grigorov, U. J. Logachev, and A. E. Chudakov, Cosmic ray measurements on Sputniks, *Dok. Akad. Nauk*, **120**(6) (1958).
110. P. A. Vinogradov, Investigations of general regularities of earth currents, *Dissertation* (Moscow, 1962).
111. K. Vozoff, R. M. Ellis, and G. D. Garland, Composition of pearls, *Nature*, **194**, 539–541 (1962).
112. R. C. Wentworth and L. R. Tepley, Hydromagnetic emissions, x-ray bursts and electron bunches, 2. Theoretical interpretation. *J. Geophys. Res.*, **67**(9), 3335–3343 (1962).
113. C. R. Wilson, Sudden commencement hydromagnetic waves and the enhanced solar wind direction, *J. Geophys. Res.*, **67**(5), 2054–2056 (1962).
114. C. R. Wilson and M. Sugiura, Hydromagnetic interpretation of sudden commencements of magnetic storms, *J. Geophys. Res.*, **66**(12), 4097–4111 (1961).
115. K. Yanagihara, Geomagnetic micropulsations with periods from 0.03 to 10 seconds in the auroral zones with special reference to conjugate-point studies, *J. Geophys. Res.*, **68**(1), 3383–3398 (1963).

CHAPTER 20

INTERNATIONAL COOPERATION IN METEOROLOGY AND THE ATMOSPHERIC SCIENCES

Thomas F. Malone

One of the consequences of the strikingly successful activities of the International Geophysical Year is the profound influence it has had in stimulating thought on new ways to bring the power of international cooperation to bear on that class of scientific problems in which progress is particularly dependent on the collaborative effort of scientists and nations all over the world. The field of meteorology, and the broader area of scientific investigation that has come to be known as the atmospheric sciences, is a case in point. A great deal of thinking has been and is being directed to cooperative measures that would permit advantage to be taken of some exciting new opportunities that have emerged in this field in recent years.

Recognition of these opportunities led to the inclusion, in a resolution on the peaceful uses of outer space, passed unanimously by the United Nations in December, 1961, of a specific provision calling the attention of member states and the scientific community to the world-wide benefits that could be derived from international cooperation in atmospheric research and meteorological operations. This portion of the resolution urged study of measures "to advance the state of science . . . to provide greater knowledge of the basic physical forces affecting climate and the possibility of large-scale weather modification" as well as to develop weather forecasting capabilities.

Except for the world-wide postal service, there is probably no human activity, scientific or otherwise, in which over the years a higher degree of coordination among the nations of the World has been developed than in the field of meteorology. Moreover, it is probably safe to say that no part of the IGY program received more attention than did those activities which had as their objective the investigation of some physical phenomena taking place in, or related to, the atmosphere. Why, then, this rising tide of interest in international cooperation in meteorology and the atmospheric sciences on the part of the scientific community and the General Assembly of the United Nations?

What are the circumstances that present new scientific opportunities? What are the considerations, other than those purely scientific, that are relevant? What might be the principal elements of an expanded program of international cooperation that would make it responsive to scientific opportunities and to nonscientific considerations? What are some of the requirements that must be met if the undertaking is to be an exciting adventure of the human spirit with real benefits to mankind rather than a cumbersome international boondoggle? Finally, what are some of the activities now under way that indicate the degree of interest and enthusiasm for this program?

1. Recent Technical Developments

What are the scientific and technological developments that make this period so promising that a substantial expansion of the international effort in this field appears to be warranted? Perhaps we can agree that scientifically—and practically—one of the most significant features of the atmosphere is that it is in motion. It is this motion that produces what we call weather and climate. An understanding and explanation of atmospheric motion (ranging in scale from planetary waves to turbulent eddies) and the physical-chemical processes that influence the energetics of that motion is probably one of the most difficult, most challenging, and most important scientific problems of our time. Four developments of recent years support the point of view that we are now in a position to make a concerted effort to solve this problem.

First, there has been a very modest but highly significant degree of success achieved in identifying some of the skeletal elements of a generalized theory of atmospheric motion. This has been accomplished by piecing together relatively fragmentary data which describe air motion over a wide range of scale sizes, analyzing the partitioning of energy, the internal energy transformations and external energy transfers, and relating all of these measurements to basic hydrodynamic and thermodynamic theory. In short, the work on the problem has progressed from the descriptive phase to the analytical phase.

Second, the availability of high-speed, large-capacity computers has provided a tool of potentially great effectiveness and flexibility for conceiving and testing theories of atmospheric motion. These theories take the form of mathematical models which relate successive states of the atmosphere through the differential equations that describe the physical processes taking place in the atmosphere. The full power of this approach, however, will not be realized until a more adequate array of global observations is available to measure the dynamical and thermodynamical variables which specify an initial state of the atmosphere.

Third, developments in the technology of measurements—most dramatically the meteorological satellite—have brought within the realm of practical possibilities a global observational system capable of supplying data points adequately distributed in space and time to meet almost any reasonable scientific or operational requirements. Converting this possibility into reality is the practical problem of international cooperation.

Fourth, the exploration of the upper atmosphere is proceeding so rapidly that the steps required to elucidate the physical and chemical process taking place there, and their consequences on motion and electromagnetic propagation, can now be outlined.

Any one of these developments, considered singly, would be significant—although scarcely compelling as far as an international program is concerned. The fact that they have all taken place almost simultaneously has this important consequence: it is now possible to formulate meaningful scientific questions concerning the atmosphere and its motion, to design an observational program that treats the entire atmosphere as a single indivisible dynamical system physically linked to the oceans and to outer space, to obtain and use the measurements in a real-time data system, and to perform the kind of quantitative analysis that will permit answers to be obtained to the questions posed. Moreover, many of the kinds of physical measurements not directly related to air motion become more meaningful because they can be made and interpreted in the context of a comprehensive view of the field of motion.

The unique justification for an international cooperative program in meteorology and the atmospheric sciences is the need for observations on a global basis. The revolution in our ability to specify what observations are needed and the particular scientific problem they are intended to solve are the considerations which sharply differentiate between the scientific opportunities today and those of only a decade ago.

2. The Social Background

Let us now turn to considerations that are not primarily scientific—to those that arise from the growing interaction between science and a composite of social-economic-political factors. The time has long passed when the scientific community can ignore the consequences of its activities on society or the influence of social forces on scientific work. Many interactions might be cited; I restrict my discussion to three.

First, the requirements for food production over the balance of this century to meet satisfactory minimum dietary standards for a growing world population are going to demand a higher degree of effectiveness in land management and total water utilization throughout the world. This, in turn, will impose special requirements on our understanding of climate, the dynamics of climate, and the interrelationships between climate on the one hand and land management and water utilization on the other hand. It scarcely seems necessary to point out that this brings us back to the need to understand air motion on a global scale because this, in fact, is what determines climate. The world-wide problems of land management and water utilization will also establish urgent requirements for substantially improved weather forecasts, particularly for time periods extending from a few weeks to a few months into the future. Here, too, it is clear that the crux of the problem is an improved understanding of the dynamics and energetics of air motion on a global scale.

Second, the development of the observational tools that hold promise of materially assisting in the solution of problems in atmospheric research is, in itself, creating circumstances that will alter the traditional kind of international cooperation in the collection and exchange of weather data among the national weather services in the world. Each nation has maintained its own network, and what has been available as a global view of air motion has been the aggregate of over a hundred national networks. The meteorological satellite will clearly require the development of new patterns of international cooperation. The concept of commonality—of joint sharing of facilities—is not a matter of choice or simply of favorable economics, but one of necessity. Imagine—if you can—the chaos that would result if there were 116 "national" weather satellites orbiting merrily about with each satellite telemetering cloud photographs and radiation data back to its "national headquarters."

Other problems arise. One of the more attractive proposals for bringing the field of middle tropospheric motion under surveillance over the entire globe, and of obtaining measurements of the exchange processes at the ocean-atmosphere interface, requires the development of a system involving interrogation of fixed and moving observation stations by a communications satellite, with subsequent data readout to centers for collection and processing of data. The observation stations would include instrumented balloons floating freely at a constant pressure and ocean buoys equipped with appropriate sensors. However, the millenium has not yet arrived, and it is unlikely that all nations would permit unrestricted movement over their boundaries of sensing platforms belonging to other nations. Moreover, there is need really for only one such system. A supranational mechanism involving a very intimate and well-thought-out mode of international cooperation would seem to be inevitable.

Third, it is unmistakably clear that any serious extension of study and experimentation in local weather control to large-scale climate modification should proceed within a framework of close international cooperation for three reasons. In the first place, the theoretical studies involving mathematical models that should precede field experimentation would require precisely the kind of global measurements to which reference has already been made. In the second place, tinkering with the large-scale features of the atmosphere in one part of the world would almost certainly have consequences in other parts of the world. Finally, a unilateral scientific breakthrough in weather control or climate modification would be a mixed blessing because it might jeopardize dedication of this kind of power over nature to humanitarian ends. More than lip service needs to be paid to this aspect of the matter. The UN resolution—in the context of the peaceful use of outer space—was a step in the right direction, but as this program takes shape this implicit objective needs to be made more explicit. Probably the most significant development in weather control or climate modification in recent years is *not* that any new light has been shed on the matter of feasibility but rather that scientific and technological accomplishments and prospects have brought us to the stage where it will soon be possible to design a program that will permit a rational and systematic examination of this feasibility.

3. Outline of an International Effort

What, then, are the principal elements of a program that would be responsive to the scientific opportunities and to the other considerations that make this an appropriate time to reexamine and strengthen international cooperation in this field? Four broad areas of activity can be identified:

1. *Design, development, and operation of a world weather system* to collect from all over the globe and to process the observations of the atmosphere that are required for weather prediction *and* for research in the atmospheric sciences, and to disseminate analyses and data to regional, national, and local weather centrals and stations. This system would be designed about the independently operated national systems and interact with them, but it would be a substantial extension in areal coverage and observational capability and may well involve new patterns of coordination and cooperation among nations. It would be designed as a unified system to produce forecasts and to provide the information needed for research. System design studies and a major effort in the area of measurement and instrumentation are clearly required—both to be carried out in close coordination with similar international programs in hydrology and oceanography.

2. *Planning and coordinating* an international scientific program of research aimed at a better understanding of the atmosphere. The scientific goal of this research would be knowledge; the practical objectives would be to improve weather prediction and to expose the crucially important problems of weather control and climate modification to a serious and sustained scientific scrutiny. Up to a rather advanced state, exactly the same research program serves both objectives.

The scientific work would cover the remarkably broad spectrum of activities encompassed within the atmospheric sciences and would substantially extend current national programs by giving special emphasis to the class of problems that arise from the global nature of the atmosphere. The research program would, in a sense, collectively provide the design specifications for that portion of the world weather system responsive to scientific needs and would be the principal user of high-altitude data, radiation measurements, observations of the exchange processes at the interface of air and ocean/land, measurements over remote and relatively inaccessible areas, and other nonroutine observations made available by the system.

The most important step now is for the scientific communities in the several nations (*a*) to convert general statements of research that can and should be done into specific proposals, (*b*) to specify the kind and the distribution of observations that are required, (*c*) to indicate the instrumentation that is needed or available to make and collect these observations, (*d*) to present detailed plans for the manner in which it is expected that the data will be analyzed, (*e*) to specify the manner in which the proposed research relates to studies already under way, and (*f*) to state the human and material resources required to carry on the research.

3. *Providing a description of world-wide climate* with a precision sufficient to identify and study small climatic changes (natural or man-made) and to be useful in improving land utilization and water management in developing nations.

4. *Developing and encouraging an educational and training program* to increase the production of scientific, professional, and technical personnel in all countries, with emphasis on those levels appropriate to the stage of scientific and technological development in each country.

The character of this program, involving an intimate blending of service, science, and education, and requiring multiple support and common use of certain parts of the world weather system, suggests an even broader program of international cooperation than that which proved to be so superbly successful during the IGY, or the kind of cooperation traditionally carried on by national weather services with the World Meteorological Organization (WMO). It is apparent that a sustained effort over a period of years will be necessary to develop the optimum framework and to perfect effective mechanisms. It would appear that emphasis during the next five or six years would be on planning, design studies, and the development of instrumentation, with a target date for full-scale operations by about 1970.

If, indeed, the decade of the 1970's is to be characterized by a concerted attack on the atmosphere, what are some of the general requirements that must be met during the 1960's? Perhaps the most important is genuine interest and enthusiasm on the part of individual scientists. The second is simply a matter of the attitude assumed by national and international governmental mechanisms and the several interested organizations in the scientific community toward this kind of cooperation. A true and a very necessary partnership of effort is developing between the private scientific community and the government activities at national and international levels. The problems may well become formidable, and special attention will be required to ensure the participation of the scientific community in the development and utilization of large data-gathering and data-processing systems which are operated by the government because they serve operational as well as research needs. Finally, there is a splendid opportunity that must be seized to develop the fundamental geophysical unity of hydrology, oceanography, meteorology, and aeronomy.

4. Present Planning

Several activities are underway which convey a sense of the forward motion of this program. At the international level, the UN General Assembly looked with favor on a preliminary report submitted by the World Meteorological Organization in the summer of 1962 and asked that the plans be developed in further detail. Member states were encouraged to strengthen their national programs, and an invitation was extended to the International Council of Scientific Unions to develop through its member unions and the national academies an expanded program of research in the atmospheric sciences that would complement those being developed by the WMO. ICSU currently has under consideration the establishment of a Special Committee, and the International Union of Geodesy and Geophysics is exploring the manner in which it can contribute most effectively to the response from ICSU to the UN General Assembly. The deep interest of scientists in COSPAR led to the establishment of a Working Group on the "Physics and Chemistry of Near Space."

WMO took some bold and constructive steps at its Fourth Congress in April of this year. An Advisory Committee with broad terms of reference in research, operations, and training was authorized to provide guidance on the program in response to the UN Resolution. A Planning Unit is being established to assist in the systems design studies for a global observing system to be known as the World Weather Watch. A new WMO Development Fund was authorized to provide support for the implementation of plans for the World Weather Watch.

Interest in this undertaking at the international level appears to be equaled by that at the national level in the United States. The National Academy of Sciences, through a special committee of its Geophysics Research Board, responded to the UN invitation and articulated the views and enthusiasm of the scientific community in this country in a report issued early in the spring of 1963. Several panels of the Academy's Committee on Atmospheric Sciences are being established to pursue specific aspects of the research planning. One, jointly with the Committee on Oceanography, is to be concerned with ocean-atmosphere interactions. Another will serve as a focal point within the Academy for the formulation of specific elements of the research program on atmospheric circulations. As we embark on an international program that has as one of its ultimate objectives exploration of possibilities for modifying the atmosphere, it seems clear that a long, thoughtful look is in order on the scientific, engineering, economic, social, ecological, and legal aspects of weather control and climate modification. Finally, a major study of education and manpower is nearing completion. Within the government area, an interagency group was established to agree on the nature of the program the United States Government should support. Although precise levels of financial support have yet to be determined, the interagency group supports the general outline now emerging.

If one senses correctly the rising tide of enthusiasm for a program of this kind within the community of scientists and of nations around the world, the growing appreciation for the intrinsic merit and challenge of the scientific problem, the emerging recognition that important aspects of it cannot be fragmented geographically nor isolated geophysically, the increasing awareness of the potential for economic and humanitarian benefits, the deepening dedication to the principle that the fruits of these scientific endeavors should be used to ameliorate and not aggravate differences among nations, the developing resolve that the program—if worth doing at all—must bear the imprint of excellence in its every aspect, the maturing will that fiscal and organizational problems can and must be solved—if one senses all these things correctly, then, clearly, the next few years will be an exciting time.

I shall conclude with a thought of President John F. Kennedy:

> When nature makes natural allies of us all, we must demonstrate that beneficial relations are possible even with those with whom we most deeply disagree—and this must some day be the basis of world peace and world law.

CHAPTER 21

THE INTERNATIONAL YEARS OF THE QUIET SUN 1964–1965

W. J. G. Beynon

The International Geophysical Year marked a historic peak in international cooperation in geophysical science, and there can be no underestimating the enormous stimulus given to geophysical research the world over by that enterprise. The basic objective of the IGY was once summarized in the phrase "the common study of our planet by all nations for the benefit of all," and it is certain that this objective was achieved in full measure.

The IGY was the third occasion on which scientists had undertaken a cooperative study of this sort. The First International Polar Year was organized in 1882–1883 and the Second, 50 years later. In both these projects studies were carried out over a period of one year, mainly in polar latitudes. In 1882–1883 the disciplines concerned were meteorology, geomagnetism, and aurora. In the 1932–1933 enterprise there were also studies of the newly discovered ionosphere. A period of 50 years separated the First and Second Polar Years, but the IGY followed after 25 years. Two main reasons lay behind this choice of 1957–1958 for the IGY. In the first place there was the need for concerted experiments at a time of maximum solar activity—and, as it turned out, the solar activity during the IGY period appreciably exceeded any recorded in the 200 years or so for which reliable sunspot numbers are available. The second factor was the enormous advance, in the two decades following the Second Polar Year, in scientific techniques—especially in the radio and electronic fields. Even in the early planning stages of the IGY it became clear that some observations should be continued at near the IGY level through the waning portion of the solar cycle, and in certain disciplines there were sound scientific reasons for an enterprise on the scale of the IGY at the next period of minimum solar activity. It was clear that the full fruits of the IGY would be reaped only if data, comparable in quantity and quality, were available for a period of low activity. Furthermore, such an enterprise could make full use of the powerful new space research techniques developed since the IGY. Hence it is that we have organized the International Years of the Quiet Sun for the period 1 January 1964 to 31 December 1965. Nearly 70 nations, including all those which took part in the IGY, are participating.

During the IQSY studies are being carried out in those disciplines which are dependent to a greater or lesser extent on solar activity. The disciplines concerned are meteorology, geomagnetism, aurora, airglow, ionospheric physics, solar activity, and cosmic rays. There is also a coordinated program of rocket and satellite investigations. The detailed proposals for studies within each of these disciplines were formulated at two IQSY General Assemblies, the first in Paris in March, 1962 and the second in Rome in March, 1963. The following summarizes the main proposals.

1. Meteorology

Although over the years, claims often have been made for direct links of one sort or another, between solar activity and meteorological conditions at the ground, such links, if they exist at all, are not obvious. It may then be asked why meteorology is found within the IQSY disciplines. There are, in fact, many good reasons for an extensive meteorological program during IQSY.

The IGY-IGC meteorological program was directed mainly to a study of the general circulation of the atmosphere, and attention was concentrated on that part of the atmosphere between the ground and a level of 30 km. During IQSY, attention will be focused on the 30- to 120-km zone, with special attention to the 25- to 60-km height range. It is planned to study the large-scale physical, dynamical, and thermodynamical characteristics of the atmosphere above the 100-mb level and to investigate the relations between the upper atmosphere and the lower atmosphere. The specific topics being studied are:

i. The climatology of the upper atmosphere—the variation in space and time of the parameters of state and the motion of the atmosphere;

ii. The morphology of the disturbances in the upper atmosphere—the thermal structure and the flow patterns in the horizontal and vertical;

iii. The relation between stratospheric circulation and temperature field, and the distributions of ozone and water-vapor;

iv. Radiative processes particularly in relation to ozone and water-vapor distribution;

v. The incidence and nature of clouds and aerosols;

vi. The relation between solar activity and the composition, motion, and temperature fields of the upper atmosphere.

The IQSY meteorological program calls for a new intensive effort with high-level balloons and with space vehicles.

Certain meteorological data such as atmospheric pressure and temperature, ozone content of the stratosphere and mesosphere, are necessary for workers in other geophysical fields. High-level aerological observations are required in certain cosmic ray studies; ionospheric workers have an interest in the propagation of atmospherics from lightning flashes; and, on the practical side, meteorological observers at weather stations will play an important part in the program for visual observation of aurora.

This very brief indication of the IQSY program is enough to show that extensive meteorological observations are an essential part of the enterprise.

2. Geomagnetism

A feature of recent advances in geophysical research has been to underline again the profound influence of the geomagnetic field on many terrestrial phenomena. Thus in the ionospheric field alone we need only recall the electric current systems associated with quiet and disturbed magnetic conditions, the geomagnetic anomalies in F-layer ionization, the influence of the field on ionospheric movements, the propagation of whistler-type atmospherics, trapped particles, auroral and polar cap radio wave absorption.

It is clear that during IQSY a full program of geomagnetic studies is required, not only for its own intrinsic interest, but also because of this intimate connection between the magnetic field and so many other geophysical phenomena.

Synoptic observations are being carried out at a network of stations which will be at least as complete as that operated during the IGY. High- and low-sensitivity instruments are being employed so that small events and effects can be studied, while at the same time permitting observations of the onset phenomena of storms. The IQSY working group on geomagnetism has called attention to the fact that the quiet-sun period is particularly appropriate for studies of solar and lunar daily variations. Two areas are suggested as appropriate for a detailed study of these variations: the Pacific Ocean and the Antarctic. Recommendations have been made for further rocket studies of the equatorial electrojet and for the use of satelliteborne magnetometers, coordinated with ground-base measurements, to study large geomagnetic anomalies such as that over the South Atlantic. It has been pointed out that the IQSY will be a very suitable occasion on which to study the secular variation of the geomagnetic field, and other plans call for the careful study of micropulsations, including the establishment of uniform procedures for describing and scaling these perturbations in the field.

A number of geomagnetic surveys are now in hand as part of the World Magnetic Survey, first proposed as a deferred IGY project, and the IQSY enterprise will benefit from these surveys which are being carried out at the same time within the framework of the World Magnetic Survey.

3. Aurora

During the solar minimum period the incidence of auroras is much reduced, and it may be anticipated that those which do occur will be of a relatively quiet nature.

Synoptic studies with all-sky cameras and visual observations are being carried out on a scale comparable with that of the IGY, and during IQSY the widespread use of photoelectric filter photometers is providing a more systematic study of the principal auroral emissions than has hitherto been possible. Following detailed discussions by members of the Special Committee for Antarctic Research (SCAR), a new 35 mm all-sky camera and photometer have been designed. Recommendations for an observing program and for the recording of reference luminance standard (to maintain uniformity) proposed by a sub-Committee of the International Association of Geomagnetism and Aeronomy (IAGA), have been adopted for IQSY.

To help visual observers, a new auroral handbook has been prepared by Dr. Jacka and Mr. Paton and published by the IQSY Secretariat. This manual gives a general account of the nature and characteristics of auroras, a detailed account of a new system of classification and of the nomenclature and symbols to be used in reporting aurora. A year or two before the Second International Polar Year of 1932–1933, Professor Carl Störmer, in collaboration with a committee of the Terrestrial Magnetism and Atmospheric Electricity Section of the International Union of Geodesy and Geophysics (IUGG), prepared a "Photographic Atlas of Auroral Forms and Scheme for Visual Observations of Aurorae." For the IQSY a completely new Auroral Atlas with explanatory text has been prepared by the IAGA sub-Committee already mentioned.

Workers in the auroral field have not been slow to appreciate the value of satellites in auroral studies. In their proposals it is pointed out that the ideal auroral experiment is the simultaneous observation, on a polar-orbiting satellite, of the nature, energy, and spatial distribution of particles descending to auroral levels, with photometric observations of the auroral emissions which result from the influx of these particles. Apart from the advantage of freedom from cloud interference, such photometric observations from a satellite would enable the study of those ultraviolet emissions which are normally absorbed by atmospheric ozone.

Special experiments are being carried out with balloons and rockets to study auroral particles and bombarding mechanisms. The relations between electron flux and auroral luminosity are being studied together with flux, spectrum, etc., of associated X-radiation. Satellite and space-probe experiments will yield information on particles in the sun-earth space, on the incidence of such particles into the geomagnetic field, and their association with auroral phenomena.

4. Airglow

One of the consequences of the diminished auroral activity during IQSY will be that airglow studies should be possible at higher latitudes than was the case during the IGY. The recommendations of the IQSY Airglow Working Group include proposals for synoptic and special experiments, for meridional chains of stations, and for improving the absolute calibration of airglow instruments. It is hoped that extensive studies of the hydrogen geocorona, first discovered in rocket experiments just before the IGY, will be carried out during the IQSY. The density and temperature of hydrogen in the terrestrial outer atmosphere, and the general shape of the geocorona, may be expected to show appreciable variation with solar activity, and reliable studies of these features during a solar minimum period will form an invaluable contribution to the airglow program. Rocket studies of airglow emissions are being made at many latitudes in an attempt to determine the height profiles of the different airglow emissions. Particular attention is being given to the red arc phenomenon discovered by Barbier and others during the IGY.

5. Ionosphere

The terrestrial ionosphere plays a central role in many geophysical phenomena; as a consequence, ionospheric studies inevitably form a very important part of any cooperative geophysical study. At the time of the Second Polar Year of 1932–1933, regular radio soundings of the ionosphere by the so called "critical frequency method" were just becoming established, and such work formed a new, but vitally important part of the whole program of that Year. In the twenty-five years following the Second Polar Year, a great network of routine radio sounding observations was established over the world, and more than 150 of these ground-based stations participated in the IGY program. During the IQSY this ground-based network is no less extensive, but on this occasion it is being supplemented by many new techniques. Not the least important of these is the use of high-power radar-type sounders to give the electron density/height profile up to levels well beyond the peak of the $F2$-layer. The sweep frequency technique of the ground-based station is also being used with very great success in the "Alouette" satellite experiment for sounding the ionosphere downward from above. New methods of studying the lowest part of the ionosphere have been developed since the IGY and are being used at a number of IQSY stations. The riometer technique for measuring the ionospheric absorption of radio waves has also assumed a new significance following the discovery of the phenomenon known as polar cap absorption and is now in regular use at many stations. Since the IGY there have also been considerable advances in the study of whistler-type atmospherics and of VLF emissions. Further intensive studies of these phenomena during the IQSY will provide new data on conditions in the outermost ionosphere at solar minimum. In recent years a feature of ionospheric and outer ionospheric studies has been the interest in geomagnetically conjugate points. During the IQSY many coordinated experiments are being carried out at a number of selected magnetically conjugate sites.

Present knowledge of movements in the ionosphere is still very inadequate, and comprehensive plans have been made for a renewed intensive study of drifts in the ionosphere. Movements at different levels in the ionosphere are being studied by different techniques, including the closely spaced receiver fading method, radio studies of drifting meteor trails, studies of radio star scintillations, and the movement of large-scale ionospheric irregularities. The IQSY ionosphere working group has emphasized the need (which still exists) for measuring ionospheric drifts by more than one technique and for critical intercomparison of the results obtained.

The IQSY represents the first opportunity for obtaining any appreciable information on the behavior of the antarctic ionosphere during a minimum sunspot period. Some very interesting facts emerged from the IGY antarctic ionospheric studies, and further study under solar minimum conditions is clearly required. Thus for some stations, as for temperature latitude stations, the electron density in the $F2$-layer reached its maximum around midday and indicated a considerable measure of solar control. At other stations of the same latitude, but at different locations in Antarctica, the electron density maximum occurred in the evening, and for the Pole station it occurred in the early hours of the morning. Then again, in local winter, the electron density at the Pole station was greater than at any other antarctic station despite the fact that the atmosphere at the Pole at this time is not illuminated below about 450 km. There is also evidence for markedly different changes with solar activity in the principal ionospheric regions.

An extensive program of radio noise studies was carried out during the IGY, and much of this work is being continued over IQSY to provide accurate information on noise intensities throughout a sunspot cycle. Certain theoretical work suggests that noise at extremely low frequencies provides a good index of the total radio noise generated over the whole world, and efforts to check this prediction are being made at a number of stations. Satellite studies of the world distribution of terrestrial radio noise are also likely to be made during the IQSY.

6. Solar Activity

Accurate prediction of the precise period of minimum solar activity is a difficult matter, and it is for this reason, together with the fact that minimum activity conditions are not simultaneous for all disciplines, that the IQSY extends over a full 2-year period, in contrast to the 18 months of the IGY. The IQSY period will include some parts of both the old and new cycles and thus provide an opportunity for making comprehensive radio, magnetic, X-ray, and particle emission observations of a few regions of both the old and new cycles.

Considerable interest is attached to a study of the solar corona under minimum activity conditions, and some radio astronomy groups are studying the outward extension of the corona by observing the occultation by it of distant radio sources. Studies of solar plasma and its propagation across the sun-earth space are being made with deep-space probes.

During the two years of IQSY there will be six solar eclipses—four partial, one annular, and one total eclipse. The total eclipse occurs on 30 May 1965 and is characterized by long duration (about 4 minutes) on the central line, but unfortunately the path of totality lies entirely in the South and Central Pacific. Two of the partial eclipses—one of maximum magnitude 0.56 on 14 January 1964 and the other of maximum magnitude 0.75 on 10 June 1964 — are visible in Antarctica, and occurring, as they do, in different seasons and at a period of low solar activity, they are of interest for the study of ionospheric and geomagnetic effects. On 9 July 1964 there is a partial eclipse (0.32 magnitude) visible in the Arctic, Canada, and Siberia; and on 3–4 December 1964 another partial eclipse of magnitude 0.75, visible in Siberia and the West Pacific. Details on the circumstances of all these eclipses are given in the IQSY World Days Instruction Manual. In the case of the total eclipse of 30 May 1965, data are given not only for ground level but also for heights 100, 200, and 300 km. These data have all been kindly supplied by the U.S. Nautical Almanac office, and the Office has also offered to undertake calculations on request for stations at which it is known observations will be made. or subsequently make calculations for stations at which observations were actually obtained.

All IQSY workers are concerned to know precisely when the minimum in solar activity occurs, and arrangements are being made for this information to be made available as quickly as possible. The solar patrol network of stations is at least as complete as during the IGY. It is also hoped to maintain over the minimum period a continuous satellite watch on the intensity of those solar ultraviolet and X-radiations which produce the lower regions of the ionosphere. The satellite observations are providing a remarkable extension of continuous monitoring observations of the solar spectrum. Hitherto, such monitoring has been possible only at wavelengths in the visible and radio range.

A new feature in the program is the proposal to study all comets that may appear during IQSY, it being recommended that frequent photographic records be obtained for the study of brightness, polarization, and spectrum changes in both the heads and tails of comets.

The quiet solar conditions are being exploited to study the solar magnetic field with instruments of the maximum possible sensitivity and resolution. Plans have also been made to study closely flare mechanisms, their relation to phenomena at all wavelengths from the radio to the X-ray end of the spectrum and to the acceleration mechanisms of solar particle streams. The full range of solar particles, from the low energies of the solar wind up to high-energy particles of cosmic rays, will be monitored in the interplanetary space.

7. Cosmic Rays

A major field of interest since the advent of rockets, space probes, and satellites has been the study of the interplanetary medium; and one of the primary objectives of cosmic ray studies during IQSY is to investigate the emission of energetic particles by the sun at the time of minimum activity, and to study their mode of propagation through the interplanetary magnetic field. The existence of quiet solar conditions is also being used to advantage in a search for intensity variations over the sidereal day, to determine the effect of meteorological factors on the intensity of the secondary radiation, and to investigate the composition, energy spectra, spatial and temporal variations of the geomagnetically trapped radiations during solar minimum.

Neutron monitors at nearly 70 stations, distributed at all latitudes from the Arctic to Antarctic, are being supplemented at some stations by a number of supermonitors with counting rates of 10^6/hour. Special investigations include studies of rapid fluctuations in meson intensity, of the relations between cosmic-ray intensity and the geomagnetic field, and measurements of the neutron albedo flux outside the earth's atmosphere. It is hoped to carry out special experiments at both ground stations and in balloons and sounding rockets, in the vicinity of the South American/South African anomaly, with the object of obtaining further information on the precipitation of particles from the inner radiation belt.

It is indicative of the progressive integrating and interrelating feature of the various geophysical disciplines that at the last meeting of the IQSY Committee in Rome the Working Group on Cosmic Rays was renamed "Cosmic Rays and Magnetically Trapped Particles."

8. Aeronomy

Direct aeronomical studies of the high atmosphere are largely conducted by means of space vehicles, and the final program for aeronomical work during IQSY has been drafted by the IQSY Working Group on Aeronomy, the reporter for which is Dr. Nicolet, and by the COSPAR Working Group for IQSY, the Chairman of which is Dr. Friedman.

Wind motions and temperature rocket measurements are being undertaken by at least 10 countries during IQSY. In addition to the measurement of wind speed and direction, the turbulent energy in the 90 to 100-km height range is being measured. The standard grenade rounds are being fired by a number of countries, and a program of atmospheric density measurements by the falling-sphere technique has also been drafted. At least a score of rocket flights will determine molecular and atmospheric density by measuring the attenuation of solar radiation with height. Electron density and electron temperature measurements by radio wave and probe methods are being made in rocket firings from at least 15 different sites over a latitude range from 30°S to 80°N. At least 30 rocket firings are planned to investigate the principal ionospheric current systems, i.e., the equatorial and auroral electrojets and Sq current system. A coordinated series of 25 rocket flights by 7 countries, specially designed to study *D*- and *E*-layer parameters, is also being carried out.

Over and above these special ionospheric rocket soundings, there is a very extensive meteorological rocket sounding program. During 1962 the United States alone carried out some 850 successful meteorological rocket soundings, and at the recent Assembly in Rome it was reported that at least 9 other countries will be firing meteorological rockets during IQSY. There can be little doubt that there will be several thousand fired during the whole 2-year period.

Satellites likely to be in orbit during the IQSY period include a number of orbiting solar observatories, geophysical observatories, an aeronomy satellite, and deep-space probes for the study of the interplanetary medium. In addition, there will be what may be called the "international satellites," in which the United States is providing satellite vehicles to carry the experiments furnished by scientists of other nations. Two highly successful examples of this generous assistance provided by United States have been the Ariel satellite which carried a number of United Kingdom experiments and the Canadian–United States ionospheric top side sounder Alouette.

9. World Data Centers

Today the World Data Centers are a well-established feature of the geophysical community, and it is interesting to recall that they are now nearly eight years old. In September, 1955, at its third meeting in Brussels, the Special Committee for the IGY (CSAGI) resolved that "The observational data to be exchanged in accordance with the IGY program shall be available to scientific institutions in all countries," and accordingly CSAGI authorized "the establishment of at least three IGY World Data Centers, of which one will consist in a number of parts. Each Center will be international in the sense that it will be at the service of all countries and scientific bodies."

The purpose of establishing several World Data Centers was, first, to ensure against catastrophic destruction of a single Center and, second, to meet the geographical convenience of workers in different parts of the world. In establishing the WDC's it was the intention of CSAGI that they should not merely be collecting centers, or data depositories, but that they should be alive and active in the task of supplying data at minimum cost to all bona fide workers and that they should freely provide all the facilities which workers might require for data analysis and study at the Centers themselves. Since the conclusion of the IGY the responsibility for World Data Centers has rested with the International Committee for Geophysics, and at the recent IQSY Assembly in Rome, considerable discussion took place on the future functions and responsibilities of the WDC's. It was decided to prepare a new Guide to World Data Centers in which the procedures for collecting and exchanging data through the WDC's for the IQSY are set forth. The task of compiling this Guide has been undertaken by Dr. H. Odishaw of World Data Center A and Chairman of the WDC Working Group. The World Data Centers played an important role in the IGY, and their role is certainly no less important during IQSY.

10. World Days

Much of the success of the IGY effort depended on the careful organization beforehand of an IGY Calendar, in which special days and periods were indicated for intensive schedules of observations, and also in the organization of a world-wide Alert system, whereby workers everywhere could be quickly warned of the imminence or commencement of some solar or geographical event of special interest. During the IGY this work was most efficiently carried out by a Working Group under the direction of Mr. A. H. Shapley. For the IQSY the corresponding task is being undertaken by the International Ursigram and World Day Service (IUWDS) acting in close consultation with the IQSY Discipline Reporters and Working Groups. The IUWDS is again under the Chairmanship of Mr. A. H. Shapley. The general plan of the World Day program is similar to that adopted for the IGY, but certain modifications have been made, based on experience gained both during and since the IGY. Furthermore, some new features are introduced which are appropriate to solar minimum activity conditions. A Geophysical Calendar for the 2-year period of IQSY has been issued and widely circulated, and arrangements are again being made for the designation of Alerts which give notice of magnetic storms, magnetic calm, cosmic-ray flux changes, stratospheric warmings, solar quiet, or solar activity. There is a plan for Retrospective World Intervals, the purpose of which will be to permit a more detailed reduction and analysis of observations taken during these periods. The RWI's are being selected in cases of outstanding ionospheric and magnetic storms, for periods of very quiet solar and geophysical activity, for certain geomagnetic micropulsations, for significant changes in cosmic-ray flux, and for periods of abnormal ionospheric absorption. Arrangements are also being made through the Regional Warning Centers for the rapid exchange of selected summaries of current observations. As during the IGY, the World Meteorological Organization is cooperating fully in facilitating the rapid world-wide distribution of Alert messages over their network of communication stations.

11. Committee for the IQSY

In setting up the Committee for IQSY the general pattern of the Special Committee for the IGY (CSAGI) has been followed, but some modifications have been thought desirable. Thus Aurora and Airglow now appear as separate disciplines, each with a Reporter. Scientific bodies with formal representation on the Committee include the World Meteorological Organization, the Special Committee on Space Research (COSPAR), the Special Committee for Antarctic Research (SCAR), the International Ursigram and World Day Service (IUWDS), and the World Data Centers. In view of the importance of space research experiments in the IQSY program, COSPAR has three representatives on the IQSY Committee. Members have been appointed to be responsible for Publications, Administration, and Finance, and in an attempt to ensure a reasonable geographical coverage, four members have been elected on a world regional basis. The membership of the IQSY Committee is as given in Table 1.

In this summary paper it has been possible to refer to only some of the features in the IQSY program, and a considerable part of what is being carried out has received no mention at all. Complete information on the IQSY is being published in *IQSY Notes* at approximately bimonthly intervals.

The International Geophysical Year gave international cooperation in geophysical science a new significance but also left its mark on the wider

TABLE 1

COMMITTEE FOR IQSY

President	W. J. G. Beynon*
Vice Presidents	M. A. Pomerantz
	N. V. Pushkov
	G. Righini
Secretary	C. M. Minnis
Reporters	
World Days	A. H. Shapley*
Meteorology	W. L. Godson
Geomagnetism	V. Laursen*
Aurora	J. Paton
Airglow	D. Barbier
Ionosphere	W. Dieminger
Solar Activity	M. A. Ellison*†
Cosmic Rays	S. N. Vernov
Aeronomy	M. Nicolet*
Space Research	H. Friedman
Representatives Other Organizations	
W.M.O.	O. M. Ashford
COSPAR	H. Friedman
	J. E. Blamont
	Z. Svestka
SCAR	F. Jacka
IUWDS	A. H. Shapley
WDC's A	H. Odishaw
B	V. F. Burkhanov
C	T. Nagata
Regional Representatives	
India	K. Ramanathan
Poland	S. Manczarski
Africa	A. Onwumechelli
S. America	J. Roederer
Publications	D. C. Martin
Administration, Finance	H. Odishaw
Ex-Officio	
Gen. Sec. ICSU	J. Van Mieghem*
Treasurer ICSU	G. Laclavere*
Gen. Sec. CIG	G. Laclavere
Exec. Sec. COSPAR	P. Beaulieu

* Former members of CSAGI.

† It is with profound sorrow that we have to record the death of Professor M. A. Ellison on 12 September 1963. Dr. R. Michard has subsequently been appointed Reporter for Solar Activity.

field of international relations. We hope that this complementary enterprise, the International Years of the Quiet Sun, will be a worthy successor to the IGY and that in the annals of science it will take its place as the well-founded fourth milestone in that endless sequence of "years of the sun" which began in 1882.

LIST OF SELECTED ABBREVIATIONS

CA	coronal activity center
COSPAR	Committee for Space Research
CSAGI	Comité Spécial de l'Année Géophysique Internationale (Special Committee for the IGY, of ICSU)
DS	daily variation of storm disturbance
IAGA	International Association of Geomagnetism and Aeronomy
IAU	International Astronomical Union
ICSU	International Council of Scientific Unions
IGC	International Geophysical Cooperation (the one-year, 1959, extension of the IGY)
IGY	International Geophysical Year (1957–1958 and extended through 1959 under IGC designation)
IPY I	First International Polar Year (1882–1883)
IPY II	Second International Polar Year (1932–1933)
IQSY	International Years of the Quiet Sun (1964–1965)
IUGG	International Union of Geodesy and Geophysics
IUWDS	International Ursigram and World Days Service
LTE	local thermodynamic equilibrium
NAS	National Academy of Sciences (Washington, D.C.)
NASA	National Aeronautics and Space Administration (Washington, D.C.)
NRL	Naval Research Laboratory, Washington, D.C.
OSO	Orbiting Solar Observatory
PCA	polar cap absorption
PP	pearl-type pulsations
SC	sudden commencement
SCAR	Scientific Committee on Antarctic Research
SID	sudden ionospheric disturbance
SIP	sudden (rapid) irregular pulsation
SSC	sudden storm commencement
SWF	short-wave fadeout
TID	traveling ionospheric disturbance
UN	United Nations
URSI	International Scientific Radio Union
VHF	very high frequency (30–300 Mc/sec)
VLF	very low frequency (<30 kc/sec)
WMO	World Meteorological Organization
WMS	World Magnetic Survey
WDC	World Data Center (geophysical)

NAME INDEX

SUBJECT INDEX